HIGHER
GCSE MATHEMATICS
FOR CCEA

Anne Connolly and
Neill Hamilton

HODDER
EDUCATION
AN HACHETTE UK COMPANY

Acknowledgements

Every effort has been made to trace all copyright holders, but if any have been inadvertently overlooked the Publishers will be pleased to make the necessary arrangements at the first opportunity.

Although every effort has been made to ensure that website addresses are correct at time of going to press, Hodder Education cannot be held responsible for the content of any website mentioned in this book. It is sometimes possible to find a relocated web page by typing in the address of the home page for a website in the URL window of your browser.

Hachette UK's policy is to use papers that are natural, renewable and recyclable products and made from wood grown in sustainable forests. The logging and manufacturing processes are expected to conform to the environmental regulations of the country of origin.

Orders: please contact Bookpoint Ltd, 130 Milton Park, Abingdon, Oxon OX14 4SB. Telephone: (44) 01235 827720. Fax: (44) 01235 400454. Lines are open 9.00–5.00, Monday to Saturday, with a 24-hour message answering service. Visit our website at www.hoddereducation.co.uk

Anne Connolly, Neill Hamilton 2010
First published in 2010 by
Hodder Education,
An Hachette UK Company
338 Euston Road
London NW1 3BH

Impression number   5 4
Year   2015 2014 2013

Cover photo © Keren Su/Corbis
Illustrations by Ken Vail Graphic Design, Cambridge, UK (kvgd.com)
Typeset in Bembo and Conduit ITC by Ken Vail Graphic Design, Cambridge, UK (kvgd.com)
Printed in Italy

A catalogue record for this title is available from the British Library

ISBN: 978 0340 889 183

Contents

Geometry and measures

Statistics and probability

Introduction

CCEA revised specification

This Student's Book covers all the changes made to the CCEA GCSE specification in Mathematics for first teaching from September 2010.

Changes in assessment

Candidates will take *either* T3 and T6 examination papers *or* T4 and T6 examination papers.

Assessment of both T3 and T4 is made by a 2-hour written examination with a calculator.

All Higher candidates must take the Higher Completion Test T6. Assessment of T6 is by two written examination papers:

- Paper 1, lasting 1 hour 15 minutes without a calculator
- Paper 2, lasting 1 hour 15 minutes with a calculator.

Available grades

The grades available to candidates taking tests T3 and T6 are A to D, with the possibility of achieving grade E. However, to attain grade A candidates must demonstrate exceptional performance on the T3 exam and sufficient work at grade A standard on the T6 Completion Test.

The grades available to candidates taking tests T4 and T6 are A★ to D with the possibility of achieving grade E.

Changes in assessment objectives

The assessment objectives for the new GCSE in Mathematics are:

A01 Candidates must recall and use their knowledge of the prescribed content.
A02 Candidates must select and apply mathematical methods in a range of contexts.
A03 Candidates must interpret and analyse problems and generate strategies to solve them.

Functional elements

The new specification addresses the functional elements of mathematics, which are the skills and abilities students need in order to take an active and responsible role in their communities. This Student's Book provides rich examples of how maths is used in our everyday lives, workplaces and educational settings. Candidates are shown how to use mathematics effectively in a wide range of contexts.

Quality of written communication

The quality of each exam candidate's written communication will be assessed through their correct use of mathematical symbols and mathematical language. In addition, marks will be gained when students demonstrate their ability to use a logical, step-by-step approach to solve the problems that have been set.

Changes in content:

The table below shows changes in content between the previous specification and the new one. While in general Units T3, T4 and T6 match up to Units N3, N4 and N6, some objectives from Units N3, N4 and N6 have been moved, and others have been removed from the new specification altogether.

Objective	Old specification	New specification
$(x + 4)(x - 2)$ and $(a \pm b)^2$	N2 (Foundation)	T3
Bias, comparing distributions, calculator statistical functions	N3	T2 (Foundation)
Similar triangles	N3	T2 (Foundation)
Area of a triangle rule: $\frac{1}{2} ab \sin C$	N3	T4
Calculating using negative indices	N3	T4
Volume of a cylinder and other solids	N3	T6
Graphical representation of linear inequalities	N3/N4	T6
Mathematical similarity	N3/N4	T6
Reciprocal functions and graphs	N3/N4	T6
3D co-ordinates	N3	R*
Using sine, cosine and tangent in problems in 3D	N4	T3
Multiplying and dividing mixed numbers	N4	T5
Sine, cosine and tangent graphs	N4	T6
The effect of enlargement for perimeter, area and volume of shapes and solids	N4	T6
Volume of cone and sphere	N4	T6
Quadratic nth term of sequence	N4	R
Calculating with negative numbers	N6	T2 (Foundation)
Direct and indirect proportion	N6	T3/T4
Irrational numbers	N6	R
Linear programming	N6	R
Proofs of triangle and quadrilateral angle properties	N6	R
Transformation of graphs	N6	R
Vectors, except for vector notation in translation	N6	R

*R = Removed from specification.

Book structure and content

This Student's Book provides full coverage of the Higher tier of the new CCEA GCSE Maths specification. The book is structured so that the chapters covering each of the three subject strands are grouped together: Number and algebra, Geometry and measures, and lastly Statistics and probability.

All the T3 and T4 content is addressed in orange-bordered chapters. Chapters covering T6 content are bordered in green. As there are common questions on the T3 and T4 examination papers, these topics are addressed together within individual chapters.

Each chapter contains:

- an overview of what the chapter is about in student-friendly language (learning intentions)
- a list of knowledge and skills which students should have gained *before* working through the chapter
- detailed and fully worked-out examples that explain clearly how to tackle the questions
- lots of questions in each exercise to provide practice in tackling the types of questions students will face at the end of the course, in addition to more open 'problem-solving' questions
- a section at the end that outlines what the students should now know (these are the success criteria)
- a summary exercise that can be used as a revision tool prior to a test being taken, or indeed used for testing the whole of the chapter
- relevant and appropriate past examination questions on topics covered in the chapter. These questions are from actual CCEA GCSE Higher Tier examination papers. You can find lots more, from 2007 until the most recent papers, online at www.ccea.org.uk. Use the 'Topic Tracker' on the Mathematics microsite to find questions on the particular chapter topics.

Prior knowledge

There are some topics that appear towards the end of the book to facilitate the prior knowledge needed before the topic can be fully addressed. For example, the chapter on bounds (Chapter 40) builds upon prior knowledge of topics including time, distance, speed and density, and area and circumference of circles, volumes of cylinders and spheres, surface area and Pythagoras' theorem. For this reason it has been placed after all these topics have been covered, rather than with the other chapters in the Number and algebra strand.

Use of calculators

Throughout the book, icons are used next to the exercises to show where calculators should and should not be used. Icons are also placed by the exam questions to show whether the questions come from a paper where a calculator can be used or from one where calculators are forbidden. However, just because a calculator can be used on a particular paper, it does not mean that it is necessary or desirable for a student to use a calculator to answer a particular question. Students need to learn to recognise for themselves where a calculator would be helpful.

Additional resources

A complete e-textbook and answers to the questions in the Exercises are provided on the HodderPlus website:

www.hodderplus.co.uk/cceagcsemaths

Details of how to access these are provided on the inside front cover of this book.

CHAPTER 1

The language of number

This chapter is about:

- the terminology used in mathematics
- powers and roots
- writing a number as a product of its prime factors
- highest common factors (HCFs) and lowest common multiples (LCMs).

You should already know:

- how to read, write and order whole numbers and decimals.

Definitions

The list below gives brief definitions of some of the important terms you will come across in your course.

- **Whole number** – a number with no tenths, hundredths, etc. The set of whole numbers includes 0, 1, 2, 3, ... (see Chapter 2).
- **Decimal** – a number which may have tenths, hundredths, etc. For example, 1.63 is a decimal (see Chapter 3).
- **Terminating decimal** – a decimal with a finite number of decimal places. For example, 0.45 is a terminating decimal (see Chapters 9 and 12).
- **Recurring decimal** – a decimal where one or more of the decimal places recur (repeat). For example, 0.6666… is recurring and can be written as $0.\dot{6}$ (see Chapters 9 and 12).
- **Fraction** – a number which can be written in the form $\frac{a}{b}$. For example, $\frac{2}{3}$ is a fraction (see Chapter 5).
- **Reciprocal** – the result when 1 is divided by a number. For example, the reciprocal of 8 is $\frac{1}{8}$ (see Chapter 10).
- **Percentage** – a fraction out of 100. For example, 45% means $\frac{45}{100}$ (see Chapter 9).
- **Square** – the result when a number is multiplied by itself. For example, $6^2 = 6 \times 6 = 36$ (see Chapter 1).
- **Square root** – finding the square root of a number is the inverse of squaring a number. For example, $\sqrt{25} = \pm 5$ (see Chapter 1).

- **Cube** – the result when a number is multiplied by itself, and then multiplied by itself again.
  For example, $4^3 = 4 \times 4 \times 4 = 64$ (see Chapter 1).
- **Cube root** – finding the cube root of a number is the inverse of cubing a number.
  For example, $\sqrt[3]{125} = 5$ (see Chapter 1).
- **Factor** – a number which divides exactly into another number.
  For example, the factors of 8 are 1, 2, 4 and 8 (see Chapter 1).
- **Multiple** – a number which another number divides exactly into.
  For example, the multiples of 3 are 3, 6, 9, 12, 15, ... (see Chapter 1).
- **Common factor** – a factor which is shared by two or more numbers.
  For example, $12 = 4 \times 3$ and $20 = 4 \times 5$, so 4 is a common factor of 12 and 20 (see Chapter 1).
- **Prime number** – a number which has only two factors (1 and itself).
  The set of prime numbers includes 2, 3, 5, 7, 11, 13, ... (see Chapter 1).
  Notice that the number 1 is not usually considered to be prime.
- **Positive number** – a number greater than zero.
  For example, the numbers 1, 2, 3, 4, ... are positive (see Chapter 4).
- **Negative number** – a number less than zero.
  For example, the numbers $-1, -2, -3, -4, \ldots$ are negative (see Chapter 4).
- **Integer** – a positive or negative whole number. The set of integers includes $\ldots -3, -2, -1, 0, 1, 2, 3, \ldots$ (see Chapter 4).
- **Natural number** – the numbers 1, 2, 3, 4, ... Notice that the number 0 appears in the set of whole numbers but not in the set of natural numbers (see Chapter 1).
- **Sum** – the result when a number of values are added.
  For example, the sum of 6 and 2 is $6 + 2 = 8$ (see Chapter 2).
- **Difference** – the result when two values are subtracted.
  For example, the difference of 6 and 2 is $6 - 2 = 4$ (see Chapter 2).
- **Product** – the result when a number of values are multiplied.
  For example, the product of 6 and 2 is $6 \times 2 = 12$ (see Chapter 2).
- **Numerator** – the top line of a fraction.
  For example, the numerator of $\frac{2}{3}$ is 2 (see Chapter 5).
- **Denominator** – the bottom line of a fraction.
  For example, the denominator of $\frac{2}{3}$ is 3 (see Chapter 5).
- **Common denominator** – a denominator which several other denominators can divide exactly into.
  For example, a common denominator for $\frac{1}{2}$ and $\frac{3}{4}$ would be 8 (see Chapter 5).
- **Equivalent** – values which are numerically equal to each other.
  For example, $\frac{1}{2}$ is equivalent to 50% (see Chapter 9).
- **Index notation** – a number written using index notation is written as a power.
  For example, $32 = 2 \times 2 \times 2 \times 2 \times 2$ and can be written as 2^5 (see Chapter 1).
- **Counter example** – an example which disproves a general statement.
  For example, a counter example which disproves the statement 'all primes are odd' is the number 2 (see for example Chapters 1 and 18).

Powers and roots

The **square** of a number is the result when a number is multiplied by itself.

For example, $6^2 = 6 \times 6 = 36$.

Finding the **square root** of a number is the inverse of squaring.

As $6^2 = 6 \times 6 = 36$, the square root of 36 is 6.

However, $(-6)^2 = (-6) \times (-6)$ is also 36.

So -6 is also a square root of 36.

You can write this as $\sqrt{36} = \pm 6$.

6 is called the **positive square root** of 36 and -6 is called the **negative square root** of 36.

> The symbol $\sqrt[+]{}$ means the positive square root.

The **cube** of a number is the result when a number is multiplied by itself, and then multiplied by itself again.

For example, $4^3 = 4 \times 4 \times 4 = 64$.

Finding the **cube root** of a number is the inverse of cubing.

As $4^3 = 4 \times 4 \times 4 = 64$, the cube root of 64 is 4.

You can write this as $\sqrt[3]{64} = 4$.

Unlike square roots, the cube root of a positive number can only be positive.

$(-4)^3 = (-4) \times (-4) \times (-4) = -64$.

So $\sqrt[3]{-64} = -4$.

You should learn these squares and the corresponding square roots:

1^2	2^2	3^2	4^2	5^2	6^2	7^2	8^2	9^2	10^2	11^2	12^2	13^2	14^2	15^2
1	4	9	16	25	36	49	64	81	100	121	144	169	196	225

You should also learn these cubes and the corresponding cube roots:

1^3	2^3	3^3	4^3	5^3	10^3
1	8	27	64	125	1000

When you write '3 squared' as 3^2, you are using **index notation**. The 2 is the **index** or **power**. In 5^3, the power is 3. You will also meet higher powers, for example $2 \times 2 \times 2 \times 2 = 2^4$.

To work out a power you do the multiplications.

EXAMPLE 1

What are the first five square numbers?

SOLUTION

$1^2 = 1 \times 1 = 1$, $2^2 = 2 \times 2 = 4$, and so on.

The numbers are 1, 4, 9, 16, 25.

EXAMPLE 2

What is the square root of 81?

SOLUTION

$\sqrt{81} = \pm 9$

> Notice the use of the symbol ± here. This is because $-9 \times -9 = 81$ too (see Chapter 4).

EXAMPLE 3

What is the third cube number?

SOLUTION

$3^3 = 3 \times 3 \times 3 = 27$

EXAMPLE 4

Find $\sqrt[3]{216}$.

SOLUTION

$6 \times 6 \times 6 = 216$

So $\sqrt[3]{216} = 6$

> -6 is *not* correct here, because $-6 \times -6 \times -6 \neq 216$.
> (In fact, it equals -216. See Chapter 4.)

EXAMPLE 5

What is the tenth prime number?

SOLUTION

The primes are 2, 3, 5, 7, 11, 13, 17, 19, 23, 29, ...

The tenth prime is 29.

> Remember that 1 is *not* prime as it has only one factor.

EXAMPLE 6

List all the factors of 24.

SOLUTION

1, 2, 3, 4, 6, 8, 12, 24

EXAMPLE 7

List the first five multiples of 9.

SOLUTION

9, 18, 27, 36, 45

EXAMPLE 8

Work out $6^2 + \sqrt[3]{125}$.

SOLUTION

$36 + 5 = 41$

EXAMPLE 9

What is the sum of 3 squared and 3 cubed?

SOLUTION

$3^2 + 3^3 = 9 + 27 = 36$

EXAMPLE 10

What is the difference between 2 cubed and 2 squared?

SOLUTION

$2^3 - 2^2 = 8 - 4 = 4$

EXAMPLE 11

What is the product of the first three square numbers?

SOLUTION

$1^2 \times 2^2 \times 3^2 = 1 \times 4 \times 9 = 36$

EXAMPLE 12

Give any value equivalent to 10%.

SOLUTION

$\frac{1}{10}$ or 0.1   There are other suitable alternatives.

EXAMPLE 13

Find a counter example to disprove the statement 'No square number is also a cube number'.

SOLUTION

1 and 64 are both counter examples.
$1 = 1^2$ and $1 = 1^3$
$64 = 8^2$ and $64 = 4^3$

EXAMPLE 14

Work out $4^4 + 3^5$.

SOLUTION

$$4^4 + 3^5 = 4 \times 4 \times 4 \times 4 + 3 \times 3 \times 3 \times 3 \times 3$$
$$= 256 + 243$$
$$= 499$$

> Remember BODMAS: you must work out the powers **of** first, then add the results.

Exercise 1.1

1 Write down the value of each of these.
   a 4^2
   b 7^2
   c 9^2
   d 14^2

2 Write down the value of each of these.
   a $\sqrt{9}$
   b $\sqrt{64}$
   c $\sqrt{100}$
   d $\sqrt{225}$

3 Write down the value of each of these.
   a 1^3
   b 2^3
   c 10^3

4 Write down the value of each of these.
   a $\sqrt[3]{27}$
   b $\sqrt[3]{64}$
   c $\sqrt[3]{125}$

5 Write each of these using index notation.
   a $3 \times 3 \times 3 \times 3 \times 3$
   b $7 \times 7 \times 7 \times 7$
   c $2 \times 2 \times 2 \times 5 \times 5 \times 5 \times 5$

6 Work out each of these.
   a 5^4
   b $4^2 + 2^3$
   c $6^2 + 2^5$

7 What is the eighth square number?

8 What is the square root of 121?

9 Which number cubed gives 729?

10 Find $\sqrt{1}$.

11 Work out $5^3 + 5^2$.

12 Find the product of the second and fourth square numbers.

13 What is the difference between 10 cubed and 10 squared?

14 Find the sum of the first, third and fifth square numbers.

15 What decimal is equivalent to the fraction $\frac{3}{5}$?

16 Find a counter example which disproves the statement
   'n^2 is always greater than n'.

17 Which factors of 20 are also multiples of 4?

18 Which odd number, greater than 1, is a factor of both 20 and 30?

19 Which are the first three consecutive non-prime numbers?

20 Use the discs shown below to make six prime numbers.
   You may use each disc only once.

(1) (2) (3) (4) (5) (6) (7) (8) (9)

21 Between which two consecutive whole numbers does the square root of 175 lie?

Primes, factors and multiples

The sieve of Eratosthenes

The set of prime numbers between 1 and 100 can be found using a method known as the sieve of Eratosthenes.

1   Write out the numbers from 1 to 100 in order, in ten rows and ten columns.

2   Shade 1, which is not a prime number.

3   Use a different colour to shade all the multiples of 2, except 2 itself.

4   Look at the unshaded numbers. Use a different colour to shade all the multiples of 3, except 3 itself.

5   Use a different colour for the multiples of 5, except 5 itself.

6   Use a different colour for the multiples of 7, except 7 itself.

All the remaining unshaded numbers are the prime numbers between 1 and 100.

1	2	3	4	5	6	7	8	9	10
11	12	13	14	15	16	17	18	19	20
21	22	23	24	25	26	27	28	29	30
31	32	33	34	35	36	37	38	39	40
41	42	43	44	45	46	47	48	49	50
51	52	53	54	55	56	57	58	59	60
61	62	63	64	65	66	67	68	69	70
71	72	73	74	75	76	77	78	79	80
81	82	83	84	85	86	87	88	89	90
91	92	93	94	95	96	97	98	99	100

Prime factorisation

Any whole number can be written as a **product of its prime factors**.

For example, $18 = 2 \times 3 \times 3$.

The next example shows two ways of carrying out the process of **prime factorisation**.

EXAMPLE 15

Write 3465 as a product of its prime factors.

SOLUTION

Method 1: Factor trees

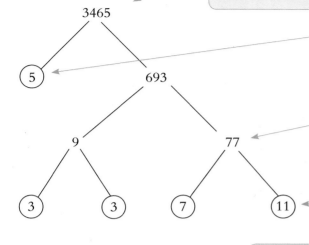

> Begin by finding two numbers that multiply together to give 3465. You could use 33×105 or 9×385 but 5 is an obvious factor of 3465, and you obtain 693 by division.

> 5 is prime so put a circle round it. Then look for two numbers that multiply together to give 693.

> Neither 9 nor 77 is prime so continue the process.

> All these numbers are prime so put a circle round each of them.
> The factor tree stops when every branch ends in a prime number (circled).

So, $3465 = 5 \times 3 \times 3 \times 7 \times 11$

$ = 3 \times 3 \times 5 \times 7 \times 11$

$ = 3^2 \times 5 \times 7 \times 11$

> It is usual to write the numbers in ascending order.

> You may want to, or be asked to, write the prime factors using **index notation**. Remember that $3 \times 3 = 3^2$ (3 squared). If the 3 had been used three times ($3 \times 3 \times 3$), you would write 3^3 (3 cubed).

Method 2: Repeated division by primes

3465

$3\overline{)3465}$

$3\overline{)1155}$

$5\overline{)385}$

$7\overline{)77}$

$11\overline{)11}$

1

> Try 2 first: 3465 is not divisible by 2 so 2 is not a factor of 3465.

> Next try 3: $3465 \div 3 = 1155$.

> Try 3 again: $1155 \div 3 = 385$.

> 385 does not divide exactly by 3 so try 5: $385 \div 5 = 77$.

> 77 does not divide exactly by 5 so try 7: $77 \div 7 = 11$.

> 11 does not divide exactly by 7 so try 11: $11 \div 11 = 1$.

> Stop when you reach 1.

So as a product of primes,

$3465 = 3 \times 3 \times 5 \times 7 \times 11$

$ = 3^2 \times 5 \times 7 \times 11$

> This version is written in **index notation** (using powers).

EXAMPLE 16

Write 5200 as a product of primes.

SOLUTION

Method 1: Factor trees

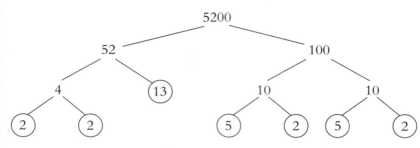

$5200 = 2 \times 2 \times 2 \times 2 \times 5 \times 5 \times 13$

$\qquad = 2^4 \times 5^2 \times 13$

Method 2: Repeated division by primes

```
2)5200
2)2600
2)1300
2)650
5)325
5)65
13)13
    1
```

Start with 2. Continue dividing by 2 until it no longer divides exactly into the result. Then continue the process with other prime numbers in ascending order (3, 5, 7, 11, 13, …) until the result is 1.

$5200 = 2 \times 2 \times 2 \times 2 \times 5 \times 5 \times 13$

$\qquad = 2^4 \times 5^2 \times 13$

Exercise 1.2

1 Write each of these numbers as a product of its prime factors.
Give your answers in index notation where appropriate.

  a 425   b 180   c 189   d 40

  e 198   f 117   g 210   h 288

  i 243   j 693   k 4000   l 7020

2 Given that $40\,500 = 2^a \times 3^b \times 5^c$, find a, b and c.

Highest common factor and lowest common multiple

The **highest common factor (HCF)** of a set of values is the largest factor that is common to all the values in the set. It can be found by listing all the factors for each value and selecting the largest number that appears in all the lists.

Find the highest common factor of 24 and 60.

SOLUTION

The factors of 24 are 1, 2, 3, 4, 6, 8, 12 and 24.
The factors of 60 are 1, 2, 3, 4, 5, 6, 10, 12, 15, 20, 30 and 60.
So the highest common factor of 24 and 60 is 12.

For larger values this method can be time consuming and may be quite difficult. A more appropriate method in this case is to use prime factorisation.

Find the highest common factor of 540 and 630.

SOLUTION

$540 = \boxed{2} \times 2 \times \boxed{3} \times \boxed{3} \times 3 \times \boxed{5}$

$630 = \boxed{2} \times \boxed{3} \times \boxed{3} \times \boxed{5} \times 7$

The highest common factor is
$2 \times 3 \times 3 \times 5 = 90$

> Write each number as a product of its prime factors using one of the methods of Example 15.

> Look at the 2s first.
> 540 has two 2s; 630 has one 2.
> Take the lower number: one 2.
> Then look at the 3s.
> 540 has three 3s; 630 has two 3s.
> Take the lower number: two 3s.
> Next look at the 5s.
> 540 and 630 have one 5 each, so take one 5.
> Finally look at the 7s.
> 540 has no 7s; 630 has one 7.
> Take the lower number: no 7s.

Find the highest common factor of 945 and 825.

SOLUTION

$945 = 3^3 \times 5 \times 7$
$825 = 3 \times 5^2 \times 11$
The highest common factor is $3 \times 5 = 15$

> Look at the 3s.
> 3^3 means there are three 3s for 945; there is one 3 for 825.
> Take the lower number: one 3.
> Look at the 5s.
> 945 has one 5; 825 has two 5s.
> Take the lower number: one 5.

The **lowest common multiple (LCM)** of a set of values is the smallest multiple that is common to all the values. It can be found by listing the first few multiples of each value in ascending order and selecting the smallest number that appears in all the lists.

Find the lowest common multiple of 5 and 8.

SOLUTION

The multiples of 5 are 5, 10, 15, 20, 25, 30, 35, 40, …
The multiples of 8 are 8, 16, 24, 32, 40, …
The lowest common multiple of 5 and 8 is 40.

You can see that this is not a very efficient method.

As for finding the highest common factor, a more appropriate method is to use prime factorisation.

Find the lowest common multiple of 24 and 36.

SOLUTION

$24 = 2 \times 2 \times 2 \times 3$

$36 = 2 \times 2 \times 3 \times 3$

The lowest common multiple is

$2 \times 2 \times 2 \times 3 \times 3 = 72$

> Write each number as a product of its prime factors.

> First look at the 2s.
> 24 has three 2s; 36 has two 2s.
> Take the higher number: three 2s.
> Then look at the 3s.
> 24 has one 3; 36 has two 3s.
> Take the higher number: two 3s.

Find the LCM of 18 and 30.

SOLUTION

$18 = 2 \times 3^2$

$30 = 2 \times 3 \times 5$

The lowest common multiple is $2 \times 3^2 \times 5 = 90$

> Look at the 2s.
> 18 has one 2; 30 has one 2.
> So the LCM has one 2.
> Look at the 3s.
> 18 has two 3s; 30 has one 3.
> Take the higher number: two 3s.
> Look at the 5s.
> 18 has no 5s but 30 has one 5.
> Take the higher number: one 5.

Lowest common multiples are useful for work with fractions (see Chapter 5). Primes, highest common factors and lowest common multiples can also be used to solve many practical problems. Take care in determining whether it is the highest common factor or the lowest common multiple that is required by the problem.

In a school, a bell rings for junior school at 9.00a.m. and again every 32 minutes.

A bell rings for senior school at 9.00a.m. and again every 40 minutes.

At what time will the bells next ring together?

SOLUTION

Junior school: 32, 64, …

Senior school: 40, 80, …

The lowest common multiple of 32 and 40 will give the required solution.

$32 = 2^5$

$40 = 2^3 \times 5$

> Write 32 and 40 as products of primes.

The lowest common multiple is $2^5 \times 5 = 160$

160 minutes = 2 hours 40 minutes

Therefore the bells next ring together at 11.40a.m.

EXAMPLE 24

Use prime factorisation to find $\sqrt{240\,100}$.

SOLUTION

$240\,100 = 2 \times 2 \times 5 \times 5 \times 7 \times 7 \times 7 \times 7$

$\sqrt{240\,100} = \sqrt{2 \times 2 \times 5 \times 5 \times 7 \times 7 \times 7 \times 7}$

$\phantom{\sqrt{240\,100}} = \sqrt{2^2 \times 5^2 \times 7^2 \times 7^2}$

$\phantom{\sqrt{240\,100}} = 2 \times 5 \times 7 \times 7$

$\phantom{\sqrt{240\,100}} = 490$

> Write 240 100 as a product of its prime factors.

> Arrange the factors in pairs and take one of each pair to find the square root.

EXAMPLE 25

Use prime factorisation to determine the smallest value that 55 125 must be multiplied by to give a cube number.

SOLUTION

$55\,125 = 3 \times 3 \times 5 \times 5 \times 5 \times 7 \times 7$

$ = 3^2 \times 5^3 \times 7^2$

> Write 55 125 as a product of its prime factors.

A cube number has each of its factors cubed.

To make a cube number, another 3 and another 7 are required.

Therefore 21 is the smallest value which 55 125 can be multiplied by to give a cube number.

Exercise 1.3

1 Find the highest common factor of each of these pairs of numbers.
   a 66 and 84   b 36 and 60   c 70 and 98
   d 36 and 54   e 128 and 144   f 132 and 286
   g 343 and 546   h 15 750 and 7350

2 Find the lowest common multiple of each of these pairs of numbers.
   a 9 and 15   b 8 and 10   c 24 and 30
   d 20 and 24   e 36 and 48   f 25 and 38
   g 90 and 70   h 99 and 66

3 Given that $777\,924 = 2^2 \times 3^4 \times 7^4$, find the square root of 777 924.

4 Use prime factorisation to find the cube root of 592 704.

5 a Write 7800 as a product of primes.
   b What is the smallest number that 7800 must be multiplied by to give a square number?

6 a Write 288 as a product of primes.
   b What is the smallest number that 288 must be multiplied by to give a cube number?

17 In a science experiment, the water content of a solution is recorded every 35 seconds, and the salt content is measured every 40 seconds. If the first readings of both are recorded at the same time, how long will it be before the readings are next recorded together?

8 120 Year 8 students and 96 Year 9 students are each to be split into groups, with the same number in every group.
What is the largest possible size for the groups?

You should now:

- know the definitions of the various mathematical terms and be able to give numerical examples of these
- be able to write any number as a product of primes
- be able to find the HCF and LCM of pairs of numbers.

Summary exercise 1

1 What are the prime factors of 30?

2 Which multiples of 3 are also factors of 24?

3 Work out $\sqrt[3]{1000} \times \sqrt[4]{100}$.

4 Find the sum of the first three cube numbers.

5 Write 3564 as a product of primes, using index notation.

6 Find the highest common factor of 630 and 4158.

7 Find the lowest common multiple of 16 and 18.

8 Use prime factorisation to work out $\sqrt{9604}$.

9 'If $x < y$, then $ax < ay$ for any value of a.'
Find a counter example to disprove this statement.

10 'The sum of two primes is never prime.'
Find a counter example to disprove this statement.

11 A bus stop is served by two routes. Buses on one route pass the stop every 25 minutes, and buses on the other route pass it every 40 minutes.
At midday, buses on both routes leave the stop together.
When is the next time that buses from the two routes should leave the stop together?

12 The sum of the factors of x is 18. What is x?

Examination questions

Questions **1** to **8** are from examination papers where you may not use a calculator.

Use 'Topic Tracker' at www.ccea.org.uk to find more exam questions.

1 Evaluate

   a 5^3
          b $2^4 + 3^2$

2 Work out the value of $2^3 \times 5^2$. Show your working.

3 Calculate

   a 4^3
          b $\sqrt{25} + \sqrt[3]{27}$

4 **a** Sadie says, 'When you divide an even number by an even number, you always get an even number'. Give an example to show that Sadie is wrong.

   b Write down the two numbers which are the square roots of 25.

5 Calculate the prime factors of 216.
Now write 216 as a product of prime factors in index form.

6 For each of the following statements, give an example which disproves the statement.

   a Every prime number is odd.

   b Every number has a reciprocal.

7 The front and back wipers of a car are switched on at exactly the same time. The back wiper begins the sweeping movement again every minute, whilst the front wiper begins every 45 seconds. How long will it be until the front and back wipers begin again together?

8 'If $x < y$, then $x^2 < y^2$.'
Give a pair of values for x and y which disproves this.

Questions **9** to **12** are from examination papers where you may use a calculator.

9 Find the value of

   a $\sqrt{2.25}$
          b 3.7^2

10 A plastic bag has been blown onto this registration plate. The missing two digit number is a cube in which both digits are even numbers. What is the missing number?

11 **a** Write 40 as a product of prime factors.

   b Find the LCM (lowest common multiple) of 40 and 28.

   c Find the HCF (highest common factor) of 40 and 28.

12 Paul says, 'The difference between the cubes of any pair of consecutive positive integers is a prime number.' Is Paul correct? Show working to justify your answer.

CHAPTER 2

Whole numbers

This chapter is about:
- addition and subtraction without a calculator
- multiplication and division without a calculator.

You should already know:
- how to read, write and order whole numbers.

Addition and subtraction without a calculator

This basic arithmetic has been covered throughout Key Stages 1, 2 and 3. When you are adding numbers together, remember to make sure that the columns are lined up properly so that each figure takes its correct place value in the calculation.

EXAMPLE 1

Work out 457 + 292.

SOLUTION

```
    4   5   7
+  ₁2   9   2
        4   9
```

Work from right to left.
Add the units: 7 + 2 = 9
Next, add the 10s column: 5 + 9 = 14
The 4 is written in the 10s column and the 1 is carried to the next column.

```
    4   5   7
+  ₁2   9   2
    7   4   9
```

Finally, add the digits in the 100s column, including the carried digit:
4 + 2 + 1 = 7

Here are two different methods for subtraction. You may have learnt a different method. It is advisable to stick to one method. Use the method you prefer.

EXAMPLE 2

Work out 647 − 372.

SOLUTION

Method 1

$$
\begin{array}{r}
6\quad 4\quad 7\\
-\;3\quad 7\quad 2\\
\hline
5
\end{array}
$$

> For the 10s: 4 − 7 cannot be done directly.

> For the units: 7 − 2 = 5.

$$
\begin{array}{r}
{}^{5}\!6\quad {}^{1}\!4\quad 7\\
-\;3\quad 7\quad 2\\
\hline
2\quad 7\quad 5
\end{array}
$$

> Exchange 10 from the 64 to give 50 and 14.
> Now 14 − 7 = 7 and 5 − 3 = 2.

Method 2

$$
\begin{array}{r}
6\quad 4\quad 7\\
-\;3\quad 7\quad 2\\
\hline
5
\end{array}
$$

> The first part of the method is the same.

> Instead of dropping 64 down to 50 and 14, you can add 1 ten to the 3 tens to make 37 up to 47.

$$
\begin{array}{r}
6\quad {}^{1}\!4\quad 7\\
-\;{}_{1}3\quad 7\quad 2\\
\hline
2\quad 7\quad 5
\end{array}
$$

> Now 14 − 7 = 7 and 6 − 4 = 2.

Addition and subtraction are **inverse** operations so one undoes the other.
This is a useful check when carrying out calculations.

For example,
6437 − 2485 = 3952

therefore
3952 + 2485 = 6437

Exercise 2.1

1 Calculate these.
  a 456 + 634   b 2347 + 6753   c 45 + 876 + 233
  d 89 456 + 34 526   e 265 + 98 765 + 345   f 23 + 457 + 348 + 3287

2 Calculate these.
  a 3457 − 458   b 3765 − 1692   c 4589 − 2361
  d 23 658 − 14 634   e 1200 − 347   f 7459 − 4583

3 Given that 4572 + 3487 = 8059, write down *only* the answer to
  each of these calculations.
  a 8059 − 4572   b 8059 − 3487
  c 8059 − 3488   d 8060 − 4572

14 There are 124 passengers on a plane from Belfast to Gatwick.
   At Gatwick 36 passengers get off, and another 52 get on for the
   flight from Gatwick to Paris.
   How many passengers are on the flight from Gatwick to Paris?

5 Tickets for a concert are available from outlet A and from outlet B.
   Outlet A sells 12 546 tickets and outlet B sells 19 573 tickets.
   On the day of the concert, 467 of the ticket-holders do not turn up.
   If no further tickets are issued, how many people actually attend the concert?

Multiplication and division without a calculator

Multiplying and dividing by powers of ten

When multiplying a whole number by 10, all the digits move one place to the left, so you need to insert an extra zero as a placeholder in the units place. When multiplying by 100, all the digits move two places to the left, so you need to insert two extra zeros; when multiplying by 1000, all the digits move three places to the left, so you need to insert three extra zeros, and so on.

When dividing a whole number by 10, all the digits move one place to the right and a placeholder zero in the units place can be removed. When dividing by 100, all the digits move two places to the right and two zeros can be removed; when dividing by 1000, all the digits move three places to the right and three zeros can be removed, and so on.

For example:

$$54 \times 100 = 5400 \qquad 43\,000 \div 10 = 4300$$
$$260 \times 1000 = 260\,000 \qquad 35\,000 \div 100 = 350$$

Multiplying and dividing by multiples of 10, 100 and 1000

The method above can be extended when multiplying or dividing by multiples of the powers of ten. For example, to multiply by 600, first multiply by 6 and then by 100; or to divide by 3000 divide by 1000 and then by 3.

For example:

$$27 \times 300 = 27 \times 3 \times 100 = 81 \times 100 = 8100$$
$$420 \times 2000 = 420 \times 2 \times 1000 = 840 \times 1000 = 840\,000$$
$$86\,000 \div 400 = 86\,000 \div 100 \div 4 = 860 \div 4 = 215$$
$$7200 \div 60 = 7200 \div 10 \div 6 = 720 \div 6 = 120$$

Long multiplication and division

When multiplying a number with three or more digits by a number with two or more digits, you need to use **long multiplication**. Here are two methods. You may have learnt others. Use the method you prefer.

EXAMPLE 3

Work out 432×37.

SOLUTION

Method 1: Long multiplication

The calculation can be broken into $(432 \times 7) + (432 \times 30)$ and so can be carried out as follows.

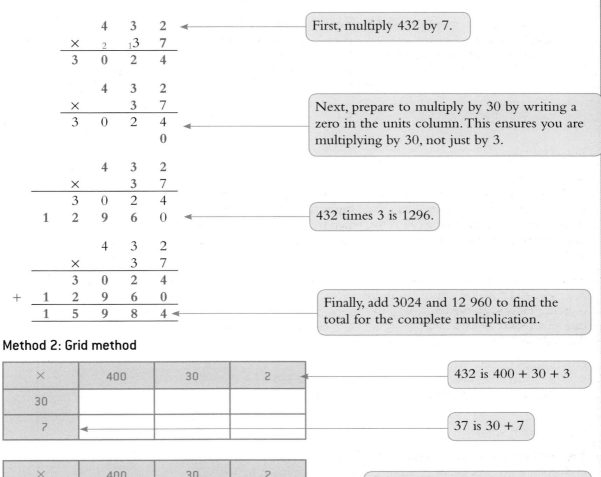

First, multiply 432 by 7.

$$
\begin{array}{ccccc}
 & & 4 & 3 & 2 \\
\times & _2 & _13 & 7 \\
\hline
 & 3 & 0 & 2 & 4 \\
\end{array}
$$

$$
\begin{array}{ccccc}
 & & 4 & 3 & 2 \\
\times & & 3 & 7 \\
\hline
 & 3 & 0 & 2 & 4 \\
 & & & & 0 \\
\end{array}
$$

Next, prepare to multiply by 30 by writing a zero in the units column. This ensures you are multiplying by 30, not just by 3.

$$
\begin{array}{ccccc}
 & & 4 & 3 & 2 \\
\times & & 3 & 7 \\
\hline
 & 3 & 0 & 2 & 4 \\
1 & 2 & 9 & 6 & 0 \\
\end{array}
$$

432 times 3 is 1296.

$$
\begin{array}{ccccc}
 & & 4 & 3 & 2 \\
\times & & 3 & 7 \\
\hline
 & 3 & 0 & 2 & 4 \\
+ \; 1 & 2 & 9 & 6 & 0 \\
\hline
1 & 5 & 9 & 8 & 4 \\
\end{array}
$$

Finally, add 3024 and 12 960 to find the total for the complete multiplication.

Method 2: Grid method

×	400	30	2
30			
7			

432 is 400 + 30 + 3

37 is 30 + 7

×	400	30	2
30	12 000	900	60
7	2 800	210	14

Multiply the parts of each number in turn: 400 × 30 = 12 000

$$
\begin{array}{cccccc}
 & 1 & 2 & 0 & 0 & 0 \\
 & & 9 & 0 & 0 \\
 & & & 6 & 0 \\
 & 2 & 8 & 0 & 0 \\
 & & 2 & 1 & 0 \\
+ & & & 1 & 4 \\
\hline
1 & 5 & 9 & 8 & 4 \\
\end{array}
$$

Add the numbers in the body of the table to find the total for the complete calculation.

Again, there are different techniques for dividing one number by another and you should use the one you feel most comfortable with.

EXAMPLE 4

Work out 2365 ÷ 19.

Method 1: Long division

```
         19 ) 2  3  6  5
```
Set up the calculation using the division bracket notation.

```
              1
         19 ) 2  3  6  5
            - 1  9  0  0
              4  6  5
```
$19 \times 1 = 19$ but since 1 represents 1 hundred, $19 \times 100 = 1900$

```
              1  2
         19 ) 2  3  6  5
            - 1  9  0  0
              4  6  5
            -   3  8  0
                8  5
```
$19 \times 2 = 38$ but since the 2 represents 2 tens, $19 \times 20 = 380$

```
              1  2  4
         19 ) 2  3  6  5
            - 1  9  0  0
              4  6  5
            -   3  8  0
                8  5
            -      7  6
                      9
```
$19 \times 4 = 76$ since the 4 represents 4 units.

So $2365 \div 19 = 124$ remainder 9.

Method 2: Long division with the remainder carried down

```
         19 ) 2  3  6  5
```
As in method 1, set up the calculation using the division bracket notation.

```
              1
         19 ) 2  3  6  5
            - 1  9
              4
```
19 will not divide into 2, so divide 19 into 23. This goes once with remainder 4.

```
              1
         19 ) 2  3  6  5
            - 1  9  ↓
              4  6
```
Bring down the next digit, 6 in this case, to give 46.

```
              1  2
         19 ) 2  3  6  5
            - 1  9
              4  6
            - 3  8
              8
```
19 divides into 46 twice, with remainder 8.

```
          1   2   4
  1  9 ) 2   3   6   5
      -  1   9
            4   6
          - 3   8
                8   5
              - 7   6
                    9
```

Bring down the digit 5 to make 85.
19 divides into 85 four times, with remainder 9.

So 2365 ÷ 19 = 124 remainder 9.

Method 3: Short division

```
  1   9 ) 2   3   6   5
```

As in methods 1 and 2, set up the calculation using the division bracket notation.

```
                1
  1   9 ) 2   3   ⁴6   5
```

19 will not divide into 2, so divide 19 into 23. This goes once with remainder 4.

```
                1   2
  1   9 ) 2   3   ⁴6   ⁸5
```

Divide 19 into 46. It goes twice, remainder 8.

```
                1   2   4   R 9
  1   9 ) 2   3   ⁴6   ⁸5
```

Divide 19 into 85. It goes four times, remainder 9.

Like addition and subtraction, multiplication and division are inverse operations and this fact can be used to check calculations.

For example,

$$156 \times 23 = 3588$$

therefore

$$3588 \div 23 = 156$$

Multiplication and division can be used to solve problems.

EXAMPLE 5

A milkman delivers 89 crates of milk, each crate holding 24 pints. How many pints of milk does he deliver in total?

SOLUTION

The problem requires you to calculate 89×24.

```
            8   9
    ×       2   4
        3   5   6
  + 1   7   8   0
    2   1   3   6
```

So the milkman delivers 2136 pints of milk.

In Example 4 there was a remainder, 9. When you use division to solve a problem, it is important to understand the significance of the remainder in the context of the problem.

EXAMPLE 6

664 students are to travel on a school outing. Each coach can carry 54 students. How many coaches are needed, and how many students are on the last coach (if all the other coaches are full)?

SOLUTION

The problem requires you to calculate $664 \div 54$.

```
              1   2
  5   4 ) 6   6   4
      -   5   4
          1   2   4
      -   1   0   8
              1   6
```

$664 \div 54 = 12$ remainder 16, so 12 coaches are filled and there are 16 students left.

The correct answer to this problem is that *13* coaches will be needed, with 16 students on the last coach.

EXAMPLE 7

812 students are to be seated in rows in an assembly hall. If each row has 34 seats, how many rows are completely filled and how many students are seated in the last row?

SOLUTION

The problem requires you to calculate $812 \div 34$.

```
              2   3
  3   4 ) 8   1   2
      -   6   8
          1   3   2
      -   1   0   2
              3   0
```

$812 \div 34 = 23$ remainder 30, so 23 rows are completely filled and there are 30 students in the last row.

Exercise 2.2

1 Calculate these.

   a $6300 \div 100$ b 240×100 c $3600 \div 10$

   d $40\,000 \div 100$ e $8 \times 10\,000$ f 540×1000

2 Calculate these.
   a   24 × 500   b   3600 ÷ 200   c   40 000 ÷ 500
   d   38 × 8000   e   24 000 ÷ 40   f   124 × 60

3 Calculate these.
   a   45 × 67   b   243 × 54   c   42 × 652
   d   4523 × 31   e   236 × 637   f   392 × 682

4 Calculate these.
   a   1242 ÷ 23   b   1728 ÷ 18   c   1944 ÷ 36
   d   7533 ÷ 31   e   55 473 ÷ 123   f   25 488 ÷ 72

5 Given that 680 × 23 = 15 640, write down the answer to each of
   these.
   a   15 640 ÷ 23   b   15 640 ÷ 68

6 Given that 222 360 ÷ 654 = 340, write down the answer to each of
   these.
   a   654 × 34   b   340 × 65 400

7 1332 eggs are to be packed into cartons, each holding 18 eggs.
   How many cartons are needed?

8 A man cycles 12 miles each day. How far does he cycle in the year?
   (Assume that it is not a leap year.)

9 How many individual stamps, each worth 23 pence, can a girl buy
   with a £5 note, and how much change will she have?

10 In a weekend Bonanza Sale, an electrical shop sells 23 washing
   machines priced at £350 each, and 18 tumble dryers at £240 each.
   What is the total income from these machines?

You should now:

- be able to add and subtract whole numbers
- be able to multiply and divide by powers, and multiples of the powers of ten
- be able to multiply and divide any whole numbers
- be able to solve problems involving addition, subtraction, multiplication and division, and
  understand the significance of the remainder in the context of division
- understand inverse operations and use them as a checking procedure.

Summary exercise 2

1 Calculate these.
   a   64 + 563 + 345   b   3476 − 1379
   c   34 762 + 14 539 − 25 673   d   6059 − 3412 + 6789

2 In September 2009 a school had 974 students. At the end of the
   school year in June 2010, 169 Year 14 students left. In September
   2010, 146 Year 8 students joined the school.
   What was the total school population in September 2010?

3 Calculate these.
   a 760×100 **b** $89\,000 \div 1000$ **c** $34\,000 \times 10$
   d 420×60 **e** $180\,000 \div 200$ **f** 350×500

4 Calculate these.
   a 56×28 **b** $15\,648 \div 32$ **c** 421×37
   d 234×463 **e** $6205 \div 17$ **f** $972 \div 27$

5 Given that $2300 \times 56 = 128\,800$, write down the answer to each of these.
   a $128\,800 \div 56$ **b** $128\,800 \div 230$ **c** $128\,800 \div 112$

6 A girl attends a fitness club three nights a week, for 24 weeks. On each of the three nights she does 75 sit-ups as part of her routine. How many sit-ups does she do in total during the 24 weeks?

7 A 380 cm length of ribbon is to be cut into equal strips, each 25 cm long. How many complete strips can be cut, and what length of ribbon will be left over?

Examination questions

Question 1 is from an examination paper where you may not use a calculator.

Use 'Topic Tracker' at www.ccea.org.uk to find more exam questions.

1 **a** Write down the number seven thousand one hundred and eight in figures.

  b From the list of numbers
     76 39 43 25 23 51 57 89 47
     write down
     i two numbers which add up to 100
     ii two numbers with a difference of 50.

Question 2 is from an examination paper where you may use a calculator.

2 Rosie wants to buy dusters which cost 85p each. How many can she buy with £15? How much change should she get?

CHAPTER 3

Decimals

This chapter is about:

- adding and subtracting decimals
- multiplying and dividing decimals.

You should already know:

- how to read, write and order whole numbers and decimals
- how to add and subtract whole numbers
- how to multiply and divide whole numbers.

Adding and subtracting decimals

Decimals are added and subtracted in exactly the same way as whole numbers. You line up the digits with the same place value in columns, and the decimal point goes in the same position in the answer.

EXAMPLE 1

Work out these.

  a $62.3 + 89.52$ b $235.37 - 42.724$

SOLUTION

a Write the numbers as a column calculation with the decimal points lined up.

```
    6   2  .  3
 +  8   9  .  5   2
 ─────────────────
    1   5   1  .  8   2
            1
```

Note the position of the decimal point in the answer; it is in line with the decimal points in the question.

b

```
    1   1   4      1   6   1
    2   3   5  .  3   7   0
 -          4   2  .  7   2   4
 ──────────────────────────
    1   9   2  .  6   4   6
```

You may wish to insert a zero here to help in the calculation.

Multiplying and dividing decimals

Multiplying and dividing by powers of ten

When multiplying by 10, all the digits move one place to the left; when multiplying by 100, all the digits move two places to the left; and when multiplying by 1000, all the digits move three places to the left. When dividing by 10, all the digits move one place to the right; when dividing by 100, all the digits move two places to the right; and when dividing by 1000, all the digits move three places to the right.

> Many people consider multiplication to be the decimal point moving to the right, and division to be the decimal point moving to the left – it is important to remember, however, that mathematically it is the digits that are moving and not the decimal point, i.e. a value in the tenths column when multiplied by 10 moves to the units.

EXAMPLE 2

Work out these.
- a 35.678×10
- b $123.46 \div 100$
- c 2.3×1000
- d $17.39 \div 1000$

SOLUTION

- a $35.678 \times 10 = 356.78$
- b $123.46 \div 100 = 1.2346$
- c $2.3 \times 1000 = 2300$
- d $17.39 \div 1000 = 0.017\,39$

> Note the extra zeros included as the digits move to the left.

> Note the extra zeros included as the digits move to the right.

Multiplication of decimals

To multiply decimals, initially ignore the decimal point and carry out the multiplication as for whole numbers. Then count the total number of digits after the decimal points in the questions and insert the decimal point into the answer so that there are same number of digits after the decimal point as this total.

The next example illustrates this. The numbers are multiplied using long multiplication, but you can use whichever method you prefer.

EXAMPLE 3

Work out these.
- a 62.34×8.6
- b 1.65×0.042

SOLUTION

a First, ignore the decimal points and work out 6234×86.

```
          6  2  3  4
    ×           8  6
    ─────────────────
       3  7  4  0  4
 +  4  9  8  7  2  0
    ─────────────────
    5  3  6  1  2  4
```

> In ignoring the decimal points you have actually multiplied 6234 (100 times too big) by 86 (10 times too big). Hence the overall answer is 1000 times too big and you need to divide it by 1000. This is often dealt with by saying that, since there are a total of three digits after the decimal points in the question, there must also be three digits after the decimal point in the answer.

So $62.34 \times 8.6 = 536.124$

b

$$
\begin{array}{rrrr}
 & 1 & 6 & 5 \\
\times & & 4 & 2 \\
\hline
 & 3 & 3 & 0 \\
+ \quad 6 & 6 & 0 & 0 \\
\hline
6 & 9 & 3 & 0 \\
\end{array}
$$

Since there are five digits after the decimal points in the question, there must also be five digits after the decimal point in the answer.

So $1.65 \times 0.042 = 0.06930$

Notice that you need to insert a zero before the digits you obtained from the multiplication ignoring the decimal points.

Notice also that, although you do not need to write the last zero in your answer (because 0.0693 is the same as 0.06930), you must count it as one of the digits after the decimal point when working out the size of the answer.

It follows that to multiply decimals by multiples of the powers of ten, for example by 400, first multiply by the 4 and then by the 100, or by the 100 and then by the 4.

EXAMPLE 4

What is 2.168×400?

SOLUTION

$2.168 \times 400 = 2.168 \times 100 \times 4 = 216.8 \times 4 =$

$$
\begin{array}{rrrrr}
2 & 1 & 6 & . & 8 \\
\times & & & & 4 \\
\hline
8 & 6 & 7 & . & 2 \\
\end{array}
$$

Division of decimals

To divide decimals, make the number you are dividing *by* (the **divisor**) a whole number by multiplying it by 10, 100 or 1000. Then multiply the number to be divided (the **dividend**) by the same power of 10. Multiplying both numbers in the division by the same amount does not change the result of the division, but it means that you are now dividing by an integer. Proceed with the division as you would for whole numbers, checking that the decimal point in the answer lines up with the decimal point in the question.

EXAMPLE 5

Work out these.
  a $0.738 \div 0.06$
  b $120.52 \div 2.3$

SOLUTION

a $0.738 \div 0.06 = 73.8 \div 6$

To make the divisor (0.06) a whole number you need to multiply it by 100, so multiply *both* numbers by 100. Here the numbers are divided using short division, but you can use long division if you prefer.

$$
\begin{array}{r}
1 \quad 2 \; . \; 3 \\
6 \overline{) \; 7 \quad {}^1 3 \; . \; {}^1 8} \\
\end{array}
$$

So $0.738 \div 0.06 = 12.3$

b $120.52 \div 2.3 = 1205.2 \div 23$ ◄───────────

$$\begin{array}{r} 5 \quad 2\ .\ 4 \\ 2 \quad 3 \overline{)\ 1 \quad 2 \quad 0 \quad {}^5 5\ .\ {}^9 2} \end{array}$$

So $120.52 \div 2.3 = 52.4$

To make 2.3 a whole number you need to multiply it by 10, so multiply *both* numbers by 10.

You may have noticed that multiplying by a number greater than 1 has an *increasing* effect. For example,

$1.62 \times 3.4 = 5.508$

and 5.508 is greater than 1.62.

However, multiplying by a number less than 1 has a *decreasing* effect. For example,

$1.62 \times 0.34 = 0.5508$

and 0.5508 is less than 1.62.

You may also have noticed that dividing by a number greater than 1 has a *decreasing* effect. For example,

$71.28 \div 2.2 = 32.4$

and 32.4 is less than 71.28.

However, dividing by a number less than 1 has an *increasing* effect. For example,

$71.28 \div 0.22 = 324$

and 324 is greater than 71.28.

This concept can provide a good check as to whether the answer to a decimal calculation is appropriate or not.

Exercise 3.1

1   Calculate these.
   a $34.567 + 54.38$
   b $673.1 + 45.789$
   c $5.621 + 76.583 + 3.57$
   d $86.2 - 45.37$
   e $126.74 - 67.52$
   f $823 - 12.507$

2   Calculate these.
   a 2.34×12
   b 0.017×8
   c 32.4×0.7
   d 4.82×1.9
   e 0.113×0.6
   f 24.62×8.36
   g 2.9×1.87
   h 0.03×0.19
   i 6.2×0.04
   j 12.4×1.68
   k 124.7×0.12
   l 1.25×2.8

3   Calculate these.
   a $0.378 \div 0.03$
   b $2.952 \div 0.12$
   c $47.58 \div 2.6$
   d $111.25 \div 12.5$
   e $0.1401 \div 0.6$
   f $1100 \div 5.5$
   g $44.16 \div 1.2$
   h $10.224 \div 0.18$
   i $0.182 \div 0.07$
   j $0.1 \div 0.008$
   k $24 \div 1.5$
   l $228.9 \div 3.5$

4 Use the correct symbol, > or <, to complete each of these statements. (Do *not* actually carry out the calculations.)

   a $18.3 \div 0.3 \ \square \ 18.3$ b $204.2 \times 0.2 \ \square \ 204.2$

   c $1.56 \times 2.4 \ \square \ 1.56$ d $0.008 \times 1.8 \ \square \ 0.008$

   e $13.92 \div 2.4 \ \square \ 13.92$ f $0.74 \div 0.85 \ \square \ 0.74$

5 A strip of wood 8.875 m long has two pieces cut from it. The first piece removed is 2.65 m long and the second piece is 3.5 m. What length of wood remains?

6 A delivery van carries parcels of weight 6.45 kg, 12.8 kg and 5.725 kg. What is the total weight of the three parcels?

7 The total time taken by four athletes to complete a 400 m relay was 40.9 seconds. The times of the first three athletes were 10.32 seconds, 10.46 seconds and 10.09 seconds. Find the time taken by the fourth athlete.

8 A 10p coin is 0.2 cm thick. A number of these coins are arranged into a pile 28.4 cm high. Find the total *value* of the pile of 10p coins.

9 I buy 0.8 kg of bananas costing £1.50 per kilogram, and 1.2 kg of apples costing 70p per kilogram. How much do I spend in total?

10 After 400 turns a machine drill penetrates to a depth of 22 cm. How far does it penetrate in each turn?

You should now:

- understand place value in decimals
- be able to order decimals
- be able to add, subtract, multiply and divide decimals, including multiplication and division by powers of ten, and multiples of powers of ten
- be able to solve problems involving addition, subtraction, multiplication and division, and understand the significance of the remainder in the context of division
- understand the increasing and decreasing effect when multiplying and dividing by decimals
- be able to solve problems involving decimals in context.

Summary exercise 3

1 Calculate these.

   a $6.36 + 0.567 + 12.8$ b $45.67 - 28.8$

   c 1.64×7.3 d $0.592 \div 0.8$

   e $8.67 - 4.654 + 2.9$ f 2.31×0.34

2 a Will the answer to the calculation 3.68×0.27 be greater than or less than 3.68?

   b Will the answer to the calculation 3.68×2.7 be greater than or less than 3.68?

   c Will the answer to the calculation $3.68 \div 0.27$ be greater than or less than 3.68? (Do *not* actually carry out the calculations.)

3 Given that $\dfrac{37\,380}{420} = 89$,

write down *only* the answer to each of these calculations.

   a 420×89 b 8.9×4.2 c 4200×8.9

4 A 5.2 kg cake is cut into equal pieces, each weighing 0.4 kg.
   How many pieces is it cut into?

5 A supermarket has cheese on sale at £3.45 per kilogram.
   A woman buys 0.4 kg. How much does her piece of cheese cost?

6 A girl training for a cross-country race runs 60 km every week.
   Each weekday (Monday to Friday), she runs along a route
   7.5 km long.
   How far does she run on Saturdays and Sundays to complete her
   training for the week? (Assume that she runs the same distance on
   Saturday and on Sunday.)

7 A square has perimeter 2.8 m. Calculate its area.

8 A taxi fare is made up of a standard charge of £1.70, plus an extra
   40p per mile for the actual journey. If the total fare is £8.50, how
   far was the journey?

Examination questions

Use 'Topic Tracker' at www.ccea.org.uk to find more exam questions.

Questions 1 to 6 are from examination papers where you may not use a
calculator.

1 Calculate:
   a 0.6 × 0.2   b   0.8 + 1.67
   c 3.7 − 1.89   d   1.47 ÷ 3

2 Calculate 0.2 × 0.7

3 a Calculate 3.6 − 1.79   b   Calculate 0.4 × 0.2
   c Given that 58 × 161 = 9338, find the value of 9338 ÷ 580.

4 Given that 63 × 426 = 26 838, find $\dfrac{26\,838}{630}$.

5 Given that 10 998 ÷ 94 = 117, find
   a 10.998 ÷ 94   b   9.4 × 117

6 Five kilograms of potatoes and two kilograms of carrots cost £4.40
   in total. The potatoes cost 60p per kilogram. How much would it
   cost to buy one kilogram of potatoes and one kilogram of carrots?

Questions 7 to 9 are from examination papers where you may use a
calculator.

7 Visitor's tax costs 2.75 euro for the first day and 1.15 euro for each
   extra day. The total tax paid by Lola was 13.10 euro. How long did
   she stay?

8 a For a trip to Norway, Debbie changed £350 into Norwegian
      kroner. £1 = 12.2 Norwegian kroner. How many kroner did
      she get?
   b In Norway, Debbie bought a camera which cost 675 kroner.
      How much would the camera be in £?

9 Together 0.6 kg of pears and 0.8 kg of apples cost £2.48. Pears cost
   £1.60 per kg. How much do apples cost per kg?

CHAPTER 4

Negative numbers

This chapter is about:

- adding and subtracting with negative numbers
- multiplying and dividing with negative numbers.

You should already know:

- how to read, write and order whole numbers and decimals
- how to add and subtract whole numbers and decimals
- how to multiply and divide whole numbers and decimals.

So far this book has only dealt with positive numbers, that is, numbers above zero on the number line. Although the sign for these was not included, they are in fact +6, +24, etc. If a number has no sign associated with it, you can assume that it is positive.

Below zero on the number line are the negative numbers. To distinguish these clearly they are always written with a negative sign. So, for example, a negative 6 is written as −6.

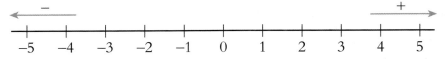

The positive whole numbers, the negative whole numbers and the value zero together make up the set of **integers**.

Negative numbers are useful in many real-life situations, for example for temperatures, bank balances and heights of geographical features above and below sea-level.

Adding and subtracting negative numbers

Look at this number pattern.

$$2 + 2 = 4$$
$$2 + 1 = 3$$
$$2 + 0 = 2$$

Continuing this pattern gives:

$$2 + (−1) = 1$$
$$2 + (−2) = 0$$
$$2 + (−3) = −1$$
$$2 + (−4) = −2$$

and so on.

Subtract 1 from the right-hand side each time.

From this you can establish that '+' and '−' immediately next to each other are equivalent to a single '−'. For example,

$$2 + (-3) = 2 - 3 = -1$$

> Note that it is good practice to include brackets around a negative value if the negative sign lies immediately next to an operation.

Now look at this number pattern.

$$4 - 2 = 2$$
$$4 - 1 = 3$$
$$4 - 0 = 4$$

Continuing this pattern gives:

$$4 - (-1) = 5$$
$$4 - (-2) = 6$$
$$4 - (-3) = 7$$
$$4 - (-4) = 8$$
and so on.

> Add 1 to the right-hand side each time.

From this you can establish that '−' and '−' immediately next to each other are equivalent to a single '+'. For example,

$$4 - (-3) = 4 + 3 = 7$$

These provide two important rules for the addition and subtraction of negative numbers.

plus and *minus* → minus	$+ - \rightarrow -$
minus and *minus* → plus	$- - \rightarrow +$

EXAMPLE 1

Work out these.

    a $6 + (-2)$ b $8 - (-3)$ c $-2 + (-4)$ d $-3 - (-7)$

SOLUTION

    a $6 + (-2) = 6 - 2 = 4$ b $8 - (-3) = 8 + 3 = 11$
    c $-2 + (-4) = -2 - 4 = -6$ d $-3 - (-7) = -3 + 7 = 4$

Exercise 4.1

1 Calculate these.

    a $2 - 7$ b $-3 + 4$ c $3 + (-3)$ d $-16 + (-3)$

    e $4 - (-2)$ f $8 + 7$ g $-10 - (-2)$ h $-8 + (-8)$

    i $3 - 7$ j $-4 - 8$ k $12 + (-22)$ l $7 - (-7)$

    m $5 - 9$ n $-8 + (-7)$ o $-23 + 5$ p $-2 + 2$

2 Copy and complete these.

    a $-6 + \square = -3$ b $8 - \square = 12$ c $4 - \square = -2$ d $-10 + \square = -8$

    e $-5 + \square = 10$ f $\square - (-7) = -2$ g $\square + (-8) = 14$ h $-4 - \square = -4$

    i $8 + \square = -1$

3 The heights above sea-level of three villages, P, Q and R, are 150 m, −20 m and −35 m, respectively.
   a How much higher is P than Q?   b How much higher is Q than R?

4 A man's bank account is overdrawn by £1250. How much must he deposit to have a credit balance of £800 in his account?

Multiplying and dividing negative numbers

Look at this number pattern.

$4 \times 2 = 8$
$4 \times 1 = 4$
$4 \times 0 = 0$

Continuing this pattern gives:

$4 \times (-1) = -4$
$4 \times (-2) = -8$
$4 \times (-3) = -12$ ← Subtract 4 from the right-hand side each time.
and so on.

From this you can establish that multiplying a positive number by a negative number results in a negative number.

Now look at this number pattern.

$-4 \times 2 = -8$
$-4 \times 1 = -4$
$-4 \times 0 = 0$

Continuing this pattern gives:

$-4 \times (-1) = 4$
$-4 \times (-2) = 8$
$-4 \times (-3) = 12$ ← Add 4 to the right-hand side each time.
and so on.

From this you can establish that multiplying a negative number by a negative number results in a positive number.

The same rules apply for division.

The rules can be extended to more than two numbers. It is usually best to ignore the signs while you work out the numerical value of the answer and then work out the sign at the end.

> Multiplying or dividing an *even* number of negative numbers results in a *positive* answer.
> Multiplying or dividing an *odd* number of negative numbers results in a *negative* answer.

EXAMPLE 2

Work out these.

a 6 × (−3)   b −2 × (−8)   c 14 ÷ (−2)   d −10 ÷ (−5)
e 5 × 5   f −5 × (−5)   g −7 × 3 × 2   h −16 ÷ 4 ÷ −4

SOLUTION

a 6 × (−3) = −18 ◄————— There is one negative number so the answer is negative.

b −2 × (−8) = 16 ◄————— There are two negative numbers so the answer is positive.

c 14 ÷ (−2) = −7 ◄————— There is one negative number so the answer is negative.

d −10 ÷ (−5) = 2 ◄————— There are two negative numbers so the answer is positive.

e 5 × 5 = 25 ◄—————
⎫ These illustrate why the square root of a number can
⎬ be positive or negative. Since 5 × 5 = 25 and −5 × −5
f −5 × (−5) = 25 ◄————— ⎭ = 25, then $\sqrt{25} = \pm 5$.

Work out the numerical value of the answer first.

g 7 × 3 × 2 = 42 ◄—————

−7 × 3 × 2 = −42 ◄————— Count the number of negative numbers to work out the sign of the answer. An odd number of negative numbers gives a negative answer.

h 16 ÷ 4 ÷ 4 = 1 ◄————— Work out the numerical value of the answer first.

−16 ÷ 4 ÷ −4 = 1 ◄————— Count the number of negative numbers to work out the sign of the answer. An even number of negative numbers gives a positive answer.

Note that the rules of negative numbers also apply to decimals and fractions.

Exercise 4.2

1 Calculate these.
a 5 × (−3)   b 8 × (−2)   c −5 × (−7)   d 18 ÷ 2
e 15 ÷ (−3)   f −24 ÷ (−4)   g −6 × (−3)   h −20 ÷ (−5)
i −8 × (−2)   j −2 × (−2)   k 4 ÷ (−8)   l −50 ÷ (−25)
m 18 × (−2)   n −36 ÷ (−6)   o 4 × (−2) × 6 p −3 × (−2) × (−4)

2 Copy and complete these.
a −6 × ☐ = 600   b −4 ÷ ☐ = 2   c ☐ × (−5) = −20
d −2 × (−40) = ☐   e ☐ ÷ (−12) = 12   f −48 ÷ ☐ = −6
g ☐² = 81   h −4 × ☐ × (−3) = −48 i ☐ × (−5)² = −75

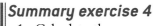

You should now:

- understand and be able to use negative numbers in context
- know the rules for addition and subtraction of negative numbers, i.e. 'plus minus → minus' and 'minus minus → plus'
- know the rules for multiplication and division of two negative numbers, i.e. when the signs are the same the answer is positive and when the signs are different the answer is negative.

Summary exercise 4

1 Calculate these.

a $2 \times (-4)$	b $-7 + (-3)$	c $4 - (-6)$
d $0 \div (-7)$	e $12 + (-4)$	f $-7 - (-2)$
g $-10 \times (-3)$	h $-14 \div (-7)$	i $-6 \times (-4)$
j $8 - (-13)$	k $-15 - 8$	l $18 + (-13)$

2 Calculate these.

a $-10 \times (-3)$	b $60 \div (-12)$	c $8 - 14$
d $-3 + (-10)$	e $-4 \times (-4)$	f $-4 \div 4$
g $-12 + (-12)$	h $8 - (-15)$	i $-1.2 + 4.8$
j $-0.5 - 6.5$	k $5.6 \times (-2)$	l $9.46 \div (-0.2)$

3 Calculate these.

a $(-6)^2$	b $(-10)^3$
c $-2 \times 7 \times (-4)$	d $-2 + (-8) - (-6)$
e $(-2)^2 + 4$	f $-600 \div (-1)^2$
g $45 + (-50) - 5$	h $0 \div (-0.5)$
i $-4 \times (-4) \times (-4)$	j $-4.2 - 4.2 - 4.2$
k $102 \div (-10)$	l $-8 \div (-16)$

Examination questions

There are no exam questions available solely on this topic. Negative numbers are often examined within topics in algebra (see Chapters 14–30).

Use 'Topic Tracker' at www.ccea.org.uk to find more exam questions.

CHAPTER 5

Fractions

> **This chapter is about:**
> - addition and subtraction of fractions and mixed numbers
> - multiplication of fractions and mixed numbers
> - division of fractions and mixed numbers
> - finding a fraction of a quantity
> - fractional change.
>
> **You should already know:**
> - the language associated with fractions
> - how to read, write and order whole numbers
> - how to add, subtract, multiply and divide whole numbers
> - how to add, subtract, multiply and divide negative numbers.

A fraction is a part of a whole.

Equivalent fractions

A fraction is written in the form $\frac{a}{b}$ where a is the **numerator** and b is the **denominator**. The value of a fraction remains the same when *both* its numerator and denominator are multiplied by or divided by the same number.

For example,

$$\frac{6}{7} = \frac{18}{21}$$

> The numerator and the denominator have both been multiplied by 3.

$\frac{6}{7}$ and $\frac{18}{21}$ are said to be **equivalent** fractions.

Similarly,

$$\frac{14}{20} = \frac{7}{10}$$

> The numerator and the denominator have both been divided by 2.

$\frac{14}{20}$ and $\frac{7}{10}$ are also equivalent fractions.

When you divide the numerator and denominator by the same number, this is known as **cancelling** or **cancelling down** or **simplifying**. When a fraction has been cancelled as much as possible, it is said to be written in its **simplest form**.

EXAMPLE 1

Write each of these fractions in its simplest form.

    a $\frac{4}{6}$ b $\frac{18}{54}$

SOLUTION

a $\frac{4}{6} = \frac{2}{3}$ ◄──────── Divide both 4 and 6 by 2.

b $\frac{18}{54} = \frac{9}{27}$ ◄──────── Divide both 18 and 54 by 2.
But notice that 9 and 27 can both be divided by 9 …

$\phantom{\frac{18}{54}} = \frac{1}{3}$ ◄──────── … so cancel again.

Ordering fractions

You use equivalent fractions when you want to compare or order fractions with different denominators. The first step is to write each of the fractions as an equivalent fraction, all with the same denominator. This denominator is known as the **common denominator**. It is a denominator into which all the other denominators divide exactly. The arithmetic is usually easier if you use the **lowest common denominator**. This is the lowest common multiple of all the denominators (see Chapter 1).

EXAMPLE 2

Order these fractions from smallest to largest. $\frac{7}{10}$ $\frac{11}{20}$ $\frac{5}{8}$ $\frac{3}{4}$

SOLUTION

40 is the lowest common multiple of the denominators 10, 20, 8 and 4.

Rewrite each fraction as an equivalent fraction with a denominator of 40.

$\frac{28}{40}$ $\frac{22}{40}$ $\frac{25}{40}$ $\frac{30}{40}$

Order the fractions.

$\frac{11}{20}\left(\frac{22}{40}\right)$ $\frac{5}{8}\left(\frac{25}{40}\right)$ $\frac{7}{10}\left(\frac{28}{40}\right)$ $\frac{3}{4}\left(\frac{30}{40}\right)$ ◄──────── Notice that the answer is the *original* fractions placed in order – not the equivalent ones.

Improper fractions and mixed numbers

An **improper**, or **vulgar**, fraction is one in which the numerator is greater than the denominator. Improper fractions can be converted to **mixed numbers** by division. If the answer to a problem is an improper fraction, you would usually convert it to a mixed number unless you have been told otherwise.

EXAMPLE 3

Write each of these improper fractions as a mixed number.

a $\frac{14}{3}$ b $\frac{25}{8}$

SOLUTION

a $\frac{14}{3} = 4\frac{2}{3}$ ◄──────── 14 divided by 3 gives 4 wholes and 2 left over.
So, as a mixed number, $\frac{14}{3}$ is $4\frac{2}{3}$.

b $\frac{25}{8} = 3\frac{1}{8}$

A mixed number can be converted to an improper fraction by finding the total number of fractional parts within the mixed number.

EXAMPLE 4

Write each of these mixed numbers as an improper fraction.

a $2\frac{3}{4}$ b $7\frac{3}{5}$

SOLUTION

a $2\frac{3}{4} = \frac{11}{4}$ ←

b $7\frac{3}{5} = \frac{38}{5}$

There are 4 quarters in 1 whole so there are 8 quarters in 2 wholes. Then add the other 3 quarters, giving a total of 11 quarters. This can be calculated using the formula

whole part × denominator + numerator.

In this case, $2 \times 4 + 3 = 8 + 3 = 11$, therefore $2\frac{3}{4} = \frac{11}{4}$.

Exercise 5.1

1 Copy and complete these.

a $\frac{4}{5} = \frac{\square}{20}$ b $\frac{8}{\square} = \frac{24}{33}$ c $\frac{1}{3} = \frac{\square}{51}$

d $\frac{5}{8} = \frac{20}{\square}$ e $\frac{10}{\square} = \frac{5}{8}$ f $\frac{24}{36} = \frac{2}{\square}$

2 Write each of these fractions in its simplest form.

a $\frac{8}{10}$ b $\frac{25}{40}$ c $\frac{54}{63}$ d $\frac{10}{30}$

e $\frac{36}{45}$ f $\frac{24}{40}$ g $\frac{39}{52}$ h $\frac{18}{45}$

i $\frac{18}{21}$ j $\frac{27}{63}$ k $\frac{28}{32}$ l $\frac{144}{180}$

3 Put each set of fractions in order from the smallest to the largest.

a $\frac{3}{10}$ $\frac{9}{20}$ $\frac{4}{5}$ $\frac{1}{2}$ b $\frac{7}{12}$ $\frac{2}{5}$ $\frac{8}{15}$ $\frac{11}{20}$

4 Write each of these improper fractions as a mixed number.

a $\frac{24}{5}$ b $\frac{31}{6}$ c $\frac{5}{2}$ d $\frac{16}{7}$

e $\frac{29}{4}$ f $\frac{30}{9}$ g $\frac{54}{7}$ h $\frac{100}{12}$

5 Write each of these mixed numbers as an improper fraction.

a $1\frac{2}{3}$ b $5\frac{3}{4}$ c $5\frac{6}{7}$ d $8\frac{1}{2}$

e $8\frac{1}{7}$ f $4\frac{2}{5}$ g $2\frac{5}{6}$ h $10\frac{1}{3}$

Adding and subtracting fractions and mixed numbers

Equivalent fractions are also used when adding or subtracting fractions. The first step is to write each fraction in the calculation as an equivalent fraction, all with a common denominator.

EXAMPLE 5

Work out these.

a $\dfrac{2}{3} + \dfrac{1}{4}$ b $\dfrac{5}{8} - \dfrac{2}{5}$

SOLUTION

a   The lowest common multiple of 3 and 4 is 12, so write both fractions with a denominator of 12.

$$\frac{2}{3} + \frac{1}{4} = \frac{2 \times 4}{3 \times 4} + \frac{1 \times 3}{4 \times 3}$$

$$= \frac{8}{12} + \frac{3}{12}$$

$$= \frac{8 + 3}{12} \quad \longleftarrow \boxed{\text{Add 8 and 3. } Do \text{ } not \text{ add 12 and 12.}}$$

$$= \frac{11}{12}$$

b   The lowest common multiple of 8 and 5 is 40 so write both fractions with a denominator of 40.

$$\frac{5}{8} - \frac{2}{5} = \frac{5 \times 5}{8 \times 5} - \frac{2 \times 8}{5 \times 8}$$

$$= \frac{25}{40} - \frac{16}{40}$$

$$= \frac{25 - 16}{40} = \frac{9}{40}$$

When you are adding or subtracting mixed numbers, there are two methods for dealing with the whole number parts. The first method is to write all the mixed numbers as improper fractions before continuing as you would for proper fractions. In the second method you deal separately with the whole number parts and the fractions. The next example shows both methods.

EXAMPLE 6

Work out these.

a $4\dfrac{3}{5} + 2\dfrac{3}{4}$ b $5\dfrac{1}{2} - 2\dfrac{2}{3}$

SOLUTION

Method 1: Changing to improper fractions

a $4\dfrac{3}{5} + 2\dfrac{3}{4} = \dfrac{23}{5} + \dfrac{11}{4}$ $\longleftarrow$ $\boxed{\text{Change to improper fractions.}}$

$= \dfrac{92}{20} + \dfrac{55}{20}$ $\longleftarrow$ $\boxed{\text{Write the fractions with a common denominator.}}$

$= \dfrac{147}{20}$

$= 7\dfrac{7}{20}$ $\longleftarrow$ $\boxed{\text{Write your answer as a mixed number.}}$

b $5\dfrac{1}{2} - 2\dfrac{2}{3} = \dfrac{11}{2} - \dfrac{8}{3}$ $\longleftarrow$ $\boxed{\text{Proceed in the same way for subtraction.}}$

$= \dfrac{33}{6} - \dfrac{16}{6}$

$= \dfrac{17}{6} = 2\dfrac{5}{6}$

Method 2: Dealing with the whole numbers and fractions separately

a Deal with the whole numbers first.

$$4 + 2 = 6$$

Then deal with the fractions.

$$\frac{3}{5} + \frac{3}{4} = \frac{12}{20} + \frac{15}{20}$$

← Write the fractions with a common denominator.

$$= \frac{27}{20}$$

$$= 1\frac{7}{20}$$

Recombine the whole numbers and the fractions.

$$4\frac{3}{5} + 2\frac{3}{4} = 6 + 1\frac{7}{20}$$

$$= 7\frac{7}{20}$$

b Deal with the whole numbers first.

$$5 - 2 = 3$$

Then deal with the fractions.

$$\frac{1}{2} - \frac{2}{3} = \frac{3}{6} - \frac{4}{6}$$

$$= -\frac{1}{6}$$

← Take care when you are subtracting using this method because subtracting the fractional parts may result in a negative answer.

Recombine the whole numbers and the fractions.

$$5\frac{1}{2} - 2\frac{2}{3} = 3 + \left(-\frac{1}{6}\right)$$

$$= 2\frac{5}{6}$$

← Convert one of the wholes to $\frac{6}{6}$ and subtract $\frac{1}{6}$ from it.

Exercise 5.2

1 Work out these.

a $2\frac{1}{3} + 3\frac{1}{4}$ b $5\frac{3}{4} - 1\frac{5}{6}$ c $6\frac{3}{5} - 2\frac{1}{3}$ d $\frac{5}{6} + \frac{7}{8}$

e $9 - 4\frac{2}{5}$ f $4\frac{3}{4} - \frac{7}{12}$ g $3\frac{2}{3} + 1\frac{1}{4} + 2\frac{1}{2}$ h $8\frac{3}{4} + 2\frac{1}{5} - 3\frac{3}{10}$

2 $\frac{3}{4}$ of the students in a class travel to school by bus, $\frac{1}{12}$ walk and the rest come by car. What fraction of the class come by car?

3 A boy works in a shop for $3\frac{3}{4}$ hours each Saturday and for $2\frac{1}{2}$ hours each Sunday. How long does he work each weekend?

4 Water is poured from a 1 litre bottle into two glasses.
   One glass holds $\frac{2}{5}$ of a litre and the other holds $\frac{1}{2}$ a litre.
   What fraction of a litre remains in the bottle?

5 The distance to my friend's house is $5\frac{1}{2}$ miles.
   I get the bus for $3\frac{4}{5}$ miles and walk the remaining distance.
   How far do I walk?

6 A survey of Year 11 students revealed that of the three sciences, $\frac{3}{7}$ prefer chemistry, $\frac{1}{3}$ prefer physics whilst the remainder prefer biology. What fraction of Year 11 prefer biology?

7 A delivery lorry carries $5\frac{1}{2}$ tonnes of sand. At one builder's yard the driver delivers $1\frac{3}{4}$ tonnes, and at another $2\frac{4}{5}$ tonnes.
The remainder of the load is delivered at a third builder's yard.
How much is delivered at the third yard?

Multiplying and dividing fractions and mixed numbers

When you are multiplying and dividing fractions and mixed numbers, you do not need to use a common denominator.

Multiplication

To multiply fractions you simply multiply the numerators and multiply the denominators. If the final answer is an improper fraction, convert it to a mixed number.

EXAMPLE 7

Work out $\frac{2}{5} \times \frac{4}{7}$.

SOLUTION

$$\frac{2}{5} \times \frac{4}{7} = \frac{2 \times 4}{5 \times 7}$$
$$= \frac{8}{35}$$

Often there is an opportunity for cancelling. The calculations are made easier if the cancelling is done first.

EXAMPLE 8

Work out $\frac{2}{3} \times \frac{7}{8}$.

SOLUTION

$$\frac{2}{3} \times \frac{7}{8} = \frac{\cancel{2}^{1} \times 7}{3 \times \cancel{8}_{4}}$$

> Here, the numerator of one fraction can be cancelled with the denominator of the other.

$$= \frac{1 \times 7}{3 \times 4}$$
$$= \frac{7}{12}$$

When the multiplication involves mixed numbers, you must first convert them to improper fractions. Unlike addition and subtraction, you cannot deal with the whole numbers and fractions separately. You then continue as for fractions.

EXAMPLE 9

Work out these.

   a $\quad 2\frac{3}{5} \times \frac{2}{5}$ $\qquad$ b $\quad 2\frac{1}{4} \times 3\frac{3}{5}$

SOLUTION

a $\quad 2\frac{3}{5} \times \frac{2}{5} = \frac{13}{5} \times \frac{2}{5}$ $\qquad$ b $\quad 2\frac{1}{4} \times 3\frac{3}{5} = \frac{9}{4} \times \frac{18}{5}$

$\qquad\qquad\quad = \frac{13 \times 2}{5 \times 5}$ $\qquad\qquad\qquad\qquad\quad = \frac{9 \times \cancel{18}^{9}}{\cancel{4}_{2} \times 5}$

$\qquad\qquad\quad = \frac{26}{25}$ $\qquad\qquad\qquad\qquad\qquad\quad = \frac{81}{10}$

$\qquad\qquad\quad = 1\frac{1}{25}$ $\qquad\qquad\qquad\qquad\qquad\quad = 8\frac{1}{10}$

Division

To divide one fraction by another, turn the second fraction upside down and then multiply them together. (This known as multiplying by the reciprocal – see Chapter 10.)

EXAMPLE 10

Work out these.

   a $\quad \frac{3}{8} \div \frac{4}{5}$ $\qquad$ b $\quad \frac{2}{5} \div \frac{9}{10}$

SOLUTION

a $\quad \frac{3}{8} \div \frac{4}{5} = \frac{3}{8} \times \frac{5}{4}$ $\qquad\qquad$ b $\quad \frac{2}{5} \div \frac{9}{10} = \frac{2}{5} \times \frac{10}{9}$

$\qquad\qquad\qquad = \frac{15}{32}$ $\qquad\qquad\qquad\qquad\qquad = \frac{2 \times \cancel{10}^{2}}{_{1}\cancel{5} \times 9}$

$\qquad\qquad\qquad\qquad\qquad\qquad\qquad\qquad\qquad\quad = \frac{4}{9}$

As with multiplication, if the division involves mixed numbers, you must first convert them to improper fractions.

EXAMPLE 11

Work out these.

   a $\quad 3\frac{1}{3} \div 2$ $\qquad$ b $\quad 3\frac{3}{8} \div 1\frac{1}{2}$

SOLUTION

a $\quad 3\frac{1}{3} \div 2 = \frac{10}{3} \div \frac{2}{1}$ $\qquad\leftarrow$ To multiply or divide by an integer, n, you can write the integer as $\frac{n}{1}$.

$\qquad\qquad\quad = \frac{10}{3} \times \frac{1}{2}$ $\qquad\leftarrow$ Note that dividing by 2 is the same as multiplying by $\frac{1}{2}$. This is known as the **multiplicative inverse**.

$\qquad\qquad\quad = \frac{\cancel{10}^{5} \times 1}{3 \times \cancel{2}_{1}}$

$\qquad\qquad\quad = \frac{5}{3} = 1\frac{2}{3}$

b $\quad 3\frac{3}{8} \div 1\frac{1}{2} = \frac{27}{8} \div \frac{3}{2}$

$\qquad\qquad = \frac{^9 27 \times 2^1}{_4 8 \times 3_1}$

$\qquad\qquad = \frac{9}{4} = 2\frac{1}{4}$

Exercise 5.3

1 Calculate these.

a $\quad \frac{3}{4} \times \frac{2}{9}$
b $\quad 6\frac{3}{4} \times \frac{2}{3}$
c $\quad 1\frac{5}{6} \times 3\frac{3}{4}$

d $\quad 2\frac{1}{2} \times 3\frac{3}{5}$
e $\quad 1\frac{2}{5} \times 2\frac{1}{7}$
f $\quad 3\frac{3}{4} \times 1\frac{2}{5}$

2 Calculate these.

a $\quad \frac{2}{5} \div \frac{9}{10}$
b $\quad 2\frac{1}{3} \div 3\frac{1}{2}$
c $\quad 4\frac{2}{3} \div 1\frac{7}{9}$

d $\quad 2\frac{4}{7} \div 1\frac{13}{14}$
e $\quad 3\frac{3}{4} \div \frac{3}{8}$
f $\quad 3 \div 2\frac{1}{3}$

Fractional change

To find a fraction of a quantity you multiply the quantity by the fraction.

EXAMPLE 12

Find each of these.

a $\quad \frac{2}{3}$ of 84 m
b $\quad \frac{5}{6}$ of £1.44
c $\quad \frac{3}{8}$ of 4 kg

SOLUTION

a $\quad \frac{2}{3}$ of 84 m $= \frac{2}{3_1} \times \frac{84^{28}}{1}$

$\qquad\qquad\quad = \frac{56}{1}$

So $\frac{2}{3}$ of 84 m = 56 m.

b $\quad \frac{5}{6}$ of £1.44 $= \frac{5}{6_1} \times \frac{144^{24}}{1}$ ← Change £1.44 into pence.

$\qquad\qquad\quad = \frac{120}{1}$

So $\frac{5}{6}$ of £1.44 = 120p = £1.20.

c $\quad \frac{3}{8}$ of 4 kg $= \frac{3}{8_1} \times \frac{4000^{500}}{1}$ ← Change 4 kg into grams.

$\qquad\qquad\quad = \frac{1500}{1}$

So $\frac{3}{8}$ of 4 kg = 1500 g = 1.5 kg.

There are two ways of calculating a fractional change. You can find the increase or reduction and then add it to or take it away from the original amount. Or you can find the fraction that represents the new amount and do the calculation in one step. The following examples show both methods.

EXAMPLE 13

A coat costs £48.

In a sale it is reduced by $\frac{1}{3}$.

What is the sale price of the coat?

SOLUTION

Method 1

$$\frac{1}{3} \text{ of } £48 = \frac{1}{\cancel{3}_1} \times \frac{\cancel{48}^{16}}{1}$$

$$= £16$$

$$\text{Sale price} = £48 - £16$$

$$= £32$$

> First find the reduction by finding $\frac{1}{3}$ of £48.

> Then find the sale price by subtracting the reduction from the original amount.

Method 2

$$\text{Sale price} = \frac{2}{3} \times \text{original price}$$

$$= \frac{2}{3} \times £48$$

$$= 2 \times \frac{\cancel{48}^{16}}{\cancel{3}_1} \times 1$$

$$= £32$$

> Think of the original price as the whole.
> If you get $\frac{1}{3}$ off in the sale you are paying
> $1 - \frac{1}{3} = \frac{2}{3}$ of the original price.

EXAMPLE 14

A youth club had 120 members last year.

This year the membership has increased by $\frac{3}{20}$.

How many members are in the club this year?

SOLUTION

Method 1

$$\frac{3}{20_1} \times \frac{\cancel{120}^6}{1} = 18$$

> First find the increase in membership by finding $\frac{3}{20}$ of 120.

$$\text{Membership this year} = 120 + 18$$

$$= 138$$

> Then find the new number by adding the increase to the original number.

Method 2

$$\text{Membership this year} = \frac{23}{20} \times \text{membership last year}$$

$$= \frac{23}{20} \times 120$$

$$= \frac{23 \times \cancel{120}^6}{_1\cancel{20} \times 1} = 138$$

> Think of the original amount as a whole.
> If there has been an increase of $\frac{3}{20}$,
> the membership can be calculated.
> $1 + \frac{3}{20} = \frac{20}{20} + \frac{3}{20} = \frac{23}{20}$

Exercise 5.4

1 Calculate these.

    a $\frac{3}{5}$ of 8.25 kg   b $\frac{7}{8}$ of 6.4 m   c $\frac{5}{6}$ of £12.60

2 A girl lives $5\frac{1}{4}$ miles from school.
She walks $\frac{2}{7}$ of the distance and travels the rest by bus.
How far does she travel by bus?

3 A man works $7\frac{1}{2}$ hours each day, $2\frac{1}{4}$ hours of which is spent on
the computer. What fraction of his working day does he spend on
the computer?

4 A garden has an area of $18\frac{1}{2}$ m².
$\frac{2}{5}$ of it is to be planted with vegetables.
What will the remaining area be?

5 A girl spends $\frac{2}{5}$ of her weekly wage on rent, $\frac{1}{3}$ on food and
$\frac{3}{8}$ of the remainder on clothes and entertainment.
She saves the rest. What fraction of her weekly wage does she save?

6 $2\frac{1}{2}$ kg of vegetables cost £4. What is the cost per kilogram?

7 Tickets for a concert were sold at £10, £12 and £15.
For one performance, 800 tickets were sold.
$\frac{2}{5}$ sold for £10, $\frac{3}{8}$ sold for £12 and the rest sold for £15.
What was the total income from the sale of the tickets?

8 A rectangular photograph with dimensions 10 cm by 6 cm is
enlarged. Its dimensions are increased by $\frac{1}{4}$.
Find the dimensions of the enlarged photograph.

9 A DVD player originally costing £150 is reduced by $\frac{1}{8}$ in the first
week of a sale. The following week it is reduced by a further $\frac{1}{3}$.
How much will it cost in the second week of the sale?

10 What fraction is midway between $\frac{4}{15}$ and $\frac{1}{3}$?

11 a Given that $\frac{5}{x} \div \frac{y}{3} = \frac{5}{8}$, find possible values for x and y.

    b Is there more than one possible answer?

You should now:

- recognise and use equivalent fractions
- be able to convert between improper fractions and mixed numbers
- be able to order fractions
- be able to solve problems involving addition, subtraction, multiplication and division of fractions
- be able to calculate a fraction of a quantity.

Summary exercise 5

1. Write each of these fractions in its simplest form.

   a $\dfrac{15}{18}$ **b** $\dfrac{24}{42}$ **c** $\dfrac{35}{50}$

2. Convert each of these improper fractions to a mixed number.

   a $\dfrac{25}{3}$ **b** $\dfrac{36}{7}$ **c** $\dfrac{15}{9}$

3. Convert each of these mixed numbers to an improper fraction.

   a $5\dfrac{2}{3}$ **b** $2\dfrac{3}{7}$ **c** $12\dfrac{1}{3}$

4. Put these fractions in order from the smallest to the largest.

   $\dfrac{2}{5}$ $\dfrac{5}{6}$ $\dfrac{7}{12}$ $\dfrac{3}{4}$ $\dfrac{1}{2}$

5. Calculate each of these.

   a $3\dfrac{1}{3} \times 1\dfrac{2}{5}$ **b** $1\dfrac{1}{3} \div 2\dfrac{2}{5}$ **c** $\dfrac{7}{10} - \dfrac{2}{3}$

   d $3\dfrac{1}{6} - 1\dfrac{1}{2}$ **e** $3\dfrac{2}{3} + 1\dfrac{3}{4}$ **f** $2\dfrac{3}{8} + 1\dfrac{2}{3}$

   g $3\dfrac{2}{5} \div \dfrac{7}{10}$ **h** $5 \times 1\dfrac{3}{10}$ **i** $1\dfrac{1}{7} + 2\dfrac{1}{2}$

   j $3\dfrac{2}{3} \div 4\dfrac{2}{5}$ **k** $\dfrac{1}{3} + \dfrac{3}{4} - \dfrac{5}{12}$ **l** $\dfrac{4\frac{1}{6} - 1\frac{2}{3}}{2\frac{1}{2}}$

6. A man's annual salary of £24 000 is increased by $\dfrac{3}{20}$.
   What is his new annual salary?

7. Divide the sum of $2\dfrac{1}{4}$ and $1\dfrac{7}{8}$ by their difference.

8. $1\dfrac{1}{4}$ kg of salad costs £2. What is the price per kilogram?

9. What fraction is $\dfrac{1}{3}$ of the way between $1\dfrac{1}{4}$ and $2\dfrac{2}{3}$?

10. A girl has already saved $\dfrac{2}{5}$ of the cost of a trip abroad.
    For her birthday her parents give her £600 towards the cost

    of the trip, which is $\dfrac{1}{2}$ of the remaining amount.

    How much does the trip cost in total?

11. Copy and complete this diagram.

    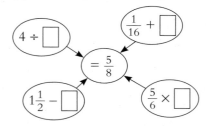

12. Complete the magic square so that each
    row, each column and each diagonal adds
    up to the same total.

$\dfrac{5}{6}$	$1\dfrac{2}{3}$	$\dfrac{1}{2}$
	1	

13 A tank is $\frac{1}{3}$ full of water. When 75 litres are added, the tank is now $\frac{3}{4}$ full. What is the total volume of the tank?

14 Calculate $\frac{1}{2} \times \frac{2}{3} \times \frac{3}{4} \times \frac{4}{5} \times \frac{5}{6} \times \frac{6}{7} \times \frac{7}{8}$.

15 On each bounce, a ball rises to $\frac{4}{5}$ of its previous height.
To what height will it rise after the third bounce if it is dropped from a height of 3 m?

Examination questions

Use 'Topic Tracker' at www.ccea.org.uk to find more exam questions.

Questions **1** to **8** are from examination papers where you may not use a calculator.

1 Which of the following fractions is the largest? Show your working clearly.

$\frac{3}{5}$ $\frac{7}{10}$ $\frac{13}{20}$ $\frac{17}{30}$

2 Which of the following is nearest in size to $\frac{1}{4}$? Show your method clearly.

$\frac{3}{10}$ $\frac{11}{60}$ $\frac{1}{5}$ $\frac{7}{30}$

3 Fiona uses $\frac{2}{5}$ of a jar of coffee per week. How many jars will she need to buy to last for nine weeks?

4 Calculate $\frac{11}{12} - \frac{1}{4}$.

5 Calculate $\frac{3}{5} \div 9$.

6 Calculate $\frac{2}{5} \times \frac{3}{4}$.

7 a Calculate $\frac{2}{7}$ of 28. **b** Calculate $\frac{2}{5} \times \frac{3}{7}$.

8 Work out the value of $3\frac{1}{3} - 1\frac{3}{5}$. Show your working.

Questions **9** to **11** are from examination papers where you may use a calculator.

9 John uses $\frac{3}{4}$ of a can of oil per week. How many cans will he need to last for 11 weeks?

10 Larry has to raise $\frac{3}{5}$ of the total cost of a trip himself. So far he has raised $\frac{1}{4}$ of the total cost. What fraction of the total cost has he still to raise?

11 A student needs to type a project of 15 pages. She only has time to type $2\frac{1}{2}$ pages on the first day, and $1\frac{3}{4}$ pages every day after the first. How many days, in total, will it take her to type the whole project?

CHAPTER 6

Approximation and estimation

> **This chapter is about:**
> - approximating numbers
> - significant figures
> - estimating the answer to a calculation.
>
> **You should already know:**
> - how to read, write and order whole numbers and decimals
> - how to add, subtract, multiply and divide whole numbers, decimals and fractions.

Approximation

There are many practical situations where calculations result in answers such as 45.678 92 km/h or 2.893 45 m. It is not always sensible to record so many digits, hence we need a method of approximating. You will already be familiar with approximating to the nearest unit, ten, hundred, thousand etc. and the process used can be extended to a given number of **decimal places** or **significant figures**.

Recall that 3.68 to the nearest unit becomes 4. The tenths digit is examined and because its value is more than 5, the units are rounded *up* to 4. In practical terms this means that 3.68 is closer to 4 than to 3.

A value of 72 to the nearest ten becomes 70. The units digit is examined and because its value is less than 5, the tens are rounded *down* to 70. In practical terms this means that 72 is closer to 70 than to 80.

And so the process continues. 853 to the nearest hundred becomes 900, and 4326 to the nearest thousand becomes 4000.

There are many occasions when an answer will be required to a greater **degree of accuracy** than to the nearest unit, for example to the nearest tenth of a millimetre or the nearest hundredth of a second. For this reason it is necessary to extend approximation to either a given number of decimal places or a given number of significant figures.

Decimal places

As discussed in Chapter 3, a decimal place is a figure after the decimal point. To round to a given number of decimal places, examine the digit to the right of the number of decimal places required. For example, if 2 decimal places are required in the answer, examine the *third* decimal place. If it is 5 or more round up; if it is less than 5 round down.

EXAMPLE 1

Write each of these numbers to the given degree of accuracy.
- a   4.672 (1 d.p.)   b   2.6743 (2 d.p.)   c   15.073 (1 d.p.)
- d   4.9898 (3 d.p.)   e   3.957 (1 d.p.)

> The abbreviation d.p. is generally used for decimal places.

SOLUTION

- a   4.672 = 4.7 (1 d.p.)   b   2.6743 = 2.67 (2 d.p.)
- c   15.073 = 15.1 (1 d.p.)   d   4.9898 = 4.990 (3 d.p.)
- e   3.957 = 4.0 (1 d.p.)

Note the inclusion of the zeros in the answers to the last two parts of the example. These *are* necessary even though 4.990 = 4.99 and 4.0 = 4. If the zeros were not included, the answers would not have the required number of decimal places and would not be accurate enough; 4.0 is accurate to the nearest tenth, whilst 4 is only accurate to the nearest unit.

Significant figures

A significant figure is the first *non-zero* figure which appears in a number when counting from the left. Once a non-zero figure is counted, *every* figure after that becomes significant (even if it is a zero).

EXAMPLE 2

How many significant figures are there in each of these numbers?
- a   2.003   b   0.005   c   0.013 04
- d   23 056   e   12.0

SOLUTION

- a   2.003 has 4 significant figures.
- b   0.005 has 1 significant figure.
- c   0.013 04 has 4 significant figures.
- d   23 056 has 5 significant figures.
- e   12.0 has 3 significant figures.

> The abbreviation s.f. is generally used for significant figures.

To round to a given number of significant figures, examine the digit to the right of the one required. For example if 3 significant figures are required, examine the *fourth* significant figure. If it is 5 or more round up; if it is less than 5 round down.

EXAMPLE 3

Write each of these numbers to the given degree of accuracy.
- a   13.37 (3 s.f.)   b   0.003 52 (2 s.f.)
- c   14.8972 (4 s.f.)   d   0.2046 (2 s.f.)
- e   4789 (1 s.f.)

SOLUTION

- a   13.37 = 13.4 (3 s.f.)   b   0.003 52 = 0.0035 (2 s.f.)
- c   14.8972 = 14.90 (4 s.f.)   d   0.2046 = 0.20 (2 s.f.)
- e   4789 = 5000 (1 s.f.)

Note that it is necessary to include extra zeros in the last part of the example to make the answer sensible. These are required to show the place value of the 5. If the extra zeros were not included, you would be saying that 4789 is approximately the same size as 5 whereas, in fact, 4789 is approximately 5000. This need to include extra zeros to make an answer sensible arises when you are dealing with a number greater than 10.

Exercise 6.1

1   Write each of these numbers to the given degree of accuracy.
    a   5.678 (2 d.p.)   b   0.0745 (1 d.p.)   c   56.347 (2 d.p.)   d   0.0078 (3 d.p.)
    e   4.506 (2 d.p.)   f   2.899 (2 d.p.)   g   3.999 (1 d.p.)   h   14.9877 (3 d.p.)
    i   0.0402 (2 d.p.)   j   14.52 (1 d.p.)   k   23.655 (2 d.p.)   l   29.998 (1 d.p.)

2   How many significant figures are there in each of these numbers?
    a   1.364   b   8965   c   0.0057   d   400   e   1003   f   0.050 807
    g   5600   h   2.052   i   2.0   j   7000   k   0.39   l   4.02

3   Write each of these numbers to the given degree of accuracy.
    a   2.354 (3 s.f.)   b   0.0067 (1 s.f.)   c   6572 (1 s.f.)   d   0.0089 (1 s.f.)
    e   2.0657 (3 s.f.)   f   20.03 (3 s.f.)   g   9.999 (3 s.f.)   h   0.007 25 (1 s.f.)
    i   4.052 (2 s.f.)   j   711.2 (1 s.f.)   k   0.0504 (1 s.f.)   l   0.0504 (2 s.f.)

Estimation

Estimation is useful when we want to have some idea of the *approximate size* of an answer, rather than an exact answer. It can serve as a check for many calculations, whether they are done mentally or using a calculator. For example, 8.96×24.2 is approximately 9×20 and so, as a rough guide, the answer should be somewhere in the region of 180.

It is good practice to estimate the answer to a calculation before calculating the exact answer, as a checking procedure. The actual answer should be somewhere in the region of the estimated answer.

Estimation is useful in many practical situations where an exact answer is not necessary and a rough estimate is sufficient. For example, suppose you need to buy 7.2 m of material priced at £7.95 per metre. A rough estimate of the cost would be $7 \times £8 = £56$.

The symbol $\approx$ is used for estimating and is read as 'approximately equal to'.

There are several *guidelines* which can be used for estimating.

An estimate does not have to be very accurate – each number in the calculation should be rounded to a figure that you can work with mentally.

For example, $297 \div 6.6$ is more easily thought of as $300 \div 6$ than as $300 \div 7$, because 300 divides easily by 6.

Approximating to numbers such as 1, 2, 5, 10 and 100 (and multiples of the powers of 10) makes calculations much more straightforward.

For example, $\dfrac{84.2 \times 267.3}{0.957} \approx \dfrac{80 \times 300}{1} = \dfrac{24\,000}{1} = 24\,000$

Where possible, look for numbers which may cancel. For example,

$\dfrac{14.97 \times 582.3}{5.21} \approx \dfrac{\overset{3}{\cancel{15}} \times 600}{\underset{1}{\cancel{5}}} = \dfrac{3 \times 600}{1} = \dfrac{1800}{1} = 1800$

Some decimals may be better estimated as fractions, as they may be easier to work with mentally.

For example, $\dfrac{0.26 \times 414}{4.68} \approx \dfrac{\frac{1}{4} \times 400}{5} = \dfrac{100}{5} = 20$

When multiplying or dividing, never round a number to zero, no matter how small it is. Rather, round to an appropriate decimal or fractional value. For example,

$\dfrac{11.94 + 7.92}{0.035} \approx \dfrac{12 + 8}{0.04} = \dfrac{20}{0.04} = \dfrac{2000}{4} = 500$

EXAMPLE 4

Estimate the answer to each of these calculations.

a 7.98×21.24

b $\dfrac{278 \times 82.4}{12.34 \times 2.81}$

c 0.0567×78.24

d $0.748 \times (49.7 + 31.24)$

e $\dfrac{5.8 \times 48.6}{0.17}$

SOLUTION

a $7.98 \times 21.24 \approx 8 \times 20 = 160$

b $\dfrac{278 \times 82.4}{12.34 \times 2.81} \approx \dfrac{300 \times 80}{10 \times 3} = \dfrac{24\,000}{30} = 800$

c $0.0567 \times 78.24 \approx 0.06 \times 80 = 0.6 \times 8 = 4.8$

d $0.748 \times (49.7 + 31.24) \approx \dfrac{3}{4} \times (50 + 30) = \dfrac{3}{4} \times 80 = 60$

e $\dfrac{5.8 \times 48.6}{0.17} \approx \dfrac{6 \times 50}{0.2} = \dfrac{300}{0.2} = \dfrac{3000}{2} = 1500$

It is important to remember that there may be several correct approaches to an estimation, and that estimated answers may vary from person to person. There is no one correct estimate – what is important is that the estimate is somewhere in the region of the exact answer to the calculation.

Exercise 6.2

1 Each of the following calculations is followed by three possible answers, only one of which is correct.
Use estimation to decide which must be the correct answer.
(Do *not* actually carry out any of the calculations.)

	Calculation	Option A	Option B	Option C
a	23.6×68.7	6213.32	1621.32	2631.21
b	$5424.88 \div 17.2$	315.4	31.54	54.13
c	$16\,416 \div 36$	45	456	654
d	0.087×47.2	1.604	0.6104	4.1064
e	$0.090\,16 \div 0.028$	32.2	0.32	3.22
f	$\dfrac{124 \times 765}{72}$	3.175	735	1317.5
g	$(157.67 - 63.83) \div 3.4$	76.2	27.6	2.76
h	$\dfrac{7.7744 + 2.68}{0.297}$	35.2	0.352	3.52

2 Estimate the answer to each of these calculations.

  a 6.8×5.14 b $68.7 \div 9.24$

  c 81.36×4.17 d $789 \div 19.6$

  e $236.5 + 472.8 - 87.9$ f $5.4 \times (3.87)^2$

  g $1.983 \div 4.12$ h $254.2 \div 0.251$

3 Estimate the answer to each of these calculations.

  a 36.2×5.48 b $32.4 \div 0.812$

  c $\dfrac{52.6 \times 0.17}{2.18}$ d $\dfrac{278.9}{3.186 + 0.79}$

  e $\dfrac{39.4 \times 9.2}{2.9 \times 3.6}$ f 0.562×6.97^2

  g $\dfrac{0.497 \times 368.79}{0.047}$ h $(0.52 \times 18.1)^2$

4 Estimate the answer to each of these problem-type questions.

  a   Given that 1 nautical mile is approximately 1.853 km, estimate the number of kilometres in 316 nautical miles.

  b   A man buys 38.2 litres of petrol, priced at 81.9p per litre. His car can travel 212 miles on this amount of petrol. Estimate the cost per mile of the petrol which his car uses.

  c   A girl walked 16 miles in 5 hours 32 minutes. Estimate the number of minutes it took her to walk 1 mile.

  d   The area of a circle is given by the formula $A = \pi r^2$ where r is the radius of the circle. Estimate the radius of a circle with area 119.32 cm².

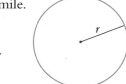

  e   A warehouse floor is to be covered with flooring which costs £12.25 per square metre. Estimate the cost, given that the floor has dimensions 61.2 m by 18.9 m.

You should now:

- be able to round a value correct to a given number of decimal places
- know the number of significant figures in any value
- be able to round a value correct to a given number of significant figures
- be able to estimate answers to practical problems, and use estimation as a check as to the appropriate size of the answer to a calculation.

Summary exercise 6

1 Write each of these values to the given degree of accuracy.

  a   2356 (nearest 100)   b   457 (nearest 10)

  c   2643 (nearest 10)   d   5607 (nearest 1000)

  e   34 670 (nearest 1000)   f   3254 (nearest 10)

  g   3256 (nearest 100)   h   798 (nearest 10)

  i   345 (nearest 10)   j   345 (nearest 100)

2 Write each of these values to the given degree of accuracy.
   a 2.567 (1 d.p.)   b 45.798 (2 d.p.)
   c 18.45 (3 s.f.)   d 6345 (3 s.f.)
   e 0.067 (1 s.f.)   f 0.306 57 (2 s.f.)
   g 0.0567 (2 d.p.)   h 52.998 (2 d.p.)
   i 0.0306 (3 d.p.)   j 3500 (1 s.f.)

3 Estimate the answer to each of these calculations.
   a $\dfrac{23.4 \times 67.8}{39.8}$ b 0.512×37.9

   c $\dfrac{14.8}{3.12 - 2.89}$ d $\dfrac{46 \times 89}{3.21 + 1.78}$

   e $0.21^2 \times 9.8^2$ f $29.88 \div 0.42$

   g $\dfrac{19.8 \times 38.6}{4.08 \times 4.72}$ h $\dfrac{51.4 \times 0.098}{9.97}$

   i 0.747×242.8 j $1.87 \div \sqrt{101.2}$

4 A bedroom floor measures 5.6 m by 2.95 m.
  Estimate the cost of carpet to cover it if the carpet is priced at
  £11.45 per square metre.

5 A train journey is 292 miles. Estimate the distance in kilometres,
  given that 1 kilometre is about 0.62 miles.

6 Jack needs 352 feet of decking timber.
  The timber is available in sheets which are 5 feet 10 inches long.
  Estimate the number of sheets of timber he will need.

Examination questions

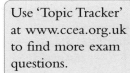

Use 'Topic Tracker' at www.ccea.org.uk to find more exam questions.

These questions are from examination papers where you may not use a
calculator.

1 Estimate the value of each of the following. Show your working.
   a $\dfrac{434 \times 279}{68}$ b $\dfrac{11.94}{3.13 - 2.72}$

2 Estimate the value of each of the following. Show your working clearly.
   a $\dfrac{62 \times 372}{28}$ b $\dfrac{5.6 + 3.9}{0.49}$

3 Estimate the value of $\dfrac{410 \times 3.98}{0.213}$.

  Show your working clearly.

4 Estimate $\dfrac{84 \times 7.89}{0.385}$.

  Show your working.

5 Estimate the value of $\dfrac{504 \times 78}{389}$.

  Show your working.

6 Estimate the value of $\dfrac{5.8 \times 21.7}{6.2 - 3.9}$.

CHAPTER 7

The order of operations

> **This chapter is about:**
> - the order of calculations
> - giving answers to calculations to an appropriate degree of accuracy
> - understanding the effects of operations on numbers of any size.
>
> **You should already know:**
> - how to add, subtract, multiply and divide positive and negative numbers, decimals and fractions
> - how to round numbers to a given degree of accuracy
> - how to estimate the answer to a calculation.

Using the correct order of operations

When a calculation involves several operations, carry them out in the order given by the BODMAS rule.

| If a calculation involves *only* multiplication and division, you can ignore the rule and do the calculation in the order it is written, because × and ÷ are of equal status. | **B**rackets
Of
Division
Multiplication
Addition
Subtraction | If a calculation involves *only* addition and subtraction, you can ignore the rule and do the calculation in the order it is written, because + and − are of equal status. |

EXAMPLE 1

Work out $7 + 8 \div 4$.

SOLUTION

$7 + 8 \div 4 = 7 + 2$ ← You must do the division first.
$ = 9$

EXAMPLE 2

Work out $6 \times 5 - 10 \div 2$.

SOLUTION

$$6 \times 5 - 10 \div 2 = 30 - 5$$

> Do the multiplication and the division first.

$$= 25$$

> Then do the subtraction with the results.

EXAMPLE 3

Work out $8 + (26 + 7) \div 3$.

SOLUTION

$$8 + (26 + 7) \div 3 = 8 + 33 \div 3$$

> Work out the brackets first.

$$= 8 + 11$$

> Then do the division.

$$= 19$$

> Finally do the addition.

EXAMPLE 4

Work out $2 + (4 - 6 \div 2) \times 5$.

SOLUTION

$$2 + (4 - 6 \div 2) \times 5 = 2 + (4 - 3) \times 5$$
$$= 2 + 1 \times 5$$
$$= 2 + 5$$
$$= 7$$

> You need to use BODMAS *within* the brackets here too. So do the division before the subtraction.

EXAMPLE 5

Work out $\dfrac{6.4}{1.3 - 0.8}$.

SOLUTION

$$\frac{6.4}{1.3 - 0.8} = \frac{6.4}{0.5}$$

> Here the division line acts like a set of brackets so you work out $1.3 - 0.8$ first.

$$= 12.8$$

EXAMPLE 6

Work out $1\frac{1}{2} + 3\frac{1}{4} \times \frac{2}{5}$.

SOLUTION

$$1\frac{1}{2} + 3\frac{1}{4} \times \frac{2}{5} = \frac{3}{2} + \frac{13}{4} \times \frac{2}{5}$$
$$= \frac{3}{2} + \frac{13}{10}$$
$$= \frac{28}{10}$$
$$= 2\frac{4}{5}$$

Example 6 shows that the BODMAS rule is used not only for calculations with whole numbers but also when calculating with fractions or decimals.

Exercise 7.1

Work out these.

1   $6 + 3 \times 2$ 2 $8 + 6 \div 2$ 3 $4 + 9 \times 2 + 3$

4   $14 \div 2 + 3$ 5 $2 \times 3 + 6 \times 4$ 6 $18 - 16 \div 2$

7   $10 \div 10 - 1 \times 1$ 8 $20 \div 2 \times 5 + 1$ 9 $14 - 2 \times 2$

10   $16 \div 8 - 2$ 11 $40 \div 4 + 2 \times 5$ 12 $3 \times 4 + 8 \times 8 \div 2$

13   $(42 - 3 \times 5) - (6 + 3 \times 2)$ 14 $2 + 3 \times 10 \div 5 + 8$ 15 $1.4 + 2.5 \times 0.5$

16   $8.2 - 4.8 \div 1.2$ 17 $1.2 \times 3 + 4 \times 0.6$ 18 $2.85 \div 0.5 \times 8$

19   $\dfrac{15 - 12 \div 4}{4 + 2 \times 4}$ 20 $\dfrac{28 - 8 \div 2}{1 + 3 \times 5}$

21   $(50 - 8 \times 6) \times 2 + [40 \div (5 \times 2)]$ 22 $[(18 - 6) \times 2] \div (10 - 2 \times 1)$

23   $3\frac{1}{4} + 2\frac{1}{2} \div \frac{3}{8}$ 24 $2\frac{2}{5} - 1\frac{1}{2} \times \frac{3}{4}$

25   $\frac{3}{8} \times (2\frac{5}{8} + 2\frac{1}{4} \times 1\frac{1}{2}) - 2\frac{2}{3}$

Inserting operations

It is useful to be able to perform the reverse procedure, that is to insert the appropriate operations in order to make a calculation correct.

In Chapter 3 you saw that multiplication by a number greater than 1 results in a bigger answer, whilst multiplication by a number less than 1 results in a smaller answer. Also, addition generally leads to a greater answer.

You also saw that division by a number greater than 1 results in a smaller answer, whilst division by a number less than 1 results in a greater answer. Also, subtraction generally leads to a smaller answer.

These are some points to consider when trying to insert the appropriate operations. It is important to realise that there may be several different combinations of operations which give the correct answer.

EXAMPLE 7

Insert the appropriate symbols, $+$, $-$, $\times$ or $\div$, to make each of these calculations correct. Insert brackets too if you need to.

a $8 \,\square\, 5 \,\square\, 4 = 28$ b $20 \,\square\, 8 \,\square\, 2 = 16$

c $8 \,\square\, 9 \,\square\, 6 \,\square\, 10 = 12$ d $8 \,\square\, 3 \,\square\, 6 \,\square\, 2 = 2$

SOLUTION

a   Since the answer is greater than any of the figures in the calculation, you would expect $+$ or $\times$.
$8 + 5 \times 4 = 8 + 20 = 28$

b   Since the answer is smaller than the 20, you would expect $-$ or $\div$.
$20 - 8 \div 2 = 20 - 4 = 16$

c Since the answer is smaller than the sum of all the figures in the calculation, you would expect − or ÷.
$8 \times 9 - 6 \times 10 = 72 - 60 = 12$

d Since the answer is small, you would expect − or ÷.
$8 - (3 + 6 \div 2) = 8 - (3 + 3) = 8 - 6 = 2$

Exercise 7.2

Insert the appropriate operations to make each of these calculations correct.

1 $4 \square 5 \square 10 = 30$ 2 $18 \square 14 \square 7 = 16$ 3 $20 \square 4 \square 4 = 4$

4 $5 \square 3 \square 12 = 27$ 5 $12 \square 8 \square 9 = 84$ 6 $41 \square 10 \square 2 = 21$

7 $21 \square 40 \square 5 = 29$ 8 $24 \square 4 \square 8 \square 2 = 4$ 9 $12 \square 4 \square 1 \square 6 = 10$

10 $20 \square 6 \square 8 \square 10 = 58$ 11 $20 \square 2 \square 1 \square 3 = 4$ 12 $20 \square 30 \square 10 \square 7 = 24$

Single-step calculations on a calculator

Modern scientific calculators have keys for many functions, but the labelling of the keys often varies from calculator to calculator. It is sensible for you to use the same calculator throughout your course so that you become familiar with it and learn ho w to use its functions.

Most calculators carry out calculations using the BODMAS rule automatically. Do some of the calculations from Examples 1 to 6 on your own calculator to check whether it works like this.

Find out how to use all the functions listed below on your own calculator. (The keys may be labelled differently on your calculator, and you may need to use the $\boxed{\textbf{SHIFT}}$ or $\boxed{\textbf{INV}}$ or $\boxed{\textbf{ALPHA}}$ 'second function' keys to access some of the functions.)

$\boxed{+}$ add	$\boxed{\sqrt{}}$ square root	$\boxed{-}$ subtract
$\boxed{x^2}$ square	$\boxed{\times}$ multiply	$\boxed{x^\blacksquare}$ power of
$\boxed{\div}$ divide	$\boxed{\sqrt[x]{}}$ xth root of	$\boxed{=}$ equals
$\boxed{(-)}$ negative	$\boxed{(}\,\boxed{)}$ brackets	$\boxed{x^{-1}}$ reciprocal

EXAMPLE 8

Use your calculator to work out each of these.

a $2.3 + 6.75$ b $5.25 - 1.67$ c 4.2×1.3

d $3588 \div 23$ e $(6.3 + 2.7) \div 2$ f 3.5^2

g 3^4 h $\sqrt{84.64}$ i $\sqrt[5]{7776}$

j $8 + (-5) - (-6)$ k $2\frac{1}{3} + 5\frac{1}{4}$ l $\frac{1}{2.5}$

SOLUTION

a $2.3 + 6.75 = 9.05$ b $5.25 - 1.67 = 3.58$

c $4.2 \times 1.3 = 5.46$ d $3588 \div 23 = 156$

e $(6.3 + 2.7) \div 2 = 4.5$ f $3.5^2 = 12.25$

g $3^4 = 81$

h $\sqrt{84.64} = \pm 9.2$ ←

> You saw in Chapter 1 that a square root can be positive or negative. Most calculators will give only the positive value.

i $\sqrt[5]{7776} = 6$

j $8 + (-5) - (-6) = 9$

k $2\frac{1}{3} + 5\frac{1}{4} = 7\frac{7}{12}$

l $\frac{1}{2.5} = 0.4$

Exercise 7.3

Use your calculator to work out each of these.

1 $7.5 - 2.6$	2 3.87×0.2	3 2.5^3
4 $\sqrt{38.44}$	5 $8 + (-2) - (-5)$	6 $-3 \times (-6) \div (-2)$
7 $7.65 + 3.5 - 2.6$	8 $(2.3 + 1.8) \div 0.02$	9 $2.3^2 + 1.2^2$
10 $\sqrt[6]{729}$	11 $\frac{1}{0.8}$	12 $2\frac{3}{4} - 1\frac{1}{2} - \left(-4\frac{2}{3}\right)$

If you need more practice, work through some of the exercises earlier in the book using your calculator.

Multistep calculations on a calculator

For a multistep calculation, plan the calculation first so that the intermediate steps are not carried out and rounded separately. This is because the slight differences caused by rounding at every stage accumulate, and the final answer could end up quite a bit different from the exact answer. Where possible, try to key in the complete calculation in one step using the following guidelines.

- Where the numerator involves a calculation, complete this before you deal with the denominator. You can do this *either* by pressing $\boxed{=}$ after the calculation required in the numerator *or* by placing the calculation required in the numerator in brackets, $\boxed{(}$ ... $\boxed{)}$.

- Where the denominator involves a calculation, *either* place that calculation within brackets, $\boxed{(}$ ... $\boxed{)}$, *or* work it out first and store the result in the calculator memory using $\boxed{\text{M}^+}$.

If you use the second method, you then calculate the numerator and divide it by the denominator by using the memory recall key $\boxed{\text{M}}$.

- A number directly in front of a bracket means you multiply the contents of the brackets by that number. On some calculators you may need to key in the $\boxed{\times}$.

- You usually need to key in a final $\boxed{=}$ at the end of the complete calculation.

Many calculator displays will show a large number of digits in the answer. It is at this stage that rounding becomes important. Sometimes the required degree of accuracy will be stated in the question. If it is not, you should round to an **appropriate degree of accuracy**, which will depend on the context of the problem. For example, if a problem involved car prices an appropriate degree of accuracy might be to the nearest £10, but for house prices it might be the nearest £1000. A general guideline is to round the answer to either the same number of decimal places or significant figures as in the figures given in the question, or to one more decimal place or significant figure. You met rounding to a given number of decimal places or significant figures in Chapter 6.

EXAMPLE 9

Calculate $(6.7 - 3.564)^2$.

SOLUTION

Key in $(\boxed{(}\ 6.7 - 3.564\ \boxed{)}\ \boxed{x^2}$
Answer: 9.834 (4 s.f.)

EXAMPLE 10

Calculate $\dfrac{4.6 + 2.35}{2.52 - 1.36}$.

SOLUTION

Key in $\quad 4.6 + 2.35\ \boxed{=}\ \boxed{\div}\ \boxed{(}\ 2.52 - 1.36\ \boxed{)}\ \boxed{=}$
or $\quad\quad \boxed{(}\ 4.6 + 2.35\ \boxed{)}\ \boxed{\div}\ \boxed{(}\ 2.52 - 1.36\ \boxed{)}$
Answer: 5.99 (3 s.f.)

EXAMPLE 11

Calculate $\dfrac{2.3 + 3.2(1.6 - 0.85)}{2.4}$.

SOLUTION

Key in
$2.3\ \boxed{+}\ 3.2\ \boxed{\times}\ \boxed{(}\ 1.6 - 0.85\ \boxed{)}\ \boxed{=}\ \boxed{\div}\ 2.4\ \boxed{=}$
or $\boxed{(}\ 2.3 + 3.2\ \boxed{\times}\ \boxed{(}\ 1.6 - 0.85\ \boxed{)}\ \boxed{)}\ \boxed{\div}\ 2.4\ \boxed{=}$
Answer: 1.96 (2 d.p.)

EXAMPLE 12

Calculate $\dfrac{13 + 4\sqrt{25}}{2}$.

SOLUTION

Key in $\quad 13 + 4\ \boxed{\times}\ \boxed{\sqrt{\ }}\ 25\ \boxed{=}\ \boxed{\div}\ 2\ \boxed{=}$
or $\quad\quad \boxed{(}\ 13 + 4\ \boxed{\times}\ \boxed{\sqrt{\ }}\ 25\ \boxed{)}\ \boxed{\div}\ 2\ \boxed{=}$
Answer: 16.5

EXAMPLE 13

Calculate $\left(\dfrac{8.4}{28.6 - 0.45}\right)^3$.

SOLUTION

Key in $\boxed{(}\ 8.4\ \boxed{\div}\ \boxed{(}\ 28.6 - 0.45\ \boxed{)}\ \boxed{)}\ \boxed{=}\ \boxed{x^\blacksquare}\ 3\ \boxed{=}$
Answer: 0.0266 (3 s.f.)

In Chapter 6 you saw that it is sensible to make an estimate before carrying out a calculation, to give you a rough idea of the approximate size of the answer. It is good practice to do this even when using a calculator – it is easy to input a wrong figure or press the wrong key, and this can distort the whole calculation.

Exercise 7.4

Use your calculator to work out each of these, giving all your answers to 4 significant figures.

1. 34.6×86.7
2. $43.67 \div 2.5$
3. $19.5 + 18.34 \div 3.4$

4. $\dfrac{2.6 + 3.67}{1.65}$
5. $\dfrac{87.56}{2.7 + 4.8}$
6. $\dfrac{10.2 + 8.3 \div 1.7}{3.65}$

7. $\dfrac{23.56 + 56.72}{12.26 - 4.58}$
8. $\dfrac{19.67}{3.5^2}$
9. $10.6 + \dfrac{5.67}{1.3}$

10. $2.4^3 + 1.2^2$
11. $(3.15 - 2.14)^2$
12. $\sqrt[3]{6.17 \times 3.26}$

13. $\dfrac{1}{6.5} + \dfrac{1}{3.5}$
14. $\left(\dfrac{7.02}{0.4}\right) + 2.365$
15. $\dfrac{1.8}{3.2} - \dfrac{2.6}{0.8}$

16. $\sqrt{\dfrac{19.68}{1.43 \times 5.2}}$
17. $\sqrt[5]{6.82^3}$
18. $4.876 + \dfrac{8}{1.6} - \dfrac{2}{3.2}$

19. $6.3^5 \div 4.1^3$
20. $3.56 + \left(19.2 \times \dfrac{1.6}{4.2}\right)$
21. $\dfrac{(5.74 - \sqrt{2.06})^2}{3.54}$

22. $\dfrac{2}{1.3^4} + \dfrac{3}{1.4^3}$
23. $\dfrac{3.6 + 4(8 + 1.2)}{2.1 + 1.6 \div 0.52}$
24. $\dfrac{\sqrt{5.65^3}}{\sqrt[3]{2.4^2}}$

25. $\left(9.5 - \dfrac{1.2}{0.52}\right)^4$
26. $\dfrac{6.78 \times 1.653}{\sqrt{3.1^3}}$

You should now:

- know and apply the BODMAS rule to calculations involving several operations
- be able to insert the appropriate operations in order to make a calculation correct
- be able to use the various functions on a calculator to evaluate answers
- be able to plan and evaluate a detailed calculation on a calculator
- be able to round to various degrees of accuracy appropriate to the context of the question.

Summary exercise 7

You must not use your calculator for questions **1** to **3**.

1. Work out each of these.

   a $8 - 2 \times 3 + 5$
   b $14 + 2(7 + 8 \div 2)$
   c $3 \times 6 + 4 \times 2$

   d $10 - 6 \div 2 \times 3$
   e $(14 + 8 \div 2) - 3 \times 6$
   f $\dfrac{40 - 10 \div 2}{3 + 2 \times 1}$

   g $18 + 3(5 - 1 \times 3)$
   h $3\tfrac{1}{2} \times 5\tfrac{3}{4} \div \tfrac{1}{2}$

2. Insert the appropriate operations to make each of these calculations correct.

   a $6 \square 2 \square 3 \square 2 = 14$
   b $18 \square 6 \square 3 = 20$
   c $4 \square 3 \square 2 \square 1 = 9$
   d $12 \square 4 \square 3 \square 1 = 10$
   e $18 \square 6 \square 3 = 0$
   f $40 \square 3 \square 7 \square 2 = 17$

3   The answer to a problem is 28.
Five students all claim to have written down a calculation which leads to the correct answer.
Which of the students are correct?

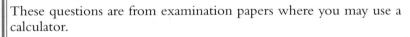

Jack
$4 \times 14 \div 2$

Kate
$2(3 \times 6 - 4)$

Mark
$3 + 1 \times 7$

Peter
$5 + 2 \times 5$

Janet
$8 \div 2 \times 7$

You may use your calculator for questions **4** and **5**.

4   Work out each of these.
 a 4.6^2
 b   the cube root of 274.625
 c $(8.6 + 0.2) \div 4$
 d $3\frac{2}{3} + 1\frac{1}{4} - 2\frac{1}{2}$
 e $5.6 + (-2.3) - (-6.4)$
 f 4^5
 g $\sqrt[4]{1296}$
 h $\frac{1}{32}$

5   Work out each of these, giving all your answers to 2 decimal places.
 a $\dfrac{24.53 + 36.28}{8.5}$
 b $(3.16 - 2.83)^2$
 c $\sqrt{2.6^3}$
 d $\dfrac{1}{8.1^2} + \dfrac{3}{2.1^3}$
 e $\dfrac{2.3 + 3(4.6 \div 1.2 - 0.8)}{2.4 + 1.65}$
 f $\left(\dfrac{3.62}{0.65}\right)^2 + \dfrac{1.8}{0.12}$
 g $\sqrt[5]{4.15} \div \sqrt{2.45^3}$
 h $\dfrac{7.45 + 3.25 \times 1.68}{\sqrt{34.2}}$

Examination questions

These questions are from examination papers where you may use a calculator.

Use 'Topic Tracker' at www.ccea.org.uk to find more exam questions.

1   Calculate
 a $\sqrt[3]{216} + \sqrt{81}$
 b $7.4^2 \div 2.4$

2   Calculate $15.6 + (660 - 78) \div (31.1 + 15.8)$ giving your answer correct to 2 decimal places.

3   a   Calculate $\dfrac{3.5 \times 7.1}{4.1 - 2.5}$.
Give your answer correct to 1 decimal place.
 b   Calculate $\sqrt{8.42^2 - 3.17^3}$.
Give your answer correct to 3 significant figures.

4   A science experiment requires the calculation:

$$\dfrac{2.36 + \sqrt{3.5^3}}{2.6 + 3.2 \times 1.8^4}$$

Work this out, describing briefly the steps of your calculation. Give your answer to an appropriate degree of accuracy.

CHAPTER 8

Ratio

This chapter is about:

- simplifying ratios
- dividing a quantity in a given ratio
- solving problems involving ratios.

You should already know:

- how to work with whole numbers, fractions and decimals
- approximate conversions between metric and imperial units
- how to convert between metric units.

Ratio is a means of comparing quantities. Here, the ratio of squares to triangles is 2 : 1. This means that for every triangle there are two squares.

It is important that the quantities are in the *same units* before any comparison is made. The notation used is $a:b$ (read as 'a is to b' or 'a to b'). The order in which a ratio is given is also very important.

Simplifying ratios

Ratios are simplified in the same way as fractions, by cancelling down as far as possible.

EXAMPLE 1

Simplify 45 : 80.

SOLUTION

Dividing both sides by 5 gives 9 : 16.

EXAMPLE 2

Simplify 240 g : 2 kg.

SOLUTION

Rewrite the ratio as 240 : 2000 (in grams). Dividing both sides by 80 gives 3 : 25. ◄

Once the units are the same, you do not need to write them in the final ratio.

In a class of 30 students, 12 wear glasses.
Find the ratio of those who wear glasses to those who do not.

SOLUTION

12 wear glasses, therefore $30 - 12 = 18$ do not.
The ratio is $12:18 = 2:3$.

Change the ratio $4:5$ into the form $1:n$.

SOLUTION

Dividing both sides by 4 gives $1:\frac{5}{4}$ or $1:1.25$.

Exercise 8.1

1 Write each of these as a ratio in its simplest form.

   a $40:65$ b $32:40$ c $25:45$
   d $36:54$ e $40:12$ f $120:300$
   g $63:49$ h $34:51$ i $24:120$
   j $40\,\text{cm}:2\,\text{m}$ k £$1.25:75\text{p}$ l $800\,\text{m}:3\,\text{km}$
   m $24\,\text{mm}:1.6\,\text{cm}$ n $6.5\,\text{kg}:450\,\text{g}$ o 1.32 litres $:450\,\text{ml}$

2 Express each of these ratios in the form $1:n$.

   a $5:20$ b $7:3$ c $2:5$ d $10:3$

3 In a class there are 14 boys and 16 girls. What is the ratio of girls to boys?

4 In April there were 12 dry days. Find the ratio of wet days to dry days.

5 Of 120 students in Year 12, 96 study French and the rest study German. What is the ratio of those studying French to those studying German?

Dividing in a given ratio

If £40 is shared equally between two people, each person gets
£40 ÷ 2 = £20. However, if the £40 is divided between the two people
in the ratio $2:3$, then the money is actually split into 5 parts (2 + 3),
with the first person getting 2 parts and the second getting 3 parts.
£40 ÷ 5 = £8. So the first person gets $2 \times$ £8 = £16 and the second gets
$3 \times$ £8 = £24. You can also think of this as the first person getting $\frac{2}{5}$ of
£40 and the second getting $\frac{3}{5}$ of £40.

A value can, therefore, be divided in a ratio. It is important to remember
that the total number of parts into which a value is divided is the total of
the individual parts of the ratio.

EXAMPLE 5

Divide 60 cm in the ratio 2 : 3.

SOLUTION

2 : 3 means that the value is to be divided into 5 parts.
Each part is worth 60 ÷ 5 = 12 cm.
Therefore dividing in the ratio 2 : 3 gives 24 cm and 36 cm. ◀

> It is good practice to check that the total end values add up to the original value. Here, 24 cm + 36 cm = 60 cm.

EXAMPLE 6

Share £120 between three boys in the ratio 1 : 3 : 4.

SOLUTION

1 : 3 : 4 implies 8 parts, with each part worth £120 ÷ 8 = £15.
Therefore sharing in the ratio 1 : 3 : 4 gives £15, £45 and £60.

EXAMPLE 7

A concrete mixture is made by mixing cement, sand and gravel in the ratio 2 : 3 : 4. What fraction of the mixture is sand?

SOLUTION

2 : 3 : 4 implies 9 parts, of which 3 are sand. Therefore, sand = $\frac{3}{9} = \frac{1}{3}$.

Exercise 8.2

1 Divide £800 in the ratio 5 : 11.

2 The angles of a triangle are in the ratio 4 : 5 : 6.
   Find the size of each angle.

3 If $\frac{3}{8}$ of the members of a youth club are girls, what is the ratio of boys to girls?

4 £108 is shared between two sisters in the same ratio as their ages.
   The sisters are aged 12 and 15.
   How much will each get?

5 A line 6 m long is split in the ratio 3 : 4 : 5.
   What is the difference in length between the longest and shortest parts of the line?

6 540 trading cards are split between John, Joseph and Dan in the ratio 4 : 3 : 2.
   John then shares his cards between himself and two other friends in the ratio 3 : 1 : 1, keeping the most for himself.
   How many cards will John then have?

7 A recipe mixture for a chocolate cake uses $2\frac{1}{2}$ times as much sugar as cocoa, and 4 times as much flour as cocoa.
   The total mixture for the chocolate cake weighs 1.5 kg.
   How much flour is used?

Solving problems using ratios

Ratio is useful for solving many different types of problems, in particular for adapting recipes, converting units, increasing or decreasing values, and finding lengths on scale drawings or distances on maps.

Ratios in the form 1 : n

Sometimes you know one of the quantities in a ratio, but not the other.

If a ratio is in the form 1 : n and you know the first quantity, you can work out the second quantity by multiplying by n.

EXAMPLE 8

The scale on a map is 1 : 25 000.
Two towns are 12 cm apart on the map.
What is the actual distance between the two towns?

SOLUTION

1 cm on map : 25 000 cm in real life.
12 cm on map : 12 × 25 000 = 300 000 cm in real life.
300 000 cm = 3000 m = 3 km
The towns are 3 km apart in real life.

If a ratio is in the form 1 : n and you know the second quantity, you can work out the first quantity by dividing by n.

EXAMPLE 9

The scale of a map is 1 : 50 000.
How far apart on the map will two towns be if they are 18 km apart in real life?

SOLUTION

1 cm on map : 50 000 cm in real life.
18 km = 18 000 m = 1 800 000 cm
1 800 000 ÷ 50 000 = 36 cm on map.
The towns are 36 cm apart on the map.

Ratios in the form m : n

For simple problems you can use an approach similar to finding equivalent fractions.

EXAMPLE 10

A recipe for 6 people uses 4 eggs, 200 g of flour and 80 g of sugar.
Adapt this recipe for 9 people.

SOLUTION

The ratio of people is $6 : 9$.
The ingredients will increase in the same ratio.

$6 : 9 = 2 : 3$ ◄───────────────── First write the ratio in its simplest form. Then find the equivalent ratio using each given quantity in turn for the first number.

Eggs: $2 : 3 \rightarrow 4 : 6$ ◄──────── Double both sides of the ratio.

Flour: $2 : 3 \rightarrow 200 : 300$ ◄──── Multiply both sides of the ratio by 100.

Sugar: $2 : 3 \rightarrow 80 : 120$ ◄──── Multiply both sides of the ratio by 40.

The recipe for 9 people requires 6 eggs, 300 g of flour and 120 g of sugar.

Look again at the ratio, in its simplest form, of the number of people and the ratio of the number of eggs in Example 10. There are, in fact, two ways to work out the answers.

Number of people		Number of people
2	$\rightarrow \times 1.5$	3
$\downarrow \times 2$		$\downarrow \times 2$
Number of eggs		Number of eggs
4	$\rightarrow \times 1.5$	6

The first way, involving the use of equivalent fractions, is the method used in the example above. To find the number you need to multiply the ratio by, you compare the quantities in the corresponding parts of the ratio, that is, 2 people initially and 4 eggs initially. To get from 2 to 4, you multiply by $4 \div 2 = 2$. Notice that you need to multiply by different numbers to find the quantities of the other ingredients.

The second method involves the use of a multiplier. To get from 2 people to 3 people, you multiply by $3 \div 2 = 1.5$, so to get from any quantity for 2 people to any quantity for 3 people, you multiply by 1.5.

EXAMPLE 11

Convert $17\frac{1}{2}$ miles to kilometres. ◄──────── Ratio is a useful means for converting between metric and imperial units.

SOLUTION

5 miles $\approx$ 8 km so the ratio of miles to kilometres is $5 : 8$. ◄──── You should learn this approximate conversion.

$$5 \xrightarrow{\times \frac{8}{5}} 8 \qquad\qquad or \qquad\qquad 5 \xrightarrow{\times 1.6} 8$$

$$17\frac{1}{2} \xrightarrow{\times \frac{8}{5}} 28 \qquad\qquad\qquad\qquad 17.5 \xrightarrow{\times 1.6} 28$$

$17\frac{1}{2}$ miles is approximately 28 kilometres.

Find the multiplier by dividing 8 by 5. Use decimals or fractions, whichever you prefer to work with.

EXAMPLE 12

A photocopier reduces in the ratio $5 : 3$.
The length of a rectangle on the reduced copy is 12 cm.
What length is it on the original?

SOLUTION

$$5 \xleftarrow{\times \frac{5}{3}} 3$$

$$20 \xleftarrow{\times \frac{5}{3}} 12$$

> This time you know the second quantity in the ratio.
> Find the multiplier by dividing 5 by 3.

The length of the rectangle on the original is 20 cm.

EXAMPLE 13

An 8 cm long photograph is enlarged so that it is now 20 cm long. What is the ratio of the enlargement?

SOLUTION

8 cm has become 20 cm, therefore the ratio of the enlargement is

$8 : 20 = 2 : 5$ ◄── Always write the ratio in its simplest form unless you are told otherwise.

Exercise 8.3

1 A map is drawn to a scale of 1 : 50 000.
  a Calculate the length of a road which appears as 4 cm long on the map.
  b Calculate the length on the map of a lake which is 8 km long in real life.

2 On a plan of a house, the scale used is 1 : 120.
  What are the actual dimensions of a room which measures 3.2 cm by 4 cm on the plan?

3 The distance from Milan to Rome is 612 km.
  How far apart do these cities appear on a map with a scale of 1 : 750 000?

4 A 4.65 km long road appears as 31 cm long on a map.
  What is the scale of the map?

5 A photocopier enlarges in the ratio 4 : 9.
  What will the enlarged diameter of a circle be if it is originally 12 cm?

6 A recipe for eight people requires 2.5 kg of meat.
  How much meat is required for six people?

7 The ratio of pigs to cows on a farm is 3 : 5.
  If there are 105 pigs, what is the total number of pigs and cows?

8 To make 30 pieces of fudge, I need 250 g of sugar and 50 g of cocoa.
  What quantity of each ingredient will I need to make only 24 pieces of fudge?

9 a Approximately how many kilograms are there in 33 pounds?
  b Approximately how many pints are there in 8 litres?

10 Two squares have lengths 15 cm and 12 cm.
   a   Find the ratio of their lengths.
   b   Find the ratio of their perimeters.
   c   Find the ratio of their areas.

You should now:
- be able to simplify ratios
- be able to divide in a given ratio
- be able to use ratios in context, for solving problems.

Summary exercise 8

You must not use your calculator for questions **1** to **6**.

1 Simplify each of these ratios.
   a $350:400$ **b** $25p:£4$
   c $80\,cm:1\,m$ **d** $144:56$
   e $2\frac{1}{2}:3\frac{3}{4}$ **f** $850\,ml:2.5l$
   g $2.4\,cm:6\,cm$ **h** $3\frac{1}{2}$ hours : 35 minutes
   i $1\,mm:5\,m$ **j** $45\,g:2.5\,kg$
   k $0.16:6.4$ **l** $3.2\,m:200\,mm$

2 Write each of these in the form $1:n$.
   a $2:3$ **b** $4:1$ **c** $10:3$ **d** $20:12$

3 $\frac{4}{9}$ of a youth club are boys. What is the ratio of boys to girls in the youth club?

4 Divide each of these in the given ratio.
   a   £280 in the ratio $3:5$
   b   184 minutes in the ratio $2:3:3$

5 A girl and her elder sister share a sum of money in the ratio $3:4$. If the sum of money is doubled, in what ratio should they divide the new amount so that the elder sister still receives the same amount of money?

6 £600 is divided between Liam, Mike and Noel.
   Liam gets twice as much as Mike and Mike gets three times as much as Noel. How much does Liam get?

You may use your calculator for questions **7** to **13**.

7 The distance between two towns is 32 km.
   How far apart will they be on a map of scale $1:400\,000$?

8 For every hectare of land planted with barley, a farmer plants 3 hectares with oats. If he sows 180 hectares altogether, how many hectares are there of each crop?

9   A shade of paint is made up of 3 parts yellow and 5 parts green. How many litres of green paint are needed to make up a mixture of 14 litres of this paint?

10 A photograph originally 8 cm by 6 cm is enlarged to have dimensions 22 cm by 16.5 cm. What is the ratio of the enlargement?

11 A passport photograph was enlarged in the ratio 5:9. The enlarged photograph was 72 mm long. How long was the passport photograph?

12 Approximately how many miles are there in 30 km?

13 A prize is divided between three people P, Q and R. If the ratio of P's share to Q's share is 3:1 and of Q's share to R's share is 2:5, calculate the ratio of P's share to R's share.

Examination questions

Use 'Topic Tracker' at www.ccea.org.uk to find more exam questions.

Questions 1 to 3 are from examination papers where you may not use a calculator.

1   To make 10 pancakes the following recipe may be used.
    400 ml milk
    2 large eggs
    175 g flour
    Adapt this recipe to make 25 pancakes.

2   The distance from Cookstown to Belfast is approximately 42 miles. What is the approximate distance in kilometres?

3   Divide £472 in the ratio 5:3.

Questions 4 to 7 are from examination papers where you may use a calculator.

4   100 g of instant cappuccino contains
    18 g protein
    36 g carbohydrate
    8 g fibre
    0.45 g sodium
    Calculate how much of each is contained in 250 g of instant cappuccino.

5   A cyclist travels 42 km on cycle paths, A roads and B roads in the ratio 4:3:1. Calculate the number of kilometres on each.

6   a   £750 is shared between James and Richard in the ratio 1:4. How much more does Richard receive than James?

    b   It takes 45 minutes to walk 5 km. How long will it take to walk 9 km, at the same speed?

7   Three sisters share £550 in the ratio 10:9:6. Calculate how much each receives.

CHAPTER 9

Percentages and finance

This chapter is about:

- converting between percentages, fractions, decimals and ratios
- finding a percentage of a quantity
- percentage change
- writing one number as a percentage of another
- financial calculations.

You should already know:

- how to work with whole numbers, decimals and fractions
- how to work with ratios
- how to write an answer to an appropriate degree of accuracy.

This chapter covers a wide range of ideas on percentages and finance. Many of the concepts can be dealt with without the use of a calculator but some more complex ideas will require one. It is important to be able to do the relevant questions without a calculator (as indicated).

Converting between percentages, fractions, decimals and ratios

A percentage is a fraction out of 100. It is important to be able to convert between percentages, fractions, decimals and ratios. Particularly on non-calculator papers, some problems are easier to solve using one form than another. For example, if you are asked to find 60% of 15 metres, it is easier to think of it as finding $\frac{3}{5}$ of 15 metres. $\frac{1}{5}$ of 15 metres is 3 metres, so $\frac{3}{5}$ or 60% of 15 metres is 9 metres.

Converting from a percentage

A percentage is a fraction out of 100 (which can be simplified) and a fraction out of 100 can be easily written as a decimal (as hundredths).

For example,

$$24\% = \frac{24}{100} = \frac{6}{25}$$
$$24\% = \frac{24}{100} = 0.24$$

$$2\% = \frac{2}{100} = \frac{1}{50}$$
$$2\% = \frac{2}{100} = 0.02$$

$$12\frac{1}{2}\% = \frac{12.5}{100} = \frac{25}{200} = \frac{1}{8}$$

$$12\frac{1}{2}\% = \frac{12.5}{100} = 0.125$$

> Here, both the numerator and denominator are multiplied by 2 to get rid of the decimal in the numerator.

$$130\% = \frac{130}{100} = \frac{13}{10} = 1\frac{3}{10}$$

$$130\% = \frac{130}{100} = 1.3$$

Converting from a decimal

A decimal is written in terms of tenths, hundredths, etc. Therefore, a decimal can be converted to the appropriate fraction and simplified. A decimal can be converted to a percentage by multiplying by 100.

For example,

$$0.35 = \frac{35}{100} = \frac{7}{20} \qquad\qquad 0.35 \times 100 = 35 \qquad \text{so } 0.35 = 35\%$$

$$0.9 = \frac{9}{10} \qquad\qquad 0.9 \times 100 = 90 \qquad \text{so } 0.9 = 90\%$$

$$0.075 = \frac{75}{1000} = \frac{3}{40} \qquad\qquad 0.075 \times 100 = 7\frac{1}{2} \qquad \text{so } 0.075 = 7\frac{1}{2}\%$$

$$1.05 = \frac{105}{100} = \frac{21}{20} = 1\frac{1}{20} \qquad\qquad 1.05 \times 100 = 105 \qquad \text{so } 1.05 = 105\%$$

Converting from a fraction

There are two types of fractions to consider here.

- If the denominator of the fraction is such that it can easily be rewritten as an equivalent fraction with a denominator of 100, then this gives the required decimal (in hundredths), which in turn leads to the percentage.

- If the denominator of the fraction is such that it cannot easily be rewritten as an equivalent fraction with a denominator of 100, then you divide the numerator of the fraction by the denominator. This will give the required decimal, which can then be converted to a percentage by multiplying by 100.

For example,

$$\frac{13}{20} = \frac{65}{100} = 0.65 \text{ or } 65\%$$

$$\frac{19}{25} = \frac{76}{100} = 0.76 \text{ or } 76\%$$

$$\frac{3}{8} = 8\,\overline{)\,3\,.\,{}^{3}0\,\,{}^{6}0\,\,{}^{4}0\,} \begin{array}{c} 0\,.\,3\ \ 7\ \ 5 \end{array} = 37\frac{1}{2}\%$$

> The denominator 8 is not easily converted to 100, so divide instead.

$$\frac{2}{3} = 3\,\overline{)\,2\,.\,{}^{2}0\,\,{}^{2}0\,\,{}^{2}0\,\,{}^{2}0\,} \begin{array}{c} 0\,.\,6\ \ 6\ \ 6\ \ 6... \end{array} = 0.\dot{6} = 66\frac{2}{3}\%$$

> When a digit repeats indefinitely in a decimal, you can write it using dot notation, as here.
> The dot indicates that the 6 repeats indefinitely.

A decimal which does not end but in which one or more of the digits repeat is called a **recurring decimal**. A decimal which ends after a fixed number of decimal places is known as a **terminating decimal**. Both terminating and recurring decimals are dealt with in more detail in Chapter 12.

It is useful to learn some of the more commonly used percentages, fractions and decimals and their equivalents so that you do not have to calculate the conversions. The most common ones are given in the table on the right. Many others can be found from these values.

Percentage	Fraction	Decimal
1%	$\frac{1}{100}$	0.01
5%	$\frac{1}{20}$	0.05
10%	$\frac{1}{10}$	0.1
$12\frac{1}{2}\%$	$\frac{1}{8}$	0.125
20%	$\frac{1}{5}$	0.2
25%	$\frac{1}{4}$	0.25
$33\frac{1}{3}\%$	$\frac{1}{3}$	$0.\dot{3}$
50%	$\frac{1}{2}$	0.5
75%	$\frac{3}{4}$	0.75
100%	1	1.0

EXAMPLE 1

Write $\frac{5}{6}$ as a decimal and as a percentage.

SOLUTION

The denominator of 6 is not easily converted to 100, so divide.

$$6 \overline{)5.\,{}^5 0\,{}^2 0\,{}^2 0} = 0.833$$

$$= 0.8\dot{3} = 83\frac{1}{3}\%$$

EXAMPLE 2

A boy scores 17 out of 25 in a test. What percentage is this?

SOLUTION

$\frac{17}{25} = \frac{68}{100} = 68\%$

EXAMPLE 3

Arrange these numbers in order from the smallest to the largest.

40%   0.36 $\frac{18}{48}$

SOLUTION

First change all the numbers to the same form.

$40\% = \frac{40}{100} = 0.4$

$\frac{18}{48} = \frac{3}{8} = 0.375$

The correct order from smallest to largest is 0.36, $\frac{18}{48}$, 40%.

EXAMPLE 4

In Year 11 there are 120 students.

35% study French, whilst 40 students study German; no student studies both languages.

Which is the more popular language?

SOLUTION

$35\% = \frac{35}{100} = \frac{7}{20}$

$\frac{1}{20}$ of $120 = 6$ students.

So $\frac{7}{20} = 7 \times 6 = 42$ students.

More students study French than German, therefore French is more popular.

EXAMPLE 5

The ratio of students who walk to school to those who travel by bus is 1 : 4. What percentage of the students come by bus?

SOLUTION

100% divided in the ratio 1 : 4 becomes 20 : 80.
80% of the students travel by bus.

Exercise 9.1

1   Convert each of these percentages to a fraction and a decimal.
    a   22%   b   8%   c   145%   d $2\frac{1}{2}\%$ e   0.05%

2   Convert each of these decimals to a fraction and a percentage.
    a   0.03   b   0.8   c   0.006   d   1.25   e   0.625

3   Convert each of these fractions to a percentage and a decimal.
    a $\frac{13}{50}$ b $\frac{5}{12}$ c $\frac{3}{5}$ d $\frac{7}{200}$ e $\frac{2}{9}$

4   32% of the members of a youth club are girls.
    What fraction of the members are boys?

5   Arrange each set of numbers in order from the smallest to the largest.
    a $42\%, 0.45, \frac{2}{5}$ b $31\%, \frac{1}{3}, 0.3$ c $70\%, \frac{7}{11}, 0.64$ d $0.1\%, 0.1, \frac{1}{100}$

6   The ratio of red paint to blue paint in a mixture is 2 : 7.
    What percentage of the mixture is blue paint?

7   A photograph is enlarged in the ratio 3 : 4.
    By what percentage are its side lengths increased?

8   Express $\frac{9}{250}$ as an exact decimal.

9   Find $0.1 \times 0.2 \times 0.3$ as a fraction in its simplest form.

10   Max receives 20% of a sum of money.
     He shares it equally between himself and his two brothers.
     What fraction of the original sum of money will they each have?

11   Here are some percentages: 30%   6%   12%   85%

     a   Which percentage is greater than $\frac{1}{2}$?   b   Which percentage lies between $\frac{1}{10}$ and $\frac{1}{20}$?

     c   Which percentage is equal to $\frac{3}{25}$?   d   Which percentage is double 0.425?

Finding a percentage of a quantity

There are several approaches for finding a percentage of a quantity. The next example shows four of these.

EXAMPLE 6

Find 45% of 6 metres.

SOLUTION

Method 1

45% of $6\,\text{m} = \frac{45}{100} \times 6\,\text{m} = 2.7\,\text{m}$

> This approach is suitable when you are allowed to use a calculator.

Method 2

45% of $6\,\text{m} = \frac{45}{100_1} \times 600^6\,\text{cm} = 270\,\text{cm} = 2.7\,\text{m}$

> This approach uses the multiplication of fractions (see Chapter 5).

Method 3

First find 1% by dividing 6 m by 100.

1% of $6\,\text{m} = \frac{6}{100} = 0.06\,\text{m}$

So $45\% = 45 \times 0.06 = 2.7\,\text{m}$

> This approach uses the multiplication of decimals (see Chapter 3).

Method 4

Convert the percentage to a fraction.

$45\% = \frac{9}{20}$

$\frac{1}{20}$ of $600\,\text{cm} = 600 \div 20 = 30\,\text{cm}$

So $\frac{9}{20} = 9 \times 30 = 270\,\text{cm} = 2.7\,\text{m}$

> This method is useful when carrying out a mental calculation.

The last three approaches are more suitable on a non–calculator paper.

EXAMPLE 7

Find 32% of £4.50 without using a calculator.

SOLUTION

$\frac{\overset{16}{32}}{\underset{50_1}{100}} \times 450^9\text{p} = 144\text{p} = £1.44$

EXAMPLE 8

Find 13% of 320 without using a calculator.

SOLUTION

1% of $320 = 3.20$
13% of $320 = 13 \times 3.20 = 41.6$

EXAMPLE 9

Find 64.5% of £8500 using a calculator.

SOLUTION

$$\frac{64.5}{100} \times £8500 = £5482.50 \quad \longleftarrow$$

> The calculator displays the answer 5482.5, but since the question involves money the appropriate format is with 2 decimal places – hence the inclusion of the extra zero.

EXAMPLE 10

Find 3.5% of £155.65 using a calculator.

SOLUTION

$$\frac{3.5}{100} \times £155.65 = £5.45 \quad \longleftarrow$$

> The calculator displays the answer 5.44775. The answer must be given to a suitable degree of accuracy (see Chapter 6).
> For money this is to 2 decimal places.

Percentage increase and decrease

A value may be increased or decreased by a given percentage. For example, someone's salary may be increased by 12%, or the number of members of a youth club may decrease by 4%. There are two appropriate methods for calculating such increases or decreases.

To increase or decrease by $x\%$, calculate $x\%$ of the quantity and either add it to or subtract it from the original quantity, as required. Alternatively, to increase by $x\%$, find $(100 + x)\%$ of the original quantity, or to decrease by $x\%$, find $(100 - x)\%$ of the original quantity.

EXAMPLE 11

Increase £60 by 4%.

SOLUTION

Method 1

4% of $£60 = \frac{4}{100} \times £60 = £2.40$

$£60 + £2.40 = £62.40$

Method 2

104% of $£60 = \frac{104}{100} \times £60 = £62.40$

EXAMPLE 12

Decrease 860 kg by 12%.

SOLUTION

Method 1

12% of $860 = \frac{12}{100} \times 860 = 103.2\,\text{kg}$

$860 - 103.2 = 756.8\,\text{kg}$

Method 2

$100 - 12 = 88$

88% of $860\,\text{kg} = \frac{88}{100} \times 860 = 756.8\,\text{kg}$

EXAMPLE 13

A television priced at £430 is reduced by 15% in a sale. Find the sale price.

SOLUTION

Method 1

15% of £430 = $\frac{15}{100}$ × 430 = £64.50

£430 − £64.50 = £365.50

Method 2

100 − 15 = 85

85% of £430 = $\frac{85}{100}$ × £430 = £365.50

EXAMPLE 14

A workforce of 550 is to be increased by 8%. Find the new workforce.

SOLUTION

Method 1

8% of 550 = $\frac{8}{100}$ × 550 = 44   550 + 44 = 594

Method 2

108% of 550 = $\frac{108}{100}$ × 550 = 594

Exercise 9.2

You must not use your calculator for questions 1 to 4.

1 Find each of these.
   a 18% of £300
   b 72% of 200 g
   c 64% of 850
   d 35% of 150 g
   e $\frac{1}{2}$% of 400 litres
   f 120% of £12
   g 85% of 2 hours
   h $62\frac{1}{2}$% of 2.4 m

2 a Increase 40 m by 6%.
   b Decrease 350 kg by 7%.
   c Decrease 600 kg by 65%.
   d Increase 1200 m by 18%.

3 A coat costing £45 is reduced by 5% in the sale. Find the sale price of the coat.

4 The price of a rail ticket, originally costing £12.50, is to be increased by 6%. Find the new price of the ticket.

You may use your calculator for questions 5 to 15.

5 Calculate each of these.
   a 17% of 4.5 kg
   b 6.4% of £15.95
   c 16% of 175 litres
   d 8% of 3450 hectares
   e 1.5% of £3
   f $5\frac{1}{2}$% of 800
   g $6\frac{2}{3}$% of 3 km
   h 110% of 6.2 kg
   i $7\frac{1}{2}$% of £312
   j 240% of 8 miles

6 a   Increase £2.50 by 35%.   b   Decrease 44 m by 6%.

   c   Decrease £4500 by $2\frac{1}{2}$%.   d   Increase 76 m by 3%.

7 A phone bill for £64.46 has $17\frac{1}{2}$% VAT added to it.
   How much VAT is added to the bill?

8 The value of a car costing £8000 decreases by 24% in its first year.
   What is its value after 1 year?

9 A joint of meat weighs 3.5 kg when frozen. It loses 8% of its weight
   when it is thawed. Find the mass of the joint when thawed.

10 A girl earns £156.50 per week, but needs to pay 24% of it in tax.
   What is her net weekly income?

Writing one number as a percentage of another

To write one number as a percentage of another, you write the values as a
fraction and then multiply by 100 to convert to a percentage. For example,
a score of 24 out of 30 becomes
$\frac{24}{30} \times 100 = 80\%$.

EXAMPLE 15

1750 ml of a 2 litre cordial mix is made up of water.
What percentage of the cordial is water?

SOLUTION

$\frac{1750}{2000} \times 100 = 87.5\%$ ◄————— Use the same units for both numerator
and denominator in the fraction.

EXAMPLE 16

What percentage of 1.5 m is 84 cm?

SOLUTION

$\frac{84}{150} \times 100 = 56\%$

EXAMPLE 17

In a class of 14 girls and 18 boys, nine students wear glasses. What
percentage of the class do not wear glasses?
(Give your answer to 1 decimal place.)

SOLUTION

Total in class = 14 + 18 = 32
9 wear glasses, so 32 − 9 = 23 do not.
$\frac{23}{32} \times 100 = 71.9\%$

Percentage change

When there is a numerical change in a value, you can find the percentage change. This could be a percentage profit, percentage loss, percentage growth, percentage decline, etc. The percentage change can be calculated using the formula

$$\text{percentage change} = \frac{\text{change}}{\text{original}} \times 100$$

EXAMPLE 18

Find the percentage profit when an item that originally cost £600 is later sold for £720.

SOLUTION

Profit = £720 − £600 = £120

Percentage profit = $\frac{120}{600} \times 100 = 20\%$

EXAMPLE 19

A man buys a car for £6500 and later sells it for £4800.
What is the percentage loss?

SOLUTION

Loss = £6500 − £4800 = £1700

Percentage loss = $\frac{1700}{6500} \times 100 = 26.2\%$ (1 d.p.)

EXAMPLE 20

A photograph originally measuring 8 cm by 6 cm is enlarged to 20 cm by 15 cm. Calculate the percentage increase in area of the photograph.

SOLUTION

Original area = 8 × 6 = 48 cm^2
Enlarged area = 20 × 15 = 300 cm^2
Increase = 300 − 48 = 252 cm^2

Percentage increase = $\frac{252}{48} \times 100 = 525\%$

Exercise 9.3

1 Of the 40 houses in North Street, 32 have a garage.
   What percentage of the houses have a garage?

2 At a drama class, two of the 28 members were absent.
   What percentage is this?

3 Pure gold is 24 carat.
   What percentage of pure gold does an 18 carat ring contain?

4 A driving instructor has 85 pupils, of which 62 are male.
   What percentage of her pupils are female?

5 What percentage of 2 kg is 44 g?

6 A girl leaves home at 8a.m. and returns at 4.30p.m.
   For what percentage of a day is she away?

7 A rectangle measuring 15 cm by 6 cm has its length and breadth
   both increased by 15%.
   a   What is the percentage increase in the perimeter of the
       rectangle?
   b   What is the percentage increase in the area of the rectangle?

8 When VAT is added to a bill of £450 the final bill is £531.
   What percentage of the final bill is VAT?

9 A girl gains £22.40 interest on her savings of £420.
   What is the percentage interest rate?

10 The length of a metal rod increases from 150 cm to 150.8 cm on
    being heated. What is the percentage increase in the length?

11 A shopkeeper buys apples at £4.32 per crate of 24.
    He sells the apples individually at 24p each.
    What is his percentage profit?

12 An employer reduces the working week from 40 hours to 38 hours,
    without any cut in weekly pay.
    Calculate the percentage increase in the wages (on an hourly rate)
    for this to happen.
    Give your answer to 2 decimal places.

Reverse percentages

If the final value of a quantity is known, after a percentage change has
already taken place, the original value can be calculated using the idea
of reverse percentages. It is important to remember that the percentage
change was a percentage of the *original* value and not of the *final* value and
to take account of this in your calculation.

EXAMPLE 21

This year there are 345 cows on a farm. This is an increase of 15% on last
year. How many cows were there on the farm last year?

SOLUTION

345 cows represents 115% (original 100% + 15% increase).

So $\frac{345}{115}$ represents 1%.

The original number of cows was 100% = $\frac{345}{115} \times 100 = 300$.

Last year there were 300 cows.

> Do *not* be tempted
> to take off 15% of
> 345, as the 15% was
> a percentage of the
> *original* value and not
> of the 345.

EXAMPLE 22

The membership of a bowls club has decreased by 8% over the last year. This year there are 138 members.

How many members were there last year?

SOLUTION

138 represents 92% (original 100% − 8% decrease).

So $\frac{138}{92}$ represents 1%.

So the original 100% = $\frac{138}{92} \times 100 = 150$.

Last year there were 150 members.

> Again, do *not* be tempted to add 8% onto the 138, as the 8% was a percentage of the *original* value and not of the 138.

EXAMPLE 23

The VAT on a bill is $17\frac{1}{2}$%. The VAT comes to £98.

What was the total bill before the VAT was added?

SOLUTION

£98 represents $17\frac{1}{2}$%.

So $\frac{£98}{17\frac{1}{2}}$ represents 1%.

The original bill was 100% = $\frac{£98}{17\frac{1}{2}} \times 100 = £560$.

Fractional change

You can use the same technique to solve problems involving fractional change as for problems involving percentage change.

EXAMPLE 24

A boy sells a motorbike for £1200. This is $\frac{3}{8}$ less than he paid for it. What did he originally pay for the bike?

SOLUTION

£1200 represents $\frac{5}{8}$.

So $\frac{£1200}{5}$ represents $\frac{1}{8}$.

The original amount was $\frac{8}{8} = \frac{£1200}{5} \times 8 = £1920$.

Exercise 9.4

1 A sound system costs £240 after a discount of 20% has been given. What was the original price of the sound system?

2 45% of the students in a school travel by bus.
   814 students do not travel by bus.
   How many students are there in the school in total?

3 The price of some trainers increases by 90p when VAT is increased from 15% to $17\frac{1}{2}\%$.
What was the original price of the trainers, excluding VAT?

4 A girl pays 22% of her weekly income in tax.
If her take-home pay each week is £265.20, what is her weekly income before tax?

5 A man's yearly salary is increased by 6% to £38 160.
What was his annual salary before the increase?

6 A return flight ticket offers a saving of 8% on two single tickets. If the difference in price between the return ticket and the total of the two single tickets is £20.48, what is the cost of a return ticket?

7 A bottle of shampoo is labelled '15% extra'.
If the bottle holds 322 ml, how much would be in an ordinary bottle?

8 The diagram shows a small rectangle and a large rectangle.
The sides of the small rectangle have been increased by 5% to give the sides of the large rectangle.

12.6 cm

The area of the large rectangle is 105.84 cm².
Find the length and width of the small rectangle.

9 A girl scored 92% in a test. She only got four questions wrong. If all the questions carried equal marks, how many questions were in the test?

10 A shopkeeper bought an article from his supplier.
He sold it for £115.92. This price included 20% profit and 15% VAT.
Find the price the shopkeeper paid the supplier.

Percentages and finance

Percentages play an important part in many financial situations. You have already met percentages in the contexts of profit, discount in a sale, tax on wages, etc. Percentages have a significant role in many other areas of finance, as illustrated below.

Interest

There are two types of interest – simple interest and compound interest.

- **Simple interest** is where the interest is calculated as a percentage of the original amount, no matter how long the money is in the account. Therefore, it is only necessary to calculate the interest for the first year, as it will remain the same in subsequent years. Simple interest can be calculated from the formula on the next page.

interest, $I = \frac{PRT}{100}$ where

P = principal (the original amount)
R = rate of interest (the percentage)
T = time for which the money remains in the account.

- **Compound interest** is where the interest is calculated as a percentage of the amount in the account the *previous* year. It is therefore compounded from year to year. The amount of interest earned in the first year is added onto the original amount, and the interest in the second year is a percentage of the amount at the end of the first year, and so on. The final amount in a compound interest account can be calculated from the formula below.

final amount, $A = P\left(\frac{100 + R}{100}\right)^n$ where

P = principal amount
R = rate of interest
n = number of years over which the interest builds.

Similarities can be drawn between this formula and the methods for increasing or decreasing by a given percentage as covered previously.

EXAMPLE 25

Find the interest earned in an account where £500 is deposited for 3 years at 5% simple interest per year.

SOLUTION

Method 1

1st year: Interest = 5% of £500 = $\frac{5}{100} \times 500$ = £25
2nd year: Interest = £25
3rd year: Interest = £25
Total interest = £25 + £25 + £25 = £75

Method 2

$I = \frac{PRT}{100} = \frac{500 \times 5 \times 3}{100} = £75$

EXAMPLE 26

Find the interest earned in an account where £2000 is deposited for 3 years at 4% compound interest per year.

SOLUTION

Method 1

1st year: Interest   = 4% of £2000

= $\frac{4}{100} \times £2000 = £80$

2nd year: Interest   = 4% of £2080

$$= \frac{4}{100} \times £2080 = £83.20$$

> This is the original £2000 plus the £80 interest from the first year.

3rd year: Interest   = 4% of £2163.20

$$= \frac{4}{100} \times £2163.20 = £86.53$$

> This is the £2080 from the end of the first year, plus the £83.20 interest from the second year.

Total interest   = £80 + £83.20 + £86.53 = £249.73

Method 2

$$A = P\left(\frac{100 + R}{100}\right)^n$$

$$A = 2000 \times \left(\frac{104}{100}\right)^3 = £2249.73$$

Interest = £2249.73 − £2000 = £249.73

What rate of simple interest must be paid per year, for a principal of £700 to amount to £752.50 over 2 years?

SOLUTION

Interest = £752.50 − £700 = £52.50

$$£52.50 = \frac{^7\cancel{700} \times R \times 2}{_1\cancel{100}} = 14R$$

$$R = \frac{£52.50}{14} = 3.75\%$$

Which would be more profitable over 5 years, £3500 in an 8% simple interest account or £3500 in a 7% compound interest account?

SOLUTION

Simple interest account: $I = \frac{3500 \times 8 \times 5}{100} = £1400$

Total now in account = £3500 + £1400 = £4900

Compound interest account: $A = 3500 \times \left(\frac{107}{100}\right)^5 = £4908.93$

Therefore the compound interest account is more profitable by £8.93.

In questions on interest it is important to read the question carefully. Sometimes you will be asked to find the interest only, whilst other questions may ask for the value of the final investment (the original value plus the interest).

Appreciation and depreciation

Appreciation is when the value of a quantity increases over time. For example, house prices generally appreciate over a period of time.

Depreciation is when the value of a quantity decreases over time. For example, the value of most cars depreciates over a period of time.

Both appreciation and depreciation work in a similar way to compound interest: the percentage is calculated as a percentage of the amount the *previous* year and not always of the original. Whilst the terms 'appreciation' or 'depreciation' are not always used, many problems involve similar types of calculations.

A car that was originally bought for £8000 depreciates by 12% over each of its first 2 years. What is the car worth at the end of the 2 years?

SOLUTION

Method 1

1st year: Depreciates by 12% (88% left).

So value $= \frac{88}{100} \times$ £8000 $=$ £7040.

2nd year: Depreciates by 12% (88% left).

So value $= \frac{88}{100} \times$ £7040 $=$ £6195.20.

Method 2

$A = 8000 \times \left(\frac{100 - 12}{100}\right)^2 =$ £6195.20

A rare postage stamp appreciates in value by 15% each year. If it is now valued at £120, what will its value be in 3 years' time (to the nearest pound)?

SOLUTION

$A = 120 \times \left(\frac{115}{100}\right)^3 =$ £183

A house is originally bought for £90 000. A year later its value has appreciated by 3%. The following year there is a slump in house prices and its value depreciates by 3%. What is the value of the house after the 2 years?

SOLUTION

1st year: 103% of £90 000 $= \frac{103}{100} \times$ £90 000 $=$ £92 700

2nd year: 97% of £92 700 $= \frac{97}{100} \times$ £92 700 $=$ £89 919

Finance in other areas

Mathematical calculations are also important in other areas, for example household bills, currency exchange and hire purchase. Some, though not all, of these calculations involve percentages. Some of them involve techniques learnt in earlier chapters.

EXAMPLE 32

An electricity bill is made up of a standing charge of £16.80 plus a charge of 5.2p per unit of electricity used.
Mr Jones uses 841 units of electricity.
    a   How much will his bill be?
    b   What percentage of his bill is made up of the standing charge?

SOLUTION

    a   Charge for units = $841 \times 5.2\text{p} = 4373.2\text{p} = £43.73$

          Standing charge = £16.80

          Total bill = £43.73 + £16.80 = £60.53

    b   Percentage from standing charge = $\dfrac{16.80}{60.53} \times 100$

                                 = 27.8% (to 1 d.p.)

EXAMPLE 33

The currency in Spain is the euro, where 1.47 euros = £1.
While he was on holiday, Jack bought some bottles of wine for 4.20 euros each, and on his return home he sold each bottle for £4.50.
What was his percentage profit on each bottle of wine?

SOLUTION

4.20 euros = $4.20 \div 1.47 = £2.86$

Profit on each bottle = $£4.50 - £2.86 = £1.64$

Percentage profit = $\dfrac{1.64}{2.86} \times 100 = 57.3\%$

EXAMPLE 34

A computer can be bought for £419.99 cash, or it can be bought on credit by paying a $12\frac{1}{2}\%$ deposit followed by 18 monthly payments of £22.50.

Find how much extra the credit price is, as a percentage of the cash price of the computer.

SOLUTION

$12\frac{1}{2}\%$ deposit = $\dfrac{12.5}{100} \times £419.99 = £52.50$

18 payments of £22.50 = $18 \times £22.50 = £405$

Total credit price = $£405 + £52.50 = £457.50$

Extra amount = $£457.50 - £419.99 = £37.51$

Percentage extra = $\dfrac{37.51}{419.99} \times 100 = 8.9\%$

£1 is worth 1.47 euros or 1.8 dollars. Convert 2000 euros into dollars.

SOLUTION

£1 = 1.47 euros
So 2000 euros = 2000 ÷ 1.47 = £1360.5442 ⟵ Do not round at this intermediate stage.
£1 = 1.8 dollars
So £1360.5442 = 1360.5442 × 1.8 = 2449 dollars.

Exercise 9.5

1 Calculate the interest on £525 invested for 4 years at 3% simple interest per year.

2 A car valued at £8500 depreciates by 20% in its first year, and by 15% in each of the next 2 years. Find its value after the 3 years.

3 £115 000 is invested for 3 years at 8% compound interest per year. Calculate the total interest earned over the 3 years.

4 £420 is invested in a simple interest account. After 4 years the interest accumulated is £117.60. What is the percentage interest rate?

5 A boy buys a motorbike. His insurance in the first year costs £780. After 1 year he receives 20% discount and in each of the following 2 years he receives a further 10% discount. How much will he have paid for insurance in total over the 4 years?

6 Approximately 20% of the surface of a pond of area 50 m² is covered by weed at the end of June. Each month a further 5% of the previous amount of weed develops. What percentage of the pond's area will be covered in weed by the end of August?

7 The population of an island increases by 5% per year. After how many years will the original population have doubled?

8 A computer depreciates in value by 5% each year. After 2 years its value is £640. What was its original value, to the nearest £10?

9 A girl wants to buy a piano that costs £3000. The shop offers a finance option of a 10% deposit, followed by monthly payments of £90 over the next 3 years. Alternatively, she can borrow the money from the bank for 3 years at 5.2% compound interest per year. Which is her better option?

10 A man can import a car from France for 16 000 euros.
The same car is available in the UK for £12 500.
What would his percentage saving be at a time when the exchange rate is £1 = 1.48 euros?

11 A telephone company charges users £20.40 per quarter for line rental. Calls are charged at 5p per minute from midnight until 6p.m. and at 4.2p per minute from 6p.m. until midnight.
VAT at 5% is added to the final bill. Find the total cost of the quarterly bill for a household which has calls totalling 254 minutes between midnight and 6p.m. and 386 minutes between 6p.m. and midnight.

> **You should now:**
> - know the meaning of a percentage
> - be able to convert between percentages, fractions, decimals and ratios
> - be able to find a percentage of a quantity, both with and without a calculator
> - be able to increase or decrease a quantity by a given percentage
> - be able to find one number as a percentage of another
> - know the formula for percentage change, and be able to apply it in various contexts
> - be able to use reverse percentages to calculate an original value
> - understand the concept of simple interest and compound interest and be able to solve a variety of problems
> - be able use percentages and other techniques for solving a variety of finance-type problems

Summary exercise 9

You must not use your calculator for questions **1** to **4**.

1 Convert each of these percentages to a fraction and a decimal.

   a   18%   **b** $37\frac{1}{2}\%$ **c**   150%

2 Convert each of these decimals to a fraction and a percentage.
   a   0.68   **b**   0.145   **c**   1.8

3 Convert each of these fractions to a percentage and a decimal.

   a $\frac{6}{25}$ **b** $\frac{11}{200}$ **c** $\frac{5}{9}$

4 The ratio of boys to girls in a swimming club is $2:3$.
   What percentage of the members are girls?

You may use your calculator for questions **5** to **24**.

5 832 letters are posted by a company in one week.
   Of these letters, 520 are posted first class and the rest second class.
   What percentage of the letters are posted second class?

6 Calculate each of these.
   a   16% of £124   **b** $22\frac{1}{2}\%$ of 27.6 kg   **c** $\frac{1}{2}\%$ of 8000 dollars

7 A holiday costing £460 has an $8\frac{1}{2}\%$ insurance surcharge.
   How much will the holiday cost including insurance?

8 A girl scores 13 out of 40 in a test. What is her percentage score?

9 A house bought for £80 000 is later sold for £92 000.
   What is the percentage profit?

10 A 7.5% discount is offered in a sale. On the last day of the sale a
   further 5% discount is given on the sale price.
   a   What will a coat cost on the last day of the sale if its original
        price was £60?
   b   What is the overall percentage discount on the coat?

11 A workforce is reduced by 2% to 539 people.
   How many people were in the original workforce?

12 A car insurance premium is £324.50 after 45% no-claims discount
   has been given. What was the original premium?

13 The final selling price of an article in a sale was £376.20. This included an original discount of 12%, followed by a further 5% discount in the last week of the sale. What was the original price of the item?

14 The price of 200 gallons of oil is £220 on Monday.
On Tuesday there is an increase of 1.5% in the cost.
On Wednesday the company announces 'a saving of 2% on yesterday's price'. What is the price of 200 gallons of oil on Wednesday?

15 *PQRS* is a square of side 80 cm. *PQ* is increased by 12% and *QR* is reduced by 4% to form a rectangle. By what percentage has the area of the shape been increased?

16 A man earns £32 000 per year. He pays 22% tax and saves 6% of the remainder of his salary. What percentage of his gross salary does he save?

17 If $W = xy$, find the percentage increase in W when x and y both increase by 8%.

18 A grocer sells a loaf of bread, making a profit of $12\frac{1}{2}$% on the price he paid for it. What is the ratio of his cost price to his selling price?

19 What is the difference in value between an investment of £12 000 which earns 3% simple interest over 3 years and the same amount invested in a compound interest account for 2 years earning 4% interest?

20 A bank pays 8% compound interest on an account. If a man deposits £8500, after how many years will his investment have trebled?

21 A piece of machinery worth £2500 is expected to depreciate by 5% over each of its first 3 years. What is the overall percentage loss if the machine is sold after 3 years?

22 After 8 years in a simple interest account, an amount of £650 has grown to £1040. What was the percentage interest rate per annum?

23 When Mr Marks visits Belfast, the buying rate for the dollar is $1.46 per pound and the selling rate is $1.32 per pound.
Mr Marks arrives in Northern Ireland with $3650 and changes it into pounds.
He spends £1850 and changes the remainder back into dollars before returning to the USA.
How many dollars does he get?

24 The rate of VAT (value added tax) is $17\frac{1}{2}$%.
Suppose that an increase in the rate causes the price of an item to rise by 2%. What is the new VAT rate?

Examination questions

Questions 1 to 7 are from examination papers where you may not use a calculator.

1 Write the following in ascending order.

53% $\frac{15}{25}$ 0.56

Show your working.

Use 'Topic Tracker' at www.ccea.org.uk to find more exam questions.

2 **a** In a survey of 600 packed lunchboxes, 80% of the lunchboxes contained sandwiches. $\frac{1}{3}$ of the 80% contained cheese sandwiches. How many of the lunchboxes surveyed contained cheese sandwiches?

  b 414 of the packed lunchboxes contained crisps. What percentage of the 600 lunchboxes contained crisps?

3 Write 165 out of 300 as a percentage.

4 A man invests £5000 in an account for two years. His money earns 5% compound interest per year. How much interest will he gain over the two years, providing he does not withdraw any money?

5 A ball is dropped from a height of 5 m above a horizontal floor. On each bounce it rises to 80% of its previous height. How far, **in total**, has the ball travelled through the air when it hits the ground for the third time?

6 £1 = 63 rupees and £1 = 182 yen. Mahish exchanges 1200 rupees into £ whilst Yumi exchanges 3800 yen into £. Who receives more money and by how much?

7 Mrs Harvey's gas bill is calculated by working out the total to be paid for the units of gas she used and adding that to the total standing charge for the number of days. She used 4685 units of gas at 3.22p per unit and the standing charge was 11.36p per day for 93 days.

  a What was her total gas bill in £s to the nearest penny?

  b VAT is added to Mrs Harvey's bill at 5%. What was the total bill after the VAT was added?

Questions **8** to **13** are from examination papers where you may use a calculator.

8 In one shop a watch costs £12.50 **plus** 17.5% VAT. In another shop the same watch costs £14.55 **including** VAT. Calculate the difference in cost.

9 A fridge–freezer costing £860 is to be reduced in price by 15% in a sale. What is the sale price of the fridge–freezer?

10 A shopkeeper buys 12 loaves of bread for £6.72, and sells them at 70p per loaf. Calculate his percentage profit.

11 Patricia bought a dress marked at a sale price of £139.70, which was a saving of 45% on the original price. What was the original price of the dress?

12 David opens a new account, depositing £4300. It earns 2.1% simple interest each year for three years. How much will then be in the account?

13 A new car costs £10 500. Its value depreciates by 20% in the first year, and by 15% in each of the following two years. What will the car be worth at the end of the three years? Show your working clearly.

CHAPTER 10

Reciprocals

> **This chapter is about:**
> - finding the reciprocal of a number
> - the properties of reciprocals.
>
> **You should already know:**
> - how to work with whole numbers, decimals and fractions.

Finding the reciprocal of a value

The **reciprocal** of a value is 1 divided by that value. The reciprocal is sometimes known as the **multiplicative inverse**.

The reciprocal of 6 is $1 \div 6 = \frac{1}{6}$.

The reciprocal of -2 is $1 \div (-2) = -\frac{1}{2}$.

The reciprocal of $\frac{1}{4}$ is $1 \div \frac{1}{4} = 1 \times \frac{4}{1} = 4$.

> Recall the method for division of fractions from Chapter 5 – turn the fraction upside down and multiply. You are, in fact, multiplying by the reciprocal of the fraction.

From the last of these, you can see that a general method to find the reciprocal of a number is as follows.

- Write the value as a fraction in the form $\frac{a}{b}$.

- Invert the fraction (turn it upside down) to give $\frac{b}{a}$.

EXAMPLE 1

Find the reciprocal of each of these.

    a $\frac{7}{8}$ b $1\frac{3}{4}$ c 10   d 1.2   e $-\frac{x}{y}$

SOLUTION

    a $\frac{7}{8} \rightarrow \frac{8}{7} = 1\frac{1}{7}$

    b $1\frac{3}{4} = \frac{7}{4} \rightarrow \frac{4}{7}$ ← Write a mixed number as an improper fraction first.

    c $10 = \frac{10}{1} \rightarrow \frac{1}{10}$

    d $1.2 = \frac{12}{10} \rightarrow \frac{10}{12} = \frac{5}{6}$

    e $-\frac{x}{y} \rightarrow -\frac{y}{x}$

Properties of reciprocals

- Zero is the only value with *no reciprocal*.
  $0 = \frac{0}{1} \rightarrow \frac{1}{0}$ which is undefined.
- Negative numbers *do* have reciprocals.
  $-\frac{2}{3} \rightarrow -\frac{3}{2} = -1\frac{1}{2}$
- The product of a value and its own reciprocal is always 1.
  $\frac{2}{3} \times \frac{3}{2} = \frac{6}{6} = 1$ ◄─────────────── Try this with other values.
- Dividing by a value is the same as multiplying by the reciprocal of that value.
  $\frac{3}{5} \div \frac{6}{7} = \frac{3}{5} \times \frac{7}{6} = \frac{7}{10}$ ◄─── Recall the division of fractions. This is why a reciprocal is sometimes known as the multiplicative inverse.

Exercise 10.1

1 Write down the reciprocal of each of these.

a $\frac{3}{8}$	b $\frac{4}{5}$	c $1\frac{2}{3}$	d 3.5	e 0.12	f −5
g $\frac{x}{y}$	h k	i 100	j $-\frac{3}{7}$	k −1.8	l $\frac{2p}{3r}$

2 What value does each of these have to be multiplied by to give the answer 1?

a $\frac{2}{9}$	b $6\frac{3}{4}$	c −2.5	d $\frac{p}{q}$
e $10\frac{1}{2}$	f 0.18	g $-\frac{5}{9}$	h $-1\frac{4}{5}$

3 Which of the following statements are true and which are false? Explain your reasoning clearly.
   a   1 has no reciprocal.
   b . The reciprocal of zero is zero.
   c   The reciprocal of the reciprocal of a is a.
   d   If x and y are positive and $x > y$, the reciprocal of x will be greater than the reciprocal of y.

Finding reciprocals on a calculator

You can find a reciprocal on a calculator by using the $\boxed{x^{-1}}$ or $\boxed{1/x}$ key. Most calculators will give the answer as a decimal. Not all reciprocals will give exact answers when a calculator is used.

EXAMPLE 2

Find the reciprocal of 2.6 on a calculator.

SOLUTION

Key in 2.6 $\boxed{x^{-1}}$ $\boxed{=}$

Answer. 0.385 (3 s.f.) ◄─── The exact answer is $\frac{1}{2.6} = \frac{10}{26} = \frac{5}{13}$

Calculate $\frac{1}{1.3^2}$ on a calculator.

SOLUTION

Key in 1.3 $\boxed{x^2}$ $\boxed{x^{-1}}$ $\boxed{=}$

Answer: 0.59 (2 d.p.)

Check your answers to Exercise 10.1, question **1** parts **a** to **f** and **i** to **k** using your calculator.

You should now:

- be able to find a reciprocal by writing the value as a fraction in the form $\frac{a}{b}$ and inverting
- know the properties of reciprocals
- know the calculator function for a reciprocal.

Summary exercise 10

You must not use your calculator for questions **1** and **2**.

1   Write down the reciprocal of each of these.

    a $\frac{5}{8}$ **b** $1\frac{5}{6}$ **c** $\frac{a}{2}$

    d 0.6   **e** -3 **f** p^2

    g 1.25   **h** 0.35   **i** t^3

    j -100 **k** 0.02   **l** $\frac{1}{c}$

2   Write down the value of the letter in each of these.

    a $a \times 8 = 1$ **b** $\frac{7}{9} \times b = 1$

    c $1\frac{3}{4} \times \frac{4}{7} = c$ **d** $\frac{5}{6} \times \frac{6}{5} + \frac{2}{3} \times \frac{3}{2} = d$

You may use your calculator for question **3**.

3   Find the reciprocal of 6.5^3.
    Give your answer to 2 significant figures.

Examination questions

These questions are from examination papers where you may not use a calculator.

1   Calculate the reciprocal of 0.02.

2   What fraction would $1\frac{2}{3}$ need to be multiplied by to give a product of 1?

Use 'Topic Tracker' at www.ccea.org.uk to find more exam questions.

CHAPTER 11

Standard form

> **This chapter is about:**
> - writing numbers in standard form
> - calculating with numbers in standard form.
>
> **You should already know:**
> - how to work with whole numbers and decimals
> - how to write answers to a suitable degree of accuracy
> - how to use the rules of indices.

Writing numbers in standard form

The radius of the Sun is about 696 000 000 000 metres.
The mass of a carbon atom is 0.000 000 000 000 000 000 000 0199 grams.
It can be seen that both these numbers are very cumbersome to write. A more suitable notation used for writing extremely large or extremely small numbers is **standard form**. (Note that *any* number can be written in standard form, but it is mainly used for very large or very small numbers.)

When a number is written in standard form, it is written like this:

$$a \times 10^n \text{ where } 1 \leqslant a < 10 \text{ and } n \text{ is an integer.}$$

For large numbers, the '10^n' part is a positive power of 10. For numbers less than 1, it is a negative power of 10.

So the radius of the Sun can be written as 6.96×10^{11} metres and the mass of a carbon atom can be written as 1.99×10^{-23} grams.

In maths or science you may be asked to write extremely large or extremely small numbers in standard form. You will also need to know how to convert numbers in standard form back into decimals.

Converting to standard form
- Rewrite the number, positioning the decimal point after the first non-zero digit. This gives the 'a' part of the notation, in $1 \leqslant a < 10$.
- Multiply by 10^n, where n is the number of times your decimal point has to be moved to the right or to the left to return to the original number. If it must be moved to the right, n is positive; if it must be moved to the left, n is negative.

EXAMPLE 1

Write each of these numbers in standard form.

    a 236 000   b 5 000 000   c 0.000 053
    d 0.0362   e 2570   f 0.0008

SOLUTION

    a $236\,000 = 2.36 \times 10^5$
    b $5\,000\,000 = 5 \times 10^6$
    c $0.000\,053 = 5.3 \times 10^{-5}$ ← Multiplying by 10^{-5} is the same as multiplying by $\frac{1}{10^5}$, so this is equivalent to 5.3 divided by 10^5.
    d $0.0362 = 3.62 \times 10^{-2}$
    e $2570 = 2.57 \times 10^3$
    f $0.0008 = 8 \times 10^{-4}$

Converting from standard form

- Move the decimal point the required number of decimal places to the right or left as determined by the power of 10. (Remember to move the decimal point to the right if n is positive, and to the left if n is negative.)
- Insert extra zeros if necessary.

EXAMPLE 2

Convert each of these numbers from standard form into decimal form.
    a 2.42×10^4 b 3×10^7 c 4.1×10^{-2}
    d 8.324×10^{-1} e 6.32×10^1 f 1.7×10^{-5}

SOLUTION

    a $2.42 \times 10^4 = 24\,200$ ← Extra zeros are needed here to show that the decimal point moves 4 places to the right.
    b $3 \times 10^7 = 30\,000\,000$
    c $4.1 \times 10^{-2} = 0.041$
    d $8.324 \times 10^{-1} = 0.8324$
    e $6.32 \times 10^1 = 63.2$
    f $1.7 \times 10^{-5} = 0.000\,017$

Exercise 11.1

1 Which of these numbers are in standard form?
    a 4.3×10^5 b 0.345×10^5 c 1.456×10^0 d 24.7×10^3
    e 0.001×10^6 f 5.67×10^{-4} g 345×10^2 h 5.0×10^{-9}

2 Write each of these numbers in standard form.
    a 34 500   b 45 000 000   c 8100   d 67 500 000 000
    e 0.000 005 4   f 0.000 07   g 60 000   h 0.003
    i 0.124   j 86 754 200   k 0.000 000 0034 l 0.9

3 Convert each of these numbers from standard form into decimal form.
    a 1.567×10^4 b 4.56×10^{-5} c 2×10^3 d 2.34×10^8
    e 1.5678×10^2 f 4.1×10^{-2} g 2.5×10^7 h 1.57×10^{-3}
    i 8×10^{-4} j 3.1×10^1 k 7×10^{-1} l 6.2×10^9

4 a The velocity of light is 300 000 000 m/s.
       Write this number in standard form.
   b A passenger ship has a mass of 3.6×10^7 kg.
       Write this number in decimal form.
   c The population of a country is estimated to be around
       230 000 000. Write this number in standard form.
   d If the number 3.567×10^8 was written in decimal form, how
       many zeros would follow the 7?
   e The surface area of the Earth is approximately 520 000 000 km².
       Write this number in standard form.
   f The diameter of an atom is 0.000 000 0002 mm.
       Write this number in standard form.
   g Light travels about 9.46×10^{15} m in a year.
       Write this number in decimal form.
   h If the number 5.62×10^{-12} was written in decimal form, how
       many zeros would there be between the decimal point and the 5?
   i Write 265 million in standard form.
   j A nanometre is 1×10^{-9} metres. Write this number in decimal form.

5 Put each set of numbers in order from the smallest to the largest.
   a 2.3×10^4, 1.2×10^2, 2.2×10^5, 1.12×10^2
   b 2.3×10^3, 1.3×10^{-2}, 3.2×10^1, 2.13×10^{-2}
   c 6.5×10^{-2}, 5.5×10^{-4}, 1.25×10^{-4}, 2.45×10^{-3}

Calculating with numbers in standard form

Numbers can be added, subtracted, multiplied and divided using standard
form. If a question has been asked in standard form, it is good practice to
give the answer in standard form too, unless you are instructed otherwise.
Check that your final answer *is*, in fact, in standard form – it may need a
slight adjustment to retain the format $a \times 10^n$ where $1 \leqslant a < 10$.

Adding and subtracting

Adding or subtracting numbers in standard from can be quite tricky. One
method is to convert the numbers into decimal form first.

• Rewrite each number in decimal form.

• Add or subtract as normal.

• Convert the final answer back into standard form.

EXAMPLE 3

Calculate each of these, giving your answers in standard form.

   a $6.3 \times 10^4 + 1.7 \times 10^3$ b $2.7 \times 10^{-2} - 1.25 \times 10^{-3}$

SOLUTION

   a $6.3 \times 10^4 + 1.7 \times 10^3$ b $2.7 \times 10^{-2} - 1.25 \times 10^{-3}$
      $= 63\,000 + 1700$ $= 0.027 - 0.001\,25$
      $= 64\,700$ $= 0.025\,75$
      $= 6.47 \times 10^4$ $= 2.575 \times 10^{-2}$

An alternative method is to adjust the numbers so that they are both multiplied by the same power of 10.

- Use the rules of indices to adjust the numbers so that they both have the same power of 10.
- Add or subtract the 'a' parts of the numbers.
- Check whether the final answer is in standard form and adjust if necessary.

> The rules of indices are covered fully in Chapter 15.

EXAMPLE 4

Calculate each of these, giving your answers in standard form.

  a $6.3 \times 10^4 + 1.7 \times 10^3$ b $2.7 \times 10^{-2} - 1.25 \times 10^{-3}$

SOLUTION

  a $6.3 \times 10^4 + 1.7 \times 10^3 = 6.3 \times 10^4 + (0.17 \times 10^1 \times 10^3)$
  $= 6.3 \times 10^4 + 0.17 \times 10^4$
  $= (6.3 + 0.17) \times 10^4$
  $= 6.47 \times 10^4$

> This is the same result as with the first method.

> **HINT**
> Remember that you add the indices when multiplying numbers written in index form, and you subtract the indices when dividing.

  b $2.7 \times 10^{-2} - 1.25 \times 10^{-3} = 2.7 \times 10^{-2} - (0.125 \times 10^1 \times 10^{-3})$
  $= 2.7 \times 10^{-2} - 0.125 \times 10^{-2}$
  $= (2.7 - 0.125) \times 10^{-2}$
  $= 2.575 \times 10^{-2}$

EXAMPLE 5

The Atlantic Ocean covers an area of about $8.2 \times 10^7 \, \text{km}^2$.
The Pacific Ocean covers an area of about $1.65 \times 10^8 \, \text{km}^2$.
  a   Find the total area covered by these two oceans.
  b   What is the difference in area between these two oceans?

SOLUTION

Method 1
  a $8.2 \times 10^7 + 1.65 \times 10^8 = 82\,000\,000 + 165\,000\,000$
  $= 247\,000\,000$
  $= 2.47 \times 10^8 \, \text{km}^2$

Method 2
  b $1.65 \times 10^8 - 8.2 \times 10^7 = (1.65 \times 10^1 \times 10^7) - 8.2 \times 10^7$
  $= 16.5 \times 10^7 - 8.2 \times 10^7$
  $= (16.5 - 8.2) \times 10^7$
  $= 8.3 \times 10^7 \, \text{km}^2$

Multiplying and dividing

It is easier to multiply or divide numbers in standard form than to add or subtract them.

- Multiply (or divide) the 'a' parts.
- Use the rules of indices to multiply (or divide) the powers of 10.
- Check whether the final answer is in standard form and adjust if necessary.

Calculate each of these, giving your answers in standard form.

     a $(3.4 \times 10^{-4}) \times (2.1 \times 10^{7})$ b $(4.75 \times 10^{-2}) \div (2.5 \times 10^{4})$

     c $(2.68 \times 10^{3}) \times (4.2 \times 10^{-5})$ d $(2.5 \times 10^{3}) \div (5.0 \times 10^{-7})$

SOLUTION

> When multiplying, add the indices. $-4 + 7 = 3$

a $(3.4 \times 10^{-4}) \times (2.1 \times 10^{7})$

     $= (3.4 \times 2.1) \times (10^{-4} \times 10^{7})$

     $= 7.14 \times 10^{3}$

> When dividing, subtract the indices. $-2 - 4 = -6$

b $(4.75 \times 10^{-2}) \div (2.5 \times 10^{4})$

     $= (4.75 \div 2.5) \times (10^{-2} \div 10^{4})$ $= 1.9 \times 10^{-6}$

c $(2.68 \times 10^{3}) \times (4.2 \times 10^{-5})$

     $= (2.68 \times 4.2) \times (10^{3} \times 10^{-5})$

     $= 11.256 \times 10^{-2}$

     $= 1.1256 \times 10^{1} \times 10^{-2}$

     $= 1.1256 \times 10^{-1}$

> These answers are not in standard form, and hence need some adjustment.

d $(2.5 \times 10^{3}) \div (5.0 \times 10^{-7})$

     $= (2.5 \div 5.0) \times (10^{3} \div 10^{-7})$

     $= 0.5 \times 10^{10}$

     $= 5 \times 10^{-1} \times 10^{10}$

     $= 5 \times 10^{9}$

The mass of an oxygen atom is 2.73×10^{-23} g.
Calculate the mass of 6000 of these atoms, giving your answer in standard form.

SOLUTION

     $(2.73 \times 10^{-23}) \times 6000 = (2.73 \times 10^{-23}) \times (6 \times 10^{3})$

                         $= (2.73 \times 6) \times (10^{-23} \times 10^{3})$

                         $= 16.38 \times 10^{-20}$

                         $= 1.638 \times 10^{1} \times 10^{-20}$

                         $= 1.638 \times 10^{-19}$ g

Exercise 11.2

1 Calculate each of these, giving your answers in standard form.
  a $2.8 \times 10^3 + 1.4 \times 10^2$
  b $4.17 \times 10^2 + 4.5 \times 10^1$
  c $3.82 \times 10^5 - 2.13 \times 10^4$
  d $8.6 \times 10^{-3} - 4.6 \times 10^{-4}$
  e $8.9 \times 10^{-2} + 5.06 \times 10^{-3}$
  f $3.67 \times 10^7 + 4.7 \times 10^6$
  g $9.68 \times 10^2 - 4.16 \times 10^{-1}$
  h $4.5 \times 10^7 - 3.8 \times 10^6$
  i $9.52 \times 10^5 - 6.6 \times 10^3$
  j $2.15 \times 10^6 + 6 \times 10^5$

2 Calculate each of these, giving your answers in standard form.
  a $(3.24 \times 10^2) \times (2.1 \times 10^3)$
  b $(2.6 \times 10^5) \div (2 \times 10^3)$
  c $(3.8 \times 10^8) \div (1.9 \times 10^5)$
  d $(4.48 \times 10^{-4}) \div (3.2 \times 10^{-1})$
  e $(3.43 \times 10^{-2}) \times (1.5 \times 10^{-3})$
  f $(4.8 \times 10^6) \div (9.6 \times 10^{-8})$
  g $(8.24 \times 10^{-2}) \times (7.4 \times 10^{-3})$
  h $(2.4 \times 10^{-5}) \div (3 \times 10^8)$
  i $(3 \times 10^{-5}) \times (6.8 \times 10^{-2})$
  j $(1.6 \times 10^4) \div (6.4 \times 10^{-2})$

3 Calculate 7 million $\times$ 360 000.

4 Light travels at a speed of 3×10^8 m/s. How far will light travel in a day? Give your answer in kilometres in standard form.

5 Mercury is 5.8×10^7 km from the Sun and Jupiter is 7.78×10^8 km from the Sun. How much farther from the Sun is Jupiter than Mercury? Give your answer in standard form.

6 The speed of light is 3×10^8 m/s. Mars is 228 million km from the Sun. Calculate, to the nearest minute, the time it takes sunlight to reach Mars.

7 The length of a rectangle is 3.6×10^3 mm and the width is 1.7×10^2 mm.
  a Calculate the perimeter of the rectangle.
  b Calculate the area of the rectangle.
  Give both your answers in standard form.

8 A sheet of paper is 9.6×10^{-3} cm thick.
  A booklet contains 24 of these pages, and 1.2×10^3 of these booklets are to be produced. If the pages are all stacked prior to the booklets being bound, how high will the pile be in metres?

9 The population of a city increases from 2.68×10^7 to 1.16×10^8 over a number of years.
  Calculate the increase in the number of people, giving your answer in standard form.

10 The mass of the Earth is approximately 5.913×10^{24} kg. The Earth is about 81 times as heavy as the Moon. Calculate the mass of the Moon, giving your answer in standard form.

11 The surface area of the Earth is approximately 1.98×10^8 square miles, of which approximately 1.4×10^8 square miles is covered by water. What percentage of the Earth's surface is covered by water? Give your answer to the nearest per cent.

12 A stamp weighs 3×10^{-5} kg and an envelope weighs 1.12×10^{-4} kg. Find the total mass of 1000 of these envelopes with stamps attached. Give your answer in standard form.

Standard form on a calculator

Very large numbers or very small numbers cannot always be keyed directly into a calculator, as the display may only have space for 8, 9 or 10 digits. It is, therefore, important to be able to enter numbers into a calculator in standard form. The result of a numerical calculation involving ordinary numbers in decimal form may also be so large or so small that the calculator can only display the answer in standard form.

The $\boxed{\text{EXP}}$ or $\boxed{\times}$ $\boxed{10^x}$ key is used to input numbers in standard form.

For example, to input 6.3×10^7, key in 6.3 $\boxed{\text{EXP}}$ 7. This will normally be displayed on the screen as 6.3E7 or 6.3^{07} or 6.3×10^7.

EXAMPLE 8

Calculate $(3.4 \times 10^8) \times (4.2 \times 10^{-2})$, giving your answer in standard form.

SOLUTION

Key in 3.4 $\boxed{\text{EXP}}$ 8 $\boxed{\times}$ 4.2 $\boxed{\text{EXP}}$ $\boxed{(-)}$ 2 $\boxed{=}$

Result on screen: 14 280 000

Converting back to standard form, this is 1.428×10^7.

EXAMPLE 9

Calculate $6.1 \times 10^7 + 8.23 \times 10^{12}$.

SOLUTION

Key in 6.1 $\boxed{\text{EXP}}$ 7 $\boxed{+}$ 8.23 $\boxed{\text{EXP}}$ 12 $\boxed{=}$

Result on screen: $8.230\,061 \times 10^{12}$ or $8.230\,061^{12}$

In standard form this is $8.230\,061 \times 10^{12}$.

> It is important that you do not copy the figures from a calculator display in this format directly – you must write your answer in the correct format for standard form.

EXAMPLE 10

Calculate $0.000\,000\,000\,0041 \div 0.000\,000\,02$.

SOLUTION

These values have too many digits to input directly into the calculator, so they must be converted to standard form first.

The calculation becomes $4.1 \times 10^{-12} \div 2 \times 10^{-8}$.

Key in 4.1 $\boxed{\text{EXP}}$ $\boxed{(-)}$ 12 $\boxed{\div}$ 2 $\boxed{\text{EXP}}$ $\boxed{(-)}$ 8 $\boxed{=}$

Result on screen: 2.05×10^{-4} or 2.05^{-04}

In standard form this is 2.05×10^{-4}.

Exercise 11.3

1 Repeat questions 1 and 2 from Exercise 11.2 using your calculator.

2 Use your calculator to work out each of these, giving your answers in standard form.

a $28\,000\,000 \times 3240\,000$

b $0.000\,000\,07 + 0.000\,000\,0324$

c $14\,400\,000 \div 1200\,000\,000$

d $365\,000\,000 - 23\,400\,000$

e $0.000\,24 \times 31\,000\,000$

f $5600\,000\,000 \div 2000\,000\,000$

g $0.000\,056 - 0.000\,003\,24$

h $248\,000\,000\,000 \div 8000\,000$

3 Use your calculator to work this out. $\dfrac{458\,000\,000\,000}{23\,000\,000 \times 4\,000\,000}$

Give your answer in standard form to 1 significant figure.

4 The radius of the Earth is approximately 6.4×10^6 m.
Calculate the volume of the Earth based on the formula

Volume $= \dfrac{4}{3} \times \pi \times r^3$

Give your answer in standard form to a suitable degree of accuracy.

5 The mass of a hydrogen atom is 1.67×10^{-24} g.
Calculate the mass of 8000 hydrogen atoms, giving your answer in kilograms in standard form.

6 The masses of four planets are given in the table.

a How much heavier is Jupiter than Venus?

b About how many times heavier is Saturn than Venus?

c What is the combined mass of Saturn and Jupiter?

d Which planet has a mass about seven times the mass of Mars?

Planet	Mass
Mars	6.57×10^{23} kg
Saturn	5.69×10^{26} kg
Venus	4.87×10^{24} kg
Jupiter	1.25×10^{27} kg

7 Water flows through a pipe at the rate of $60\,\text{m}^3$ per second.
About how long will it take to fill a tank of volume $1.2 \times 10^6\,\text{m}^3$?

8 A light year is the distance that light can travel in a year.
If the speed of light is 1.85×10^5 miles per second, how far in miles is 1 light year?
Give your answer in standard form to 3 significant figures.

You should now:

- be able to write numbers in standard form
- be able to convert numbers from standard form into decimal form
- be able to add, subtract, multiply and divide numbers in standard form without a calculator
- be able to use standard form on a calculator
- be able to solve a variety of problems using standard form in context.

Summary exercise 11

You must not use your calculator for questions **1** to **11**.

1. Write each of these numbers in standard form.
   a. 345 000
   b. 0.000 0089
   c. 567 000 000
   d. 0.0009
   e. 50 000
   f. 1 230 000 000 000

2. Convert each of these numbers from standard form into decimal form.
   a. 2.3×10^5
   b. 1×10^{-4}
   c. 8.6×10^2
   d. 4×10^{-8}
   e. 5.6234×10^3
   f. 9.86×10^{-7}

3. If the number 6.2×10^7 was written in full, how many zeros would there be after the 2?

4. Avogadro's number is 602 300 000 000 000 000 000 000.
   Write this in standard form.

5. Write 252 million in standard form.

6. Which of these numbers is the greatest?
   2.3×10^4,   230 thousand,   2 300 000, 0.23×10^4

7. Work out each of these, giving your answers in standard form.
   a. $(6.5 \times 10^9) \div (5 \times 10^7)$
   b. $5.6 \times 10^7 + 3.1 \times 10^6$
   c. $(6.4 \times 10^{-3}) \div (8 \times 10^{-6})$
   d. $(7.9 \times 10^6)^2$
   e. $7.61 \times 10^{-3} - 8.4 \times 10^{-4}$
   f. $(130 000)^4$
   g. $(3.7 \times 10^8) \times (2 \times 10^{-3})$
   h. $4.75 \times 10^{-5} - 9.2 \times 10^{-6}$
   i. $2.56 \times 10^4 + 1.6 \times 10^5$
   j. $\dfrac{(7.6 \times 10^{-4} \times 5.2 \times 10^{-5})}{4 \times 10^{-8}}$

8. A particle has mass 1.68×10^{-24} g.
   Find the total mass of $2\frac{1}{2}$ million of these particles.

9. A ream of paper has 500 sheets and is 3.5 cm thick.
   Calculate the thickness of each sheet of paper in millimetres.

10. The area of India is about 3.3×10^6 km² and the area of the UK is about 2.41×10^5 km².
    What is the difference between the two areas?

11. A large stone has a mass of 5.5×10^2 kg and a volume of 2.5×10^{-1} m³. Find the density of the stone.

You may use your calculator for questions **12** to **14**.

12. Use your calculator to work out each of these, giving your answers in standard form.
    a. $2.3 \times 10^5 + 1.65 \times 10^4$
    b. $(5.8 \times 10^{-3}) \div (2 \times 10^{-5})$
    c. $1.8 \times 10^{-3} - 2.1 \times 10^{-4}$
    d. $(7.6 \times 10^4) \times (8.4 \times 10^{-2})$
    e. $(23 000 000 000)^2$
    f. $(5.6 \times 10^4)^3$
    g. $240 000 \times 340 000$
    h. $32 000 000 000 \div 400 000$
    i. $0.000 0056 + 0.000 000 04$
    j. $5 000 000 000 \times 27 000 000$

13 Five million electrons have a total mass of 4.5545×10^{-24} g.
Calculate the mass of a single electron.

14 The distance from Earth to Mars is 2.3×10^8 km.
A spacecraft takes 710 days to travel from Earth to Mars.
Find its average speed in km/h, correct to 2 significant figures.

Examination questions

Question **1** is from an examination paper where you may not use a calculator.

1 a Write 3 245 000 in standard form.

b Write 4.32×10^{-4} in decimal form.

Questions **2** to **4** are from examination papers where you may use a calculator.

2 a i Express 146 700 000 000 in standard form.

ii Express 0.000 000 867 in standard from.

b The population of England is 5.3×10^7.

i The average amount of money spent by each person in a week is £39. Calculate the total amount of money spent in a week. Give your answer in standard form.

ii A very wealthy man is said to have £2.3×10^9.
If this money was shared equally between the population of England, how much would each person get?
Give your answer to a suitable degree of accuracy.

3 a An oxygen atom has a mass of 2.7×10^{-23} grams.
Find the total mass of 4000 oxygen atoms.
Give your answer in standard form.

b A hydrogen atom has a mass of 1.7×10^{-24} grams.
Calculate how many times heavier an oxygen atom is than a hydrogen atom.

4 The planet Umer orbits its sun, Zenath. When they are closest to each other the distance between them is 6.5×10^{11} m, to 2 significant figures.
Light travels in a straight line from Zenath to Umer and the speed of light is 3×10^8 m/s to 1 significant figure.
Calculate, to the nearest second, the shortest time that light might take to travel from Zenath to Umer.

> Use 'Topic Tracker' at www.ccea.org.uk to find more exam questions.

CHAPTER 12

Rational and irrational numbers

This chapter is about:

- rational and irrational numbers
- recurring decimals.

You should already know:

- how to work with whole numbers, decimals and fractions
- how to convert a fraction to a decimal
- how to find squares, square roots, cubes and cube roots
- how to solve equations
- how to use Pythagoras' theorem
- how to find the perimeter and area of a rectangle
- how to find the circumference and area of a circle.

Definitions

A **rational number** is a number which can be expressed as a fraction in the form $\frac{a}{b}$ where a and b are integers.

Rational numbers include integers, fractions, mixed numbers, **terminating decimals** (decimals with a finite number of decimal places), **recurring decimals** (decimals in which one or more of the digits repeat), the square roots of square numbers, and the cube roots of cube numbers. It can be shown that each of these types of number can be written in the form $\frac{a}{b}$.

Rational numbers can all be placed *exactly* on a number line. For example:

- 4 is an integer and can be written in the form $\frac{a}{b}$ as $\frac{4}{1}$ (shown as **A** on the number line below).
- The fraction $\frac{5}{6}$ is already in the form $\frac{a}{b}$ (**B** on the number line).
- $1\frac{3}{4}$ is a mixed number, which can be converted to $\frac{7}{4}$, which is now in the correct format (**C** on the number line).
- 0.28 is a terminating decimal and can be written as $\frac{28}{100} = \frac{7}{25}$, which is now in the form $\frac{a}{b}$ (**D** on the number line).
- $2.\dot{3}$ is a recurring decimal but can be written as $\frac{7}{3}$ and hence is in the form $\frac{a}{b}$ (**E** on the number line). ◄——— A more detailed explanation of recurring decimals is given later in this chapter.
- $\sqrt{36}$ is the square root of a square number. Its value is 6 – an integer – which can be written in the form $\frac{a}{b}$ as $\frac{6}{1}$ (**F** on the number line).
- $\sqrt[3]{27}$ is the cube root of a cube number. Its value is 3 – an integer – which can be written in the form $\frac{a}{b}$ as $\frac{3}{1}$ (**G** on the number line).

An **irrational number** is one which cannot be written in the form $\frac{a}{b}$.

Irrational numbers include the square roots of non-square numbers, the cube roots of non-cube numbers, and decimals which neither repeat nor terminate. A common example is π. Its value is 3.141 592 654... . The number π continues forever without ever ending or forming a pattern that repeats.

Irrational numbers *cannot* be placed exactly on the number line.

For example, $\sqrt{5}$ is approximately 2.236 (given to 3 d.p.). However, using the inverse operation, if 2.236 is squared the result is 4.999 696, whilst if 2.2361 is squared the result is 5.000 143 21. Therefore between 2.236 and 2.2361 there is a number whose square is 5, but this number cannot be found exactly.

The number representing $\sqrt{5}$ is somewhere here, but cannot be found exactly.

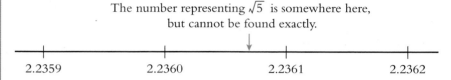

Although irrational numbers cannot be placed exactly on the number line, you can still work with them. For example, you can multiply π by 2 to give $2 \times \pi$. Its value is 6.283 185 307... . Often you just write 2π rather than writing it as a number. 2π is an exact value but 6.283 185 307... is not.

Operations involving irrational numbers will be considered in more detail in Chapter 13.

Recurring decimals

You met recurring decimals in Chapter 9.

A common example is the decimal equivalent of $\frac{1}{3}$. When you divide 1 by 3 you get 0.333 333... . When a digit repeats indefinitely in a decimal, you can write it using dot notation. 0.333 333... is written as $0.\dot{3}$. The dot indicates that the 3 repeats indefinitely.

In some recurring decimals there is more than one figure that repeats. To write these decimals using dot notation, you put a dot over the first and last figures in the pattern. For example, 0.090 909 090 909... is written as $0.\dot{0}\dot{9}$ and 0.203 203 203 203... is written as $0.\dot{2}0\dot{3}$.

It is also possible to have some non-repeating digits before the recurring part of the decimal. For example, 2.999 999 999 999... is written as $2.\dot{9}$ and 0.011 111 111 111... is written as $0.0\dot{1}$.

Converting a recurring decimal to a fraction

To convert a recurring decimal to a fraction take the following steps.

- Use the letter *r* for the recurring decimal written out in full.
- Multiply *r* by a suitable power of 10 (10 if there is one recurring digit, 100 if there are two recurring digits, etc.).
- Subtract *r* from the product you got from the previous step.
- Rearrange to find *r* as a fraction in the form $\frac{a}{b}$.

EXAMPLE 1

Write $2.\dot{3}$ as a fraction.

SOLUTION

Let $r = 2.333\,333\,333\ldots$

Then $10r = 23.333\,333\,333\ldots$

> Multiply by 10 as there is only one recurring digit.

Writing these results one below the other, and subtracting:

$$10r = 23.333\,333\,333\ldots$$
$$-\ r = 2.333\,333\,333\ldots$$
$$9r = 21$$

So $r = \dfrac{21}{9} = \dfrac{7}{3}$

> A fraction in the form $\dfrac{a}{b}$.

You may have recognised $0.\dot{3}$ as $\dfrac{1}{3}$, in which case you could have written down the answer straight away.

EXAMPLE 2

Write $0.2\dot{5}$ as a fraction.

SOLUTION

Let $r = 0.255\,555\,555\ldots$

$$10r = 2.555\,555\,555\ldots$$
$$-\ r = 0.255\,555\,555\ldots$$
$$9r = 2.3$$

So $r = \dfrac{2.3}{9} = \dfrac{23}{90}$

EXAMPLE 3

Write $0.\dot{8}1\dot{6}$ as a fraction.

SOLUTION

Let $r = 0.816\,816\,816\ldots$

$$1000r = 816.816\,816\,816\ldots$$
$$-\ r = 0.816\,816\,816\ldots$$
$$999r = 816$$

> Multiply by 1000 as there are three recurring digits.

So $r = \dfrac{816}{999} = \dfrac{272}{333}$

A common mistake is to think that recurring decimals are irrational. They are not, since they can be written as a fraction in the form $\dfrac{a}{b}$ (as you have seen in the examples above). However, you frequently find questions that combine asking you to distinguish between rational and irrational numbers and asking you to convert a recurring decimal to a fraction.

EXAMPLE 4

Decide whether each of these values is rational or irrational, giving reasons. For those that are rational, write them in the form $\frac{a}{b}$.

a 0.6   b $\sqrt{30}$ c $\frac{6\pi}{4\pi}$ d $-1\frac{1}{2}$

e $0.1\dot{5}$ f 5.4   g $\sqrt{7} - 1$ h $2.\dot{4}\dot{2}$

SOLUTION

a 0.6 is a terminating decimal – rational.
$0.6 = \frac{6}{10} = \frac{3}{5}$

b $\sqrt{30}$ is the square root of a non-square number – irrational.

c $\frac{6\pi}{4\pi} = \frac{3}{2}$, which is a fraction – rational. ◄——— Notice that, although π occurs in the fraction, it cancels.

d $-1\frac{1}{2} = -\frac{3}{2}$, which is a fraction – rational.

e $0.1\dot{5}$ is a recurring decimal – rational.

Let $r = 0.155\,555\,555...$

$10r = 1.555\,555\,555...$

$- r = 0.155\,555\,555...$

$\overline{\quad 9r = 1.4 \quad}$ So $r = \frac{1.4}{9} = \frac{14}{90} = \frac{7}{45}$

f 5.4 is a terminating decimal – rational.
$5.4 = \frac{54}{10} = \frac{27}{5}$

g $\sqrt{7}$ is the square root of a non-square number.
So $\sqrt{7} - 1$ is irrational.

h $2.\dot{4}\dot{2}$ is a recurring decimal – rational.

Let $r = 2.424\,242\,424...$

$100r = 242.424\,242\,424...$

$- r = 2.424\,242\,424...$

$\overline{\quad 99r = 240 \quad}$ So $r = \frac{240}{99} = \frac{80}{33}$

Exercise 12.1

1 Decide whether each of these values is rational or irrational, giving reasons for your answers.

a 3.5   b $\sqrt{49}$ c 5π d $\frac{33}{40}$ e $1.2\dot{5}$

f $\frac{3}{\sqrt[3]{25}}$ g $\sqrt[3]{125}$ h $\frac{2}{\pi}$ i $1.\dot{7}$ j 0.2888

2 Decide whether each of these values is rational or irrational, giving reasons for your answers.
For those that are rational, write them in the form $\frac{a}{b}$ in their lowest terms.

a $\sqrt{6}$ b $0.4\dot{5}$ c 1.2   d $\frac{8\pi}{2\pi}$ e $\frac{\sqrt{100}}{2}$

f 0.28   g $2\frac{3}{4}$ h -2.5 i 4.565   j $\frac{3}{1.5}$

3 a Write down an irrational number between $\sqrt{2}$ and $\sqrt{5}$.
  b Write down a rational number between $\sqrt{2}$ and $\sqrt{5}$.

4 Find two different irrational numbers m and n such that $\frac{m}{n}$ is rational.

5 Write down two rational numbers between 0 and 1, one equal to a terminating decimal and one equal to a recurring decimal. Show that the sum of your two numbers is rational.

6 N is a rational number. Is the reciprocal of N rational or irrational?

7 For each of these calculations, decide whether the answer is rational or irrational, giving reasons.
  a $\sqrt{6\frac{1}{4}}$ b $\frac{1}{3} + \sqrt{3}$ c $(1\frac{1}{2})^2$ d $\sqrt{6} \times 1\frac{1}{2}$
  e $\pi \times \frac{2}{\pi}$ f $(\sqrt{3})^2$ g 0.2^3 h $\frac{2.5}{0.2}$
  i $\sqrt{4\frac{1}{4}}$ j $3^{-1} + 3^{-2}$

8 For each of these, decide whether the value would be rational or irrational, giving reasons.
  a The area of a circle of radius 5 cm.
  b The perimeter of a rectangle of length 10 m and breadth 8 m.
  c The diagonal of a rectangle of length 10 m and breadth 8 m.
  d The area of a triangle with base π and perpendicular height $\frac{5}{\pi}$.

9 Is it possible to multiply two irrational numbers to give a rational number? If so, give possible values.

10 For each of these numbers, find an irrational number which can be multiplied by it to give a rational result.
  a $\frac{2}{\sqrt{5}}$ b $\frac{10}{\pi}$ c $3\sqrt{2}$

11 Write each of these recurring decimals as a fraction of the form $\frac{p}{q}$ in its lowest terms.
  a $0.\dot{2}\dot{7}$ b $1.0\dot{5}\dot{6}$ c $0.363636\ldots$ d $0.5\dot{1}\dot{2}$

You should now:

- be able to distinguish between a rational and an irrational number
- be able to write all rational numbers as fractions of the form $\frac{a}{b}$
- be able to solve problems involving rational and irrational numbers in context.

Summary exercise 12

1 Decide whether each of these values is rational or irrational, giving reasons for your answers. For those that are rational, write them as a fraction in its lowest terms.
  a $0.\dot{8}$ b 2^3 c $\sqrt{2.25}$ d $\sqrt{8}$ e $\sqrt[3]{8}$
  f $0.8\dot{2}$ g 5.12 h $4\frac{2}{3}$ i $\pi + 2$ j 10^{-1}

2   Where possible, write down an example of a number that matches
    each of these descriptions.
    Give both the fractional and decimal versions of your answer.
    a A rational number which is a terminating decimal.
    b An irrational number which is a terminating decimal.
    c A rational number which is a recurring decimal with just one
       repeating digit.

3   For the right-angled triangle shown, decide whether
    a the length of the hypotenuse is rational or irrational
    b the area is rational or irrational.

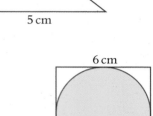

4 cm

5 cm

4   Write down a rational number between $\sqrt{8}$ and $\sqrt{10}$.

5   a Write down a rational number between 1.2 and 1.25.
    b Write down an irrational number between 1.2 and 1.25.

6   A circle just fits inside a square of side 6 cm.
    Decide whether each of these would give a rational or an irrational
    value, giving reasons.
    a The area of the square.   b The diagonal of the square.
    c The perimeter of the square.   d The diameter of the circle.
    e The area of the circle.   f The circumference of the circle.

6 cm

7   a Write $\frac{5}{6}$ as a decimal.
    b Use your answer to part a to calculate:
       i   a fraction equivalent to $0.41\dot{6}$.   ii   a fraction equivalent to $0.348\dot{3}$.

8   Write down a number between 11 and 12 that has a
    rational square root.

9   Adding two irrational numbers can result in a rational
    solution. Give an example to illustrate this.

10 a Write down three rational numbers between 9 and 10.
    b Write down three irrational numbers between 9 and 10.

Examination questions

Use 'Topic Tracker'
at www.ccea.org.uk
to find more exam
questions.

Questions 1 to 3 are from examination papers where you may not use a
calculator.

1   For each of these equations, decide whether the solutions are
    rational or irrational. Explain your answers.
    a $2x^2 + 1 = 19$ b $2x^2 + 1 = 16$ c $2x^2 + 1 = 13.5$

2   a Which one of these equations has solutions which are rational?
       Explain why this is the case.

       i $\frac{2x^2}{5} = 4$ ii $\frac{2x^2}{7} = 5$ iii $\frac{2x^2}{3} = 6$

    b Calculate $0.3\dot{1}2\dot{6}$ as a fraction in its lowest terms.

3   a Express $\frac{7}{9}$ as a recurring decimal.   b   Express $0.03\dot{5}$ as a fraction.

       Show your working.

This question is from an examination paper where you may use a calculator.

4   Give an example to show that the square of an irrational number
    is **not** always rational.

12 Rational and irrational numbers

CHAPTER 13

Surds

This chapter is about:
■ simplifying surds
■ working with surds
■ rationalising a denominator which contains a surd.
You should already know:
■ the square numbers
■ how to distinguish between rational and irrational numbers
■ how to expand brackets.

Simplifying surds

Irrational numbers such as $\sqrt{5}$, $1 - \sqrt{3}$ and $4\sqrt{7}$, which involve the square roots of non-square numbers, are called **surds**. You will meet surds in work using Pythagoras' theorem and in trigonometry (see Chapter 33).

A surd can sometimes be simplified by rewriting the number inside the root as a product of two numbers, one of which is its largest square factor. The square root of this square factor is then written outside the root.

> Recall the square numbers from Chapter 1: 1, 4, 9, 16, 25, 36, 49, 64, 81, 100, 121, 144, 169, etc.

EXAMPLE 1

Simplify each of these.

a $\sqrt{80}$ b $\sqrt{28}$ c $3\sqrt{20}$

SOLUTION

a $\sqrt{80} = \sqrt{16 \times 5} = 4\sqrt{5}$
b $\sqrt{28} = \sqrt{4 \times 7} = 2\sqrt{7}$
c $3\sqrt{20} = 3\sqrt{4 \times 5} = 6\sqrt{5}$

> When dealing with surds you only need to consider the *positive* square root.

Exercise 13.1

Simplify each of these.

1 $\sqrt{450}$	2 $\sqrt{147}$	3 $\sqrt{324}$	4 $\sqrt{50}$
5 $\sqrt{52}$	6 $\sqrt{288}$	7 $4\sqrt{90}$	8 $2\sqrt{800}$
9 $10\sqrt{1000}$	10 $6\sqrt{162}$	11 $3\sqrt{45}$	12 $3\sqrt{44}$

The rules of surds

Look at these calculations involving surds.

$$\sqrt{9} \times \sqrt{9} = 3 \times 3 = 9$$

$$\sqrt{9} \times \sqrt{4} = 3 \times 2 = 6 = \sqrt{36}$$

$$\frac{\sqrt{36}}{\sqrt{4}} = \frac{6}{2} = 3 = \sqrt{9}$$

$$2\sqrt{9} + 5\sqrt{9} = 2 \times 3 + 5 \times 3 = 6 + 15 = 21 = 7 \times 3 = 7\sqrt{9}$$

These illustrate four general rules which can be used to simplify surds.

$$\sqrt{a} \times \sqrt{a} = a \qquad \sqrt{a} \times \sqrt{b} = \sqrt{ab}$$

$$\frac{\sqrt{a}}{\sqrt{b}} = \sqrt{\frac{a}{b}} \qquad a\sqrt{b} \pm c\sqrt{b} = (a \pm c)\sqrt{b}$$

EXAMPLE 2

Simplify each of these.

   a $\sqrt{3} \times \sqrt{6}$ b $\dfrac{\sqrt{36}}{\sqrt{3}}$ c $5\sqrt{3} \times \sqrt{3}$ d $\sqrt{12} - \sqrt{3}$

   e $\sqrt{8} \times \sqrt{5}$ f $(2 + \sqrt{5})^2$ g $\sqrt{8} \times \sqrt{18}$ h $\sqrt{75} - \sqrt{48}$

SOLUTION

   a $\sqrt{3} \times \sqrt{6} = \sqrt{18} = \sqrt{9 \times 2} = 3\sqrt{2}$

   b $\dfrac{\sqrt{36}}{\sqrt{3}} = \sqrt{\dfrac{36}{3}} = \sqrt{12} = \sqrt{4 \times 3} = 2\sqrt{3}$

   c $5\sqrt{3} \times \sqrt{3} = 5 \times 3 = 15$

   d $\sqrt{12} - \sqrt{3} = \sqrt{4 \times 3} - \sqrt{3} = 2\sqrt{3} - \sqrt{3} = \sqrt{3}$

   e $\sqrt{8} \times \sqrt{5} = \sqrt{40} = \sqrt{4 \times 10} = 2\sqrt{10}$

   f $(2 + \sqrt{5})^2 = (2 + \sqrt{5})(2 + \sqrt{5})$

           $= 4 + 2\sqrt{5} + 2\sqrt{5} + 5$

           $= 9 + 4\sqrt{5}$

> Expanding brackets is covered in Chapter 16.

   g $\sqrt{8} \times \sqrt{18} = \sqrt{144} = 12$

   h $\sqrt{75} - \sqrt{48} = \sqrt{25 \times 3} - \sqrt{16 \times 3} = 5\sqrt{3} - 4\sqrt{3} = \sqrt{3}$

Exercise 13.2

1 Simplify each of these.

   a $\sqrt{6} \times \sqrt{6}$ b $\sqrt{9} \times \sqrt{9}$ c $\sqrt{28} \div \sqrt{7}$

   d $\sqrt{27} \times \sqrt{3}$ e $\sqrt{5} \times \sqrt{12}$ f $\sqrt{50} \div \sqrt{2}$

   g $\dfrac{\sqrt{20}}{2}$ h $\dfrac{\sqrt{6}}{\sqrt{3}} \times \sqrt{2}$ i $2\sqrt{5} \times 5\sqrt{2}$

   j $2\sqrt{12} \div 4\sqrt{3}$ k $3\sqrt{5} \times 6\sqrt{75}$ l $3\sqrt{18} \times \sqrt{6}$

2 Simplify each of these as far as possible.
   a $3\sqrt{5} - 2\sqrt{5}$ b $2\sqrt{3} + \sqrt{12}$ c $\sqrt{8} + 3\sqrt{2}$
   d $3\sqrt{12} - 2\sqrt{3}$ e $\sqrt{60} - \sqrt{15}$ f $3\sqrt{50} - 2\sqrt{8}$

3 Expand and simplify these. ◄──────────────
   a $(\sqrt{5} + 2)^2$ b $(\sqrt{6} - 1)^2$ c $(2 + \sqrt{7})(3 - \sqrt{7})$
   d $(3 + \sqrt{3})(3 - \sqrt{3})$ e $(2 + 3\sqrt{5})^2$

> Expanding brackets is covered in Chapter 16.

4 $(7 - \sqrt{5})^2$ can be simplified to $a + b\sqrt{5}$ where a and b are integers. Find the values of a and b.

5 Will the diagonal of each of these rectangles be rational or irrational?

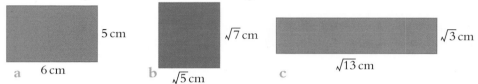

a   6 cm   5 cm
b $\sqrt{5}$ cm $\sqrt{7}$ cm
c $\sqrt{13}$ cm $\sqrt{3}$ cm

6 x is a positive integer greater than 2 such that $\sqrt{x} \times \sqrt{2}$ is rational. Find a possible value for x.

Rationalising the denominator

A fraction which has a surd of the form $\sqrt{b}$ in the denominator can be **rationalised**, by multiplying by $\frac{\sqrt{b}}{\sqrt{b}}$. Since $\frac{\sqrt{b}}{\sqrt{b}}$ equals 1, the numerical value is not changed but the denominator becomes rational.

EXAMPLE 3

Simplify each of these by rationalising the denominator.

a $\dfrac{2}{\sqrt{5}}$ b $\dfrac{27}{\sqrt{3}}$ c $\dfrac{4\sqrt{7}}{\sqrt{2}}$ d $\dfrac{24}{\sqrt{12}}$

SOLUTION

a $\dfrac{2}{\sqrt{5}} = \dfrac{2}{\sqrt{5}} \times \dfrac{\sqrt{5}}{\sqrt{5}} = \dfrac{2\sqrt{5}}{5}$ ◄──────

b $\dfrac{27}{\sqrt{3}} = \dfrac{27}{\sqrt{3}} \times \dfrac{\sqrt{3}}{\sqrt{3}} = \dfrac{27\sqrt{3}}{3} = 9\sqrt{3}$

c $\dfrac{4\sqrt{7}}{\sqrt{2}} = \dfrac{4\sqrt{7}}{\sqrt{2}} \times \dfrac{\sqrt{2}}{\sqrt{2}} = \dfrac{4\sqrt{14}}{2} = 2\sqrt{14}$

d $\dfrac{24}{\sqrt{12}} = \dfrac{24}{\sqrt{12}} \times \dfrac{\sqrt{12}}{\sqrt{12}} = \dfrac{24\sqrt{12}}{12}$ ◄──────

   $= 2\sqrt{12} = 2 \times \sqrt{4 \times 3} = 4\sqrt{3}$ ◄──────

> Multiply top and bottom by $\sqrt{5}$. Using the rules of surds, $\sqrt{5} \times \sqrt{5} = 5$. The denominator is now rational.

> Now the $\sqrt{12}$ needs to be simplified further.

> This could also have been rationalised by multiplying through by $\frac{\sqrt{3}}{\sqrt{3}}$. The $\sqrt{12} \times \sqrt{3}$ in the denominator will become $\sqrt{36}$ or 6.
> $\dfrac{24}{\sqrt{12}} \times \dfrac{\sqrt{3}}{\sqrt{3}} = \dfrac{24\sqrt{3}}{6} = 4\sqrt{3}$
> This method can be used if you can spot an appropriate smaller surd which would rationalise the denominator. It reduces the simplification needed at the end.

Exercise 13.3

1 Simplify each of these by rationalising the denominator.

a $\dfrac{6}{\sqrt{3}}$　　　b $\dfrac{\sqrt{20}}{\sqrt{5}}$　　　c $\dfrac{\sqrt{39}}{\sqrt{3}}$　　　d $\dfrac{8}{\sqrt{2}}$

e $\dfrac{12}{\sqrt{8}}$　　　f $\dfrac{2+\sqrt{3}}{\sqrt{3}}$　　　g $\dfrac{\sqrt{5}+10}{\sqrt{5}}$　　　h $\dfrac{\sqrt{7}+2\sqrt{3}}{\sqrt{3}}$

2 Simplify each of these as far as possible.

a $\dfrac{\sqrt{2}}{5}+\dfrac{3}{\sqrt{2}}$　　　b $10\sqrt{2}+\dfrac{5}{\sqrt{2}}$　　　c $\sqrt{18}-\dfrac{1}{\sqrt{2}}$

3 Which of the following statements are true and which are false?

a $\sqrt{4}+\sqrt{4}=\sqrt{8}$　　b $\sqrt{4}\times\sqrt{4}=4$　　c $(\sqrt{8})^2=8$

d $\dfrac{\sqrt{8}}{\sqrt{2}}=4$　　　　e $\sqrt{8}\times\sqrt{4}=4\sqrt{2}$　　f $\sqrt{8}-\sqrt{4}=4$

You should now:

- **be able to simplify surds using square numbers**
- **know and apply the rules of surds**

  $\sqrt{a}\times\sqrt{a}=a$

  $\sqrt{a}\times\sqrt{b}=\sqrt{ab}$

  $\dfrac{\sqrt{a}}{\sqrt{b}}=\sqrt{\dfrac{a}{b}}$

  $a\sqrt{b}\pm c\sqrt{b}=(a\pm c)\sqrt{b}$

- **be able to rationalise the denominator of a surd.**

Summary exercise 13

1 Simplify each of these.

a $\sqrt{72}$　　b $\sqrt{300}$　　c $\sqrt{432}$　　d $\sqrt{18}$　　e $\sqrt{125}$

f $\sqrt{96}$　　g $\sqrt{45}$　　h $\sqrt{338}$　　i $3\sqrt{40}$　　j $5\sqrt{75}$

k $2\sqrt{200}$　　l $5\sqrt{8}$　　m $2\sqrt{150}$　　n $5\sqrt{250}$　　o $5\sqrt{242}$

2 Simplify each of these as far as possible.

a $\sqrt{2}\times\sqrt{10}$　　　b $2\sqrt{3}\times\sqrt{27}$　　　c $3\sqrt{5}\times2\sqrt{8}$

d $\sqrt{5}\times\sqrt{10}$　　　e $\sqrt{200}\div\sqrt{8}$　　　f $\sqrt{1}\times\sqrt{1}$

g $\sqrt{24}\times\sqrt{8}$　　　h $\dfrac{8\sqrt{6}}{\sqrt{3}}$　　　i $2\sqrt{45}\times\sqrt{18}$

j $\dfrac{\sqrt{12}\times\sqrt{12}}{\sqrt{2}}$　　k $\sqrt{6}\times\sqrt{48}$　　　l $\sqrt{7}\times2\sqrt{3}$

m $3\sqrt{72}\times2\sqrt{6}$　　n $\sqrt{8}\times\sqrt{8}\times\sqrt{8}$　　o $(2\sqrt{3})^2$

3 Simplify each of these by rationalising the denominator.

a $\dfrac{3}{\sqrt5}$ b $\dfrac{2}{\sqrt7}$ c $\dfrac{8}{\sqrt8}$ d $\dfrac{40}{\sqrt8}$

e $\dfrac{1+\sqrt3}{\sqrt2}$ f $\dfrac{10\sqrt3}{\sqrt6}$ g $\dfrac{2-\sqrt{10}}{\sqrt5}$ h $\sqrt{\dfrac{2}{3}}$

4 Simplify each of these as far as possible.

a $3\sqrt2+\sqrt2$ b $\sqrt{63}-\sqrt7$ c $5\sqrt{10}+\sqrt{40}$

d $\sqrt{20}+\sqrt{45}$ e $\sqrt{32}-2\sqrt8$ f $3\sqrt2+2\sqrt{18}$

5 Expand and simplify these.

a $(\sqrt5+3)^2$ b $(\sqrt2-\sqrt3)^2$ c $(4\sqrt3+2)(2-2\sqrt3)$

d $(\sqrt5-\sqrt2)^2$ e $(4+\sqrt3)(1+\sqrt2)$

6 Simplify each of these as far as possible.

a $\dfrac{2}{\sqrt3}+3\sqrt3$ b $\sqrt{20}-\dfrac{2}{\sqrt5}$ c $\sqrt{27}-\dfrac{2}{\sqrt3}$

7 Sort these into four pairs of equal value.

$\dfrac{1}{\sqrt2}$ 6 $\sqrt8\times\sqrt5$ $3\sqrt4$ $\dfrac{\sqrt{40}}{\sqrt{10}}$ 2 $\dfrac{\sqrt8}{4}$ $\sqrt{40}$

8 Prove that $\sqrt{32}+\dfrac{6}{\sqrt2}=7\sqrt2$.

Examination questions

Questions 1 to 5 are from examination papers where you may not use a calculator.

1 Simplify $\dfrac{\sqrt{50}}{10}$.

2 Simplify

a $\sqrt{45}$

b $\sqrt{12}\times\sqrt3$

3 Rationalise the denominator of $\dfrac{8}{\sqrt2}$.

4 Expand and simplify $(5-\sqrt3)^2$.

5 a Show that $(\sqrt{12}+\sqrt3)^2=27$.

b $p^2=\dfrac{3}{5q^2}$

Find the value of q when $p=15$. Give your answer in the form $a\sqrt b$.

Question 6 is from an examination paper where you may use a calculator.

6 Calculate $(3-\sqrt5)(2+3\sqrt5)$, giving your answer in the form $a+b\sqrt5$.

> Use 'Topic Tracker' at www.ccea.org.uk to find more exam questions.

CHAPTER 14

Algebra review

This chapter is about:

- algebraic expressions
- the conventions used in algebra
- collecting like terms
- substitution
- using indices in algebraic expressions.

You should already know:

- about the order of operations, BODMAS
- how to work with powers.

Algebraic expressions

In mathematics, many problems can be solved by using letters to represent unknown values. A mathematical problem can then be written as an algebraic **expression**. An algebraic expression consists of letters and numbers but does not contain an equals sign.

When you want to write an algebraic expression to represent a problem, it is helpful to work out which mathematical process or processes you would carry out if you had been given numerical values, and then carry out the same mathematical process on the letters.

EXAMPLE 1

'I start with a number x, I double it and then subtract 6.
What number am I left with?'
Write an algebraic expression to represent this problem.

SOLUTION

The final number is $x \times 2 - 6$. ◄——— | Use x to represent the original number. |

Conventions in algebra

There are a number of conventions used when you write algebra.

- $x \times 2$ is written as $2x$ ◄——— | It is not necessary to write the multiplication signs in algebra. |
- $b + b + b$ is written as $3b$
- $1a$ written as a ◄——— | It is not necessary to include the 1 in algebra. |

- $a \times b \times 2$ is written as $2ab$ ←

  It is usual to write the letters in alphabetical order.

- $y \times y$ is written as y^2
- $a \div b$ is written as $\frac{a}{b}$

Terms which have the same letter or combination of letters are called **like terms**. But note that, although x and $2x$ are like terms, x and x^2 are not.

Like terms can be added or subtracted. When collecting together like terms, it is important to remember that the sign in front of a term belongs to that term and must be taken into account when adding or subtracting.

EXAMPLE 2

Simplify these.

Simplifying means collecting together like terms where possible.

a $4a + 3a - 2a$
b $2x + 3y - 5x + 7y$
c $4x^2 + 3x - 5 + 10x^2 - 7x$
d $2a + 3b - 5c + 8a - 10b + 5c$
e $6bc + 3cd + 5cb$

SOLUTION

The first step is to collect together the x terms and the y terms, keeping the negative sign with the $5x$.

a $4a + 3a - 2a = 5a$
b $2x + 3y - 5x + 7y = 2x - 5x + 3y + 7y$
               $= -3x + 10y$
c $4x^2 + 3x - 5 + 10x^2 - 7x = 14x^2 - 4x - 5$
d $2a + 3b - 5c + 8a - 10b + 5c = 10a - 7b$
e $6bc + 3cd + 5cb = 11bc + 3cd$

Note that x and x^2 are *not* like terms so they are treated separately.

$-5c + 5c = 0$ and so is not written down. There is no need to write $0c$.

The bc term and the cb term *are* like terms and so can be collected together. (Numerically, $2 \times 3 = 3 \times 2$ and algebra works the same way. So, algebraically, $a \times b = b \times a$.) You usually write the letters in alphabetical order.

Using index notation in algebra

In Chapter 1 you saw that you can write $2 \times 2 \times 2 \times 2$ using index notation as 2^4. You can also use index notation in algebra. You have already met y^2. It means y squared or y to the power 2. x^4 is another example of an algebraic expression written using index notation. It means $x \times x \times x \times x$.

EXAMPLE 3

Simplify these, writing your answers using index notation.

a $p \times p \times p \times p \times p$
b $x \times x \times x \times x \times y \times y \times y \times y$
c $3a \times 4a \times 5a$

a $\quad p \times p \times p \times p \times p = p$ to the power 5 $= p^5$

b $\quad x \times x \times x \times y \times y \times y \times y = x^3 \times y^4$

$\qquad\qquad\qquad\qquad\qquad = x^3 y^4$

c $\quad 3a \times 4a \times 5a = (3 \times 4 \times 5) \times (a \times a \times a)$

$\qquad\qquad\qquad = 60 \times a^3$

$\qquad\qquad\qquad = 60a^3$

> x and y are not like terms so you must deal with them separately.

> You do not need to write the $\times$ signs in algebra.

> Multiply the numbers together first, then multiply the as.

Exercise 14.1

1 Simplify each of these expressions.

a $\quad 2a + 5a - 9a$

b $\quad 5x + 3y - 2x + 7y$

c $\quad 4k + 6 - 8k - 9$

d $\quad 5u - 9u + 4u$

e $\quad 6ab - 2ab + 5ba$

f $\quad 4p + 10q - 3p + 6p$

g $\quad 6t - 11r + 5t - 8r$

h $\quad 3e - 6e^2 + 5e - 2e^2$

i $\quad 2a + k - 6a + 3k - 8a$

j $\quad 9p^2 - 4p + 6p^2 - 5p + p^2$

k $\quad 4a - 7 + 3b - 2a - 9$

l $\quad pq - 3qp + 8 - 6pq + 7$

m $\quad 5abc - 2bc + 6cba + 4cb$

n $\quad 3k - 5t + 6tk - 4k - 9tk$

o $\quad 8a^2b - 3b^2 + 2a^2 - 6b^2 - 2a^2b$

p $\quad 6 + 5t^2 - 3 - 10t^2 - 4$

q $\quad 6a^2 - 3b^2 + 2a^2 - 9 + 4b^2$

r $\quad 2w^3 - 3w^2 + 5w^2 - 10w^3$

s $\quad 10 - 3qp + p^2 + 6qp - q^2$

t $\quad 6h^2 - 3h^3 + 10 - 5h^2 + 2h^3 - h^2$

u $\quad n \times n \times n \times n \times n \times n$

v $\quad k \times k \times k \times k \times k \times k \times k$

w $\quad a \times a \times b \times b \times b \times b$

x $\quad m \times 4m \times 7m$

2 Which of the following expressions simplify to $x + y$?

a $\quad 3x + 2y - 4x + 6y - 7y$

b $\quad 5xy + 2y - 4yx - y + x - xy$

c $\quad -x + y - x + y - y + 3x$

d $\quad 2x^2 - 3y + 2x - x^2 + 4y - x$

3 The length of a rectangle is a and the width is b.
Find each of these in its simplest form:

a $\quad$ an expression for the perimeter of the rectangle

b $\quad$ an expression for the area of the rectangle.

4 Find an expression (in its simplest form) for the perimeter of this shape.

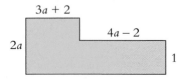

5 What must be added to each of these expressions to make $4x - y$?

a $\quad 4x + 2y$

b $\quad 2x^2 - 3x + y$

c $\quad 6 + 5x + 3y$

d $\quad -x - y$

Substitution

In earlier work you will have met function machines. You carry out the operations described by the function machine on the input number to get an output number.

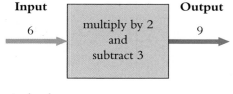

This is similar to substitution. The letters in an algebraic expression represent unknown numbers. Sometimes you are told the numerical value of each of the letters. You can then **substitute** these values for the letters to give an overall numerical value for an expression. The function machine above represents the expression $2x - 3$ and you are being told that $x = 6$.

When you substitute numbers into an expression, you must be careful to follow the correct order of operations. You can use the mnemonic **BODMAS** to remind yourself to work out **B**rackets first, then powers **O**f (such as squares, cubes or roots), then **D**ivision and **M**ultiplication and, finally, **A**ddition and **S**ubtraction.

EXAMPLE 4

Given that $a = 4$, $b = 2$ and $c = 1$, find the value of each of these expressions.

 a $2a + 3b$ b $a^2 b$ c $3b^2 + c$ d $(3b)^2$ e $\dfrac{10c - 2b}{a}$

SOLUTION

Rewrite the expression, replacing each letter with the numerical value given for it.

 a $2a + 3b = 2 \times 4 + 3 \times 2$
$= 8 + 6$
$= 14$

Do the multiplications first.

Then do the addition.

 b $a^2 b = 4^2 \times 2$
$= 16 \times 2$
$= 32$

Work out the powers of the numbers first.

Then do the multiplication.

 c $3b^2 + c = 3 \times 2^2 + 1$
$= 3 \times 4 + 1$
$= 12 + 1$
$= 13$

Again, work out the powers of the numbers first.

Then do the multiplication.

Then do the addition.

 d $(3b)^2 = (3 \times 2)^2$
$= 6^2$
$= 36$

Work out the brackets first.

Then work out the power.

 e $\dfrac{10c - 2b}{a} = \dfrac{10 \times 1 - 2 \times 2}{4}$
$= \dfrac{10 - 4}{4}$
$= \dfrac{6}{4}$
$= 1\frac{1}{2}$

In an algebraic fraction, the dividing line acts like brackets. Work out the numerator and the denominator separately first. Then do the division.

When you are substituting numbers into an expression, you may also need to remember the rules for working with negative numbers and how to calculate with fractions.

Given that $p = 5$, $q = -3$ and $r = 2$, find the value of each of these expressions.

a pqr

b $\dfrac{q}{p} + \dfrac{r}{q}$

SOLUTION

a $pqr = 5 \times -3 \times 2$
$\qquad = -30$

> There is an odd number of negative numbers, so the answer is negative.

b $\dfrac{q}{p} + \dfrac{r}{q} = \dfrac{-3}{5} + \dfrac{2}{-3}$

$\qquad = \dfrac{-3}{5} + \dfrac{-2}{3}$

> Write the negative signs in the numerators.

$\qquad = \dfrac{-9 + (-10)}{15}$

> Write the fractions with a common denominator and add the numerators.

$\qquad = \dfrac{-19}{15}$

$\qquad = -1\dfrac{4}{15}$

Exercise 14.2

1 Find the missing values for this function machine.

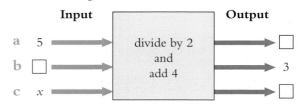

2 Evaluate each of these expressions when $x = 5$, $y = 2$ and $z = 1$.

a $2x + 3y$ b xy^2 c $3y^2$ d $y - 2x$

e z^3 f $y - 3z$ g $2x^2$ h $(2x)^2$

i xyz j $\dfrac{2y - x}{2z}$ k $3y - 10$ l $\dfrac{x^2 y}{10}$

3 Evaluate each of these expressions when $p = 4$, $q = -2$ and $r = -1$.

a $p + 3q$ b $4r - 5$ c $p^2 q$ d $\dfrac{r^2}{p}$

e $12 - qr$ f $4q^2 - 2r^2$ g $\sqrt[3]{pqr}$ h $3q^3$

i $p(q - r)$ j $\dfrac{10p^2}{q}$ k $\dfrac{p}{q} + \dfrac{r}{q}$ l $\dfrac{q^3 - p^2}{4r^2}$

4   Evaluate each of these expressions when $k = 6$, $m = -3$ and $n = 2$.

    a $k(m - n)$ **b** kmn **c** $\dfrac{10k}{mn}$

    d $\dfrac{4k + 3n}{m - n}$ **e** m^2n^2 **f** $6m^2 - 10$

    g $(3m)^3$ **h** $\dfrac{m^2}{k}$ **i** $m + n + m^2 - n^2$

    j $\dfrac{k}{m} + \dfrac{m}{n}$ **k** $m(k - n^2)$ **l** $\sqrt{m^2n + 3k}$

5   Given that $g = \frac{1}{2}$, $h = 1$ and $j = 2$, find the value of this expression.

$$\frac{gh\,(3j^2 + 4h - 5g)}{ghj}$$

6   Given that $a = 10$, $b = -5$, $c = 1$ and $d = -\frac{1}{2}$, find the value of this expression.

$$\frac{(a + c)(b + c) + abd}{5c - 2b}$$

You should now:

- be able to form an algebraic expression for given information
- be able to simplify algebraic expressions by gathering like terms
- be able to evaluate algebraic expressions by substituting in various numerical values
- be able to operate function machines for numerical and variable terms.

Summary exercise 14

1   The width of a rectangle is w cm.
The length is 3 cm more than double the width.
Find an expression for the perimeter of the rectangle.

2   The price of a holiday for an adult is £A, and the price for a child
is 75% of the adult price.
Write an expression for the total cost of the holiday for two adults
and three children.

3   Write an expression for the number of pounds in k 20p pieces.

4   If t is the largest of five consecutive odd numbers, write an
expression for the smallest of these odd numbers.

5   Simplify each of these expressions.

    a $2a - 3b + 5c - 3a + 2b + c - b$

    b $6pq + 3qr - 4qp + 5qr - pq$

    c $6x^2 - 2x + 4 - 3x^2 + 2x + 1$

    d $a^2 + 2a - 1 + 2a - 3a^2 - 1 - 3a$

6   A picture of dimensions a cm by b cm is surrounded by a frame
6 cm wide. Find an expression for the perimeter of the frame.

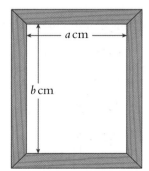

7 Given that $a = 5$, $b = 10$ and $c = \frac{1}{2}$, evaluate each of these.

a a^2b **b** $\dfrac{ab}{c}$ **c** $c(b - a)$

d $b - 3a$ **e** $\dfrac{a}{b} + c$ **f** c^3

g $2b^2$ **h** $(2b)^2$ **i** $bc - a$

8 Given that $x = -2$, $y = -3$ and $z = -1$, evaluate each of these.

a xyz **b** xy^2 **c** $3x - 2y$

d $\dfrac{4y - 3z}{2x}$ **e** $y^2 - 4y - 2$ **f** $6xy^2z^3$

g $\dfrac{z}{x} + \dfrac{z}{y}$ **h** $100 - 10x - 5y$ **i** $(2xy)^2$

9 Find the missing values for this function machine.

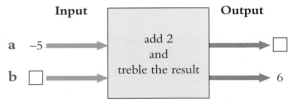

c What is the output when the input is the variable k?

Examination questions

Use 'Topic Tracker' at www.ccea.org.uk to find more exam questions.

Questions **1** to **3** are from examination papers where you may not use a calculator.

1 Simplify $7d + 5e - 4d + 2e$.

2 $R = \dfrac{J - 30}{D}$

Calculate the value of R when $J = -6$ and $D = 12$.

3 a $a = 5$ and $b = 2$

Find the value of $4ab$.

b $x = 4$ and $y = -3$

Find the value of $3x + 5y$.

Questions **4** and **5** are from examination papers where you may use a calculator.

4 Simplify $5p - 2q - 3p + 5q$.

5 $p = 5$ and $q = \dfrac{1}{2}$

Find the value of $6p - 8q$.

CHAPTER 15

Indices

This chapter is about:

- the rules of indices
- simplifying algebraic expressions involving indices
- evaluating numerical powers and roots expressed in index notation
- solving equations involving indices.

You should already know:

- how to work with positive and negative whole numbers, decimals and fractions
- how to use index notation.

The rules of indices

You met indices in Chapter 1, principally for the squares and cubes of numbers. You also met algebraic expressions involving indices in Chapter 14. In an expression of the form a^n, n is known as the **index** (plural **indices**) and a is known as the **base**.

There are several useful rules which can be established for working with indices.

> The notation a^n will be used throughout this chapter to represent a general power or number given in index notation.
>
> a^n — index, base

Rule 1

Look at the expression $a^5 \times a^3$.

This can be rewritten as $a \times a \times a \times a \times a \times a \times a \times a = a^8$.

From this you can see that $a^5 \times a^3 = a^{5+3} = a^8$.

In general, when powers of the *same base* are multiplied, the indices are added.

$$a^m \times a^n = a^{m+n}$$

Rule 2

Look at the expression $a^5 \div a^3$.

This can be rewritten as $\dfrac{a \times a \times a \times a \times a}{a \times a \times a} = a^2$.

From this you can see that $a^5 \div a^3 = a^{5-3} = a^2$.

In general, when powers of the *same base* are divided, the indices are subtracted.

$$a^m \div a^n = a^{m-n}$$

Rule 3

Look at the expression $(a^3)^2$.

This can be rewritten as $(a \times a \times a) \times (a \times a \times a) = a^6$.

From this you can see that $(a^3)^2 = a^{3 \times 2} = a^6$.

In general, when a power is raised to another power, the two powers are multiplied.

$$(a^m)^n = a^{mn}$$

Rule 4

Look at this sequence.

$a^4 = a \times a \times a \times a$

$a^3 = a \times a \times a$

$a^2 = a \times a$

Then, continuing the sequence,

$a^1 = a$

In general, a base raised to the power 1 is simply the base number.

$$a^1 = a$$

Rule 5

Look at the expression $a^m \div a^m$.

From rule 2, $a^m \div a^m = a^{m-m} = a^0$.

But, since $a^m \div a^m = \dfrac{a^m}{a^m} = 1$, it can be established that $a^0 = 1$.

In general, a base to the power zero will always equal 1 (providing the base itself is not equal to zero).

$$a^0 = 1$$

Rule 6

Look at the expression $a^0 \div a^m$.

From rule 2, $a^0 \div a^m = a^{0-m} = a^{-m}$.

But since $a^0 = 1$ (from rule 5), it can be established that

$$1 \div a^m = \frac{1}{a^m} = a^{-m}$$

In general, a negative index represents 1 divided by a positive power.

$$a^{-m} = \frac{1}{a^m}$$

Rule 7

Look at the expression $a^{\frac{1}{2}} \times a^{\frac{1}{2}}$.

From rules 3 and 4, $a^{\frac{1}{2}} \times a^{\frac{1}{2}} = (a^{\frac{1}{2}})^2 = a^1 = a$.

The inverse of this would suggest that $\sqrt{a} = a^{\frac{1}{2}}$.

Now look at the expression $a^{\frac{1}{3}} \times a^{\frac{1}{3}} \times a^{\frac{1}{3}}$.

From rules 3 and 4, $a^{\frac{1}{3}} \times a^{\frac{1}{3}} \times a^{\frac{1}{3}} = (a^{\frac{1}{3}})^3 = a^1 = a$.

The inverse of this would suggest that $\sqrt[3]{a} = a^{\frac{1}{3}}$.

In general, a fractional power represents a root.

$$a^{\frac{1}{m}} = \sqrt[m]{a}$$

Rule 8

Look at the expression $a^{\frac{n}{m}}$.

Combining rules 3 and 7, this can be rewritten as:

$a^{\frac{n}{m}} = (a^{\frac{1}{m}})^n = \sqrt[m]{a^n}$ or $(\sqrt[m]{a})^n$.

For example, $a^{\frac{2}{3}} = (a^{\frac{1}{3}})^2 = \sqrt[3]{a^2}$ or $(\sqrt[3]{a})^2$

and $a^{\frac{3}{5}} = (a^{\frac{1}{5}})^3 = \sqrt[5]{a^3}$ or $(\sqrt[5]{a})^3$.

In general,

$$a^{\frac{n}{m}} = \sqrt[m]{a^n} \quad \text{or} \quad (\sqrt[m]{a})^n$$

The rules of indices can be used in three different areas:

- simplifying algebraic expressions involving indices
- evaluating numerical powers and roots expressed in index notation
- solving equations involving indices.

Simplifying algebraic expressions

The rules of indices can be used to simplify many algebraic expressions.

EXAMPLE 1

Simplify each of these expressions.

   a $p^6 \times p^3$ b $10x^5y^2 \div 2x^2y^6$ c $(3a^2)^4$

SOLUTION

   a $p^6 \times p^3 = p^{6+3}$
                  $= p^9$

   b $10x^5y^2 \div 2x^2y^6 = 5x^{5-2}y^{2-6}$
                          $= 5x^3y^{-4}$

                          $= \dfrac{5x^3}{y^4}$

   c $(3a^2)^4 = 3^4 \times a^{2 \times 4}$
               $= 81a^8$

> Note that 3^4 becomes 81 (*not* 3×4), as 3 is the base and 4 is the index, whereas $(a^2)^4$ becomes $a^{2 \times 4}$ as *both* the 2 and the 4 are indices and so are multiplied together.

EXAMPLE 2

Simplify each of these expressions.

   a $8p^{-2} \div 4p^{-2}$ b $(49a^8)^{\frac{1}{2}}$ c $x^{-2} \times x^{\frac{1}{2}}$

SOLUTION

   a $8p^{-2} \div 4p^{-2} = 2 \times p^{-2-(-2)}$
                       $= 2 \times p^{-2+2}$
                       $= 2 \times p^0$
                       $= 2 \times 1$
                       $= 2$

> The rules of negative numbers are applied when subtracting the indices here.
> $-2 - (-2) = -2 + 2 = 0$

   b $(49a^8)^{\frac{1}{2}} = \sqrt{49} \times \sqrt{a^8}$
                 $= 7 \times a^{8 \div 2}$
                 $= 7a^4$

> When evaluating indices it is *not* necessary to give the negative square root.

c $\quad x^{-2} \times x^{\frac{1}{2}} = x^{-2 + \frac{1}{2}}$

$\qquad\qquad = x^{-\frac{3}{2}}$

$\qquad\qquad = \dfrac{1}{x^{\frac{3}{2}}}$

$\qquad\qquad = \dfrac{1}{\sqrt{x^3}}$

Exercise 15.1

1 Express each of these in index form.
   a $\quad 2 \times 2 \times 2 \times 2$
   b $\quad 3 \times 3 \times 4 \times 4 \times 4$
   c $\quad t \times t \times t \times t \times t \times t$

2 Simplify these.
   a $\quad x^6 \times x^2$
   b $\quad p^{10} \div p^2$
   c $\quad (a^2)^4$
   d $\quad t^{10} \times t^{10}$
   e $\quad n^{12} \div n^{11}$

3 Simplify these.
   a $\quad 2g^3 \times 4g^2$
   b $\quad 6k \times 9k^8$
   c $\quad 18k^6 \div 6k^2$
   d $\quad 72r^8 \div 12r^4$
   e $\quad \dfrac{20y^7}{15y^3}$
   f $\quad (5g^2)^2$
   g $\quad (2n^2)^3$
   h $\quad (2a^3)^2$
   i $\quad (2a)^2 \times (3a)^3$
   j $\quad a^2y^2 \times a^5y^3$
   k $\quad p^5q^9 \div p^3q^4$
   l $\quad (3m^2n^3)^3$

4 Write each of these expressions as a power of a single base number.
   a $\quad \dfrac{2^3 \times 2^7}{2^4}$
   b $\quad \dfrac{25^2 \times 5}{125}$

5 Simplify these.
   a $\quad \dfrac{1}{y} \times \dfrac{1}{y}$
   b $\quad w^5 \div w^{-2}$
   c $\quad \dfrac{x^5}{x^7}$
   d $\quad k^{-3} \times k^3$
   e $\quad (y^{-3})^{-4}$
   f $\quad a^2 \div a \times a^{-1}$
   g $\quad \sqrt[5]{a}$
   h $\quad \sqrt{x^6}$
   i $\quad x^{2.5} \div x^{0.5}$
   j $\quad \dfrac{x}{\sqrt{x}}$
   k $\quad \dfrac{\sqrt{x}}{x^3}$
   l $\quad p^{-3} \times p^{\frac{1}{3}}$
   m $\quad \dfrac{\sqrt{x} \times \sqrt{x}}{x}$
   n $\quad \dfrac{t^{\frac{3}{4}} \div t^{-\frac{1}{2}}}{t}$
   o $\quad \sqrt{k^{1\frac{1}{3}} \times k^{\frac{2}{3}}}$

6 Simplify these.
   a $\quad (8t)^0$
   b $\quad (3m)^{-3}$
   c $\quad (64w^9)^{\frac{1}{3}}$
   d $\quad (8c^2)^{-2}$
   e $\quad (25y^2)^{\frac{1}{2}}$
   f $\quad (2h)^{-3}$
   g $\quad \dfrac{4p^2 \times 6p}{8p^4}$
   h $\quad 5y^4 \times y^{-7}$
   i $\quad \sqrt[3]{64k^6}$
   j $\quad 8x^{\frac{3}{2}} \div 2x^{\frac{1}{2}}$
   k $\quad (4n)^{-1} \times (4n)^2$
   l $\quad p^3q^6 \times pq^{-2}$
   m $\quad t^3u \div tu^5$
   n $\quad \dfrac{12xy^{-2}}{4x^2y}$
   o $\quad \sqrt{9b^4c^2}$

7 Simplify these.
   a $\quad 3^{-p} \div 3^{-p}$
   b $\quad \dfrac{4^a \times 4^b}{4^{-c}}$
   c $\quad \dfrac{2^c \times 2^d}{2^e}$
   d $\quad (4e^y)^{-1}$

8 Write each of these expressions as a power of a single base number.

 a $\dfrac{81^{2x}}{3^x}$

 b $\dfrac{16^{2a} \times 2^b}{4^c \times 8^{3a}}$

9 Given that $10^a = 9$ and $10^b = 4$, find the value of each of these.

 a 10^{a+b} b 10^{a-b} c 10^{2a}

Evaluating numerical powers and roots

Numerical powers can be evaluated (without the use of a calculator) by applying one or more of the rules of indices.

EXAMPLE 3

Evaluate each of these.

 a $64^{\frac{1}{2}}$ b 8^0 c $(2^3)^2$

 d $16^{\frac{3}{4}}$ e 0.01^{-2} f $25^{-1\frac{1}{2}}$

SOLUTION

a $64^{\frac{1}{2}} = \sqrt{64}$
$= 8$

b $8^0 = 1$

c $(2^3)^2 = 2^{3 \times 2}$
$= 2^6$
$= 64$

d $16^{\frac{3}{4}} = (16^{\frac{1}{4}})^3$
$= (\sqrt[4]{16})^3$
$= 2^3 = 8$

e $0.01^{-2} = \dfrac{1}{0.01^2}$
$= \dfrac{1}{0.0001}$
$= 10\,000$

f $25^{-1\frac{1}{2}} = 25^{-\frac{3}{2}}$
$= \dfrac{1}{25^{\frac{3}{2}}}$
$= \dfrac{1}{(25^{\frac{1}{2}})^3} = \dfrac{1}{(\sqrt{25})^3} = \dfrac{1}{5^3}$
$= \dfrac{1}{125}$

Exercise 15.2

Evaluate each of these.

1 4^3

2 $27^{\frac{1}{3}}$

3 10^0

4 4^{-2}

5 $(3^2)^2$

6 2×2^4

7 5^{-3}

8 $(4^{-1})^{-2}$

9 $81^{\frac{1}{2}}$

10 $8^{\frac{2}{3}}$

11 $3^{-2} \times 3^3$

12 $(16^{\frac{1}{2}})^{-2}$

13 $0.01^{\frac{3}{2}}$

14 3.56^0

15 $49^{-\frac{1}{2}}$

16 $\left(\dfrac{1}{4}\right)^{\frac{1}{2}}$

17 $16^{\frac{3}{4}} \times 16^{-1}$

18 $5^{-3} \div 5^{-2}$

19 $125^{-\frac{2}{3}}$

20 $\left(\dfrac{1}{3}\right)^{-3}$

21 $8^0 \times 10^0$

22 $\left(\dfrac{1}{25}\right)^{-\frac{1}{2}}$

23 $8^{1\frac{1}{3}}$

24 $0.001^{-\frac{2}{3}}$

25 $32^{0.6}$

26 $\left(11\dfrac{1}{9}\right)^{\frac{1}{2}}$

27 $4^{-\frac{5}{2}}$

28 What is half of 2^{10}?

29 Find 1% of 100^9.

30 Evaluate $\dfrac{2^3 \times 2^8}{2^4 \times 2^3}$

31 Evaluate $\dfrac{49^3 \times 7^2}{\sqrt{49} \times (7^2)^2}$

32 Find the value of the missing index in each of these.

    a $\sqrt{60} = 60^?$
    b $(\sqrt{5})^7 = 5^?$
    c $\dfrac{1}{\sqrt[3]{6}} = 6^?$

33 Put these numbers in order of size from the smallest to the largest.

    $6^2 \quad 2^{-6} \quad 2^6 \quad 6^{\frac{1}{2}} \quad 6^{-2}$

34 Which of these numbers have the same value?

    $16^{0.25} \quad 2^0 \quad 4^{-\frac{1}{2}} \quad 4^{\frac{1}{2}} \quad 2$

35 Evaluate $16^{1\frac{1}{4}} \times 8^{-\frac{2}{3}}$.

36 Evaluate $4^{\frac{5}{2}} \times 16^{\frac{1}{3}} \div 4^{\frac{1}{6}}$.

37 Write $100\,000$ as a power of 100.

Solving equations involving indices

An equation involving indices can be solved by writing each side of the equation as a power of the same base number. Then, using the rules of indices, the powers are equated and a new equation, involving just the indices, is written. This is then solved like a linear equation.

EXAMPLE 4

Find the value of x if $4^x = 8$.

SOLUTION

$$4^x = 8$$
$$(2^2)^x = 2^3$$
$$2^{2x} = 2^3$$
So $\quad 2x = 3$
$$x = 1\tfrac{1}{2}$$

> Since 4 and 8 are both powers of 2, rewrite each side of the equation as a power of 2.

> The base numbers are now the same, so the indices must be the same.

EXAMPLE 5

Find the value of p if $6^p = \dfrac{1}{\sqrt[3]{6^4}}$.

SOLUTION

$$6^p = \frac{1}{\sqrt[3]{6^4}} = \frac{1}{6^{\frac{4}{3}}} = 6^{-\frac{4}{3}}$$

So $\quad p = -\dfrac{4}{3} = -1\tfrac{1}{3}$

EXAMPLE 6

Find the value of n if $\left(\frac{1}{3}\right)^n = 81$.

SOLUTION

$$\left(\frac{1}{3}\right)^n = 81$$
$$(3^{-1})^n = 3^4$$
$$3^{-n} = 3^4$$

So $\quad -n = 4$

$$n = -4$$

EXAMPLE 7

Find the value of y if $25^{y+1} = 5^y$.

SOLUTION

$$25^{y+1} = 5^y$$
$$(5^2)^{y+1} = 5^y$$
$$5^{2y+2} = 5^y$$

So $\quad 2y + 2 = y$

$$2y - y = -2$$
$$y = -2$$

Exercise 15.3

Find the value of x in each of these equations.

1   $2^x = 32$

2   $8^x = \frac{1}{2}$

3   $3^{-x} = \frac{1}{27}$

4   $6^x = 1$

5   $x^{-1} = 3^{-4}$

6   $1000^x = 10$

7   $6^{-x} = \frac{1}{36}$

8   $3^{2x} = 729$

9   $x^{\frac{1}{2}} = 4$

10   $7^{2x} = 49$

11   $3^x = \sqrt[3]{9}$

12   $8^{x+1} = 2^x$

13   $2^{x-1} = \frac{1}{16}$

14   $10^x = 0.1$

15   $x^{-1} = 2^{-5}$

16   $2^{-2x} = 32$

17   $2^{x+4} = 4^x$

18   $64^{\frac{1}{2}} = 2^{-3x}$

19   $3 \times 27^x = 81$

20   $3^{\frac{x}{2}} = 243$

21   $\frac{1}{5^x} = \sqrt{25^3}$

22   $0.01x = 1000^{-\frac{1}{3}}$

23   $5 \times 5^{3x} = 25^4$

24   $\frac{16}{4^{\frac{x}{2}}} = 4$

25   $4x = \frac{1}{\sqrt{2^6}}$

26   $3^{x+4} = 27^x$

27   $4^{\frac{x}{2}} = 64$

28   $125^x = 25^2$

29   $4 \times 8^{2x} = 2$

30   $1000^{2x} = \frac{1}{10 \times 10^3}$

Summary exercise 15

1 Write each of these using index notation.

   a $10 \times 10 \times 10 \times 10$ **b** $k \times k \times k \times k \times k$ **c** $\dfrac{1}{100}$ **d** $\dfrac{1}{y \times y}$

   e $\sqrt{20}$ **f** $\sqrt[4]{t}$ **g** $\sqrt{7^3}$ **h** $a \times a \times b \times b \times b \times b$

2 Simplify these.

   a $k^6 \div k^2$ **b** $t^9 \times t^3$ **c** $(x^4)^2$ **d** $m^{-2} \div m^6$

   e $(4c^2)^3$ **f** $n^3 \div n^{-3}$ **g** $\sqrt{36a^6}$ **h** $(m^{-3})^{-4}$

   i $(a^{\frac{1}{2}})^6$ **j** $x^{\frac{1}{7}} \times x^{\frac{6}{7}}$ **k** $\sqrt[6]{x^3}$ **l** $x^4 \times x^0$

3 Simplify these.

   a $4t^6 \times 3t^4$ **b** $10h^8 \div 2h^2$ **c** $5a^2b \times 3ab^2$ **d** $4y^6 \times 3y^{-5}$

   e $\sqrt{x^{-4}}$ **f** $(k^{\frac{3}{4}})^8$ **g** $\dfrac{14m^2n^3}{20mn^2}$ **h** $(8a^{-3})^2$

   i $(3a^2)^2 - 6a^4$ **j** $\sqrt[3]{x^{1.5}}$ **k** $(27a^3b^6)^{\frac{2}{3}}$ **l** $2a^2 \times 3a^3 \times 5a^{-5}$

4 Evaluate each of these.

   a 7^0 **b** 4^{-3} **c** $9^{\frac{2}{3}}$ **d** $8^{\frac{5}{3}}$

   e $36^{-\frac{1}{2}}$ **f** $(0.001)^{\frac{1}{3}}$ **g** $\left(\dfrac{1}{2}\right)^{-1}$ **h** $27^{-\frac{5}{3}}$

   i $\left(\dfrac{9}{25}\right)^{\frac{1}{2}}$ **j** $16^{0.75}$ **k** $\left(\dfrac{1}{8}\right)^{-\frac{2}{3}}$ **l** $2.25^{\frac{1}{2}}$

5 Evaluate each of these.

   a $169^{\frac{1}{4}} \times 13^{\frac{1}{2}}$ **b** $36^{\frac{7}{8}} \div 6^{\frac{3}{4}}$

6 What is one quarter of 2^{20}?

7 Given that a is a positive integer greater than 1, arrange these numbers in order of size, from the smallest to the largest.

   a^6 a^{-6} $\sqrt[6]{a}$ a^0 a

8 Write $\dfrac{16^{2a} \times 2^b}{4^a}$ as a single power.

9 Solve each of these equations to find n.

    a $3^n = \frac{1}{9}$ b $9^n = (\sqrt{3})^8$ c $32^{-n} = \frac{1}{8}$

    d $2^{\frac{n}{2}} = 8$ e $3^{n+3} = 3$ f $\frac{1}{125} = 5^{-2n}$

    g $10^{3n} = 0.001$ h $9^{2n} = 27^2$ i $5^{-n} = \frac{1}{\sqrt{125}}$

    j $0.25 = 2^n$ k $2^{-n} = \sqrt{2^{10}}$ l $36^{3n} = \frac{1}{6}$

Examination questions

Use 'Topic Tracker' at www.ccea.org.uk to find more exam questions.

Questions **1** to **9** are from examination papers where you may not use a calculator.

1   Simplify

    a $x^3 \times x^7$ b $12x^3 \div 6x$ c $(x^3)^5$ d $\frac{12x^4y^2}{15xy^3}$

2   Simplify $(3x^2)^3$

3   Evaluate

    a 2^{-4} b 2^0

4   Evaluate

    a 10^{-2} b 10^0 c $49^{\frac{1}{2}}$

5   Evaluate

    a $36^{\frac{1}{2}}$ b $32^{0.2}$ c $16^{\frac{3}{4}}$ d $125^{-\frac{2}{3}}$

6   Evaluate

    a $32^{\frac{3}{5}}$ b $27^{-\frac{2}{3}}$

7   Evaluate $16^{0.5} \times 4^{-3}$.

    Give your answer in its simplest form.

8   Given that $a > 1$, arrange in ascending order:

    a^{-3}, a, $a^{\frac{1}{2}}$, $\frac{1}{a}$

    Show your working clearly.
    Describe the effect, if any, on the order when $0 < a < 1$.

9   a   Simplify

       i $t^2 \times t^7$

       ii $\frac{r^2}{r^5}$

       iii $(27a^3b^6)^{\frac{2}{3}}$

    b   Find the value of x for which $2^x = \sqrt[3]{4}$

Questions **10** and **11** are from examination papers where you may use a calculator.

10   Simplify

    a $4x^2y^3 \times x^3y$ b $\frac{m^2}{m^7}$

11   Simplify $(5a^3b^4) \times (ab^2)$

CHAPTER 16

Brackets

> **This chapter is about:**
> - expanding brackets.
>
> **You should already know:**
> - about the order of operations, BODMAS
> - how to find the area of rectangles and triangles.

Expanding brackets

Look at this rectangle.

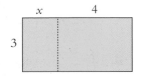

The area of the large rectangle can be calculated by adding the areas of the two smaller rectangles.

$$3 \times x + 3 \times 4 = 3x + 12$$

You could also calculate the area directly as $3 \times (x + 4)$. Remember that when you are writing algebraic expressions you do not need to write the multiplication sign, so you write this as $3(x + 4)$. The area is the same as before, $3x + 12$.

The mathematical process of multiplying out brackets is known as **expanding** the brackets.

When expanding brackets there are a few points to consider.

- A term directly in front of a bracket means that *everything* inside the bracket is multiplied by the term in front of the bracket.
- If there is no term directly in front of the bracket, a '1' can be inserted.
- You need to take care when multiplying by a negative term. Use the rules for multiplying negative numbers. A negative term in front of a bracket will change the sign of every term inside the bracket because you are multiplying every term inside the bracket by a negative number.
- Once the brackets are expanded, all the like terms should be collected together.

EXAMPLE 1

Expand these and simplify where possible.

  a $4(2x + 3)$

  b $-7(3y - 2)$

  c $6 + 3(5t - 3)$

  d $x(3x - 5)$

  e $4(5p - 3) + 3(2p + 1)$

  f $3(2x + 1) - 4(x + 5)$

  g $3 + 4(3a - 4) - (2a + 6)$

  h $x^2(x^3 + 4)$

SOLUTION

a $4(2x + 3) = 4 \times 2x + 4 \times 3$
$$= 8x + 12$$

> Multiply each term inside the bracket by the term outside the bracket. In this case, the term outside the bracket is a number, 4.

> Be careful when multiplying by a negative number.

b $-7(3y - 2) = -7 \times 3y + (-7 \times -2)$
$$= -21y + 14$$

c $6 + 3(5t - 3) = 6 + 15t - 9$
$$= 15t - 3$$

> Notice how multiplying by a negative number has changed the signs of both of the terms in the bracket.

> Remember BODMAS: you need to deal with the brackets first.

> Then you do the subtraction.

d $x(3x - 5) = x \times 3x - x \times 5$
$$= 3x^2 - 5x$$

> The term outside the bracket can be a letter.

> In the same way as 2×2 can be written as 2^2, $x \times x$ can be written as x^2. Remember also that $3x$ means $3 \times x$ so that $x \times 3x$ means $x \times 3 \times x$. You write this as $3x^2$.

e $4(5p - 3) + 3(2p + 1) = 20p - 12 + 6p + 3$
$$= 26p - 9$$

> When you have two sets of brackets, work out each of the brackets separately first.

> Then simplify the result by collecting together like terms.

f $3(2x + 1) - 4(x + 5) = 3(2x + 1) + (-4)(x + 5)$
$$= 6x + 3 + (-4 \times x) + (-4 \times 5)$$
$$= 6x + 3 + (-4x) + (-20)$$
$$= 6x + 3 - 4x - 20$$
$$= 2x - 17$$

> Look back at part b. The minus sign in front of the bracket there meant you multiplied everything inside the bracket by -7. Just as when you are collecting like terms, the minus sign belongs with the term that follows it. Remember the rules for negative numbers: '+' and '−' adjacent to each other mean '−'. Use the reverse of this to rewrite the expression to make it clear that you must multiply everything in the bracket by -4.

g $3 + 4(3a − 4) − (2a + 6)$ $= 3 + 4(3a − 4) + (−1)(2a + 6)$
$= 3 + 12a − 16 + (−1 × 2a) + (−1 × 6)$
$= 3 + 12a − 16 + (−2a) + (−6)$
$= 3 + 12a − 16 − 2a − 6$
$= 10a − 19$

> There is no term directly in front of the second bracket here but you can insert a 1 to remind yourself that you need to multiply the second bracket by −1.

h $x^2(x^3 + 4)$ $= (x^2 × x^3) + (4 × x^2)$
$= x^{2+3} + 4x^2$
$= x^5 + 4x^2$

> Use the rules of indices (see Chapter 15).

Exercise 16.1

1 Expand each of these.
   a $3(2x − 5)$ b $4(5x − 2)$ c $6(a + 5)$ d $2(4 − 3a)$
   e $5(3k − 1)$ f $7(5d − 3)$ g $8(3z − 2)$ h $5(5p + 5)$
   i $4(3t + 5s)$ j $2(3a − 2b)$ k $10(100 − x)$ l $7(a − 3c)$

2 Expand each of these.
   a $−4(2a − 3)$ b $−3(7c − 1)$ c $−5(5a + 2)$ d $−6(t − 5)$
   e $−3(x + y)$ f $−4(3 + 2y)$ g $−(4c + 7)$ h $−5(2a − 3b)$
   i $−8(9y + 8)$ j $−3(1 − 3x)$ k $−5(k + m)$ l $−10(1 − 10a)$

3 Expand each of these.
   a $x(x + 2)$ b $x(3x − 1)$ c $x(y − 2)$ d $y(2y + 3)$
   e $2x(3x − 1)$ f $a(ab + c)$ g $y(3x + 2y)$ h $−a(2a + 1)$
   i $ab(a + b)$ j $4k(2k − 3)$ k $−3b(b + 6)$ l $3x^2(2x − 7)$

4 Expand and simplify these.
   a $2 + 3(2a + 5)$ b $4t + 3(2t − 1)$ c $5r + 3(3r − 5)$
   d $6a + 4(3a − 2)$ e $2 − 4(3x − 4)$ f $6 + 3(2m − 5)$
   g $5 + 3(2a − 7) + 9a$ h $9b − (3b + 2) − 7b$ i $6t − (3t + 5) − 4t$
   j $10 − 4(2u − 3) + 7u$ k $4 − 3(3x − 2) + 6x$ l $5 + 3(3y − 4) + 6y$

5 Expand and simplify these.
   a $x(2x − 1) + 3x^2$ b $2a(3a − 5) + 7a$ c $5(3x^2 − 2) − 7x^2$
   d $2 + y(5y − 3) + 6y^2$ e $k(5k − 1) + 3k^2$ f $6 − (p^2 + 5) − 3p^2$
   g $p(p + 2) − 5p^2$ h $t + 6t(t + 3) − 7t$ i $4a(3a + 7) − 2a$
   j $−2x(3x + 2) + 6x^2$ k $y(xy + 2) − 4y$ l $3e(5e − 1) + 2e^2$

6 Expand and simplify these.
   a $2(3a + 4) + 4(5a + 2)$ b $4(2x − 3) + 3(5x + 1)$
   c $6(3x − 1) − 2(4x + 3)$ d $3(x + 3) − (2x + 1)$
   e $5(a + 2) + 6(a − 5)$ f $2(5t + 7) − 3(6 − 7t)$
   g $6(2x − 3) − (5x − 3)$ h $a(2a + 3) + a(3a + 4)$
   i $2x(5x + 3) + x(3 − 4x)$ j $7(a − 2) − (a − 2)$
   k $−y(5y −2) + y(3y +1)$ l $2t^2(3t + 4) + t^2(6 − t)$

7   Find the area of this shape in terms of x.

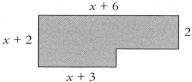

8   The width of a solid cuboid is y cm.
    Its length is three times its width and its height is 4 cm more than its width.
    Find an expression in terms of y for the surface area of the solid cuboid.

Multiplying two brackets together

Look at this rectangle. It has been split into four smaller rectangles.

The area of the large rectangle can be found by adding the areas of the four smaller rectangles.

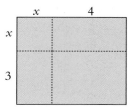

$$\begin{aligned}\text{Area} &= x \times x + x \times 4 + x \times 3 + 4 \times 3 \\ &= x^2 + 4x + 3x + 12 \\ &= x^2 + 7x + 12\end{aligned}$$

You could also work out the area directly.

The length of the rectangle is $(x + 4)$ and the width is $(x + 3)$.

So the area of the rectangle is $(x + 3)(x + 4)$.

The area is the same as before, so $(x + 3)(x + 4) = x^2 + 7x + 12$.

Here you are expanding two sets of brackets, $(x + 3)(x + 4)$. In this case you multiply one bracket by another bracket. You must multiply *each* term in the second bracket by *each* term in the first bracket. There are several possible methods and these are shown in the next example.

Expand $(x + 3)(x + 4)$.

SOLUTION

Method 1

×	x	$+3$
x	x^2	$3x$
$+4$	$4x$	12

Write the terms from the first bracket along the top of the grid and the terms from the second bracket down the side. Then fill in the cells by multiplying together the corresponding terms.

$$\begin{aligned}(x + 3)(x + 4) &= x^2 + 4x + 3x + 12 \\ &= x^2 + 7x + 12\end{aligned}$$

Add the terms from the body of the table.

Simplify by collecting like terms.

Method 2

Multiply each term in the second bracket separately by each term in the first bracket.

$$\begin{aligned}(x + 3)(x + 4) &= x(x + 4) + 3(x + 4) \\ &= x^2 + 4x + 3x + 12 \\ &= x^2 + 7x + 12\end{aligned}$$

Simplify by collecting like terms.

Method 3

Use the word **FOIL** to make sure you multiply each term in the second bracket by each term in the first bracket.

> First × First
> Outer × Outer
> Inner × Inner
> Last × Last

If you draw arrows to show the multiplications, you can think of a smiley face.

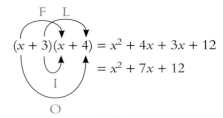

$$(x + 3)(x + 4) = x^2 + 4x + 3x + 12$$
$$= x^2 + 7x + 12$$

Any of these methods is acceptable, but method 3 is probably the quickest way of reaching the final expression.

As with expanding a single bracket, you need to take care when minus signs are involved.

EXAMPLE 3

Expand and simplify these.

a $(x + 7)(x - 2)$ b $(3y - 1)(2y - 5)$ c $(a + x)(b - x)$

SOLUTION

Use whichever method you prefer to ensure you multiply each term in the second bracket by each term in the first bracket.

a $(x + 7)(x - 2)$ $= x \times x + x \times (-2) + 7 \times x + 7 \times (-2)$
$= x^2 - 2x + 7x - 14$
$= x^2 + 5x - 14$

> Notice that the minus sign in front of the 2 stays with the 2.

b $(3y - 1)(2y - 5)$ $= 3y \times 2y + 3y \times (-5) + (-1) \times 2y + (-1) \times (-5)$
$= 6y^2 - 15y - 2y + 5$
$= 6y^2 - 17y + 5$

c $(a + x)(b - x)$ $= a \times b + a \times (-x) + x \times b + x \times (-x)$
$= ab - ax + bx - x^2$

> ax and bx are not like terms so you cannot simplify this any further.

Sometimes you will be asked to square a bracket, for example $(3a - 2)^2$. This means you must multiply the bracket by itself. A common mistake is simply to square each term. It is good practice to rewrite the squared bracket as the multiplication of two separate brackets.

EXAMPLE 4

Expand $(3a - 2)^2$.

$$(3a - 2)^2 = (3a - 2)(3a - 2)$$
$$= 9a^2 - 6a - 6a + 4$$
$$= 9a^2 - 12a + 4$$

Sometimes you will meet a pair of brackets multiplied by another factor, for example $5(2x - 1)(3x + 2)$. You can tackle this in two ways. *Either* you can multiply the brackets together and then multiply by the single factor (5 in this case) *or* you can multiply the first bracket by 5 first and then multiply the result by the second bracket. The answer is the same whichever method you use.

EXAMPLE 5

Expand $5(2x - 1)(3x + 2)$.

SOLUTION

Method 1

$$5(2x - 1)(3x + 2) = 5(6x^2 + 4x - 3x - 2)$$
$$= 5(6x^2 + x - 2)$$
$$= 30x^2 + 5x - 10$$

Method 2

$$5(2x - 1)(3x + 2) = (10x - 5)(3x + 2)$$
$$= 30x^2 + 20x - 15x - 10$$
$$= 30x^2 + 5x - 10$$

EXAMPLE 6

Expand $6 - (x - 2)^2$.

SOLUTION

Remember the order of operations (BODMAS). In this example you must expand the squared bracket first.

$$6 - (x - 2)^2 = 6 - (x - 2)(x - 2)$$
$$= 6 - (x^2 - 2x - 2x + 4)$$
$$= 6 - (x^2 - 4x + 4)$$
$$= 6 - x^2 + 4x - 4$$
$$= 2 - x^2 + 4x$$

Look at the equation below.

$$(p + 2)^2 + 3(p - 2) - 7p + 2 \equiv p^2$$

This is an example of an **identity**. The left-hand side will always equal the right-hand side, no matter what value is used for p. The symbol '$\equiv$' is used. It means 'is identical to'.

If you are asked to prove an identity, you need to show that the left-hand side simplifies to give the right-hand side.

EXAMPLE 7

Prove that $(p + 2)^2 + 3(p - 2) - 7p + 2 \equiv p^2$.

SOLUTION

$$(p + 2)(p + 2) + 3p - 6 - 7p + 2 = p^2 + 2p + 2p + 4 + 3p - 6 - 7p + 2$$
$$= p^2$$

Exercise 16.2

1 Expand and simplify these.
   a $(x + 2)(x + 4)$ b $(a + 5)(a + 3)$ c $(t - 7)(t - 1)$
   d $(y + 5)(y - 3)$ e $(u - 5)(u - 6)$ f $(p + 6)(p + 2)$
   g $(a - 2)(a - 1)$ h $(c + 3)(c - 3)$ i $(g - 7)(g - 9)$
   j $(a + x)(a - y)$ k $(r - 3)(r - 3)$ l $(c + d)(c - d)$

2 Expand and simplify these.
   a $(2x + 1)(3x - 2)$ b $(5a + 2)(a - 1)$ c $(3t + 5)(2t + 3)$
   d $(6e - 1)(2e + 1)$ e $(4y - 1)(4y - 1)$ f $(7k - 3)(7k + 3)$
   g $(3b - 2)(4b + 5)$ h $(6 + d)(4 - 3d)$ i $(2a + x)(3a - x)$
   j $(3p - 5q)(6p + q)$ k $(4 + 3x)(2 - x)$ l $(5y - 10)(6y - 5)$

3 Expand and simplify these.
   a $(x + 7)^2$ b $(4e - 3)^2$ c $(3d + 2)^2$
   d $(x - 1)^2$ e $4 + (2x - 1)^2$ f $10 - (5x - 3)^2$
   g $(2y + 1)^3$ h $6(2a - 3)(3a - 2)$ i $(x - 3)^2 + (x + 3)^2$
   j $(2a + 3)^2 - (a + 4)^2$ k $(x + 2)(x^2 - 3x + 5)$ l $(a - b)(a + b)(a - b)$

4 Find an expression for the area of a rectangle of length $(2x + 3)$ and width $(3x - 1)$.

5 Find an expression for the area of a triangle with base $(4a + 3)$ and perpendicular height $(6a - 2)$.

6 A picture measuring 40 cm by 30 cm is surrounded by a frame of width x cm. Find the area of the frame in terms of x.

7 Prove the identity $(x + 2)^2 - (x - 2)^2 \equiv 8x$.

8 For any even number n, prove that the product of it and the next two consecutive even numbers will be $n^3 + 6n^2 + 8n$.

You should now:

- be able to expand a single bracket
- be able to expand and simplify an expression with brackets
- be able to multiply two sets of brackets
- be able to square brackets
- be able to solve problems involving brackets (including proof of identities).

Summary exercise 16

1 Expand each of these.
 a $4(y + 3)$ b $2(3x - 1)$ c $-3(2a + 5)$ d $-(3y - 2)$
 e $6(7g + 3)$ f $-5(2 - 3p)$ g $x(6x + 7)$ h $y(6y + 1)$
 i $x(3x + 2y)$ j $-4c(c - 3)$ k $2k(-3 - 5k)$ l $7t^2(t - 5)$

2 Expand and simplify these.
 a $3 + 4(2n - 3)$ b $3 - x + 2(4 - 3x)$ c $4y^2 + y(3 + 2y)$
 d $x(3x - 1) - x$ e $5x^2 + 3(2x^2 - 3x)$ f $8 - (3a + 5) - 7a$
 g $2 - 3(5e - 3) + 2e$ h $4(3a - 2) + 2(3 - a)$ i $x(3x + 5) - 2x^2 - 5x$
 j $5(6 - 2g) - (3g + 5)$ k $-2y(3y + 1) + y(2y - 1)$ l $3 - 6p - p(2 + 3p)$

3 Expand and simplify these.
 a $(x - 3)(x + 6)$ b $(a + 6)(a + 7)$ c $(d + 5)(d + 3)$
 d $(2a + 3)(2a + 7)$ e $(3p + 5)(2p - 1)$ f $(10 + y)(3 - 2y)$
 g $4(3k - 1)(2k + 1)$ h $(a + 3)^2$ i $(5t + 3)^2$
 j $2(3e + 1)^2$ k $6 - (3y - 2)^2$ l $(2x + 1)^2 - (1 - 2x)^2$

4 A wooden rod is $(3x + 5)$ cm long and a second rod
 is $(2x - 3)$ cm long.
 a What is the difference between the two lengths?
 b If the two rods are joined together, what is the combined length?

5 Floor tiles are arranged as shown in the diagram opposite.
 The central square tile is surrounded by four identical
 rectangular tiles. Find the area of the central square tile.

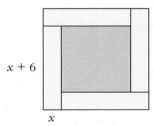

$x + 6$

x

Examination questions

Questions **1** to **5** are from examination papers where you
may not use a calculator.

1 Simplify $3(2c + d) + 2(c - 5d)$.

2 a Expand $4x(x^2 - 3)$.
 b Simplify $5(2c + 3) - 4(3c - 2)$.

3 Expand and simplify $(x - 3)(x + 5)$.

4 Show that $(2n + 3)(3n - 2) + 6(1 - n)(1 + n) \equiv 5n$.

5 Find the values of c and d for which
 $y^2 - 12y + c \equiv (y + d)^2$.

Questions **6** to **8** are from examination papers where you may use a
calculator.

Use 'Topic Tracker'
at www.ccea.org.uk
to find more exam
questions.

6 Multiply out and simplify $(x - 5)^2$.

7 Simplify $\dfrac{3(x - 1)^2}{(x - 1)}$.

8 Prove that $(x + 1)^2 - 2x - (x + 1) \equiv x^2 - x$.

CHAPTER 17

Linear equations

This chapter is about:

- solving linear equations, including equations with the variable on both sides, equations involving brackets and equations involving fractions.

You should already know:

- about the order of operations, BODMAS
- how to work with negative numbers
- how to work with fractions
- how to expand brackets
- the geometrical properties of rectangles and triangles
- how to find the perimeter and area of rectangles and triangles
- how to use Pythagoras' theorem
- the angle properties of straight lines, triangles and quadrilaterals
- how to work out speed, distance and time
- how to work with money
- how to calculate a percentage increase.

Solving simple equations

The general aim when solving an equation is to find a numerical value for the unknown quantity. This can be done by collecting all the numerical terms onto one side of the equation. You do this by performing the same operation on both sides of the equation.

EXAMPLE 1

Solve the equation $2a + 3 = 13$.

SOLUTION

$$2a + 3 = 13$$
$$2a + 3 - 3 = 13 - 3$$
$$2a = 10$$
$$\frac{2a}{2} = \frac{10}{2}$$
$$a = 5$$

> Subtract 3 from both sides.

> Divide both sides by 2.

 HINT

It is good practice to substitute the numerical result back into the original equation as a check.

EXAMPLE 2

Solve the equation $8 = 6 - 2x$.

SOLUTION

Method 1
$$8 = 6 - 2x$$
$$8 + 2x = 6 - 2x + 2x$$
$$8 - 8 + 2x = 6 - 8$$
$$2x = -2$$
$$\frac{2x}{2} = -\frac{-2}{2}$$
$$x = -1$$

Add $2x$ to both sides. This makes the x term positive, which is easier to work with.

Subtract 8 from both sides.

Divide both sides by 2.

Method 2
$$8 = 6 - 2x$$
$$8 - 6 = 6 - 6 - 2x$$
$$2 = -2x$$
$$\frac{2}{-2} = \frac{-2x}{-2}$$
$$-1 = x$$
$$x = -1$$

Subtract 6 from both sides.

Divide both sides by -2.

It is good practice to give the answer with the variable first.

If you use this method, you must take great care with the manipulation of the negative numbers.

EXAMPLE 3

Solve the equation $-12 = 3x + 3$.

SOLUTION

$$-12 = 3x + 3$$
$$-12 - 3 = 3x$$
$$-15 = 3x$$
$$-\frac{15}{3} = x$$
$$-5 = x$$
$$x = -5$$

It is not necessary to show all your working.

EXAMPLE 4

Solve the equation $5p - 2 = 12$.

SOLUTION

$$5p - 2 = 12$$
$$5p = 12 + 2$$
$$5p = 14$$
$$p = \frac{14}{5}$$
$$p = 2\frac{4}{5}$$

Exercise 17.1

Solve these equations.

1 $5a + 7 = 32$	2 $x + 9 = 20$	3 $x - 2 = -5$	4 $2a - 3 = 1$
5 $3e - 1 = 1$	6 $7y + 12 = -2$	7 $4 + 3y = 12$	8 $8 = 5a + 1$
9 $0 = 1 - 2x$	10 $9p - 4 = 2$	11 $5y + 3 = -2$	12 $-2 = 5t + 3$
13 $14e + 4 = 10$	14 $3 - 6d = 1$	15 $9k - 2 = 5$	16 $12 - y = 5$
17 $-45 = 3x + 3$	18 $100 = 40 - 2a$	19 $6x + 3 = -2$	20 $4p - 3 = 7$
21 $6k - 3 = -12$	22 $0 = 5 - 2t$	23 $-6 - 4r = -2$	24 $-4a - 2 = -5$

Equations with the variable on both sides

If an equation has the variable on both sides, then all the variable terms need to be collected onto one side of the equation and all the numerical values need to be collected onto the other side. It is usual to collect the variable terms onto the side which will mean that the final variable term will be positive.

EXAMPLE 5

Solve the equation $8a + 2 = 5a + 8$.

SOLUTION

$$8a + 2 = 5a + 8$$
$$8a - 5a + 2 = 5a - 5a + 8$$
$$3a + 2 = 8$$
$$3a + 2 - 2 = 8 - 2$$
$$3a = 6$$
$$\frac{3a}{3} = \frac{6}{3}$$
$$a = 2$$

> Subtract $5a$ from both sides.

> Subtract 2 from both sides.

> Divide both sides by 3.

> **HINT**
> Again, it is good practice to check the numerical answer by substituting it back into the original equation.
> $8 \times 2 + 2 = 18$ $5 \times 2 + 8 = 18$.
> Both sides are equal, as required.

EXAMPLE 6

Solve the equation $4x + 7 = 10 - 2x$.

SOLUTION

$$4x + 7 = 10 - 2x$$
$$4x + 2x = 10 - 7$$
$$6x = 3$$
$$x = \frac{3}{6}$$
$$x = \frac{1}{2}$$

> Again, it is not necessary to show all your working. Here, in order to get all the variable terms on one side and all the numerical terms on the other, $2x$ has been added to both sides and 7 has been subtracted from both sides. The '$-2x + 2x$' and '$7 - 7$' parts of the calculation have not been written down.

EXAMPLE 7

Solve the equation $6 - 3y = 2y + 8$.

SOLUTION

$$6 - 3y = 2y + 8$$
$$6 - 8 = 2y + 3y$$
$$-2 = 5y$$
$$\frac{-2}{5} = y$$
$$y = -\frac{2}{5}$$

Here the variable terms are collected onto the right-hand side so that the overall variable term will be positive.

EXAMPLE 8

Solve the equation $12k - 3 + 2k = 5k - 21$.

SOLUTION

$$12k - 3 + 2k = 5k - 21$$
$$12k + 2k - 5k = -21 + 3$$
$$9k = -18$$
$$k = -\frac{18}{9}$$
$$k = -2$$

Exercise 17.2

Solve these equations.

1   $6x + 4 = 5x + 2$

2   $4a - 2 = 2a + 3$

3   $5t - 3 = 2t$

4   $6e - 3 = e + 7$

5   $3y - 2 = y - 8$

6   $7k - 3 = 2k + 1$

7   $5 + 3y = 2y + 1$

8   $4z - 3 = 6z + 1$

9   $8h - 1 = 4h - 1$

10   $3e + 11 = 2 - 3e$

11   $7 - 2t = t + 4$

12   $1 - 5g = 2g$

13   $9j + 3 = j - 1$

14   $7x - 5 = x$

15   $20 - 2e = 3e - 20$

16   $8d + 3 = 9d + 1$

17   $4t + 3 - 2t = 1 + 3t$

18   $3 + 2e - 7 = 5e - 4$

19   $6 + 3g + 2 = 3 + 8g$

20   $6a - 3 - 5a = 4 + 2a$

21   $5y - 1 = 4y - 1 + 2y$

22   $7 - 3e = 5 - 2e$

23   $4 - x = 14 - 2x$

24   $10 - x = 3 - 2x + 4 - 2x$

25   $5a = 8 - 2a - 5$

26   $3e + 5 = -5 + 2e - 1$

Equations with brackets

If an equation has one or more sets of brackets, these should be expanded first. Then you solve the equation in the usual way.

EXAMPLE 9

Solve the equation $3(2x - 1) = 2(x - 3)$.

$$3(2x - 1) = 2(x - 3)$$
$$6x - 3 = 2x - 6$$
$$6x - 2x = -6 + 3$$
$$4x = -3$$
$$x = -\frac{3}{4}$$

EXAMPLE 10

Solve the equation $2 + 5(3t - 1) = 1 + 4(t - 2)$.

SOLUTION

$$2 + 5(3t - 1) = 1 + 4(t - 2)$$
$$2 + 15t - 5 = 1 + 4t - 8$$
$$15t - 4t = 1 - 8 - 2 + 5$$
$$11t = -4$$
$$t = -\frac{4}{11}$$

HINT

Remember BODMAS: expand the brackets first. Do *not* add the 2 and the 5.

EXAMPLE 11

Solve the equation $6y - (2 + 3y) + 2y = 1 - 5y$.

SOLUTION

$$6y - (2 + 3y) + 2y = 1 - 5y$$
$$6y + (-1)(2 + 3y) + 2y = 1 - 5y$$
$$6y - 2 - 3y + 2y = 1 - 5y$$
$$6y - 3y + 2y + 5y = 1 + 2$$
$$10y = 3$$
$$y = \frac{3}{10}$$

HINT

Remember that you can insert a 1 here to help in this expansion (see Chapter 16).

EXAMPLE 12

Solve the equation $5(2x - 1) + 3x = 10 - 2x$.

SOLUTION

$$5(2x - 1) + 3x = 10 - 2x$$
$$10x - 5 + 3x = 10 - 2x$$
$$10x + 3x + 2x = 10 + 5$$
$$15x = 15$$
$$x = \frac{15}{15}$$
$$x = 1$$

EXAMPLE 13

Solve the equation $4(2a + 3) - 2(a + 4) = -6$.

SOLUTION

$$4(2a + 3) - 2(a + 4) = -6$$
$$8a + 12 - 2a - 8 = -6$$
$$8a - 2a = -6 - 12 + 8$$
$$6a = -10$$
$$a = -\frac{10}{6}$$
$$a = -1\frac{2}{3}$$

Exercise 17.3

Solve these equations.

1. $3(2x + 1) + 2(4x + 2) = 21$
2. $2(4a + 3) + 3(2a + 1) = 23$
3. $3(2a + 3) = 2(2a - 1)$
4. $5(5e - 3) - 10 = 5$
5. $2 + 3(3e + 2) - 4e = -10$
6. $6(5w - 2) = 3(2w + 1) - 3$
7. $4x - 2(x - 3) = 6x + 3(2x + 2)$
8. $7(2k - 3) = 13 - 3k$
9. $3(c + 1) = 4 - (c - 3)$
10. $7y = 3y - (y + 20)$
11. $6(1 - t) + 5 = 3(2 - t) - 4$
12. $8 - (h + 1) = 9 - (2h - 1)$
13. $3(2a + 5) + 8(3a - 1) = 24$
14. $8 - (4e + 3) = e + 3(5 - 2e)$
15. $2 + 3(1 - 2e) = 4e - 2$
16. $4 - 6y = 4(2y + 6)$
17. $1 - (x + 10) - 10 = 10 - 2x$
18. $3(y - 2) + (y + 2) = 8$

Equations with fractions

If an equation has two fractions equal to each other then the method of **cross-multiplication** can be used to solve the equation. This means that you multiply each numerator by the denominator of the other fraction. This removes the fractions from the equation, which can then be solved in the usual way.

It is important to remember that you only use this method when you are working with an equation that contains *only two fractions* which are equal. Some equations may involve other terms, and some preliminary rearrangement may be necessary before cross-multiplying.

EXAMPLE 14

Solve the equation $\dfrac{x}{3} = \dfrac{2}{5}$.

SOLUTION

$$\frac{x}{3} \diagup\!\!\!\!\diagdown \frac{2}{5}$$
$$5x = 6$$
$$x = \frac{6}{5}$$
$$x = 1\frac{1}{5}$$

HINT

The numerator of the first fraction is multiplied by the denominator of the second and is equated to the numerator of the second fraction multiplied by the denominator of the first — forming an X shape across the equation.

The cross-multiplying method used in Example 14 is effectively a short-hand way of multiplying both sides of the equation by 3 to remove the fraction on the left-hand side and then multiplying both sides of the resulting equation by 5 to remove the fraction on the right-hand side.

$$\frac{x}{3} = \frac{2}{5}$$

$$3 \times \frac{x}{3} = 3 \times \frac{2}{5}$$

$$x = \frac{6}{5}$$

$$5 \times x = 5 \times \frac{6}{5}$$

$$5x = 6$$

You can see that you did not, in fact, need to get rid of the fraction on the right-hand side in this case. In cases such as the next examples, however, the method of cross-multiplication is helpful.

EXAMPLE 15

Solve the equation $\frac{5}{2c} = -\frac{1}{4}$.

SOLUTION

$$\frac{5}{2c} = -\frac{1}{4}$$
$$20 = -2c$$
$$2c = -20$$
$$c = -\frac{20}{2}$$
$$c = -10$$

EXAMPLE 16

Solve the equation $\frac{5}{x+1} = \frac{10}{x}$.

SOLUTION

$$\frac{5}{x+1} = \frac{10}{x}$$
$$5x = 10(x+1)$$
$$5x = 10x + 10$$
$$-10 = 10x - 5x$$
$$-10 = 5x$$
$$-\frac{10}{5} = x$$
$$-2 = x$$
$$x = -2$$

 HINT
Brackets are used here because the numerator of the second fraction, 10, must be multiplied by *all* of the denominator of the first fraction, $x + 1$.

EXAMPLE 17

Solve the equation $\frac{8}{x} - 2 = 6$.

SOLUTION

$$\frac{8}{x} - 2 = 6$$

$$\frac{8}{x} = -6 + 2$$

$$\frac{8}{x} = -\frac{4}{1}$$

$$8 = -4x$$

$$4x = -8$$

$$x = -\frac{8}{4}$$

$$x = -2$$

> **HINT**
>
> This equation requires some rearrangement before cross-multiplying. The -2 is brought to the right and made positive, and then the right-hand side is simplified. This leaves two fractions equal to each other, which can then be cross-multiplied.

Exercise 17.4

Solve these equations.

1 $\dfrac{2x}{3} = 4$

2 $\dfrac{3a}{5} = 6$

3 $\dfrac{3y}{4} = 45$

4 $\dfrac{8}{x} = 2$

5 $\dfrac{30}{5x} = 6$

6 $-\dfrac{2}{x} = 4$

7 $\dfrac{a}{7} = \dfrac{5}{8}$

8 $\dfrac{7}{2a} = \dfrac{4}{5}$

9 $\dfrac{3x}{4} = \dfrac{5}{2}$

10 $-\dfrac{2a}{3} = \dfrac{7}{2}$

11 $\dfrac{5x}{4} = -20$

12 $\dfrac{6}{x} + 1 = 2$

13 $2 - \dfrac{a}{3} = 8$

14 $\dfrac{2a}{3} + 3 = 10$

15 $\dfrac{2x + 1}{5} = 1$

16 $-\dfrac{x}{3} + 1 = -1$

17 $12 = 3 + \dfrac{x}{4}$

18 $\dfrac{3x + 1}{5} = \dfrac{2x}{3}$

19 $\dfrac{2 + p}{3} = \dfrac{3p - 2}{2}$

20 $\dfrac{18}{x - 2} = 10$

21 $2(3x - 1) = \dfrac{5x}{3}$

22 $\dfrac{8a - 4}{3} + 15 = 7$

More complicated equations with fractions

For more complicated equations with fractions, it is more suitable to multiply the whole equation through by the common denominator of all the fractional parts, in order to remove the fractions from the equation.

EXAMPLE 18

Solve the equation $\frac{1}{2}(3a + 1) + \frac{3}{4}(2a - 1) = 4\frac{1}{4}$.

SOLUTION

$$\frac{1}{2}(3a + 1) + \frac{3}{4}(2a - 1) = 4\frac{1}{4}$$

$$2(3a + 1) + 3(2a - 1) = 17$$

$$6a + 2 + 6a - 3 = 17$$

$$12a = 17 - 2 + 3$$

$$12a = 18$$

$$a = \frac{18}{12}$$

$$a = 1\frac{1}{2}$$

> **HINT**
>
> Multiply the *whole* equation by 4 to eliminate the fractions, as 4 is the lowest common multiple of 2 and 4 (the denominators).

EXAMPLE 19

Solve the equation $\frac{1}{4}(x - 1) - \frac{1}{5}(2x - 3) = \frac{1}{20}$.

SOLUTION

$$\frac{1}{4}(x - 1) - \frac{1}{5}(2x - 3) = \frac{1}{20}$$
$$5(x - 1) - 4(2x - 3) = 1$$
$$5x - 5 - 8x + 12 = 1$$
$$-5 + 12 - 1 = 8x - 5x$$
$$3x = 6$$
$$x = \frac{6}{3}$$
$$x = 2$$

 HINT

The lowest common multiple of 4, 5 and 20 is 20, so multiply the whole equation by 20.

EXAMPLE 20

Solve the equation $\frac{3(x + 1)}{4} - \frac{x}{3} = \frac{1}{12}$.

SOLUTION

$$\frac{3(x + 1)}{4} - \frac{x}{3} = \frac{1}{12}$$
$$9(x + 1) - 4x = 1$$
$$9x + 9 - 4x = 1$$
$$9x - 4x = 1 - 9$$
$$5x = -8$$
$$x = -\frac{8}{5}$$
$$x = -1\frac{3}{5}$$

Multiply through by 12.

Exercise 17.5

Solve these equations.

1. $\frac{1}{2}(2p + 1) - (3p + 2) = \frac{3}{4}$

2. $\frac{2(3a - 1)}{3} + \frac{4a - 2}{5} = -1$

3. $\frac{1}{5}(4x + 2) - \frac{1}{2}(2x - 1) = 10$

4. $\frac{2x + 1}{8} - \frac{x - 1}{3} = \frac{5}{24}$

5. $\frac{2}{3}(a + 6) + \frac{3}{4}(2a - 1) + 1\frac{1}{12} = 0$

6. $\frac{1}{2}(4p + 3) + 5 - p = 4\frac{1}{2}$

7. $\frac{3(2k + 1)}{2} - \frac{k - 2}{3} = 14\frac{1}{6}$

8. $\frac{3}{5}(5x + 1) - \frac{2}{3}(2x + 3) = -3\frac{1}{15}$

Forming equations to solve problems

Equations can be used to solve a wide variety of mathematical problems. The following steps should be taken.

- Use a suitable letter to represent the unknown quantity.
- Write the given mathematical information in the form of an equation.
- Solve the equation.

- Use the solution of the equation to answer the original question.
- Check that your answer fits the *original mathematical information*.

Checking your solution against the original information you were given is more reliable than substituting into your equation, as you might have made an error in forming the equation.

EXAMPLE 21

I think of a number, treble it, subtract 4 and double the result.
My final answer is 28.
What was the number?

SOLUTION

Use x to represent the original number.

Then $2(3x - 4) = 28$

$$6x - 8 = 28$$
$$6x = 28 + 8$$
$$6x = 36$$
$$x = \frac{36}{6}$$
$$x = 6$$

The original number was 6.

Build up the equation using the information you are given. Note that you need to use brackets to show that the *result* of trebling the number then subtracting 4 is doubled.

Check
Treble 6 is 18, subtract 4 gives 14, double it gives 28, as required.

EXAMPLE 22

Find the perimeter of this rectangle.

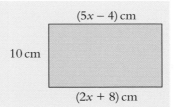

$(5x - 4)$ cm

10 cm

$(2x + 8)$ cm

SOLUTION

Opposite sides of a rectangle are equal so

$$5x - 4 = 2x + 8$$
$$5x - 2x = 8 + 4$$
$$3x = 12$$
$$x = \frac{12}{3}$$
$$x = 4$$
Perimeter $= 16 + 10 + 16 + 10$
$$= 52 \text{ cm}$$

Check
Top length is $5 \times 4 - 4 = 16$ cm and bottom length is
$2 \times 4 + 8 = 16$ cm. These are equal, as required.

Note that the question asks you to find the *perimeter* of the rectangle, not just the value of x.

EXAMPLE 23

Danielle has five times as many sweets as Nicola.
If Danielle gives Nicola 16 sweets, they will each have the same number.
How many sweets does each girl have to start with?

SOLUTION

Use x to represent Nicola's starting number.
Then Danielle has $5x$ to start with.
Nicola gains 16 so she now has $x + 16$.
Danielle gives away 16 so she now has $5x - 16$.

It is good practice to use a letter for the *smaller* quantity, as it makes the equation easier to solve.

They now have the same number so
$$5x - 16 = x + 16$$
$$5x - x = 16 + 16$$
$$4x = 32$$
$$x = \frac{32}{4}$$
$$x = 8$$
At the start Nicola has 8 sweets and Danielle has 40.

> **Check**
> Danielle has 40 and gives away 16, so she now has 24.
> Nicola has 8 and gains 16, so she now has 24.
> They now have the same number of sweets.

EXAMPLE 24

The sides of a rectangle are 5 m and $(x + 2)$ m. The diagonal is $(x + 3)$ m. Find the area of the rectangle.

SOLUTION

By Pythagoras' theorem,
$$(x + 3)^2 = 5^2 + (x + 2)^2$$
$$x^2 + 6x + 9 = 25 + x^2 + 4x + 4$$
$$x^2 - x^2 + 6x - 4x = 25 + 4 - 9$$
$$2x = 20$$
$$x = \frac{20}{2}$$
$$x = 10$$
The sides are 5 m and 12 m.
Area $= 5 \times 12 = 60\,\text{m}^2$.

> **Check**
> $5^2 + (x + 2)^2 = 25 + 12^2 = 25 + 144 = 169 = 13^2 = (x + 3)^2$

EXAMPLE 25

In 18 years' time, Mrs Jones will be twice as old as she was 7 years ago. Find her present age.

SOLUTION

Use a to represent Mrs Jones's present age.
In 18 years' time she will be $a + 18$.
7 years ago she was $a - 7$.
$$a + 18 = 2(a - 7)$$
$$a + 18 = 2a - 14$$
$$18 + 14 = 2a - a$$
$$32 = a$$
Mrs Jones's present age is 32.

> **Check**
> $32 + 18 = 50$ which is $2 \times (32 - 7)$.

Exercise 17.6

Solve each of these problems by forming and solving a suitable equation.

1   When 8 is subtracted from 3 times a certain number, the result is 19.
    What is the number?

2   The sum of three consecutive odd numbers is 195.
    Find the numbers.

3   I buy two cans of lemonade costing 54p each, and several packets of
    crisps costing 32p each.
    I get 64p change from £3.
    How many packets of crisps did I buy?

4   Find the size of each angle on the line.

5   Jack is 3 years younger than Martin.
    Rob is 7 years older than Jack.
    The total age of the three boys is 25.
    Find the age of each boy.

6   Find the perimeter of this equilateral triangle.

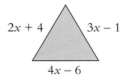

7   The length of a rectangle is 3 cm more than 4 times its width.
    Given that the perimeter of the rectangle is 51 cm, find its area.

8   The difference between two numbers is 17.
    Find the numbers if their sum is 67.

9   A train has 180 passengers on board.
    At the first stop x passengers get off and 24 get on.
    At the second stop half of the passengers get off and 40 get on.
    There are now 134 passengers on board.
    How many passengers got off at the first stop?

10 A man jogs to the shop and back in half an hour.
    On the way he jogs at 4 m/s and on the way back he jogs at 5 m/s.
    Ignoring any time spent in the shop, find the distance to the shop.

11 A woman's salary increases by 15% after the first year, and then by a
    further 10% after the second year.
    If her total salary for the three years amounts to £81 960, find her
    starting salary.

12 Find the length of each side of this right-angled triangle.

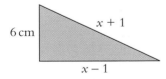

13 The area of the rectangle shown here exceeds the area of the square
    by 6 cm². Find k.

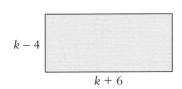

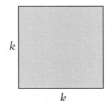

Summary exercise 17

1 Solve each equation to find x.
     a $x - 7 = -1$ **b** $4 - 3x = 9$ **c** $8 = 2x - 7$
     d $4x + 8 = 2$ **e** $-2 - x = -1$ **f** $5x - 2 = 0$

2 Solve each equation to find y.
     a $3y - 2 = 4y + 7$ **b** $8y + 3 = 2y - 9$
     c $5 + 3y = 5y + 2$ **d** $3 - 7y = 8 + 2y - 1$
     e $1 + 10y = 12y - 1$ **f** $9 - y = 4y - 3$

3 Solve each equation to find w.
     a $2 + 3(2w - 1) = 10$ **b** $6(5w + 2) - 3(2w + 3) = 4$
     c $-8 - 4(5 - 2w) = 2(1 - 6w)$ **d** $10 - 3(4w + 1) - 2w = 5$
     e $5(3w + 2) - 2w = 9$ **f** $10 - 3w = 4 + 2(2w + 1)$

4 Solve each equation to find k.
     a $\dfrac{3k}{2} = 6$ **b** $\dfrac{8}{5k} = -2$

     c $\dfrac{2k}{3} + 4 = 1$ **d** $\dfrac{k + 3}{2} = \dfrac{3k}{4}$

     e $\dfrac{3k - 1}{2} + \dfrac{3}{4} = 1\frac{1}{4}$ **f** $\dfrac{2}{3}(4k + 1) - \dfrac{3}{4}(2k - 1) = \dfrac{1}{2}$

5 The sum of five consecutive whole numbers is 615.
   Find the middle number.

6 In an isosceles triangle the two equal angles are each 10 degrees less
   than double the third angle.
   Find the size of each angle.

7 Find the value of w such that the areas of the two shaded rectangles
   are equal.

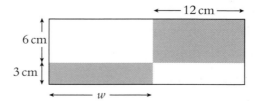

8 I travel on a bus for half an hour at an average speed of
   $(2x - 10)$ km/h, and then on a train for 2 hours at an average speed
   of $(2x + 10)$ km/h. My total journey is 165 km.
   Find the average speed of the train.

9 Find four consecutive multiples of 3 which have a sum of 474.

10 A child's money box has 50 coins in it, with a total value of £7.20.
The coins are either 5p, 10p or 20p.
There are twice as many 10p coins as 5p coins.
How many 20p coins are there?

Examination questions

Use 'Topic Tracker' at www.ccea.org.uk to find more exam questions.

Questions **1** to **4** are from examination papers where you may not use a calculator.

1 Solve the equation $6x - 2 = 2x + 8$.
Show your working.

2 a Solve $5(x - 3) = 20$.
b Solve $8y + 6 = 7 - 2y$.

3 Solve the equation $\frac{1}{4}(2x - 1) + \frac{1}{2}(3x - 2) = 2\frac{1}{4}$.

Show your working.
A solution by trial and improvement will not be accepted.

4 Write an equation and solve it to find the size of angle $x°$ in the quadrilateral.
Show your working.

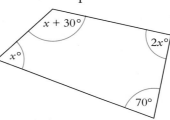

Questions **5** to **10** are from examination papers where you may use a calculator.

5 Solve $3(2x + 1) = 4(x - 3)$.

6 Solve $\frac{2(x - 1)}{3} - \frac{3(2x - 3)}{5} = 1$.

A solution by trial and improvement will not be accepted.
Show your working clearly.

7 Solve $\frac{1}{5}(2x + 1) - \frac{2}{3}(x - 5) = 5$.

Show your working.
A solution by trial and improvement will not be accepted.

8 Solve
a $7x - 2 = 19$
b $\frac{1}{2}(x + 3) - \frac{1}{5}(x - 4) = 5$

9 Sam bought 15 bottles of water at x pence each and 4 bottles of sports drinks at 80 pence each. The total cost was £12.50.
Write down an equation in x for this.
Solve your equation to find the cost of a bottle of water.

10 Joel bought 3 yoghurts at x pence each and 2 cartons of fruit juice at $2x$ pence each. He got £1.85 change from £5.
Write down an equation in terms of x and solve it to find the value of x.

Sequences

This chapter is about:

- continuing sequences
- generating sequences
- finding the rule for linear sequences
- finding the rule for quadratic sequences
- using a counter example.

You should already know:

- how to solve simple linear equations
- how to substitute into an algebraic expression
- how to expand brackets.

Continuing sequences

A **sequence** is a list of **terms** which have a special pattern or relationship between them. You have already met some special sequences.

1, 4, 9, 16, 25, ... is the sequence of *square numbers*
1, 8, 27, 64, 125, ... is the sequence of *cube numbers*
3, 6, 9, 12, 15, ... is a sequence of the *multiples of 3*
2, 3, 5, 7, 11, ... is the sequence of *prime numbers*

Once the pattern for a sequence has been recognised it can be used to find subsequent terms.

EXAMPLE 1

For each of the following sequences, give a rule in words for the sequence, and use the rule to find the next three terms.

a   3, 7, 11, 15, ...   b   2, 6, 18, 54, ...
c   32, 16, 8, 4, ...   d   1, 1, 2, 3, 5, ...

SOLUTION

a   3   7   11   15   ...
    +4   +4   +4   +4

Each term is found by adding 4 to the previous term.
The next three terms are:

15 + 4 = 19
19 + 4 = 23
23 + 4 = 27

b

Each term is found by multiplying the previous term by 3.
The next three terms are:

$54 \times 3 = 162$
$162 \times 3 = 486$
$486 \times 3 = 1458$

c
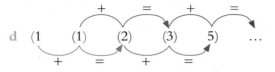

Each term is found by dividing the previous term by 2.
The next three terms are:

$4 \div 2 = 2$
$2 \div 2 = 1$
$1 \div 2 = \frac{1}{2}$

d (1   (1)   (2)   (3)   5)   ...

This sequence is known as the Fibonacci sequence.

Each term is found by adding the two previous terms.
The next three terms are:

$3 + 5 = 8$
$5 + 8 = 13$
$8 + 13 = 21$

If you are only given the first few terms of a sequence, it is not always possible to find its rule. A particular rule may apply to the first few terms but not to later terms. For example, a sequence beginning 1, 2, 4, … could be part of the sequence 1, 2, 4, 8, 16, 32, … (where each term is found by doubling the previous term) or it could be part of the sequence 1, 2, 4, 7, 11, 16, … (where each term is found by adding 1 more than was previously added).

The difference method

If the pattern in a sequence is not easily recognised, the **difference method** can be used to find further terms. This involves finding the differences between successive terms. If the differences between the terms are not the same, you then find the **second differences,** which are the differences between the first differences. You can continue to find third or fourth differences if necessary until the differences are the same. You can use the patterns in the differences to find subsequent terms in the sequence.

EXAMPLE 2

Find the next two terms in the sequence 6, 7, 11, 18, 28, … .

SOLUTION

Find the difference between the two numbers above: $7 - 6 = 1$.

6   7   11   18   28   41   57
  1   4   7   10   13   16
    3   3   3   3   3

To find subsequent terms, work from the bottom and continue the sequences.
The second differences are all 3 so add 3 to continue the sequence of first differences: $10 + 3 = 13$ and $13 + 3 = 16$.
Add the first differences to the terms of the sequence: $28 + 13 = 41$ and $41 + 16 = 57$.

The first differences are not the same so continue the process, finding the difference between the two numbers above: $4 - 1 = 3$.

The next two terms are 41 and 57.

EXAMPLE 3

Find the next two terms in the sequence 1, 5, 10, 16, 23, … .

SOLUTION

1   5   10   16   23   31   40
    4   5   6   7   8   9
        1   1   1   1   1

The next two terms are 31 and 40.

EXAMPLE 4

Find the next two terms in the sequence 0, 1, −2, −6, −8, … .

SOLUTION

0   1   −2   −6   −8   −5   6
    1   −3   −4   −2   3   11
       −4   −1   2   5   8
          3   3   3   3

Care must be taken with the negative differences here.

You need to continue to the third differences here because the second differences are not the same.

The next two terms are −5 and 6.

Exercise 18.1

1. Find the missing number in each of these sequences.
   a 2, 4, …, 8, 10, 12
   b 1, 4, 9, 16, 25, …, 49, 64
   c 1, 2, 4, 8, …, 32, 64
   d 4, 8, 12, 16, …, 24, 28
   e 160, 80, …, 20, 10

2. Write down a rule in words which generates each of these sequences.
   a 2, 7, 12, 17, 22, …
   b 20, 10, 5, $2\frac{1}{2}$, …
   c 10, 7, 4, 1, −2, …
   d 3, 9, 27, 81, 243, …
   e 10, 9, 7, 4, 0, −5, …

3. Write down the next two terms in each of these sequences.
   a 2, 10, 18, 26, 34, …
   b 6, 11, 17, 24, 32, …
   c 40, 36, 32, 28, 24, …
   d 95, 87, 79, 71, 63, …
   e 2, 5, 11, 20, 32, …
   f 10, 8, 5, 1, …
   g −5, −1, 3, 7, …
   h 120, 60, 30, 15, …
   i 9, 9, 11, 15, 21, …
   j 6, 11, 21, 36, …

4. Use the difference method to find the next three terms in each of these sequences.
   a 1, 5, 12, 25, 47, …
   b 2, 5, 10, 17, 26, …
   c 3, 10, 29, 66, 127, …
   d 2, 10, 30, 68, 130, …
   e −1, 4, 21, 56, 115, …
   f 9, 7, 7, 9, 13, 19, 27, …
   g −3, 3, 13, 27, 45, …
   h −4, 3, 22, 59, 120, …
   i 0, −1, 4, 27, 80, 175, …
   j −6, 6, 26, 54, 90, …

The rule for the nth term of a sequence

In all the examples in the previous section, each term was found from the preceding term by some pattern or relationship. The disadvantage of this is that to find the 100th term of a sequence, say, you need to know the 99th term. However, if you can find a *general* rule for a sequence, known as the rule for the nth term of the sequence, then this rule can be used to find *any* term without having to know the preceding term.

The rule for the nth term of a linear sequence

A **linear sequence** is one in which the differences between the terms (the **first differences**) are the same. It is called a *linear* sequence because, if the terms of the sequence were plotted on a graph, they would form a straight-line or linear graph. There is much similarity between the rule for the nth term of a linear sequence and the equation of a straight line. This will be discussed further in Chapter 25.

The rule for the nth term of a linear sequence is

$$n\text{th term} = an + b$$

where a is the difference between the terms.

To find b you substitute in any value of n and equate this with the corresponding term of the sequence. By solving the resulting equation, b can be found. An alternative method for finding b is to work back one term from the first term of the original sequence.

The rule for the nth term can be used to find any term in the sequence. Alternatively, given the value of a term in a sequence, you can use the rule to work out its position in the sequence.

EXAMPLE 5

Find the rule for the nth term of the sequence 4, 7, 10, 13, … and use it to find the 50th term of the sequence.

SOLUTION

The difference between the terms is 3 so $a = 3$.

nth term $= 3n + b$
1st term $= 3 \times 1 + b$

The 1st term is 4, so $4 = 3 + b$.
Solving this equation gives $b = 1$.

So the rule for the nth term is $3n + 1$.

The 50th term is $3 \times 50 + 1 = 150 + 1 = 151$.

> The 1st term is given by substituting $n = 1$ in the rule.

> Alternatively, having found $a = 3$, working back a term (to $n = 0$) gives 1, 4, 7, 10, 13, … .
> So $b = 1$.
> Hence the rule for the nth term is $3n + 1$, as before.

> **Check**
> 3rd term $= 3 \times 3 + 1 = 9 + 1 = 10$
> It is good practice to check your rule on one of the given terms of the sequence, to ensure it works properly, before using it to predict any further terms.

EXAMPLE 6

Find the rule for the nth term and the 10th term of the sequence 3, −2, −7, −12, −17, … .

SOLUTION

The difference between the terms is −5 so $a = -5$.

nth term $= -5n + b$
1st term $= -5 \times 1 + b$

The 1st term is 3, so $3 = -5 + b$.
Solving this equation gives $b = 8$.

So the rule for the nth term is $-5n + 8$.

The 10th term is $-5 \times 10 + 8 = -50 + 8 = -42$.

> Alternatively, b = 1st term − a
> = 3 − (−5)
> = 8

> **Check**
> 2nd term $= -5 \times 2 + 8 = -10 + 8 = -2$

EXAMPLE 7

Find the rule for the nth term of the sequence 6, 11, 16, 21, 26, … .
Also find the 20th term of the sequence.
Which term in the sequence will equal 601?

SOLUTION

The difference between the terms is 5 so $a = 5$.

nth term $= 5n + b$
1st term $= 5 \times 1 + b$

The 1st term is 6, so $6 = 5 + b$.
Solving this equation gives $b = 1$.

So the rule for the nth term is $5n + 1$.

$$
\begin{aligned}
\text{The 20th term} \quad &= 5 \times 20 + 1 \\
&= 100 + 1 \\
&= 101
\end{aligned}
$$

To find which term equals 601, you need to find the value of n in
$5n + 1 = 601$

$$
\begin{aligned}
5n &= 601 - 1 \\
5n &= 600 \\
n &= \frac{600}{5} \\
n &= 120
\end{aligned}
$$

> This involves solving a simple linear equation, as covered in Chapter 17.

Hence 601 is the 120th term of the sequence.

The rule for the nth term of a quadratic sequence

A **quadratic sequence** is one in which the differences between the terms are not the same, but the differences *between the differences* (the **second differences**) *are* the same. It is called a *quadratic* sequence because, if the terms of the sequence were plotted on a graph, they would form a curve known as a quadratic curve. This will be discussed further in Chapter 26.

Look at the sequence of square numbers, which can be represented symbolically as n^2.

$$
\begin{array}{ccccccc}
1 & & 4 & & 9 & & 16 & & 25 & & \ldots \\
& 3 & & 5 & & 7 & & 9 & & \\
& & 2 & & 2 & & 2 & & &
\end{array}
$$

> The first differences.

> The second differences.

When the differences are the same (here it is the second differences), that difference is called the **common difference**. Half the common difference gives the coefficient of the n^2. For the square numbers this is 1 and so the rule for the nth term is $1n^2$, which is written as n^2.

This introduces a method for finding the nth term for any quadratic sequence.

The rule for the nth term of a quadratic sequence is

$$n\text{th term} = an^2 + bn + c$$

where a is half the common difference.

Once a is known, you can find the values of b and c by writing out the terms of the sequence an^2, and subtracting them from the original sequence. The resulting sequence will be a linear sequence of the form $bn + c$, from which b and c can be found in the usual way. Then you combine the two parts to give the rule for the nth term in the form $an^2 + bn + c$.

An alternative method for finding b and c is to use the fact that c is the value of the term before the first term of the original sequence. Then b can be found by subtraction because $a + b$ is the value you obtain when you work back from the first differences of the sequence.

EXAMPLE 8

Find the rule for the nth term of the sequence $5, 10, 17, 26, 37, \ldots$.

SOLUTION

Method 1

$$
\begin{array}{ccccccccc}
5 & & 10 & & 17 & & 26 & & 37 \\
& 5 & & 7 & & 9 & & 11 & \\
& & 2 & & 2 & & 2 & &
\end{array}
$$

a is half the second difference, so $a = 1$.

The original sequence is
Subtracting the sequence $1 \times n^2$
results in the linear sequence
This sequence follows the rule $2n + 2$.

$$
\begin{array}{rccccc}
 & 5 & 10 & 17 & 26 & 37 \\
- & 1 & 4 & 9 & 16 & 25 \\
\hline
 & 4 & 6 & 8 & 10 & 12
\end{array}
$$

> Using the rule for the nth term for a linear sequence.

Hence the rule for the nth term of the quadratic sequence is $n^2 + 2n + 2$.

> **Check**
> 3rd term $= 3^2 + 2 \times 3 + 2 = 9 + 6 + 2 = 17$

Method 2

Alternatively, having found $a = 1$, working back a term (to $n = 0$) gives:

$2, 5, 10, 17, 26, 37, \ldots$.

So $c = 2$.
1st term $= a + b + c = 1 + b + 2$
The 1st term is 5, so $5 = 1 + b + 2$.
Solving this equation gives $b = 2$.

Hence the rule for the nth term is $n^2 + 2n + 2$, as before.

EXAMPLE 9

Find the rule for the nth term and the 20th term in the sequence of triangular numbers $1, 3, 6, 10, 15, \ldots$.

SOLUTION

$$
\begin{array}{ccccccccc}
1 & & 3 & & 6 & & 10 & & 15 \\
& 2 & & 3 & & 4 & & 5 & \\
& & 1 & & 1 & & 1 & &
\end{array}
$$

$a = \frac{1}{2} \times 1 = \frac{1}{2}$

The original sequence is
Subtracting the sequence $\frac{1}{2} \times n^2$
results in the linear sequence

$$
\begin{array}{ccccc}
1 & 3 & 6 & 10 & 15 \\
0.5 & 2 & 4.5 & 8 & 12.5 \\
\hline
0.5 & 1 & 1.5 & 2 & 2.5
\end{array}
$$

which is a linear sequence with the rule $\frac{1}{2}n$.

Hence the rule for the nth term is $\frac{1}{2}n^2 + \frac{1}{2}n$.

> **Check**
> 4th term $= \frac{1}{2} \times 4^2 + \frac{1}{2} \times 4 = 8 + 2 = 10$

The 20th term is $\frac{1}{2} \times 20^2 + \frac{1}{2} \times 20 = 210$.

EXAMPLE 10

Find the rule for the nth term and hence the 10th term of the sequence
$-1, 5, 15, 29, 47, \ldots$.

SOLUTION

Using the alternative method and working back a term:

$$-3 \qquad -1 \qquad 5 \qquad 15 \qquad 29 \qquad 47$$
$$2 \qquad 6 \qquad 10 \qquad 14 \qquad 18$$
$$4 \qquad 4 \qquad 4 \qquad 4$$

So $a = \frac{1}{2} \times 4 = 2$ and $c = -3$.

nth term $= 2n^2 + bn - 3$

1st term $= 2 + b - 3$

The 1st term is -1, so $-1 = 2 + b - 3$.
Solving this equation gives $b = 0$.

So the rule for the nth term is $2n^2 - 3$. ◄

Check
4th term $= 2 \times 4^2 - 3 = 32 - 3 = 29$

The 10th term is $2 \times 10^2 - 3 = 200 - 3 = 197$.

Exercise 18.2

1 Find the rule for the nth term and the 20th term of each of these sequences.
  a 1, 5, 9, 13, 17, … $4n-3$ b 6, 4, 2, 0, −2, … $-2n+8$ c 12, 24, 36, 48, … $12n$
  d 5, 12, 19, 26, 33, … $7n-2$ e 2, 3.5, 5, 4.5, 6, … $1.5n+0.5$ f 13, 10, 7, 4, 1, … $-3n+16$
  g 7, 12, 17, 22, 27, … $5n+2$ h 10, 9, 8, 7, 6, … $-n+11$ i 100, 95, 90, 85, 80, … $-5n+105$
  j −3, −5, −7, −9, −11, … $-2n-1$

2 Find the rule for the nth term and the 10th term of each of these sequences.
  a 2, 5, 10, 17, 26, …   b 1, 3, 7, 13, 21, …   c 1, 10, 25, 46, 73, …
  d 6, 11, 18, 27, 38, …   e 4, 5, 4, 1, −4, −11, …   f −1, 2, 7, 14, 23, 34, …
  g 3, 19, 45, 81, 127, …   h 20, 80, 180, 320, 500, …   i 0, 3, 8, 15, 24, 35, …
  j 10, 9, 7, 4, 0, −5, …

3 Find the rule for the nth term, and hence the 15th term, of the sequence where the fourth
  term is 12, the fifth term is 14, the sixth term is 16 and the seventh term is 18.

4 Find the rule for the nth term, and hence the 100th term, of the
  sequence where the third term is 8, the fourth term is 11, the fifth
  term is 14 and the sixth term is 17.

5 Find the rule for the nth term, and hence the 12th term, of the
  sequence where the second term is 9, the third term is 20, the
  fourth term is 35 and the fifth term is 54.

6 Which term of the sequence 2, 8, 14, 20, 26, … will equal 98?

7 Which term of the sequence 40, 37, 34, 31, … will equal −29?

8 Show that the rule for the nth term of the sequence
  2, 6, 12, 20, 30, … can be represented by $n(n + 1)$.

Applying sequences to practical problems

Sequences can be used to solve a wide variety of mathematical problems. What may seem to be a very complex task can be split into simpler smaller steps for which the rules of sequences can be used.

EXAMPLE 11

In a group of people, each person must shake hands with every other person in the group.
How many handshakes will there be if there are 20 people in the group?

SOLUTION

Breaking this into simpler tasks:

if there is 1 person there will be 0 handshakes
if there are 2 people there will be 1 handshake
if there are 3 people there will be 3 handshakes
if there are 4 people there will be 6 handshakes, etc.

Now look at the sequence of the numbers of handshakes.

$$0 \qquad 1 \qquad 3 \qquad 6$$
$$\quad 1 \qquad 2 \qquad 3$$
$$\qquad 1 \qquad 1$$

This is a quadratic sequence with $a = \frac{1}{2}$.

$\frac{1}{2}n^2$ gives the sequence 0.5, 2, 4.5, 8, ...

Subtracting this from original sequence gives $-0.5, -1, -1.5, -2, ...$ which is the linear sequence with the rule $-\frac{1}{2}n$.

So the rule for the nth term is $\frac{1}{2}n^2 - \frac{1}{2}n$.

So for 20 people the number of handshakes will be

$$\frac{1}{2} \times 20^2 - \frac{1}{2} \times 20 = 190.$$

EXAMPLE 12

The diagram shows a sequence of squares, made from sticks.
One square needs four sticks, two squares need seven sticks, three squares need 10 sticks, etc.

    a   How many sticks will be needed for seven squares?
    b   Find a rule connecting the numbers of squares (S) and sticks (M).
    c   Use your rule to find how many sticks are needed to make 50 squares.
    d   How many squares can be formed using 223 sticks?

SOLUTION

    a   Continuing the sequence of sticks by using the rule 'add 3 to the previous term' gives 4, 7, 10, 13, 16, 19, 22.
       So 22 sticks are needed for 7 squares.

    b   This is a linear sequence with nth term $= 3n + 1$.
       Therefore $\qquad\qquad\qquad\qquad M = 3S + 1.$

> Notice how the rule for the nth term can be adapted to suit other variables.

c $M = 3S + 1$
    $M = 3 \times 50 + 1 = 151$ ← *Substitute $S = 50$.*

    151 sticks are needed for 50 squares.

d $M = 3S + 1$
            $223 = 3S + 1$ ← *Substitute $M = 223$.*
      $223 - 1 = 3S$
          $222 = 3S$
          $\dfrac{222}{3} = S$
          $74 = S$

    74 squares can be made with 223 sticks.

EXAMPLE 13

Prove that the numerical value of every term of the sequence below is 8.
       $3 \times 5 - 1 \times 7$
       $4 \times 6 - 2 \times 8$
       $5 \times 7 - 3 \times 9$
       $6 \times 8 - 4 \times 10$

SOLUTION

Taking each column of numbers as a separate sequence gives:

3, 4, 5, 6, … $n + 2$ ←
5, 6, 7, 8, … $n + 4$
1, 2, 3, 4, … n
7, 8, 9, 10, … $n + 6$

Combining the rules for the nth terms gives:

$(n + 2)(n + 4) - n(n + 6) \quad = n^2 + 6n + 8 - n^2 - 6n$
$\qquad\qquad\qquad\qquad\qquad = 8$, no matter what n is.

> If a sequence involves several sets of numbers, for example sequences of fractions or products, it is usually easier to find the rule for the nth term by considering each set of numbers as a *separate sequence* first, and then combining the rules for the nth terms.

EXAMPLE 14

Find a rule connecting n and K.

n	2	3	5	8
K	8	11	17	26

SOLUTION

It is important to realise here that the only two *successive* terms of the sequence that are given are term 2 and term 3. These have a difference of 3. This would lead to a first term of 5, a fourth term of 14, etc.

So the overall sequence is actually 5, 8, 11, 14, 17, 20, 23, 26, which is a linear sequence.

The difference between the terms is 3, so $a = 3$.

nth term $= 3n + b$
2nd term $= 3 \times 2 + b$

The second term is 8, so $8 = 6 + b$.
Solving this equation gives $b = 2$.

Hence $K = 3n + 2$.

Exercise 18.3

1 Towels are hung on a clothesline with pegs, as shown.
   a How many pegs are needed to hang 17 towels?
   b How many towels could be hung with 25 pegs?

2 A bucket contains $1000\,\text{cm}^3$ of water.
   Every second, $0.5\,\text{cm}^3$ of water leaks out from the bucket.
   Write an expression for the volume of water remaining in the
   bucket after t seconds.

3 A set of tables and chairs are arranged as shown.
   a How many chairs are needed for three tables arranged in a
      similar way?
   b Find a rule connecting the numbers of tables, T, and chairs, C.
   c How many chairs would be needed for 12 tables?
   d How many tables are used if 96 chairs are used?

4 a Find a rule connecting n and P.

n	2	5	6	10
P	5	17	21	37

   b Find a rule connecting n and T.

n	4	7	10	12
T	17	26	35	41

5 Find the rule for the nth term and the 20th term in each of these sequences.

   a $\dfrac{1}{2}, \dfrac{2}{3}, \dfrac{3}{4}, \dfrac{4}{5}, \ldots$ b $1 \times 1, 2 \times 4, 3 \times 9, 4 \times 16, \ldots$ c $1, \dfrac{4}{5}, \dfrac{6}{10}, \dfrac{8}{17}, \dfrac{10}{26}, \ldots$

6 Bricks are stacked vertically in 34 layers.
   If the bottom layer has 42 bricks and each layer above has one fewer
   brick in it, how many bricks are in the top layer?

7 What is the 30th triangular number?

8 A quadrilateral has two diagonals, a pentagon has five diagonals and a
   hexagon has nine diagonals.
   a Find a rule for the number of diagonals in a polygon with n sides.
   b Use the rule to find the number of diagonals in a 12-sided polygon.

9 Points are placed around the edge of a circle and each point is joined
   to every other point by a chord.
   In doing so, regions are also created within the circle.

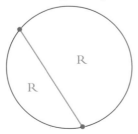
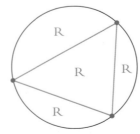
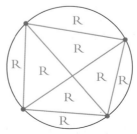

2 points are joined by
1 chord, creating 2
regions.

3 points are joined by
3 chords, creating 4
regions.

4 points are joined by
6 chords, creating 8
regions.

By drawing out the next three diagrams, confirm or reject (with the use of a counter example) each of these suggestions.

a For n points the number of chords is given by $0.5n^2 - 0.5n$.

b For n points the number of regions created is given by $2n^{-1}$.

10 A student states 'In any linear sequence the sum of the first four terms is always less than the sum of the fifth and sixth terms.' Are they correct?
Explain your answer.

> **You should now:**
>
> - recognise special number sequences
> - be able to describe the pattern for a sequence in words
> - be able to continue a sequence (including use of the difference method)
> - be able to write a sequence from given information
> - be able to find the nth term of a linear sequence
> - be able to find the nth term of a quadratic sequence
> - be able to solve a variety of problems using sequences
> - recognise the role of counterexamples in the context of sequences.

Summary exercise 18

1 Write down a rule in words which generates each of these sequences.
a 35, 30, 24, 17, ...   b 12, 14, 18, 24, ...   c 4, 4, 7, 13, 22, ...

2 Given a first term of 10 and these sets of instructions, find the first five terms in each sequence.
a Double the previous term.   b Halve the previous term.
c Subtract 4 from the previous term.

3 Write down the next three terms in each of these sequences.
a 32, 30, 26, 20, ...   b 6, 9, 14, 21, ...   c 5, 11, 6, 12, 7, ...

4 Use the difference method to find the next two terms in each of these sequences.
a 11, 12, 16, 23, 33, ...   b 11, 17, 33, 71, 143, 261, ...   c −1, 6, 25, 62, 123, 214, ...

5 Find the rule for the nth term and the 15th term of each of these sequences.
a −1, 1, 3, 5, 7, ...   b 5, 14, 27, 44, 65, ...   c 16, 13, 10, 7, ...
d 1, 8, 21, 40, 65, ...   e −1, 0, 3, 8, ...

6 The third term of a sequence is 15, the fourth term is 18, the fifth term is 21 and the sixth term is 24.
Find the 25th term.

7 How many terms of the sequence given by the rule 'nth term $= 8n - 2$' need to be listed before a value greater than 1000 occurs?

8 Each rung of a ladder is 1.25 cm shorter than the rung below it.
If the bottom rung is 35 cm long, how long is the 14th rung?

9 The fourth term of a sequence is 43, the fifth term is 64, the sixth term is 89 and the seventh term is 118.
Find the 30th term.

10 The diagram shows a sequence of stacked cubes.

 a How many cubes are needed for the fourth arrangement?
 b Find a rule for the number of cubes needed for the nth arrangement.
 c How many cubes would be needed to make the tenth arrangement?

Examination questions

Use 'Topic Tracker' at www.ccea.org.uk to find more exam questions.

Questions 1 to 3 are from examination papers where you may not use a calculator.

1 a This sequence of shapes is made from matchsticks.
     i   How many matchsticks will be needed for Shape 6?
     ii Explain how you worked out your answer.
   b Write down the next two terms in the sequence
      21, 19, 15, 9, …, …

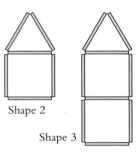

Shape 1

Shape 2

Shape 3

2 a Write down the first three terms of the sequence where the nth term is $n^2 + 7$.
   b Find the nth term for each of these sequences.
     i   11, 22, 33, 44, …   ii   3, 7, 11, 15, …

3 Find the nth term for each of the following sequences.
   a 5, 3, 1, −1, …
   b $\frac{1}{2}$, $\frac{2}{3}$, $\frac{3}{4}$, $\frac{4}{5}$, …

   c $\frac{1}{4}$, $\frac{2}{7}$, $\frac{3}{12}$, $\frac{4}{19}$, …

Questions 4 to 6 are from examination papers where you may use a calculator.

4 Write down the next two numbers in the sequence
   23, 21, 17, 11, …, … .

5 The first four terms of a sequence are
   4, 7, 10, 13, …
   a Find the eighth term.
   b Find an expression for the nth term of the sequence.
   c Find the 25th term of the sequence.

6 a Find the nth term of the sequence
      1, 5, 9, 13, 17, …
   b i Hence write down the nth term of the sequence

         1, $\frac{5}{4}$, 1, $\frac{13}{16}$, $\frac{17}{25}$, …

     ii Hence prove that, although the sequence has two terms equal
         to 1, no other term of the sequence will equal 1.

CHAPTER 19

Factorisation

> ## This chapter is about:
> - factorising by taking out a common factor
> - factorising by grouping
> - difference of two squares
> - factorising quadratic expressions in which the coefficient of x^2 is 1
> - factorising quadratic expressions in which the coefficient of x^2 is not 1
> - using a combination of these methods.
>
> ## You should already know:
> - how to work with negative numbers
> - how to work with indices
> - how to expand brackets
> - how to find the area of a rectangle
> - how to find the area of a circle.

In Chapter 16 you met the various methods used to expand brackets. The reverse process, when you put brackets in, is known as **factorisation**.

There are several methods for factorisation.

Common factors

This is the reverse of expanding a single set of brackets.

When you **expand** $2x(x + 3)$, the result is $2x^2 + 6x$.
When you **factorise** $2x^2 + 6x$, the result is $2x(x + 3)$.

It is good practice, as a check, to expand your factorised answer.

All terms which are common throughout the expression should be placed in front of the bracket. In the example above, $2x^2 + 6x$ could have been written as $2(x^2 + 3x)$, but since x is still common to both terms inside the bracket, it too must be placed outside the bracket for the expression to be *completely* factorised. It is the highest common factor (HCF) which should be placed in front of the bracket.

Common factors will play an important role when changing the subject of a formula (see Chapter 20).

EXAMPLE 1

Factorise fully each of these expressions.

    a $2x + 8$ b $4w + 6x - 10y$ c $6a^2 + 9a$

    d $12x^2y + 16xy$ e $8a^2c + 16bc$ f $6k^2 - k$

SOLUTION

    a $2x + 8 = 2(x + 4)$

    b $4w + 6x - 10y = 2(2w + 3x - 5y)$

    c $6a^2 + 9a = 3a(2a + 3)$

    d $12x^2y + 16xy = 4xy(3x + 4)$

    e $8a^2c + 16bc = 8c(a^2 + 2b)$

    f $6k^2 - k = k(6k - 1)$

> 2 is the highest common factor of $2x$ and 8.

> 3 and a are both common factors. The highest common factor is $3a$.

> It is important to include the 1 as a second term inside the bracket here, even though the k has come to the front.

Exercise 19.1

1 Complete each of these.

    a $4x + 8 = 4(\ldots + \ldots)$ b $16 + 4n = \ldots (4 + n)$

    c $12k + 9 = \ldots (4k + \ldots)$ d $10x - 15 = 5(\ldots - \ldots)$

    e $21 + 6p = \ldots (\ldots + 2p)$ f $40x + 24 = \ldots (5x + \ldots)$

2 Factorise fully each of these.

    a $24a - 36$ b $4x - 20$ c $5n + 5$

    d $12 + 16p$ e $8 - 8k$ f $7x + 21$

    g $8 + 16y$ h $9x - 3$ i $32 - 40n$

    j $18y + 24$ k $25t - 40$ l $6g - 18$

3 Complete each of these.

    a $4x^2 + 2x = 2x(\ldots + \ldots)$ b $ay - ab = \ldots (y - b)$

    c $2h^2 + h = h(\ldots + \ldots)$ d $6x^2 + 3x = 3x(\ldots + \ldots)$

    e $4a^2 - 8a = 4a(\ldots - \ldots)$ f $8p^2q + 4pq = 4pq(\ldots + \ldots)$

4 Factorise fully each of these.

    a $15n - 20n^2$ b $k^3 + k^2$ c $10a^2 - 5a$

    d $a^2b + ab^2$ e $8r^2 - 10r^3$ f $18a - 6a^2$

    g $\pi r^2 + 2\pi rh$ h $12c^2d + 18cd^2$ i $2xyz + 4x^2z$

    j $30p^3 - 25p^2$ k $x^2y + wxy$ l $4k^3 - 10k^2$

5 Factorise each of these expressions.

    a $m^2 + 4m$ b $16e - 2e^2$ c $6x - x^2$ d $56x + 21x^2$

    e $4r^2 - r$ f $10x - 25x^2$ g $p^3 - 3p^2$ h $15y - 9y^2$

    i $\pi r^2 + 2\pi r$ j $ab^2 - abc$ k $8a^3 + 4a^2$ l $4pq + 2q$

    m $4a^2c + 6c$ n $a^3d - ad^2$ o $5a^3b + 2a^2b$ p $6xy + 2xz - 4wx$

    q $awx + a^2x + a^3y$ r $6xy^2 + 4xy - 2xy^2$

Grouping

When an expression has four terms, it can sometimes be factorised by removing the common factor from two pairs of terms, leaving an expression which can then be factorised further by removing another common factor.

EXAMPLE 2

Factorise $ax + ay + bx + by$.

SOLUTION

Taking a common factor of a from the first two terms and a common factor of b from the second two terms gives

$a(x + y) + b(x + y)$ ←————————————

It can now be seen that $(x + y)$ is a common factor of the expression.

Hence $ax + ay + bx + by = (a + b)(x + y)$.

> When grouping, aim to get the terms inside the two sets of brackets the same, so that these can then be clearly seen as another common factor.

EXAMPLE 3

Factorise $mk + 2mn^2 - tk - 2tn^2$.

SOLUTION

Taking a common factor of m from the first two terms and a common factor of t from the second two terms gives

$m(k + 2n^2) - t(k + 2n^2)$ ←————————————

It can now be seen that $(k + 2n^2)$ is a common factor of the expression.

Hence $mk + 2mn^2 - tk - 2tn^2 = (m - t)(k + 2n^2)$.

> To make the second bracket the same as the first, a *negative t* comes out. As a result, the remaining $-2n^2$ becomes $+2n^2$ (by the rules for multiplying negative numbers).

EXAMPLE 4

Factorise $12c - 3cd + 4d - d^2$.

SOLUTION

$$12c - 3cd + 4d - d^2 = 3c(4 - d) + d(4 - d)$$
$$= (3c + d)(4 - d)$$

EXAMPLE 5

Factorise $1 + x + y + xy$.

SOLUTION

$$1 + x + y + xy = 1(1 + x) + y(1 + x)$$
$$= (1 + y)(1 + x)$$

EXAMPLE 6

Factorise $ab - cd - ca + db$.

SOLUTION

$$ab - cd - ca + db = ab - ca - cd + db$$
$$= a(b - c) + d(b - c)$$
$$= (a + d)(b - c)$$

> There was no common factor in the first two terms in the original expression, so it has been rearranged to allow a common factor to be removed.

EXAMPLE 7

Factorise $pq + 3 - p - 3q$.

SOLUTION

$$pq + 3 - p - 3q = pq - p + 3 - 3q$$
$$= p(q - 1) - 3(q - 1)$$
$$= (p - 3)(q - 1)$$

> You should check your answers by the reverse procedure of expanding the brackets – in this case by any of the three methods for expanding two sets of brackets covered in Chapter 16.

Exercise 19.2

Factorise each of these expressions.

1. $by + bz + ay + az$
2. $xy - xz - wy + wz$
3. $ax^2 + bx^2 + ay + by$
4. $ef + gd + ge + df$
5. $x^2 + ax + ay + xy$
6. $cd^2 - 1 + c - d^2$
7. $15cd - 4ef + 10ed - 6cf$
8. $2xy + 6y - x - 3$
9. $1 + t + t^2 + t^3$
10. $ay + by - ax - bx$
11. $3ay + ax + 6by + 2bx$
12. $4u^2 - uv - 20u + 5v$
13. $e^3 - 3e^2 + 2e - 6$
14. $6g^2 - 3gh - hn + 2gn$
15. $3cd - 10ef + 2cf - 15ed$
16. $24p^2 - 4p^2t - 18t + 3t^2$
17. $ak - 5 + a - 5k$
18. $xy^2 - 1 + x - y^2$

The difference of two squares

If you expand the expression $(x - y)(x + y)$, you obtain $x^2 - y^2$, which is the difference of two square terms. You can use the reverse of this to factorise an expression that is written as the **difference of two square terms.** This can also be used to evaluate numerical calculations written as the difference of two square terms.

EXAMPLE 8

Factorise $a^2 - b^2$.

SOLUTION

$$a^2 - b^2 = (a - b)(a + b)$$

> Again, all these factorised expressions can be checked by the reverse procedure of expanding the brackets.

EXAMPLE 9

Factorise $k^2 - 100$.

SOLUTION

$k^2 - 100 = (k - 10)(k + 10)$

EXAMPLE 10

Factorise $36c^2 - 49d^2$.

SOLUTION

$36c^2 - 49d^2 = (6c - 7d)(6c + 7d)$ ← $36c^2 = (6c)^2$ and $49d^2 = (7d)^2$

EXAMPLE 11

Factorise $p^2 - \frac{1}{9}$.

SOLUTION

$p^2 - \frac{1}{9} = (p - \frac{1}{3})(p + \frac{1}{3})$

EXAMPLE 12

Evaluate $102^2 - 101^2$.

SOLUTION

$$102^2 - 101^2 = (102 - 101)(102 + 101)$$
$$= 1 \times 203$$
$$= 203$$

This method can be useful on non-calculator papers. Many students overlook it and try squaring both values – which can be quite cumbersome!

EXAMPLE 13

Evaluate $2.81^2 - 2.8^2$.

SOLUTION

$$2.81^2 - 2.8^2 = (2.81 - 2.8)(2.81 + 2.8)$$
$$= 0.01 \times 5.61$$
$$= 0.0561$$

Exercise 19.3

1 Factorise each of these.

a $c^2 - d^2$ b $a^2 - y^2$ c $100 - p^2$ d $c^2 - \frac{1}{d^2}$ e $36y^2 - 1$

f $64 - t^2$ g $9k^2 - m^2$ h $16a^2 - 49b^2$ i $81a^2 - 25$

2 Evaluate each of these.

  a $68^2 - 67^2$ b $6.1^2 - 5.9^2$
  c $(4\frac{1}{2})^2 - (3\frac{1}{2})^2$ d $32\,005^2 - 32\,003^2$

3 Use the difference of two squares to simplify each of these expressions.

  a $(x + y)^2 - (x + z)^2$ b $(4n - 1)^2 - n^2$ c $(3x + 2)^2 - (2x + 1)^2$

4 a Write 9999 as the difference of two squares.
  b Use this to write 9999 as a product of its prime factors.

Factorising quadratic expressions

A **quadratic expression** is one of the form $ax^2 + bx + c$. The factorisation
of quadratic expressions plays an important role in the solution of
quadratic equations, which you will meet in Chapter 24. There are various
methods of factorisation for quadratics, and you have already met some of
these.

For example, the expression $6x^2 + 4x$ is a quadratic with the c term equal
to zero. It can be factorised by the method of common factors, leading to
$2x(3x + 2)$.

Another example is $4x^2 - 25$, which is a quadratic with the b term equal
to zero. It can be factorised by the difference of two squares, leading to
$(2x - 5)(2x + 5)$.

We will now look at quadratics in which all three terms are non-zero, and
at how they can be factorised.

Quadratics in which the coefficient of x^2 is 1

We will first look at quadratics in which the coefficient of x^2 is 1, that is
$a = 1$. Look at the constant term, c, find factors of c which will add to give
the coefficient of the x term, b, and arrange these in a pair of brackets.
This is the reverse of the 'FOIL' method used in Chapter 16.

EXAMPLE 14

Factorise $x^2 + 7x + 12$.

SOLUTION

Factors of +12 are +1 and +12, +2 and +6, and +3 and +4.

> You can ignore −1 and −12, etc. as b is positive.

The pair of factors which add to give +7 are +4 and +3.
Hence $x^2 + 7x + 12 = (x + 4)(x + 3)$.

> A quadratic factorisation can be checked by any
> of the methods discussed in Chapter 16.
> Here $x \times x = x^2$, $x \times 3 = 3x$, $4 \times x = 4x$,
> $4 \times 3 = 12$,
> leading to $x^2 + 3x + 4x + 12 = x^2 + 7x + 12$,
> as required.

EXAMPLE 15

Factorise $x^2 - 2x - 15$.

SOLUTION

Factors of -15 are $+1$ and -15, -1 and $+15$, $+3$ and -5, and -3 and $+5$.
The pair of factors which add to give -2 are -5 and $+3$.
Hence $x^2 - 2x - 15 = (x - 5)(x + 3)$.

EXAMPLE 16

Factorise $x^2 + 5x - 14$.

SOLUTION

The pair of factors of -14 which add to give $+5$ are $+7$ and -2.
Hence $x^2 + 5x - 14 = (x + 7)(x - 2)$.

Quadratics in which the coefficient of x^2 is not 1

We will now look at quadratic expressions in which the coefficient of x^2 is not 1. The factorisation process is a little more complex. Firstly, find the product of a and c, and then find factors of ac which add to give the coefficient of the x term, b. Rewrite the whole quadratic expression as the sum of four terms and then factorise by the grouping method.

EXAMPLE 17

Factorise $2x^2 + 7x + 3$.

SOLUTION

$ac = 2 \times 3 = 6$

Factors of $+6$ are $+1$ and $+6$, and $+2$ and $+3$.
The pair of factors which add to give $+7$ are $+1$ and $+6$.
The expression can now be written as

$2x^2 + 1x + 6x + 3$

and factorised as

$x(2x + 1) + 3(2x + 1) = (2x + 1)(x + 3)$.

EXAMPLE 18

Factorise $6x^2 - 11x + 4$.

SOLUTION

$ac = 6 \times 4 = 24$

Factors of $+24$ are -1 and -24, -2 and -12, -3 and -8, and -4 and -6.
The pair of factors which add to give -11 are -3 and -8.
The expression can now be written as

> You need two negative factors so that they multiply together to give a positive number, but add to give a negative number.

$6x^2 - 3x - 8x + 4$

and factorised by grouping as

$3x(2x - 1) - 4(2x - 1)$
$= (2x - 1)(3x - 4)$.

> Notice that you need to take -4 out of the second bracket to make the expressions inside the two brackets the same.

EXAMPLE 19

Factorise $4x^2 - 4x - 15$.

SOLUTION

$ac = 4 \times (-15) = -60$

The pair of factors of -60 which add to give -4 are $+6$ and -10.
The expression can now be written as

$4x^2 + 6x - 10x - 15$

and factorised by grouping as

$2x(2x + 3) - 5(2x + 3) = (2x - 5)(2x + 3)$.

> Notice that you need one negative factor and one positive factor here to make both b and c negative.

With practice you may be able to factorise quadratics much more quickly by opening two sets of brackets and trying the 'FOIL' method in reverse. If you do this, you must take care with the positioning of the terms within the brackets and the signs of the terms.

For instance, in Example 19 above, you could factorise the expression $4x^2 - 4x - 15$ by considering $4x \times x$ or $2x \times 2x$ as the first terms, and 15×1 or 3×5 as the last terms, and positioning these in the brackets with the correct signs such that the outer and inner terms combine to give $-4x$.

Exercise 19.4

1 Factorise each of these.
   a $x^2 + 14x + 45$
   b $x^2 - 2x - 35$
   c $x^2 - x - 20$
   d $a^2 - 13a + 30$
   e $p^2 - 13p - 30$
   f $y^2 + 11y + 24$
   g $a^2 - 4a - 21$
   h $k^2 + 2k + 1$
   i $x^2 - 5x - 24$
   j $p^2 - 10p + 9$
   k $m^2 + 2m - 35$
   l $t^2 - 5t - 36$

2 Factorise each of these.
   a $3a^2 + 17a + 10$
   b $3x^2 - 5x - 8$
   c $2x^2 - x - 3$
   d $3y^2 + 14y + 11$
   e $2p^2 - 11p + 5$
   f $3x^2 - 11x - 20$
   g $3p^2 - 31p + 10$
   h $10y^2 - 3y - 4$
   i $6x^2 - 7x - 20$
   j $12y^2 + 13y - 4$
   k $4n^2 + 11n - 3$
   l $25x^2 - 20x + 4$

3 Use common factors, the difference of two squares or quadratic factorisation, as appropriate, to factorise each of these quadratic expressions.
   a $5x^2 - 3x$
   b $a^2 - 121$
   c $2x^2 - x - 3$
   d $x^2 - 4x - 21$
   e $p^2 - 9$
   f $3x^2 - 11x + 6$
   g $10x^2 - 5x$
   h $10x^2 + 9x + 2$
   i $49x^2 - 36$
   j $8p^2 - 10p - 3$
   k $4p - 8p^2$
   l $y^2 - 5y + 6$

Expressions requiring several methods for factorisation

To factorise some expressions completely, you may need to apply more than one method of factorisation.

For example, an expression may become the difference of two squares if you remove a common factor first, or a quadratic expression may be easier to factorise if a common factor can be removed from all three terms first.

More complicated algebraic expressions can also be simplified, by factorising numerators and denominators separately, and then simplifying further by cancelling if possible.

These techniques are illustrated in the examples below.

EXAMPLE 20

Factorise fully $8a^2 - 50$.

SOLUTION

$$8a^2 - 50 = 2(4a^2 - 25)$$ — Take out the common factor first ...

$$= 2(2a - 5)(2a + 5)$$ — and now use the difference of two squares.

EXAMPLE 21

Factorise fully $24x^2 + 4x - 8$.

SOLUTION

$$24x^2 + 4x - 8 = 4(6x^2 + x - 2)$$ — Take out the common factor first ...

$$= 4(3x + 2)(2x - 1)$$ — and now factorise the resulting quadratic expression.

Note that the same answer would have been reached by factorising the quadratic first, as $(12x + 8)(2x - 1)$, and then removing the common factor from the first bracket, as $4(3x + 2)(2x - 1)$. However, by removing the common factor *first*, the quadratic becomes much easier to factorise.

EXAMPLE 22

Simplify $\dfrac{8a + 4}{2a^2 + 7a + 3}$.

SOLUTION

$$8a + 4 = 4(2a + 1)$$ — Factorise the numerator by common factors.

$$2a^2 + 7a + 3 = (2a + 1)(a + 3)$$ — Factorise the denominator.

So $\dfrac{8a + 4}{2a^2 + 7a + 3} = \dfrac{4\cancel{(2a + 1)}}{\cancel{(2a + 1)}(a + 3)}$ — Cancel by $2a + 1$.

$$= \dfrac{4}{a + 3}$$

EXAMPLE 23

Simplify $\dfrac{12a^2 + 2ab + 6ac + bc}{2a^2 + ac}$.

SOLUTION

$$12a^2 + 2ab + 6ac + bc = 2a(6a + b) + c(6a + b)$$

Factorise the numerator by grouping.

$$= (2a + c)(6a + b)$$

$$2a^2 + ac = a(2a + c)$$

Factorise the denominator by common factors.

Hence $\dfrac{12a^2 + 2ab + 6ac + bc}{2a^2 + ac} = \dfrac{(2a + c)(6a + b)}{a(2a + c)}$

Cancel by $2a + c$.

$$= \dfrac{6a + b}{a}$$

Simplifying algebraic fractions will be dealt with in more detail in Chapter 23.

Exercise 19.5

1 Use an appropriate method to factorise each of these expressions.
   a $5a^3 + 15$
   b $1 - 64y^2$
   c $pq + rq + ps + rs$
   d $x^2 + 4x - 5$
   e $15y^2 - y - 2$
   f $3p^2 - 17p - 6$
   g $x^3 + xy$
   h $x^2 + xy - xk - yk$

2 Factorise *fully* each of these expressions.
   a $2x^2 - 4x - 6$
   b $2x^2 - 18$
   c $4xy + 12y - 2x - 6$
   d $5x^2 + 5x - 60$
   e $4a^2 - 4b^2$
   f $10a^2b - 40ab^2$
   g $2k^2 - 10k + 12$
   h $4pq + 8p - 8q - 16$

3 Simplify each of these expressions as fully as possible.
   a $\dfrac{2ab + 4b^2}{3a^2 + 6ab}$
   b $\dfrac{k^2 - 4}{k^2 + 5k + 6}$
   c $\dfrac{a^2 + ab - ac - bc}{4ab - 4bc}$
   d $\dfrac{12a^2 - 3}{6a^2 - a - 1}$

4 Given that the area of this rectangle is $6y^2 + 15xy$ and its width is $3y$, find an expression for its length.

area = $6y^2 + 15xy$ | $3y$

5 By factorising, find the value of $4 \times 7.6^2 - 4 \times 2.4^2$.

6 The outer circle has radius $20\,cm$ and the inner circle has radius $18\,cm$. Use factorisation to show that the shaded area is $76\pi\,cm^2$. The formula for the area of a circle is $A = \pi r^2$.

You should now:

- be able to factorise using common factors
- be able to factorise using grouping
- be able to factorise using the difference of two squares
- be able to factorise using quadratics
- be able to simplify expressions involving several types of factorisation
- be able to solve problems which require factorisation.

Summary exercise 19

1 Use the method of common factors to factorise each of these.
   a $6a + 20$ b $12x - 20$ c $10x + 5$ d $x^2 - 3x$
   e $10y^2 + 5y$ f $6k^2 - 9k$ g $4ab - 6bc$ h $mn^2 - m^2n$
   i $15xy - 20y$ j $3x^2 + 6xy + 9xz$ k $x^3 + 3x^2 - 2x$ l $6d^4 + 6d^2$

2 Use the method of grouping to factorise each of these.
   a $ah + ak + bh + bk$ b $6wy - 3hy + 2wx - hx$
   c $x^2a + x^2b + ya + yb$ d $2mn + 3mk - 2pn - 3pk$
   e $5yz - xz + ax - 5ay$ f $ab + ac + b^2 + bc$
   g $c^2 - 10d - 5c + 2cd$ h $3x^2 - ax - 9xy + 3ay$
   i $8b^2 + 4ab - 6b - 3a$ j $18xz - y^2 - 3yz + 6xy$

3 Use the difference of two squares to factorise each of these.
   a $p^2 - q^2$ b $100 - t^2$ c $25h^2 - 1$ d $b^2 - 0.01$
   e $36 - y^2$ f $\dfrac{1}{100} - a^2$ g $4x^2 - 25y^2$ h $1 - \dfrac{1}{c^2}$
   i $25k^2 - 36d^2$ j $49x^2 - \dfrac{y^2}{25}$ k $(2x + 1)^2 - (x + 1)^2$ l $(a - b)^2 - (a + b)^2$

4 Use quadratic factorisation to factorise each of these.
   a $a^2 + 7a + 10$ b $d^2 - 4d - 21$ c $2x^2 + 11x - 21$ d $p^2 + 3p - 40$
   e $3k^2 - 14k + 8$ f $x^2 + 7x - 18$ g $6h^2 + 23h - 4$ h $8x^2 - 14x - 15$
   i $m^2 - 5mn + 6n^2$ j $8 + 2x - x^2$

5 Factorise *fully* each of these expressions.
   a $4x^2 + 8x - 60$ b $5x^2 - 125$ c $3ac + 3bc + 6a + 6b$
   d $6x^2 - 26x - 20$ e $10x^2 - 90$ f $80 - 12y - 8y^2$

6 Use an appropriate method to factorise each of these.
   a $9b^2 + 27b$ b $a^2 + 12a + 27$ c $mn + 2n - m - 2$
   d $a^2b^2 - 1$ e $4x^2 + 23x + 15$ f $5a^2 - 6a - 8$
   g $4ax - 8ay + 8by - 4bx$ h $15p^2 + 22p + 8$ i $4\pi r^2 + 2\pi rh$
   j $\dfrac{x^2}{4} - 25$

7 Simplify each of these expressions.
   a $\dfrac{12a^2 - 2a - 4}{12a - 8}$ b $\dfrac{3x^2 - 27}{x^2 - 5x + 6}$ c $\dfrac{5c^2 - 10c}{10cd - 30c}$

8 Evaluate $514^2 - 486^2$.

9 By factorising, evaluate $2 \times 5 \times 89 \times 90 - 2 \times 5 \times 89^2$.

10 Write 391 as the difference of two squares, and hence write 391 as a product of its prime factors.

11 Prove the identity $2(x - 1) + (2x + 1)^2 + (2x - 1)^2 \equiv 2x(4x + 1)$.

Examination questions

Use 'Topic Tracker' at www.ccea.org.uk to find more exam questions.

Questions 1 to 4 are from examination papers where you may not use a calculator.

1 Factorise fully
   a $6cd - 9c^2$ b $3a^2 - 27d^2$

2 Factorise $y^2 - 4y - 12$.

3 a Factorise fully $6pq + 2p^2$.

   b Simplify $\dfrac{x^2 - 16}{2x^2 + 7x - 4}$.

4 a Factorise $a^2 - 9b^2$.

   b Simplify $\dfrac{x - 2}{2x^2 - 3x - 2}$.

Questions 5 to 7 are from examination papers where you may use a calculator.

5 Factorise
   a $9b - 12c$ b $y^2 - 9y$ c $w^2 + w$

6 Factorise
   a $p^2 + 5p$ b $2k^2 - k$ c $p^2 - 25q^2$

7 a Factorise fully $xy + 5x - 3y - 15$.

   b i Factorise fully $3x^2 - 48$.

      ii Hence simplify $\dfrac{3x^2 - 48}{2x^2 + 9x + 4}$.

CHAPTER 20

Formulae

This chapter is about:

- formulae and how to use them
- changing the subject of a formula.

You should already know:

- how to work with positive and negative whole numbers, fractions and decimals
- how to work with surds
- how to expand brackets
- how to factorise algebraic expressions
- how to solve linear equations.

Using formulae

In a **formula**, letters are used to represent defined quantities or variables. For example, the formula $F = ma$ represents the relationship 'force = mass $\times$ acceleration', which is a law of physics.

A formula is a concise way of writing down a mathematical process, which can then be applied to any suitable numerical quantities. Although the variables within the formula will usually be defined, it is not necessary at GCSE level to actually *know* any of these formulae – it is the application of them which is required.

When the formula is given, you can use the process of substitution, which you met in Chapter 14, to calculate the numerical value of the **subject** of the formula. The subject is the variable which is written in terms of other variables. In the formula $F = ma$, for example, F is the subject.

If a formula is not given, you can use the mathematical information provided to construct a suitable formula, which can then be used repeatedly for various numerical values.

EXAMPLE 1

The final speed v of a car is given by the formula $v = u + at$, where u is the initial speed, a is the acceleration and t is the time.
Find v when $u = 30$, $a = 2.5$ and $t = 5$.

SOLUTION

$$v = u + at$$

$$v = 30 + 2.5 \times 5$$
$$= 30 + 12.5$$
$$= 42.5$$

> Substitute in the values you are given for u, a and t.

EXAMPLE 2

The surface area of a cylinder is given by the formula $A = 2\pi r^2 + 2\pi rh$, where r is the radius and h is the height of the cylinder. Find the surface area of a cylinder of radius $3\frac{1}{2}$ cm and height 14 cm. Take $\pi = \frac{22}{7}$.

SOLUTION

$$A = 2\pi r^2 + 2\pi rh$$
$$= 2 \times \frac{22^{11}}{7} \times \frac{7}{2} \times \frac{7}{2} + 2 \times \frac{22^{11}}{7} \times \frac{7}{2} \times 14$$
$$= 77 + 308$$
$$= 385 \text{ cm}^2$$

EXAMPLE 3

$s = ut + \frac{1}{2}at^2$ is a formula used to calculate the distance s travelled in time t by a particle with initial velocity u and acceleration a.
Calculate the distance travelled in a time of 3 seconds by a particle whose initial velocity is 100 m/s and whose acceleration is -5 m/s^2.

SOLUTION

$$s = ut + \frac{1}{2}at^2$$
$$= 100 \times 3 + \frac{1}{2} \times (-5) \times 3^2$$
$$= 300 + \frac{1}{2} \times (-5) \times 9$$
$$= 300 - 22.5$$
$$= 277.5 \text{ m}$$

> Some of these examples include work with fractions and negative numbers. It is important to realise that using formulae can require you to work with whole numbers, decimals, fractions, negative numbers, standard form, surds, etc. and so a lot of work covered in the Number chapters is vital for this topic.

EXAMPLE 4

Use the formula $K = 4L + 3M$ to calculate L when K is 26 and M is 6.

SOLUTION

$$26 = 4L + 3 \times 6$$
$$26 = 4L + 18$$
$$26 - 18 = 4L$$
$$8 = 4L$$
$$L = 2$$

> Substitute in the values you are given for K and M.

> At this point, the substitution has resulted in an equation, which can be solved using the techniques covered in Chapter 17. An alternative method is to 'change the subject of the formula', which is dealt with later in this chapter.

A plumber charges a call-out fee of £50, plus £12 per hour for every hour (or part of an hour) worked.

  a Write a formula for the total charge £C for working n hours.
  b Use your formula to calculate the total charge for a job which takes 6 hours.

SOLUTION

  a Total charge $= £50 + £12$ for every hour.
     So $C = 50 + 12 \times n$
               $C = 50 + 12n$
  b For 6 hours, $C = 50 + 12 \times 6$
                   $= 50 + 72$
                   $= 122$
     The total charge is £122.

Exercise 20.1

1 $d = \frac{1}{2}(u + v)t$ is the formula used to calculate the distance d travelled by a particle in t seconds, when its initial velocity is u m/s and its final velocity is v m/s.
   Find the distance travelled by a particle in 24 seconds, if its initial velocity is 6 m/s and its final velocity is 20 m/s.

2 $F = \frac{9C}{5} + 32$ is the formula used to convert temperatures from degrees Celsius (C) to degrees Fahrenheit (F).
   Convert 40 °C to Fahrenheit.

3 Find the value of f in the formula $f = \frac{uv}{u + v}$ when $u = -10$ and $v = -5$.

4 $E = mc^2$ is a famous formula of Einstein's, connecting energy, mass and the speed of light.
   Calculate E when $m = 2 \times 10^{-3}$ and $c = 3 \times 10^8$.

5 The sum of all the integers from 1 to n is given by the formula
   $S = \frac{n}{6}(n + 1)(2n + 1)$.
   Calculate the sum of the first 100 integers.

6 The total resistance R in a circuit when two resistors are connected in parallel is given by the formula $\frac{1}{R} = \frac{1}{R_1} + \frac{1}{R_2}$.
   Calculate R when $R_1 = 3.5$ and $R_2 = 2.5$.

7 The stopping distance of a vehicle can be calculated using the formula $D = \frac{S^2 + 20S}{60}$ where S is the speed of the car in miles per hour and D is the stopping distance in metres.
   How many metres will it take a car to stop if it is travelling at 60 miles per hour?

8   The tension in a spring is given by the formula $T = \dfrac{kx}{l}$.
    Find the tension T when $k = 15$, $x = 5$ and $l = 2$.

9   $T = 2\pi \sqrt{\dfrac{l}{g}}$
    Find T when $l = 20$ and $g = 9.8$.
    Give your answer to 2 decimal places.

10 The surface area of a solid cone is given by the formula
    $A = \pi r^2 + \pi r l$.
    Find the surface area of a cone, to the nearest square centimetre,
    when $r = 5\,cm$ and $l = 13\,cm$.

11 $V = \dfrac{1}{6}\pi x^2 h$
    Find the value of x when $V = 16\tfrac{1}{2}$, $h = 14$ and $\pi = \dfrac{22}{7}$.

12 A girl's weekly wage in a factory is a fixed payment of £160.40,
    plus a bonus of £5.50 for every completed garment she made in
    that week.
    a   Write a formula for her total wage £W, if she completes
        g garments in the week.
    b   Use your formula to find her total weekly wage in a week
        when she completes 15 garments.

13 An article is bought for £C and later sold for £S, making a profit.
    Write a formula for the percentage profit P, in terms of C and S.

Changing the subject of simple formulae

Remember that the **subject** of a formula is the 'leading term' or 'the
variable which is written in terms of other variables'. In the formula
$F = ma$, for example, we said above that F was the subject. Likewise, in the
formula $v = u + at$, v is the subject, and in the formula $I = \dfrac{PRT}{100}$, I is the
subject.

Sometimes we may want to 'change the subject of the formula' (also
known as 'transforming the formula'). This is particularly useful when
we wish to find the numerical value of one of the other variables in the
formula rather than the leading term.

The steps involved in changing the subject of the formula are similar to
those involved in solving equations, as covered in Chapter 17. Inverse
operations are used to transform the formula.

The required subject is brought to one side of the formula, and all the
other terms are collected on the other side of the formula. As with solving
equations, you must always perform the same operation on both sides of
the formula.

Changing the subject of a formula will be important when you study
proportion and variation (see Chapter 21).

EXAMPLE 6

Make y the subject of the formula $By + C = D$.

SOLUTION

$$By + C = D$$
$$By = D - C$$
$$y = \frac{D - C}{B}$$

> You want y by itself on the left-hand side of the formula.
> First subtract C from both sides …

> then divide both sides by B.

EXAMPLE 7

Make x the subject of the formula $K = Lx - C$.

SOLUTION

$$K = Lx - C$$
$$K + C = Lx$$
$$\frac{K + C}{L} = x$$
$$x = \frac{K + C}{L}$$

> In this case leave Lx on the right-hand side (so that the required subject is positive) and collect all other terms to the left-hand side.
> First add C to both sides …

> then divide both sides by L

> Finally, rewrite the formula with the subject on the left-hand side.

EXAMPLE 8

Make a the subject of the formula $b - ac + e = d$.

SOLUTION

$$b - ac + e = d$$
$$b + e = d + ac$$
$$b + e - d = ac$$
$$\frac{b + e - d}{c} = a$$
$$a = \frac{b + e - d}{c}$$

> Add ac to both sides of the formula as a first step so that the required subject is positive.

> Subtract d from both sides.

> Divide both sides by c.

> Finally, rewrite the formula with the subject on the left-hand side.

EXAMPLE 9

Make c the subject of the formula $bcd = e$.

SOLUTION

$$bcd = e$$
$$c = \frac{e}{bd}$$

> c is multiplied by both b and d, that is c is multiplied by bd.
> Therefore you can divide both sides by bd in a single step.

Exercise 20.2

1 Make x the subject of each of these formulae.

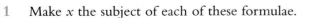

   a $P = kx$ b $x - t = c$ c $cx - d = e$ d $ax + b = c - d$

   e $f = g - x$ f $4x - 3 = y$ g $t = 3x - u$ h $2y + 3z = w - yx$

   i $Ny - x = y$ j $D - tx = E$ k $p^2 - 3x = q^2$ l $Px + T - Q = 0$

2 Make y the subject of each of these formulae.

   a $y + k = z$ b $ay = b$ c $a + ty = d$ d $4 - y = k$

   e $Gy + H = L$ f $a - cy = d$ g $My + B = A$ h $3 - ty - e = f$

   i $h = y - j$ j $xy = z$ k $r = 5 - ty$ l $A = byc$

3 Make r the subject of each of these formulae.

   a $A = \pi rl$ b $C = 2\pi r$ c $d = 2r$

4 Make a the subject of the formula $v^2 = u^2 + 2as$.

5 Make T the subject of the formula $pV = RT$.

Changing the subject of formulae with brackets

When a formula contains brackets, you should expand these first.

EXAMPLE 10

Make k the subject of the formula $p(k - t) = e$.

SOLUTION

$$p(k - t) = e$$
$$pk - pt = e \qquad \longleftarrow \qquad \text{Expand the brackets first.}$$
$$pk = e + pt$$
$$k = \frac{e + pt}{p}$$

EXAMPLE 11

Make a the subject of the formula $y = m(3 - a) + 2$.

SOLUTION

$$y = m(3 - a) + 2$$
$$y = 3m - ma + 2 \qquad \longleftarrow \qquad \text{Expand the brackets first.}$$
$$ma = 3m + 2 - y$$
$$a = \frac{3m + 2 - y}{m}$$

Changing the subject of formulae with fractions

As in equations, when fractions occur in formulae, you need to eliminate the fractions.

EXAMPLE 12

Make Q the subject of the formula $P = \dfrac{Q + R}{5}$.

SOLUTION

$$P = \frac{Q + R}{5}$$

$$5P = Q + R$$

$$5P - R = Q$$

$$Q = 5P - R$$

> Multiply both sides by 5.

> Subtract R from both sides.

> Rewrite the formula with the subject on the left-hand side.

EXAMPLE 13

Make x the subject of the formula $\frac{x}{2} - y = k$.

SOLUTION

$$\frac{x}{2} - y = k$$

$$\frac{x}{2} = k + y$$

$$x = 2(k + y) \qquad \text{or} \qquad x = 2k + 2y$$

> Add y to both sides.

> Multiply both sides by 2.

EXAMPLE 14

Make x the subject of the formula $a = \frac{2c}{x - b}$.

SOLUTION

$$a = \frac{2c}{x - b}$$

$$a(x - b) = 2c$$

$$ax - ab = 2c$$

$$ax = 2c + ab$$

$$x = \frac{2c + ab}{a}$$

> Multiply both sides by $(x - b)$.

> Expand the brackets.

EXAMPLE 15

Make b the subject of the formula $A = \frac{1}{2}(a + b)h$.

SOLUTION

$A = \frac{1}{2}(a + b)h$ can be rewritten as $A = \frac{(a + b)h}{2}$

> Recall that multiplication by $\frac{1}{2}$ is the same as dividing by 2. This is a useful first step when formulae are given in this format.

$$A = \frac{ah + bh}{2}$$

$$2A = ah + bh$$

$$2A - ah = bh$$

$$\frac{2A - ah}{h} = b$$

$$b = \frac{2A - ah}{h}$$

> Expand the brackets.

> Multiply both sides by 2.

> Subtract ah from both sides.

> Divide both sides by h.

Exercise 20.3

1 Make a the subject of each of these formulae.

   (a) $x(y - a) = b$ b $C(a + B) = D$ c $h(a + n) = y$ d $5(a - 1) = b$

   e $c = k(a + t)$ (f) $6(1 - a) = r$ g $g = d(a - e)$ h $p(x + a) = qn$

   i $L = l(2 + at)$ j $T = 100(p - a)$ (k) $2(a + b) = P$ l $3(m - a) = b - 2m$

2 Make b the subject of each of these formulae.

   a $A = \dfrac{\pi b}{4}$ b $F = \dfrac{ma - mb}{t}$ c $\dfrac{1}{b} = \dfrac{a}{c}$ d $V = \dfrac{2E}{A + b}$

   e $K = e + \dfrac{bc}{100}$ f $T = \dfrac{f}{b}$ g $I = \dfrac{3}{4}mb$ h $a = \dfrac{(40 + b)t}{5}$

   i $h = \dfrac{a + b}{2a}$ j $L = \dfrac{1}{3(8b - c)}$ k $T = \dfrac{a}{1 - b}$ l $P = \dfrac{Q}{A + b} - 4P$

3 $V = \dfrac{1}{3}\pi r^2 h$ is the formula used to find the volume V of a cone of radius r and vertical height h.
   Make h the subject of the formula.

4 The surface area of a solid cylinder of radius r and height h is given by the formula $A = 2\pi r(r + h)$.
   Write a formula for finding the height of the cylinder.

5 $T = a + (n - 1)d$ is a formula for the value T of the nth term in a sequence of numbers.
   Change the subject of the formula to n.

Changing the subject of formulae where a power or root of the subject occurs

Recall that raising a number to a power and taking the root of a number are **inverse operations**. This concept is used when changing the subject of formulae involving powers and roots.

Also recall that a number has *two* square roots – negative as well as positive. If the variables in a formula containing a square root are not defined, then the square root should include a '$\pm$' symbol. However, in some cases when the variables of a formula *are* defined, it may not be possible to have the negative square root. For example, if r represented the radius of a circle then it would not make sense to give a negative value for r, as a radius cannot be negative. You need to take the context of the question into account when deciding whether or not to include the negative value.

EXAMPLE 16

Make x the subject of the formula $\sqrt{x + a} = b$.

SOLUTION

$$\sqrt{x + a} = b$$

$$x + a = b^2 \quad \longleftarrow \qquad \boxed{\text{Square both sides of the formula.}}$$

$$x = b^2 - a$$

EXAMPLE 17

Make y the subject of the formula $(Ay - B)^2 = P$.

SOLUTION

$$(Ay - B)^2 = P$$
$$Ay - B = \pm\sqrt{P}$$
$$Ay = \pm\sqrt{P} + B$$
$$y = \pm\frac{\sqrt{P} + B}{A}$$

> Square root both sides of the formula. As P is undefined you must include $\pm$ with the square root.

> You could rewrite this as $y = \dfrac{B \pm \sqrt{P}}{A}$

EXAMPLE 18

Make A the subject of the formula $D = C\sqrt{\dfrac{A}{B}}$.

SOLUTION

$$D = C\sqrt{\frac{A}{B}}$$
$$\frac{D}{C} = \sqrt{\frac{A}{B}}$$
$$\left(\frac{D}{C}\right)^2 = \frac{A}{B}$$
$$\frac{D^2}{C^2} = \frac{A}{B}$$
$$\frac{BD^2}{C^2} = A$$
$$A = \frac{BD^2}{C^2}$$

> Square both sides.

> Multiply both sides by B.

> Rewrite the formula with the subject on the left-hand side.

EXAMPLE 19

Make r the subject of the formula $V = \frac{4}{3}\pi r^3$.

SOLUTION

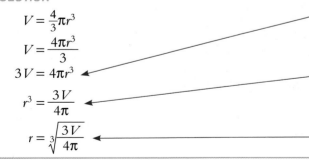

$$V = \frac{4}{3}\pi r^3$$
$$V = \frac{4\pi r^3}{3}$$
$$3V = 4\pi r^3$$
$$r^3 = \frac{3V}{4\pi}$$
$$r = \sqrt[3]{\frac{3V}{4\pi}}$$

> Multiply both sides by 3 to eliminate the fraction.

> Divide both sides by 4π. Notice that you can swap the sides of the formula at any stage.

> Take the cube root of both sides.

Exercise 20.4

1 Make a the subject of each of these formulae.

a $c^2 = a^2 + b^2$ b $a^2 + 5 = c$ c $\dfrac{a^2}{4} = b$ d $d = \sqrt{a}$

e $\sqrt{x + a} = b$ f $t = a\sqrt{b}$ g $k = \sqrt{a - p}$ h $\dfrac{ea^2}{b} = d$

i $s = \frac{1}{2}at^2$ j $ga^3 = h$ k $2\pi\sqrt{\dfrac{a}{b}} = c$ l $n = \dfrac{m}{\sqrt{a}}$

2 Make x the subject of each of these formulae.

a $x^2 = C$ b $x^3 = D$ c $k^2 = \dfrac{t}{x^2}$ d $\sqrt{x} + T = E$

e $c\sqrt{a + x} = d$ f $p = q - x^2$ g $2\pi\sqrt{x + t} = r$ h $\sqrt{c - x} = a$

i $x^3 + y = w$ j $\frac{1}{3}\pi x^3 = r$ k $\dfrac{3}{\sqrt{x}} = 2k$ l $x\sqrt[3]{t} = p$

3 Given that $\dfrac{a}{b} = \dfrac{b}{c}$ write b in terms of a and c.

4 The surface area of a sphere is given by the formula $A = 4\pi r^2$ where r is the radius. Write an expression for the radius of a sphere.

5 $T = 2\pi\sqrt{\dfrac{l}{g}}$ Express l in terms of T and g.

Changing the subject of formulae where the subject appears more than once

In some formulae the required subject may occur more than once. To find the formula for the new subject, first gather all the terms containing the required subject to one side of the formula, and collect all the other terms to the other side of the formula. Then, take out the required subject as a common factor of the variables on one side, as covered in Chapter 19. The subject will now occur only once in the formula so it can be transformed as necessary.

EXAMPLE 20

Make x the subject of the formula $r = px + qx$.

SOLUTION

$$r = px + qx$$
$$r = x(p + q)$$
$$\frac{r}{p + q} = x$$
$$x = \frac{r}{p + q}$$

> All the terms involving x are already on one side of the formula so factorise straight away.

> Divide both sides by $(p + q)$.

> Rewrite the formula with the subject on the left-hand side.

EXAMPLE 21

Make y the subject of the formula $cy - m = dy + n$.

SOLUTION

$$cy - m = dy + n$$

$$cy - dy = n + m$$

$$y(c - d) = n + m$$

$$y = \frac{n + m}{c - d}$$

> Gather all the y terms to one side.

> Factorise.

> Rearrange.

EXAMPLE 22

Make a the subject of the formula $a + x = \dfrac{a + b}{c}$.

SOLUTION

$$a + x = \frac{a + b}{c}$$

$$(a + x)c = a + b$$

$$ac + xc = a + b$$

$$ac - a = b - xc$$

$$a(c - 1) = b - xc$$

$$a = \frac{b - xc}{c - 1}$$

> Multiply both sides by c to eliminate the fraction.

> Expand the brackets.

> Collect all the terms involving a onto the left-hand side.

> Factorise by taking the common factor, a, outside the bracket. Remember that a divided by a is 1, so a 1 needs to be included in the bracket.

> Divide both sides by $(c - 1)$.

EXAMPLE 23

Make x the subject of the formula $a = \dfrac{3x}{x - 1}$.

SOLUTION

$$a = \frac{3x}{x - 1}$$

$$a(x - 1) = 3x$$

$$ax - a = 3x$$

$$ax - 3x = a$$

$$x(a - 3) = a$$

$$x = \frac{a}{a - 3}$$

> Multiply both sides by $(x - 1)$ to eliminate the fraction.

> Collect all the terms involving x onto the left-hand side.

> Factorise by taking the common factor, x, outside the bracket.

> Divide both sides by $(a - 3)$.

Exercise 20.5

1 Make x the subject of each of these formulae.

  a $ax + bx = c$
  b $dx = e(x + f)$
  c $f - gx = x(g - h) + kx$

  d $y = \dfrac{1 + x}{1 - x}$
  e $a + bx = \dfrac{c - x}{3}$

2 Make y the subject of each of these formulae.

  a $ty = u - 4y$
  b $y(p + q) = q(n - y)$
  c $a = \dfrac{y + m}{y - n}$

  d $6y - 7 = py - 9$
  e $x = \dfrac{100(b - y)}{y}$

3   The formula for an electric current is $I = \dfrac{nE}{R + nr}$.
    Make n the subject of the formula.

4   Make y the subject of the formula $\dfrac{a(y + n)}{y} = p$.

You should now:

- be able to find the value of a defined quantity using a formula
- be able to change the subject of any basic formula
- be able to change the subject of a formula involving brackets
- be able to change the subject of a formula involving fractions
- be able to change the subject of a formula involving powers or roots
- be able to change the subject of the formula where the subject appears more than once
- be able to solve problems requiring formulae and changing the subject.

Summary exercise 20

1   $C = \frac{5}{9}(F - 32)$ is a formula that can be used to convert a temperature
    from degrees Fahrenheit (F) to degrees Celsius (C).
    Convert $-13\,°F$ to Celsius.

2   Use the formula $a = \dfrac{t^2 - s^2}{2d}$ to find a when $t = 0$, $s = 12.5$ and
    $d = -2.5$.

3   Find p in the formula $a = bp + c$, given that $a = 1\frac{5}{8}$ when
    $b = \frac{3}{4}$ and $c = 2$.

4   Make a the subject of each of these formulae.
    a $3 + 4a = y$ **b** $t - ay = z$ **c** $b + c + ad = y$

5   Make b the subject of each of these formulae.
    a $2(3b - 1) = 5c$ **b** $k(m - b) = r$ **c** $p^2 = p + q(3 - b)$

6   Make c the subject of each of these formulae.
    a $a = \dfrac{b}{c} + d$ **b** $\dfrac{P}{c + d} = Q$ **c** $\dfrac{f(Nc - e)}{m} = D$

7   Make the letter in square brackets the subject of each of these formulae.
    a $v = u + ft$ $[f]$ **b** $\dfrac{a}{c} - d = b$ $[c]$
    c $x = \dfrac{p(p - a)}{qr}$ $[a]$ **d** $m = \frac{3}{4}(b + g)$ $[g]$

8   Make k the subject of each of these formulae.
    a $(k - d)^2 = x$ **b** $\dfrac{k + 1}{2} = y$ **c** $\dfrac{k^3}{q} = \dfrac{p}{r}$

9   Make e the subject of each of these formulae.
    a $\dfrac{a - e}{a + e} = y$ **b** $n - e = \dfrac{5e - n}{m}$ **c** $\dfrac{A}{e} + C = \dfrac{D}{e}$

10 Make p the subject of each of these formulae.
    a $\dfrac{x}{p} = k^2$ **b** $y + p = \dfrac{4 + p}{t}$ **c** $1 - p^2 = x^2$

11 Make k the subject of each of these formulae.
    a $k + c = kd$ **b** $h = 4\sqrt{k}$ **c** $h + 2 = \dfrac{mk - 3}{k}$

12 $R = \dfrac{kL}{d^2}$

    a Change the subject of the formula to d.

    b Hence, calculate d when $k = 7.5$, $L = 3$ and $R = 2.5$.

13 Make the letter in square brackets the subject of each of these formulae.

    a $\dfrac{x + y}{x - y} = 6$ $[x]$ **b** $\sqrt{z - at} = h$ $[a]$

    c $(Ax - B)^2 = K$ $[x]$ **d** $F = P\sqrt{1 + t^2}$ $[t]$

    e $T = \dfrac{mg(2a - x)}{a}$ $[a]$ **f** $\dfrac{m_1 - m_2}{1 + m_1 m_2} = \dfrac{3}{4}$ $[m_1]$

    g $x - yz = z + w$ $[z]$ **h** $v = \sqrt{u^2 - w^2}$ $[w]$

    i $y = \dfrac{a}{\sqrt{t}}$ $[t]$ **j** $us = v - s(w - x)$ $[s]$

14 An approximate relationship between an adult's height h cm and the length of their forearm f cm is given by the formula

    $f = \dfrac{1}{10}(3h - 256)$.

    Jack's forearm measures 26 cm.
    What height would you expect him to be?

Examination questions

Use 'Topic Tracker' at www.ccea.org.uk to find more exam questions.

Questions **1** to **4** are from examination papers where you may not use a calculator.

  1 The surface area of a solid is given by the formula $A = 7\pi r^2$.
     Find the value of A when $\pi = \dfrac{22}{7}$ and $r = \dfrac{3}{2}$.
     Give your answer as a mixed number.

  2 **a** Using the formula $P = 2L + 2W$, find the value of W when $P = 28$ and $L = 9$.

     b Using the formula $s = ut + \dfrac{1}{2}at^2$, calculate s when $u = 65$, $t = 2$ and $a = -5$.

  3 **a** Rearrange $d = 10c + 15$ to make c the subject of the formula.

     b Rearrange $4(3 + g) = h(7 - 2g)$ to make g the subject of the formula.

  4 $x = \dfrac{2y + 7}{3y - 3}$ Make y the subject of the formula.

Questions **5** to **7** are from examination papers where you may use a calculator.

  5 **a** Use the formula $Q = 3P - 2T$
       to find the value of Q when $P = 9$ and $T = 4$.

     b Use the formula $W = 4G + 3K$
       to find the value of G when $W = 17$ and $K = 3$.

  6 $2p + q = r$ Make p the subject of the formula.

  7 **a** $v^2 = u^2 - 2gh$ Make u the subject of the formula.

     b $y = \dfrac{1 - x}{1 + x}$ Make x the subject of the formula.

CHAPTER 21

Proportion and variation

This chapter is about:

- solving numerically problems involving direct or inverse proportion
- finding and using formulae to represent direct or inverse variation
- recognising graphs which represent variables that are directly or inversely proportional to one another.

You should already know:

- how to solve problems involving ratios
- how to solve linear equations
- how to change the subject of a formula.
- how to work with speed, distance and time
- how to work with numbers in standard form
- how to calculate percentage change.

Proportion

When two values are related to one another, they are said to be **proportional**. If, as one value increases, the other increases at the same rate or in the same ratio, the values are said to be **directly proportional** to one another. If, however, as one value increases the other *decreases* by the same ratio, the values are said to be **inversely proportional** to one another.

Direct proportion

An increase in one quantity causes a proportional increase in the other. If one quantity trebles, for example, so does the other, or if one quantity halves, so does the other.

EXAMPLE 1

Six books cost £8.52.
What will the cost of 10 similar books be?

SOLUTION

As the number of books increases, so too will the cost.

6 books cost £8.52.
So 1 book will cost £8.52 ÷ 6 = £1.42
and 10 books will cost £1.42 × 10 = £14.20.

As the cost will *increase*, this type of problem is commonly solved like this:
$\frac{10}{6} \times £8.52 = £14.20$

EXAMPLE 2

It takes 110 minutes to cycle 20 miles.
How long will it take to cycle 8 miles?

SOLUTION

As the distance decreases, so too will the time.
It takes 110 minutes for 20 miles.
So it will take $110 \div 20 = 5.5$ minutes for 1 mile
and $5.5 \times 8 = 44$ minutes for 8 miles.

> This type of problem can also be
> solved using ratios, like this:
> $$110 : 20 = x : 8$$
> $$x = 110 \times \frac{8}{20}$$
> $$= 44 \text{ minutes}$$

Inverse proportion

An increase in one quantity causes a proportional *decrease* in the other. If
one quantity doubles, for example, the other will halve, or if one quantity
is divided by 4, the other will become 4 times greater.

EXAMPLE 3

Three men build a wall in 20 days.
How long would it take five men to build the wall?

SOLUTION

As the number of men is increased, the time taken
to build the wall will decrease.

3 men take 20 days.
So 1 man would take $3 \times 20 = 60$ days
and 5 men would take $60 \div 5 = 12$ days.

> As time will *decrease*, this type of
> problem is commonly solved like this:
> $$\frac{3}{5} \times 20 = 12 \text{ days}$$

EXAMPLE 4

A farmer has enough grain to feed 60 animals for 24 days.
How long would the same amount of grain last if he had 80 animals?

SOLUTION

As the number of animals increases, the time for which the grain will last
decreases.

It will last 60 animals for 24 days.
So it would last 1 animal for $60 \times 24 = 1440$ days
and 80 animals for $1440 \div 80 = 18$ days.

> Alternatively, as time
> will decrease,
> $$\frac{60}{80} \times 24 = 18 \text{ days.}$$

Exercise 21.1

1   Nine pencils cost £1.62. What will 16 pencils cost?

2   An aeroplane takes 6 hours to travel 4200 km.
    How far will it travel in $4\frac{1}{2}$ hours at the same speed?

3   15 metres of cloth cost £48.
    How many metres of the same cloth could be bought for £72?

4   Nine identical bottles hold $22\frac{1}{2}$ litres altogether.
    How many bottles would be needed to hold 30 litres?

5   12 taps fill a tank in 3 hours. How long would it take to fill the
    same tank if there were 15 taps, each working at the same rate?

6   Three men paint a house in 20 days. How long would it take four
    men?

7   Using four pumps, it takes 21 hours to drain a swimming pool.
    If one of the pumps is broken, how long will it take the other
    three pumps to drain the pool?

8   60 machines produce 5400 CDs in 3 hours.
    a   Find how many CDs each machine produces in 1 hour.
    b   Find how many CDs would be produced during a 12-hour
        shift, if only $\frac{3}{4}$ of the machines were in operation.

9   x men take n hours to tarmac a particular road. How long would it
    take to tarmac the same road, if 5 more men were available?

10 A 44-seater coach costs £p to hire.
    How much would a 56-seater coach cost, if the charge per
    passenger remains the same?

Variation

When quantities are directly or inversely proportional to one another, you
can say that one **varies** as the other changes, or **varies inversely** as the
other changes. The symbol for variation is '$\propto$'.

Direct variation

You have already learnt that direct variation or proportion occurs when
both quantities increase or decrease in the same ratio. For example, if you
can buy five loaves of bread for £3.80, then eight loaves of bread will cost
more. You can say that the cost c is directly proportional to the number
of loaves l. This can be written as $c \propto l$, and this implies that $c = kl$, where
k is the **constant of proportionality**. The value of this constant can be
found by substitution, giving an algebraic formula connecting the two
variables. This formula can then be used to find any further values of c or l.

In general, $y \propto x$ (which can be rewritten as $y = kx$) represents any
function of the form 'y is proportional to x', 'y varies as x', 'y varies
directly as x', etc.

The idea can also be extended to other functions of the form 'y is directly
proportional to the square of x' (which becomes $y \propto x^2$ or $y = kx^2$),
'y varies as the cube root of x' (which becomes $y \propto \sqrt[3]{x}$ or $y = k\sqrt[3]{x}$), etc.

EXAMPLE 5

y varies directly as x. Given that $y = 9$ when $x = 6$, find:

    a y when $x = 15$ b x when $y = 3.75$.

SOLUTION

y varies directly as x, so $y \propto x$, which can be written as $y = kx$.

$9 = k \times 6$

So $k = \dfrac{9}{6} = 1\frac{1}{2}$

The formula is $y = 1\frac{1}{2}x$.

First find the formula connecting x and y.

Substitute in the values you are told for y and x to find the value of k.

Note the rearrangement to find k. This is the same method as was used for solving equations (see Chapter 17) and for changing the subject of a formula (see Chapter 20).

a $y = 1\frac{1}{2}x$

$y = 1\frac{1}{2} \times 15$

$y = 22.5$

Simply substitute $x = 15$ into the formula.

b $y = 1\frac{1}{2}x$

$3.75 = 1\frac{1}{2} \times x$

$x = 3.75 \div 1.5$

$x = 2.5$

Substitute for y and then solve this equation to find x.

Alternatively, you could change the subject of the formula to x first, and then substitute for y.

EXAMPLE 6

The volume V of a sphere varies directly as the cube of its diameter d. When the diameter is 6 cm, the volume of the sphere is 108 cm^3.

 a Find a formula connecting V and d.
 b Find the volume of a sphere with diameter 8 cm.
 c Find the diameter of a sphere with volume 500 cm^3.

SOLUTION

a V varies directly as d^3, so $V \propto d^3$ or $V = kd^3$.
  When $d = 6$, $V = 108$, so

   $108 = k \times 6^3$

   $108 = k \times 216$

  So $k = \dfrac{108}{216}$

    $= 0.5$

  The formula is $V = 0.5d^3$.

b $V = 0.5d^3$

   $V = 0.5 \times 8^3$

    $= 256$ cm^3

Substitute $d = 8$ in the formula.

c $V = 0.5d^3$

  $500 = 0.5d^3$

  So $d^3 = \dfrac{500}{0.5}$

    $= 1000$

   $d = \sqrt[3]{1000}$

    $= 10$ cm

Substitute $V = 500$ in the formula.

EXAMPLE 7

Given that p varies as the square of q, complete this table of values.

q	4	7	
p	8		72

SOLUTION

p varies as q^2, so $p \propto q^2$ or $p = kq^2$.

$8 = k \times 4^2$

$8 = k \times 16$

$k = \dfrac{8}{16}$

$\quad = \dfrac{1}{2}$

> The only pair of corresponding values are $q = 4$ and $p = 8$, so substitute these to find k.

The formula is $p = \frac{1}{2}q^2$.

When $q = 7$, $p = \frac{1}{2} \times 7^2 = 24.5$

When $p = 72$, $72 = \frac{1}{2} \times q^2$

$$\dfrac{72}{\frac{1}{2}} = q^2$$

$$144 = q^2$$

$$q = \sqrt{144} = 12$$

You can represent direct variation graphically. The graphs all pass through the origin.

- y varies directly as x.

  $y = kx$

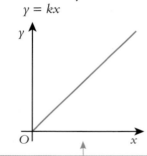

> This is a linear graph passing through the origin.

- y varies directly as x^2.

  $y = kx^2$

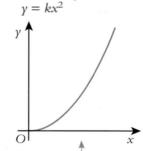

> This is a curved graph passing through the origin.

Exercise 21.2

1 P is proportional to Q, and when Q is 5, P is 16.
   Find a formula connecting P and Q.

2 y is proportional to the square root of x, and when $x = 1.96$, $y = 4.2$.
   a Find a formula for y in terms of x.
   b Use the formula to find y when x is 36.

3 The capacity C of a set of similar jugs varies directly as the cube of their height h.
   A jug of height 12 cm has a capacity of 864 cm^3.
   Find the capacity of a jug of height 20 cm.

4   The current I in a wire is proportional to the voltage V.
    When the current is 24 amperes, the voltage is 15 volts.

    a   Find the current when the voltage is 5 volts.

    b   Find the voltage when the current is 10 amperes.

5   The energy e of an object in motion is proportional to the square
    of its speed v m/s.
    An object moving at 20 m/s has 720 units of energy.
    At what speed will the object have 405 units of energy?

6   m varies directly as $(n + 3)$, and when $n = 5$, $m = 4.8$.
    a   Find m when $n = 12$.   b   Find n when $m = 6$.

7   $a \propto \sqrt{b - 3}$, and when $b = 12$, $a = 3.75$.

    a   Find a formula connecting a and b.   b   Find b when $a = 2.25$.

    c   Find a when $b = 7$.

8   When an object falls from rest, the distance d it falls is proportional
    to the square of the time t it takes to fall.
    A particle falling for 5 seconds covers a distance of 245 m.
    What distance will an object fall in 12 seconds?

9   In an experiment, the results in the table were obtained.

x	2	4	6
y	32	256	864

    Which of the following laws connects all three results:

    $y \propto x$, $y \propto x^2$, or $y \propto x^3$?

10 Given that $p \propto q^2$, what is the effect on p when
    a q is doubled?   b q is divided by 4?

11 The heat, H joules, that is produced in a wire varies directly
    as the square of the current I *and* as the time t for which the
    current flows.
    When a current of 5 amperes flows for 10 minutes, the heat
    produced is 9000 J.

    a   Find a formula connecting H, I and t.

    b   Use the formula to find the heat produced when 8 amperes
        flows for 2 minutes.

    c   Use the formula to find what current would need to flow for
        3 minutes to produce a heat of 1728 J.

Inverse variation

You have already learnt that inverse variation or proportion occurs when, as
one quantity increases, the other decreases proportionally. For example, if a car
travelling at 60 miles per hour can complete a journey in 40 minutes, then
a car travelling at 30 miles per hour will take longer (as it is travelling more
slowly). It will in fact take 80 minutes – as the speed has halved, the time
taken will double. You can say that the time t is inversely proportional to the

speed v. This can be written as $t \propto \dfrac{1}{v}$, and this implies that $t = k \times \dfrac{1}{v}$ or $t = \dfrac{k}{v}$, where k is the **constant of proportionality**. The value of this constant can be found by substitution, giving an algebraic formula connecting the two variables. This formula can then be used to find any further values of t or v.

In general, $y \propto \dfrac{1}{x}$ (which can be written as $y = \dfrac{k}{x}$) represents any function of the form 'y is inversely proportional to x', 'y varies inversely as x', 'y varies indirectly as x', etc.

The idea can be extended to other functions of the form 'y is inversely proportional to the square of x' (which becomes $y \propto \dfrac{1}{x^2}$ or $y = \dfrac{k}{x^2}$ and is commonly known as the **inverse square law**) and 'y varies inversely as the cube root of x' (which becomes $y \propto \dfrac{1}{\sqrt[3]{x}}$ or $y = \dfrac{k}{\sqrt[3]{x}}$), etc.

EXAMPLE 8

y varies inversely as x. Given that $y = 3$ when $x = 5$, find

    a y when $x = 2$ b x when $y = 20$.

SOLUTION

y varies inversely as x, so $y \propto \dfrac{1}{x}$, which can be written $y = \dfrac{k}{x}$ First find the formula connecting x and y.

$$3 = \frac{k}{5}$$

So $k = 3 \times 5 = 15$

The formula is $y = \dfrac{15}{x}$.

a $y = \dfrac{15}{x}$ b $y = \dfrac{15}{x}$

$y = \dfrac{15}{2}$ Simply substitute $x = 2$ into the formula. $20 = \dfrac{15}{x}$

$y = 7.5$ $20x = 15$

$$x = \frac{15}{20}$$

$$= 0.75 \ \text{ or } \ y = \frac{3}{4}$$

EXAMPLE 9

The force of attraction F between two magnets varies inversely as the square of the distance d between them.
When the magnets are 6 cm apart, the force of attraction is 2 newtons.

    a   Find a formula connecting F and d.
    b   Find the force of attraction between two magnets that are 2 cm apart.
    c   How far apart do two magnets need to be to result in a force of 4.5 newtons between them?

SOLUTION

a F varies inversely as d^2, so $F \propto \dfrac{1}{d^2}$ or $F = \dfrac{k}{d^2}$.

   When $d = 6$, $F = 2$, so

   $$2 = \frac{k}{6^2}$$

   $$2 = \frac{k}{36}$$

   $$k = 2 \times 36 = 72$$

   The formula is $F = \dfrac{72}{d^2}$.

b $F = \dfrac{72}{2^2}$ ⟵ Substitute $d = 2$ in the formula.

   $= \dfrac{72}{4} = 18$ newtons

c $F = \dfrac{72}{d^2}$

   $4.5 = \dfrac{72}{d^2}$ ⟵ Substitute $F = 4.5$ in the formula.

   $4.5d^2 = 72$

   $d^2 = \dfrac{72}{4.5}$

   $= 16$

   $d = \sqrt{16} = 4$ cm

EXAMPLE 10

Given that $v \propto \dfrac{1}{\sqrt{r}}$ complete this table of values.

r	1	16	
v	12		$\dfrac{3}{4}$

SOLUTION

$v \propto \dfrac{1}{\sqrt{r}}$ so $v = \dfrac{k}{\sqrt{r}}$ ⟵ The only pair of corresponding values are $r = 1$ and $v = 12$, so substitute these to find k.

$$12 = \frac{k}{\sqrt{1}}$$

$$= \frac{k}{1}$$

$$k = 12 \times 1 = 12$$

The formula is $v = \dfrac{12}{\sqrt{r}}$.

When $r = 16$, $v = \dfrac{12}{\sqrt{16}} = 3$

When $v = \dfrac{3}{4}$, $\dfrac{3}{4} = \dfrac{12}{\sqrt{r}}$

$$3 \times \sqrt{r} = 4 \times 12$$

$$\sqrt{r} = \frac{4 \times 12}{3}$$

$$= 16$$

$$r = 16^2 = 256$$

You can represent inverse variation graphically. The graphs are all curves that approach, but never touch, the two axes.

- y varies inversely as x.
  $$y = \frac{k}{x}$$

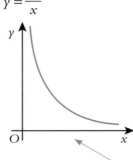

- y varies inversely as x^2.
  $$y = \frac{k}{x^2}$$

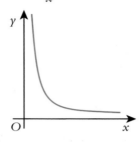

> This is a **reciprocal** graph. You will learn more about reciprocal graphs in Chapter 26.

Exercise 21.3

1 T is inversely proportional to M, and when T is $\frac{1}{2}$, M is 3.
   Find a formula connecting T and M.

2 y is inversely proportional to the square of x, and when $x = 3$, $y = 4$.
   a Find a formula connecting x and y.
   b Use the formula to find y when x is 1.5.

3 The volume V of a gas is inversely proportional to its pressure P.
   When the pressure is 40 cm of mercury, the volume is 450 cm³.
   Find the volume when the pressure is 25 cm of mercury.

4 Ohm's law states that the current, A amperes, in a resistor is
   inversely proportional to the resistance, R ohms.
   When the current is 6 amperes, the resistance is 40 ohms.
   a Find the current when the resistance is 48 ohms.
   b Find the resistance when the current is 2×10^{-3} amperes.
      Give your answer in standard form.

5 The intensity of light on an object is inversely proportional to the
   square of the distance of the object from the light source.
   If the intensity of the light is 12.5 units at a distance of 4 m, find
   the intensity at a distance of 2.5 m.

6 p varies inversely as $(q - 2)$, and when $q = 6$, $p = 1.2$.
   a Find p when $q = 8$.
   b Find q when $p = 0.5$.

7 The frequency of radio waves varies inversely as the wavelength.
   Radio R broadcasts on a wavelength of 200 metres and a frequency
   of 1.4×10^6 cycles per second.
   Another station, Radio M, operates on a frequency of
   8×10^5 cycles per second.
   What is the wavelength for Radio M?

8   $A \propto \dfrac{1}{\sqrt{B - 4}}$, and when $A = 2$, $B = 6.25$.

   a Find a formula connecting A and B.

   b Find A when $B = 20$.

   c Find B when $A = 15$.

9   The air pressure in a pump is inversely proportional to the square
of the diameter of the pump.
The pressure from a pump of diameter 20 mm is 12.5 units.
Find the diameter of a pump which can produce 8 units of pressure.

10 The number of swings per minute of a pendulum is inversely
proportional to the square root of its length.
A pendulum of length 0.25 m makes 120 swings per minute.

   a How many swings per minute will a pendulum of length
0.64 m make?

   b Find what length of pendulum would produce twice as many
swings per minute as a 1.44 m pendulum.

11 The number of ball bearings which can be manufactured from a
particular quantity of steel varies inversely as the cube of the radius
of the ball bearings.
When the radius is 0.25 mm, the number of ball bearings which
can be produced is 3456.
What is the maximum radius (to the nearest hundredth of a
millimetre), if at least 5000 ball bearings are to be produced?

12 The force F acting on a mass moving in a circle varies directly as
the square of its velocity v and inversely as the radius r of the circle
in which it is moving.

   a What will happen to the force if the radius is doubled and the
velocity is halved?

   b What will happen to the force if the velocity is ten times
greater and the radius is halved?

You should now:

- be able to solve numerically problems involving direct or inverse proportion
- be able to solve problems involving direct or inverse variation, algebraically by setting up a formula involving the constant of proportionality
- be able to use the formula derived for direct or inverse variation to find further unknown quantities
- recognise graphs which represent variables which are directly or inversely proportional.

Summary exercise 21

1   A car can travel 299 km on 26 litres of fuel.
How many litres of fuel would be needed to travel 460 km?

2   Six men can unload a delivery lorry in 20 minutes.
How long would it take if there were 10 men?

3   A man working x hours per day can complete a job in 12 days.
How many days would it take him to complete the job if he
worked an extra 2 hours per day?

4 The energy E of a rotating wheel varies as the square of its angular speed ω.

    a Given that $E = 16$ when $\omega = 2$, find a formula connecting E and ω.

    b Use your formula to find E when $\omega = 1.5$.

    c Use your formula to find ω when $E = 196$.

5 The mass m of a cube is proportional to the cube of its length l.
A cube of length 5 cm has a mass of 400 g.
What is the mass of a cube of length 8 cm?

6 **a** $y \propto x^2$
       What is the effect on y when

       i x is trebled?   **ii** x is halved?

    b $p \propto \sqrt{q}$
       What is the effect on p when

       i q is multiplied by 4?   **ii** q is divided by 16?

7 The time taken to cook something in a microwave oven is inversely proportional to the power of the oven. The time taken to cook a ready meal in a 500 W oven is $8\frac{1}{2}$ minutes.
How long would it take the same meal to cook in an 850 W oven?

8 Given that $p = \dfrac{k}{q^n}$ find k and n and hence complete this table.

q	0.5	2		8
p		80	10	1.25

9 a varies directly as the square of b *and* inversely as c.
What is the percentage change in a when b is decreased by 5% and c is increased by 25%?

10 Match each of these graphs with the correct statement below.

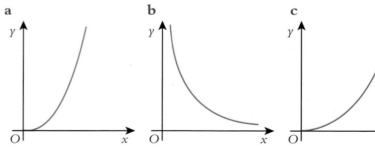

  a   **b**   **c**

    i y varies directly as the square of x.

    ii y varies directly as the cube of x.

    iii y varies inversely as x.

Examination questions

Use 'Topic Tracker' at www.ccea.org.uk to find more exam questions.

Question **1** is from an examination paper where you may not use a calculator.

1 P varies inversely as V.
When $V = 100$, $P = 0.6$

  a Express P in terms of V.

  b Calculate the value of P when $V = 300$.

Questions **2** and **3** are from examination papers where you may use a calculator.

2 p varies directly as the cube of q.
When $q = 4$, $p = 16$.

  a Express p in terms of q.

  b Find q when $p = 128$.

3 The resistance, R, of a copper wire is inversely proportional to the square of the diameter, d, of the wire.
When the diameter is 4, the resistance is 360.

  a Find an expression for R in terms of d.

  b Hence calculate

    i the resistance when the diameter is 7.

    ii the diameter when the resistance is 160.

CHAPTER 22

Trial and improvement

This chapter is about:

- solving polynomial equations by trial and improvement
- solving problems by trial and improvement to a suitable degree of accuracy.

You should already know:

- how to round numbers to a given number of decimal places
- how to square and cube numbers
- how to solve linear equations
- how to use and rearrange formulae
- how to expand brackets
- how to find the area of rectangles and triangles
- how to use Pythagoras' theorem
- how to find the volume of a cuboid
- how to find the surface area of a pyramid.

Solving polynomial equations by trial and improvement

In Chapter 17, you learnt how to solve a **linear equation.** A linear equation is one which has only one variable, such as x or a, without a power. An equation which has a *squared* term, for example $2x^2 - 3x = 5$, is known as a **quadratic equation**. An equation with a *cubed* term, for example $2x^3 + 3x^2 = 7$, is known as a **cubic equation**. Equations like these that are the sums of terms raised to different powers are more generally called **polynomial equations**. Polynomial equations cannot be solved in the same way as linear equations.

One way to solve such equations is known as **trial and improvement**, which can be used to find a reasonable answer to an appropriate degree of accuracy, for problems which may not have an exact answer. You will learn alternative ways of solving quadratic equations, which may be more accurate, in Chapter 24.

When you find a solution to a polynomial equation by trial and improvement, you substitute a trial value for the variable into the equation and then improve on that value until you find a solution to the required degree of accuracy.

Trial and improvement should be done in a systematic way. Usually you work with whole numbers first, until you find the two consecutive whole numbers between which the solution lies. (One of them will be too big and the other too small.) Then progress to numbers with 1 decimal place and, if necessary, to numbers with 2 decimal places. Finally, test the number halfway between the two consecutive decimals to determine which value is closer to the exact answer.

EXAMPLE 1

Solve the equation $x^2 + x = 83$, giving your answer correct to 1 decimal place.

SOLUTION

Trial x value	$x^2 + x$	Value (target = 83)	Result
7	$7^2 + 7$	56	too small
8	$8^2 + 8$	72	too small
9	$9^2 + 9$	90	too big

Your first trial may not be very accurate, but that is not important. So long as you progress in a systematic manner, you will eventually reach the required solution.

Trial x value	$x^2 + x$	Value (target = 83)	Result
7	$7^2 + 7$	56	too small
8	$8^2 + 8$	72	too small
9	$9^2 + 9$	90	too big
8.6	$8.6^2 + 8.6$	82.56	too small

This indicates that the solution must lie between 8 and 9 – *possibly* closer to 9 (as 90 is closer to 83 than 72 is). For the next trial, try 8.6.

8.6 is too small, but not by much. For the next trial, try 8.7.

Trial x value	$x^2 + x$	Value (target = 83)	Result
7	$7^2 + 7$	56	too small
8	$8^2 + 8$	72	too small
9	$9^2 + 9$	90	too big
8.6	$8.6^2 + 8.6$	82.56	too small
8.7	$8.7^2 + 8.7$	84.39	too big

This indicates that the solution lies between 8.6 and 8.7. To determine which is more accurate, you *must* test halfway, at 8.65.

Trial x value	$x^2 + x$	Value (target = 83)	Result
7	$7^2 + 7$	56	too small
8	$8^2 + 8$	72	too small
9	$9^2 + 9$	90	too big
8.6	$8.6^2 + 8.6$	82.56	too small
8.7	$8.7^2 + 8.7$	84.39	too big
8.65	$8.65^2 + 8.65$	83.4725	too big

Since using $x = 8.65$ gives an answer which is too big, the solution must be between 8.6 and 8.65. Any number in this range will round to 8.6 when written correct to 1 decimal place.

The solution to $x^2 + x = 83$ is $x = 8.6$ (to 1 d.p.).

EXAMPLE 2

Solve the equation $x^3 + 3x = 25$, giving your answer correct to 1 decimal place.

SOLUTION

Trial x value	$x^3 + 3x$	Value (target $= 25$)	Result
2	$2^3 + 3 \times 2$	14	too small ←
3	$3^3 + 3 \times 3$	36	too big
2.4	$2.4^3 + 3 \times 2.4$	21.024	too small
2.5	$2.5^3 + 3 \times 2.5$	23.125	too small
2.6	$2.6^3 + 3 \times 2.6$	25.376	too big
2.55	$2.55^3 + 3 \times 2.55$	24.231 375	too small ←

The solution to $x^3 + 3x = 25$ is $x = 2.6$ (to 1 d.p.).

> It is useful to be familiar with the square and cube numbers from Chapter 1, as this will help you to find a reasonably good starting point.

> Since using $x = 2.55$ gives an answer which is too small, the solution must be between 2.55 and 2.6. Any number in this range will round to 2.6 when written correct to 1 decimal place.

EXAMPLE 3

Solve the equation $2x^3 = x + 1.8$, giving your answer correct to 2 decimal places.

SOLUTION

First rearrange the equation as $2x^3 - x = 1.8$. ←

Trial x value	$2x^3 - x$	Value (target $= 1.8$)	Result
2	$2 \times 2^3 - 2$	14	too big
1	$2 \times 1^3 - 1$	1	too small
1.1	$2 \times 1.1^3 - 1.1$	1.562	too small ←
1.2	$2 \times 1.2^3 - 1.2$	2.256	too big ←

Trial x value	$2x^3 - x$	Value (target $= 1.8$)	Result
2	$2 \times 2^3 - 2$	14	too big
1	$2 \times 1^3 - 1$	1	too small
1.1	$2 \times 1.1^3 - 1.1$	1.562	too small
1.2	$2 \times 1.2^3 - 1.2$	2.256	too big
1.14	$2 \times 1.14^3 - 1.14$	1.823 088	too big
1.13	$2 \times 1.13^3 - 1.13$	1.755 794	too small
1.135	$2 \times 1.135^3 - 1.135$	1.789 2708	too small ←

The solution to $2x^3 = x + 1.8$ is $x = 1.14$ (to 2 d.p.).

> As with linear equations, all variable terms should be brought to one side of the equation. For example, an equation of the form $x^2 = 3x + 6$ should be rewritten as $x^2 - 3x = 6$ before any trials are carried out.

> Since a solution to 2 decimal places is required here, continue to look at values between 1.1 and 1.2.

> To decide between 1.13 and 1.14 as the best solution, test halfway between them.

> Since using $x = 1.135$ gives an answer which is too small, the solution must be between 1.135 and 1.14. Any number in this range will round to 1.14 when written correct to 2 decimal places.

In Chapter 17 you saw that a linear equation has a single solution. A quadratic equation has in fact *two* possible solutions and a cubic equation can have up to *three* possible solutions. But when you are using trial and improvement to solve an equation in this course, it is sufficient to find *just one* possible solution.

Exercise 22.1

1 Solve each of these polynomial equations by trial and improvement, giving your answers correct to 1 decimal place.

  a $x^3 + 2x = 200$
  b $4x^2 + x = 10$
  c $x^2 - 3x = 8$
  d $x^3 + x^2 + x = 20$
  e $2x^3 - 4x^2 = 38$
  f $x^3 - 3x^2 + 4 = 16$
  g $x^3 = 50$
  h $x^3 = 250 - 8x$
  i $2x^2 - x = 30$
  j $x(x + 3) = 19$

2 Solve each of these polynomial equations by trial and improvement, giving your answers correct to 2 decimal places.

  a $x^3 = 30$
  b $2x^2 = 80 + x$
  c $x^3 + x^2 = 120$
  d $4x^3 - 1 = 16$
  e $3x^2 - 5x - 7 = 0$
  f $x^4 = 120$
  g $3x^3 - x = 2.5$
  h $(3x)^2 = 54$
  i $2x^2 - 7x = -2$
  j $x^4 - x^3 = 30$

Problem solving using trial and improvement

Trial and improvement can be used to solve many practical problems for which there is not an exact answer, as illustrated in the examples below.

EXAMPLE 4

A building is to be extended so that the total floor area becomes 350 m². The original floor area is a square of side n, as shown in the diagram.

The shaded area in the diagram represents the extension.

Form an equation for the total floor area after the extension.

Solve your equation by trial and improvement to find the dimensions of the original floor area, correct to 1 decimal place.

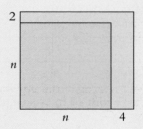

SOLUTION

The total floor area becomes $(n + 4)(n + 2)$, which must equal 350 m².

So $(n + 4)(n + 2) = 350$
    $n^2 + 2n + 4n + 8 = 350$
    $n^2 + 6n + 8 = 350$

> Recall the 'FOIL' method for expanding brackets (see Chapter 16).

Trial n value	$n^2 + 6n + 8$	Value (target $= 350$)
14	$14^2 + 6 \times 14 + 8$	288
15	$15^2 + 6 \times 15 + 8$	323
16	$16^2 + 6 \times 16 + 8$	360
15.6	$15.6^2 + 6 \times 15.6 + 8$	344.96
15.7	$15.7^2 + 6 \times 15.7 + 8$	348.69
15.8	$15.8^2 + 6 \times 15.8 + 8$	352.44
15.75	$15.75^2 + 6 \times 15.75 + 8$	350.5625

> n must be between 15 and 16.

> n must be between 15.7 and 15.8.

> n must be between 15.7 and 15.75 therefore $n = 15.7$ (to 1 d.p.).

> **Check**
> The extended floor area is $(15.7 + 4) \times (15.7 + 2) = 19.7 \times 17.7 = 348.69$
> This is approximately 350 m², as required.

The original floor was approximately 15.7 m by 15.7 m.

EXAMPLE 5

The length of a rectangle is 4 cm more than its width.
Given that the width is x and the diagonal of the rectangle is 12 cm, find the width of the rectangle, correct to 1 decimal place.

SOLUTION

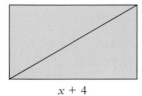

x

$x + 4$

Start by drawing and labelling a diagram. Since the length is 4 cm more than the width, it can be written as $x + 4$.

By Pythagoras' theorem,
$$x^2 + (x + 4)^2 = 12^2$$
$$x^2 + x^2 + 8x + 16 = 144$$
$$2x^2 + 8x = 128$$
$$x^2 + 4x = 64$$

This equation can be simplified by dividing through by 2. This will make the trial and improvement easier.

Trial x value	$x^2 + 4x$	Value (target = 64)
5	$5^2 + 4 \times 5$	45
6	$6^2 + 4 \times 6$	60
7	$7^2 + 4 \times 7$	77
6.2	$6.2^2 + 4 \times 6.2$	63.24
6.3	$6.3^2 + 4 \times 6.3$	64.89
6.25	$6.25^2 + 4 \times 6.25$	64.0625

x must be between 6 and 7.

x must be between 6.2 and 6.3.

x must be between 6.2 and 6.25 so $x = 6.2$ to 1 decimal place.

The width of the rectangle is 6.2 cm (to 1 d.p.).

Check
A width of 6.2 cm implies a length of 10.2 cm, and hence the diagonal will be $\sqrt{6.2^2 + 10.2^2} = 11.9$ cm. This is approximately 12 cm, as required. (Any difference is due to the rounding to 1 decimal place − remember that this is not an *exact* solution.)

EXAMPLE 6

A juice carton that holds 750 ml has a square base of side y.
Its height is 3 times the length of the base. Use trial and improvement to find the length of the base, correct to 1 decimal place.

SOLUTION

Height of carton $= y \times 3 = 3y$
Volume of carton $= y \times y \times 3y = 3y^3$
$$3y^3 = 750$$
$$y^3 = 250$$

The length of the base of the carton is 6.3 cm (to 1 d.p.).

Check
Volume $= 6.3 \times 6.3 \times (3 \times 6.3)$
$= 750.141$
≈ 750 cm^3, as required

Trial y value	y^3	Value (target = 250)
6	6^3	216
7	7^3	343
6.4	6.4^3	262.144
6.3	6.3^3	250.047
6.2	6.2^3	238.328
6.25	6.25^3	244.140 63

Exercise 22.2

Use the method of trial and improvement to solve each of the following problems.

1　The cube of a number, added to five times the original number, is 300.
　　Find the original number, correct to 1 decimal place.

2　A rectangle has length 5 cm more than its width.
　　The area of the rectangle is 64 cm².
　　Find the width, correct to 2 decimal places.

3　A square based pyramid has a base of side x cm.
　　The distance from the vertex to the midpoint of each edge is 8 cm as shown.

　　The total surface area of the pyramid is 400 cm².
　　Find the length of the sides of the base, correct to 0.1 cm.

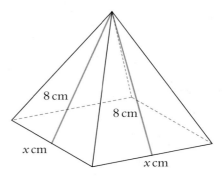

4　A rectangular sheet of paper has dimensions w by $w + 6$.
　　Four identical right-angled triangles are cut from the corners as shown.
　　a　Write an expression for the remaining area, in terms of w.
　　b　Given that the remaining area is 60 cm², find the value of w, correct to 1 decimal place.

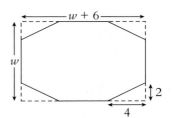

5　An object slides down a slope.
　　At any time t seconds, the distance, d metres, of the object from the top of the slope is given by the formula $d = 10 + 4t + t^2$.
　　a　How far is the object from the top of the slope at the starting time?
　　b　How far is the object from the top of the slope after 2 seconds?
　　c　How far has the object travelled after 3 seconds?
　　d　The slope is 50 metres long.
　　　　Find the time taken for the object to slide to the bottom of the slope, to the nearest tenth of a second.

You should now:

- be able to solve a polynomial equation by trial and improvement, correct to 1 decimal place
- be able to solve a polynomial equation by trial and improvement, correct to 2 decimal places
- be able to solve a problem, in context, by trial and improvement, to a suitable degree of accuracy.

Summary exercise 22

1   Solve each of these equations by trial and improvement, giving your answers correct to 1 decimal place.

   a $x^3 - 2x = 4.5$ **b** $3x^2 + 5x = 75$ **c** $2x^3 = 40 + x^2$

2   Solve each of these equations by trial and improvement, giving your answers correct to 2 decimal places.

   a $5x^2 - 4x = 24$ **b** $x^3 - 2x^2 = 50$ **c** $3x^2 - 20 = 4x$

3   Find, by trial and improvement, the number whose cube is 50 times its square root.
    Give your answer correct to 1 decimal place.

Examination questions

These questions are from examination papers where you may use a calculator.

1   Use trial and improvement to solve

    $x^3 - x = 30$

    giving your answer correct to 1 decimal place.

2   Taking values of x between 4 and 5, use trial and improvement to solve the equation $x^3 - 4x = 88$.
    Give your answer correct to 1 decimal place.
    Show each stage of your working.

3   Use trial and improvement to solve the equation $x^3 + 2x = 26$.
    Give your answer correct to 1 decimal place.
    Show each stage of your working.

> Use 'Topic Tracker' at www.ccea.org.uk to find more exam questions.

CHAPTER 23

Algebraic fractions

This chapter is about:

- simplifying algebraic fractions using factorisation and the rules of indices
- adding and subtracting algebraic fractions
- multiplying and dividing algebraic fractions.

You should already know:

- how to simplify, add, subtract, multiply and divide numerical fractions
- the rules of indices
- how to factorise simple algebraic expressions
- how to calculate the area of a rectangle
- how to work with speed, distance and time.

An **algebraic fraction** is a fraction with variable terms, rather than numerical terms. Many of the operations which you learnt for numerical fractions are also applicable to algebraic fractions. Also, some of the algebraic processes learnt in earlier chapters can be applied to algebraic fractions.

Simplifying algebraic expressions

In Chapter 5 you saw how numerical fractions can be simplified by cancelling both numerator and denominator by the same number, that is by dividing by a common factor. In the same way, an algebraic fraction can be simplified by dividing both numerator and denominator by the same algebraic factor. You have already encountered some simplifications of this type in Chapters 15 and 19.

EXAMPLE 1

Simplify $\dfrac{8x^2}{12xy}$.

SOLUTION

$$\frac{8x^2}{12xy} = \frac{2x}{3y}$$

Divide both the numerator and the denominator by $4x$, using the rules of indices. $8x^2 \div 4x = 2x$ and $12xy \div 4x = 3y$.

EXAMPLE 2

Simplify $\dfrac{4k^2m}{10k^3}$.

SOLUTION

$$\frac{4k^2m}{10k^3} = \frac{2m}{5k}$$

> Divide both the numerator and the denominator by $2k^2$.

EXAMPLE 3

Simplify $\dfrac{a^2 + 2a}{a^2 - 3a}$.

> A common mistake is to cancel the two a^2 terms, but remember that a^2 is not a *factor* of the complete numerator or denominator here. So you need to *factorise* both numerator and denominator first, before any cancelling is carried out.

SOLUTION

$$a^2 + 2a = a(a + 2)$$

> Factorise the numerator by common factors.

$$a^2 - 3a = a(a - 3)$$

> Factorise the denominator by common factors.

Hence $\dfrac{a^2 + 2a}{a^2 - 3a} = \dfrac{a(a + 2)}{a(a - 3)}$

> Cancel by a.

$$= \frac{a + 2}{a - 3}$$

As you can see from these two examples, the process of factorisation plays a vital role in the simplification of many algebraic fractions.

EXAMPLE 4

Simplify $\dfrac{x^2 + 7x + 10}{x^2 - 4}$.

SOLUTION

$$x^2 + 7x + 10 = (x + 5)(x + 2)$$

> Factorise the numerator, using whichever method for factorising a quadratic you prefer (see Chapter 19).

$$x^2 - 4 = (x - 2)(x + 2)$$

> Factorise the numerator, using the difference of two squares (see Chapter 19).

Hence $\dfrac{x^2 + 7x + 10}{x^2 - 4} = \dfrac{(x + 5)(x + 2)}{(x - 2)(x + 2)}$

> Now cancel by $(x + 2)$.

$$= \frac{x + 5}{x - 2}$$

Exercise 23.1

1 Simplify each of these fractions.

a $\dfrac{24}{60}$ b $\dfrac{35}{40}$ c $\dfrac{56}{64}$

2 Simplify each of these fractions.

a $\dfrac{6p}{3p}$ b $\dfrac{5ac}{10c}$ c $\dfrac{8pq^2}{12pq}$ d $\dfrac{21ac^2}{36c^3}$ e $\dfrac{4t^2}{10t^3}$ f $\dfrac{(5a)^2}{25a}$

3 Simplify each of these.

a $\dfrac{9a + 3}{3a}$ b $\dfrac{12p + 6}{6p}$ c $\dfrac{x^2 + x}{x^2}$ d $\dfrac{5x + 10y}{15xy}$

e $\dfrac{4pq + 8q^2}{2pq}$ f $\dfrac{4k + 5k^2}{5k}$ g $\dfrac{m^2 + mn}{m^2 - n^2}$ h $\dfrac{e^2 - 4}{e^2 + 5e + 6}$

i $\dfrac{9y^2 - 1}{9y + 3}$ j $\dfrac{a^2 + 2ab}{ab + 2b^2}$ k $\dfrac{2t^2 - 18}{t^2 + 2t - 3}$ l $\dfrac{a^2 - 7a}{a^2 - 49}$

4 Simplify each of these.

a $\dfrac{a^2 - 4a}{a^2 - 2a - 8}$ b $\dfrac{p^2 + 4p}{p^2 + 5p + 4}$ c $\dfrac{a^2 + 3a}{a^2 - 9}$ d $\dfrac{x^2 - 1}{x^2 + x - 2}$

$$\text{e} \quad \frac{h^2 - h - 6}{h^2 - 8h + 15} \qquad \text{f} \quad \frac{k^2 + k - 6}{k^2 + 3k} \qquad \text{g} \quad \frac{y^2 - 2y - 15}{2y^2 - 9y - 5} \qquad \text{h} \quad \frac{3a^2 - 48}{6a + 24}$$

$$\text{i} \quad \frac{5ab}{15a + 10a^3} \qquad \text{j} \quad \frac{a^2 + 4a}{2a^2 - 10a} \qquad \text{k} \quad \frac{ap - aq}{bq - bp} \qquad \text{l} \quad \frac{a^2 + ax - ay - xy}{ay + xy}$$

Adding and subtracting algebraic fractions

In Chapter 5 you saw how numerical fractions can be added or subtracted by first rewriting them as equivalent fractions with a common denominator. The numerators could then be added or subtracted.

For example, $\frac{2}{3} + \frac{1}{4} = \frac{8}{12} + \frac{3}{12} = \frac{11}{12}$.

Algebraic fractions are added or subtracted in a similar way.

EXAMPLE 5

Simplify $\frac{a}{4} + \frac{7b}{12}$.

SOLUTION

The lowest common multiple of 4 and 12 is 12, so write both fractions with a denominator of 12.

$$\frac{a}{4} + \frac{7b}{12} = \frac{3a}{12} + \frac{7b}{12} = \frac{3a + 7b}{12}$$

EXAMPLE 6

Simplify $\frac{2}{3x} - \frac{3}{2y}$.

SOLUTION

The lowest common multiple of $3x$ and $2y$ is $6xy$, so write both fractions with a denominator of $6xy$.

$$\frac{2}{3x} - \frac{3}{2y} = \frac{4y}{6xy} - \frac{9x}{6xy} = \frac{4y - 9x}{6xy}$$

> Recall the procedure for finding equivalent fractions with a common denominator.
> $6xy \div 3x = 2y$; $2y \times 2 = 4y$
> $6xy \div 2y = 3x$; $3x \times 3 = 9x$

EXAMPLE 7

Simplify $\frac{3}{5x} + \frac{2}{5x^2}$.

SOLUTION

Write both fractions with a denominator of $5x^2$.

$$\frac{3}{5x} + \frac{2}{5x^2} = \frac{3x}{5x^2} + \frac{2}{5x^2} = \frac{3x + 2}{5x^2}$$

EXAMPLE 8

Simplify $\frac{4}{x + 2} - \frac{2}{x - 1}$.

SOLUTION

Write both fractions with a denominator of $(x + 2)(x - 1)$.

$$\frac{4}{x + 2} - \frac{2}{x - 1} = \frac{4(x - 1)}{(x + 2)(x - 1)} - \frac{2(x + 2)}{(x + 2)(x - 1)}$$

$$= \frac{4x - 4 - 2x - 4}{(x + 2)(x - 1)}$$

$$= \frac{2x - 8}{(x + 2)(x - 1)} = \frac{2(x - 4)}{(x + 2)(x - 1)}$$

> Brackets are used here to ensure that *all* of the numerator of the second fraction is subtracted.

Exercise 23.2

1 Simplify each of these.

a $\dfrac{3x}{8} + \dfrac{x}{4}$
b $\dfrac{2a}{3} + \dfrac{a}{12}$
c $\dfrac{11a}{8} - \dfrac{3a}{4}$

d $\dfrac{3p}{4} + \dfrac{2p}{5}$
e $\dfrac{7x}{4} - \dfrac{2x}{3}$
f $\dfrac{x}{2} + \dfrac{x + 2}{3}$

2 Simplify each of these.

a $\dfrac{3}{10x} + \dfrac{2}{5x}$
b $\dfrac{5}{6x} - \dfrac{2}{3x}$
c $\dfrac{3}{x} + \dfrac{7}{2x}$

d $\dfrac{8}{3x} - \dfrac{3}{x^2}$
e $\dfrac{2}{p} + \dfrac{3}{p^2}$
f $\dfrac{4c}{3d} + \dfrac{3c}{d}$

3 Simplify each of these.

a $\dfrac{x + 4}{4} + \dfrac{x + 3}{6}$
b $\dfrac{p - 2q}{3} + \dfrac{p - 5q}{2}$
c $\dfrac{t - u}{5} - \dfrac{t + u}{4}$

d $\dfrac{a + 2}{2} - \dfrac{a + 1}{5}$
e $\dfrac{x}{5} + x + \dfrac{3}{2}$
f $\dfrac{2x - 1}{3} + \dfrac{x + 4}{4}$

4 Simplify each of these.

a $\dfrac{5}{a} + \dfrac{2}{a + 1}$
b $\dfrac{4}{2a} - \dfrac{1 - 1}{a - 2}$
c $\dfrac{3}{x - 2} - \dfrac{5}{x + 1}$

d $\dfrac{2t}{t + 1} - \dfrac{t}{t - 1}$
e $\dfrac{2k - 1}{6k^2} + \dfrac{7}{10k}$
f $\dfrac{a}{a - b} + \dfrac{b}{b - a}$

5 Simplify each of these.

a $\dfrac{a + 3}{a - 2} + \dfrac{a + 5}{a + 1}$
b $\dfrac{6y}{y^2 - 1} - \dfrac{5}{y - 1}$

c $\dfrac{2a - 3}{2a + 3} + \dfrac{12a}{4a^2 - 9}$
d $\dfrac{4}{p^2 + p} + \dfrac{3}{p^2 - p}$

6 A rectangular piece of material has an area of $50\,\text{cm}^2$ and length $x\,\text{cm}$. A second piece of material has an area of $40\,\text{m}^2$, and its length is $4\,\text{cm}$ less than that of the first piece. In terms of x, how much wider is the first piece than the second piece?

Multiplying and dividing algebraic fractions

Multiplying

In Chapter 5 you saw how fractions can be multiplied. The fractions were simplified first if possible, by dividing a numerator and a denominator by the same number or factor. This left the remaining fractions easier to multiply. Then the numerators were multiplied together and the denominators were multiplied together.

For example, $\dfrac{25}{49} \times \dfrac{21}{50} = \dfrac{25^1}{_749} \times \dfrac{21^3}{50_2} = \dfrac{3}{14}$.

Algebraic fractions can be multiplied in a similar way, simplifying first if possible by factorising all the numerators and all the denominators. It may then be possible to cancel a factor from a numerator and a denominator, leaving the remaining fractions easier to multiply.

EXAMPLE 9

Simplify $\dfrac{y + 3}{y^2 - 3y + 2} \times \dfrac{2y - 4}{y^2 - 9}$.

SOLUTION

$$\dfrac{y + 3}{y^2 - 3y + 2} \times \dfrac{2y - 4}{y^2 - 9} = \dfrac{y + 3}{(y - 2)(y - 1)} \times \dfrac{2(y - 2)}{(y - 3)(y + 3)}$$

$$= \dfrac{y + 3}{(y - 2)(y - 1)} \times \dfrac{2(y - 2)}{(y - 3)(y + 3)}$$

$$= \dfrac{2}{(y - 1)(y - 3)}$$

> Factorised by common factors.

> Factorised by the difference of two squares.

> Factorised into a pair of brackets.

> Cancel by the common factors $(y - 2)$ and $(y + 3)$.

EXAMPLE 10

Simplify $\dfrac{x^2 - 4}{x} \times \dfrac{3x^2 - 6x}{x + 2}$.

SOLUTION

$$\dfrac{x^2 - 4}{x} \times \dfrac{3x^2 - 6x}{x + 2} = \dfrac{(x - 2)(x + 2)}{x} \times \dfrac{3x(x - 2)}{x + 2}$$

$$= \dfrac{(x - 2)(x + 2)}{x} \times \dfrac{3x(x - 2)}{x + 2}$$

$$= 3(x - 2)^2$$

Dividing

In Chapter 5 you saw how fractions can be divided. The second fraction was inverted (turned upside down), and the process of multiplication was then carried out.

For example, $\dfrac{3}{5} \div \dfrac{9}{10} = \dfrac{3^1}{5_1} \times \dfrac{10^2}{9_3} = \dfrac{2}{3}$.

Algebraic fractions can be divided in a similar way, by inverting the second fraction and then carrying out the process of multiplication as above.

EXAMPLE 11

Simplify $\dfrac{y^2 - 4}{y} \div \dfrac{2y + 4}{5y}$.

SOLUTION

$$\dfrac{y^2 - 4}{y} \div \dfrac{2y + 4}{5y} = \dfrac{y^2 - 4}{y} \times \dfrac{5y}{2y + 4}$$

> Turn the second fraction upside down and multiply.

$$= \frac{(y-2)(y+2)}{y} \times \frac{5y}{2(y+2)}$$

← Factorise where possible.

$$= \frac{(y-2)(y+2)}{y} \times \frac{5y}{2(y+2)}$$

← Cancel by y and by $(y+2)$.

$$= \frac{5(y-2)}{2}$$

EXAMPLE 12

Simplify $\dfrac{x^2 + 7x + 10}{2x + 3} \div \dfrac{3x + 15}{12x + 18}$.

SOLUTION

$$\frac{x^2 + 7x + 10}{2x + 3} \div \frac{3x + 15}{12x + 18} = \frac{x^2 + 7x + 10}{2x + 3} \times \frac{12x + 18}{3x + 15}$$

$$= \frac{(x+5)(x+2)}{2x+3} \times \frac{6(2x+3)}{3(x+5)}$$

$$= \frac{(x+5)(x+2)}{2x+3} \times \frac{{}^2 6(2x+3)}{3(x+5)}$$

$$= 2(x+2)$$

Exercise 23.3

1 Simplify each of these.

a $\dfrac{4a}{b} \times \dfrac{b^2}{a}$

b $\dfrac{c^3}{24d^2} \times \dfrac{40d}{c^2}$

c $\dfrac{pq^2}{2} \times \dfrac{4p}{q}$

d $\dfrac{a}{y} \div \dfrac{b}{y}$

e $\dfrac{8x^3}{27y^2} \div \dfrac{40x}{9y^3}$

f $\dfrac{a^2 - b^2}{45} \div \dfrac{a + b}{36}$

2 Simplify each of these.

a $\dfrac{a^2 - b^2}{27c} \times \dfrac{36c}{a + b}$

b $\dfrac{x + 1}{x^2 - x - 6} \times \dfrac{x + 2}{2x + 2}$

c $\dfrac{a^2 - 1}{(a + 1)^2} \times \dfrac{a + 1}{a - 1}$

d $\dfrac{3p^2 + p - 2}{2} \times \dfrac{8p + 4}{6p^2 - p - 2}$

e $\dfrac{k^2 - 4k + 4}{k^2 - 2k} \times \dfrac{k - 2}{k^2 - 4}$

f $\dfrac{2x^2 - 4x - 16}{x^2 - 16} \times \dfrac{3x + 12}{4x + 8}$

3 Simplify each of these.

a $\dfrac{10a - 5b}{48} \div \dfrac{2a - b}{36}$

b $\dfrac{4x^2 - 9}{3 - 2x} \div \dfrac{3 + 2x}{2x - 3}$

c $\dfrac{p + 1}{2p} \div \dfrac{4p^2 - 4}{p^2}$

d $\dfrac{x^2 + x - 2}{x + 1} \div \dfrac{2x - 2}{x^2 + 2x + 1}$

e $\dfrac{4a^2 - 9}{(2a - 3)^2} \div \dfrac{8a + 12}{16a - 24}$

f $\dfrac{x^2 - ax + bx - ab}{x} \div \dfrac{10x - 10a}{5x^2}$

4 Simplify each of these.

a $\dfrac{4y^2 + 8y}{6y + 9} \times \dfrac{12y + 18}{5y^2 + 10y}$

b $\dfrac{(p + q)^2}{3p - 3q} \div \dfrac{5p + 5q}{p - q}$

c $\dfrac{a^2 - 4a + 4}{a^2 + 3a} \times \dfrac{a^2 + 6a + 9}{a^2 + a - 6}$

d $\dfrac{3x^2 - 6xy}{5y^2z} \times \dfrac{4z^2}{x^2 - 4y^2} \div \dfrac{9x}{10y}$

You should now:

- be able to simplify an algebraic fraction, using factorisation and the rules of indices
- be able to add and subtract algebraic fractions
- be able to multiply and divide algebraic fractions
- be able to simplify problems involving algebraic fractions.

Summary exercise 23

1 Simplify each of these.

a $\dfrac{2p + 2}{p^2 - 1}$ **b** $\dfrac{x + 1}{x^2 - 2x - 3}$ **c** $\dfrac{4y - 6z}{24yz}$

d $\dfrac{9y^2 - 3y + 12}{6y^2 - 2y + 8}$ **e** $\dfrac{3c^2 + 6cd}{2cd + 4d^2}$ **f** $\dfrac{4a - 4b}{6b - 6a}$

2 Simplify each of these.

a $\dfrac{2a}{3} + \dfrac{a}{5}$ **b** $\dfrac{3}{4x} + \dfrac{4}{5x}$ **c** $\dfrac{2}{a} - \dfrac{3}{a + 1}$

d $\dfrac{a + 3b}{2} - \dfrac{a - 3b}{4}$ **e** $\dfrac{4}{a - 2} - \dfrac{3}{2a + 1}$ **f** $\dfrac{3}{x^2 + x} + \dfrac{3}{x^2 - x}$

3 Simplify each of these.

a $\dfrac{2x + 8}{5} \times \dfrac{1}{x^2 - 16}$ **b** $\dfrac{5a^2}{a^2 + 6a - 7} \div \dfrac{a}{a^2 - 1}$

c $\dfrac{3k^2 + 12k + 12}{k^2 - 4} \times \dfrac{5k^2 - 5k - 10}{10k}$ **d** $\dfrac{4y - 12}{3y + 9} \div \dfrac{3 - y}{y^2 - 9}$

e $\dfrac{8p^2q}{8p + 4q} \times \dfrac{16p}{3q} \div \dfrac{48p + 24q}{(2p + q)^2}$ **f** $\left(\dfrac{2}{c + 4} - \dfrac{3}{c}\right) \div \dfrac{c + 12}{c^2 - 16}$

4 a A car travelled a km at an average speed of x km/h. Write an expression for the time taken.

b On the return journey, the average speed of the car was 2 km/h faster than on the outward journey. Write an expression for the time taken for the return journey.

c Write an expression for the total distance travelled.

d Write an expression for the total time taken, as a single fraction.

e Hence find an expression for the average speed for the complete journey.

Examination questions

Question **1** is from an examination paper where you may not use a calculator.

1 Express $\dfrac{x - 1}{x} + \dfrac{x}{x + 1}$ as a single fraction in its simplest form.

Questions **2** and **3** are from examination papers where you may use a calculator.

2 a Factorise $x^2 - 9y^2$. **b** Simplify $\dfrac{x^2 - 9y^2}{x^2 - 9xy + 18y^2}$.

3 Prove that

$$\dfrac{x - y}{x + y} - \dfrac{y}{x - y} + \dfrac{2xy}{x^2 - y^2} \equiv \dfrac{x}{x + y}$$

Use 'Topic Tracker' at www.ccea.org.uk to find more exam questions.

Whilst there are few examination questions available solely on this topic, it is important to remember that these skills *will* be examined in greater detail within questions on other topics, in particular those on quadratic equations (see Chapter 24).

CHAPTER 24

Solving quadratic equations

This chapter is about:

- solving quadratic equations by factorisation
- solving quadratic equations using the quadratic formula
- solving quadratic equations involving algebraic fractions
- selecting the most appropriate method to solve a quadratic equation resulting from a problem.

You should already know:

- how to work with negative numbers and fractions
- how to expand brackets
- how to factorise quadratic expressions
- how to simplify expressions involving algebraic fractions
- how to round numbers to a given degree of accuracy
- how to simplify surds
- how to find the perimeter and area of rectangles and compound shapes made from rectangles
- how to work with speed, distance and time
- how to use Pythagoras' theorem
- how to find the probability of two events occurring
- how to find the rule for the nth term of a sequence
- what a triangular number is
- how to find the area of a circle
- how to find the volume of a cuboid
- what a reciprocal is
- how to find the mean.

A **quadratic expression** is one of the form $ax^2 + bx + c$. (The b or the c term may in fact be zero, but there *must* be a squared term.) You have already met such expressions in Chapters 18 and 19.

When a quadratic expression is equated to zero, it becomes a **quadratic equation**, for example $ax^2 + bx + c = 0$. The solutions to the equation are the points at which the quadratic graph cuts the x–axis.

In general, quadratic equations have *two* different solutions.

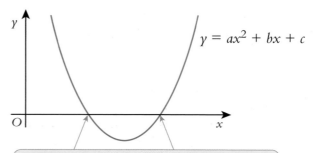

These are the solutions to the quadratic equation $ax^2 + bx + c = 0$.

There are several methods for solving a quadratic equation. Some of these are illustrated in this chapter. You will also see how to solve a quadratic equation by a graphical method in Chapters 26 and 29.

Solving quadratic equations by factorisation

In Chapter 19 you saw how a quadratic expression can be factorised by common factors, quadratic factorisation or the difference of two squares. Any of these methods leads to a product of two terms or expressions, which can be written as AB.

For example, $x^2 - x - 6$ can be factorised to give $(x + 2)(x - 3)$, with $A = (x + 2)$ and $B = (x - 3)$. Similarly, you can factorise the left–hand side of the quadratic equation $x^2 - x - 6 = 0$, giving $(x + 2)(x - 3) = 0$. If $AB = 0$, either $A = 0$ or $B = 0$. This fact is used to solve quadratic equations that factorise.

EXAMPLE 1

Solve the equation $(x + 2)(x - 3) = 0$.

SOLUTION

Either $x + 2 = 0$ or $x - 3 = 0$

so $x = 0 - 2$ or $x = 0 + 3$

              $x = -2$ or $x = 3$

EXAMPLE 2

Solve the equation $x^2 - 13x - 30 = 0$.

SOLUTION

$$x^2 - 13x - 30 = 0$$
$$(x - 15)(x + 2) = 0$$

Either $x - 15 = 0$ or $x + 2 = 0$

                      $x = 15$ or $x = -2$

Here, $15^2 - 13 \times 15 - 30 = 225 - 195 - 30 = 0$

and $(-2)^2 - 13 \times (-2) - 30 = 4 + 26 - 30 = 0$.

> First factorise the quadratic expression using one of the methods from Chapter 19.

> As with linear equations, you should check the solutions to a quadratic equation by substituting them back into the original equation.

EXAMPLE 3

Solve the equation $2x^2 + 11x + 12 = 0$.

SOLUTION

$$2x^2 + 11x + 12 = 0$$
$$(2x + 3)(x + 4) = 0$$

Either $2x + 3 = 0$ or $x + 4 = 0$

                $2x = -3$

                $x = -1\frac{1}{2}$ or $x = -4$

> At this stage you should be able to factorise quadratics fairly easily and quickly, but if you are still unsure look back to Chapter 19 for more details.

EXAMPLE 4

Solve the equation $16x^2 - 25 = 0$.

$$16x^2 - 25 = 0$$
$$(4x - 5)(4x + 5) = 0$$

Either $\quad 4x - 5 = 0 \quad$ or $\quad 4x + 5 = 0$
$$4x = 5 \quad \text{or} \quad 4x = -5$$
$$x = 1\tfrac{1}{4} \quad \text{or} \quad x = -1\tfrac{1}{4}$$

> The difference of two squares is used to factorise here.

EXAMPLE 5

Solve the equation $3x^2 + x = 10$.

SOLUTION

$$3x^2 + x = 10$$
$$3x^2 + x - 10 = 0$$
$$(3x - 5)(x + 2) = 0$$

Either $\quad 3x - 5 = 0 \quad$ or $\quad x + 2 = 0$
$$3x = 5$$
$$x = 1\tfrac{2}{3} \quad \text{or} \quad x = -2$$

> First rearrange the equation so that the right-hand side is zero ...

> ... then factorise and solve the equation as before.

EXAMPLE 6

Solve the equation $a^2 = \dfrac{a}{4}$.

SOLUTION

The variable used here is a but this is still a quadratic equation because there is a squared term.

$$a^2 = \frac{a}{4}$$
$$4a^2 = a$$
$$4a^2 - a = 0$$
$$a(4a - 1) = 0$$

Either $\quad a = 0 \quad$ or $\quad 4a - 1 = 0$
$$4a = 1$$
$$a = 0 \quad \text{or} \quad a = \tfrac{1}{4}$$

> Multiply both sides by 4 to eliminate the fraction.

> Common factors are used to factorise here.

Exercise 24.1

1 Solve these equations.
   a $(x + 3)(x - 4) = 0$
   b $(a - 7)(a + 1) = 0$
   c $(2x + 3)(x - 2) = 0$
   d $(4t + 5)(3t + 10) = 0$
   e $(x - 3)(x + 3) = 0$
   f $(2x - 1)(x - 3) = 0$
   g $x(4x - 5) = 0$
   h $3a(2a - 1) = 0$
   i $x(x + 2) = 0$
   j $(2x + 1)^2 = 0$

2 Solve these equations by factorisation.
   a $x^2 + 3x + 2 = 0$
   b $2y^2 - 5y - 3 = 0$
   c $6x^2 - x - 1 = 0$
   d $x^2 - 14x + 13 = 0$
   e $a^2 - 2a - 8 = 0$
   f $p^2 - 11p + 24 = 0$
   g $3y^2 - 10y + 3 = 0$
   h $4k^2 - 3k - 10 = 0$
   i $8a^2 - 2a - 3 = 0$
   j $12m^2 + 7m - 12 = 0$

3 Solve these equations by factorisation.

a $9x^2 - 1 = 0$ b $4x^2 - 2x = 0$ c $3a^2 + a = 0$

d $x^2 - 25 = 0$ e $6y^2 + 9y = 0$ f $36y^2 - 3y = 0$

g $a^2 - \frac{1}{4} = 0$ h $5y^2 + 5y = 0$ i $2t^2 - 18 = 0$

j $10x^2 - 45x = 0$

4 Solve each of these equations by factorisation.
You may need to rearrange the equation into the correct format before factorising.

a $x^2 = 5x - 6$ b $2x^2 + 7x = 15$ c $2a^2 = a + 10$

d $x^2 = 1$ e $(x - 2)^2 = 1$ f $a^2 - 8a = 33$

g $20 = 9p - p^2$ h $(x + 4)(x - 2) = 7x - 2$ i $k(k + 4) = 60$

j $2n^2 = \frac{n}{3}$

5 Solve each of these quadratic equations by factorisation.

a $(2x + 7)(x - 2) = 0$ b $2x^2 + 5x - 3 = 0$ c $a^2 + 12 = 8a$

d $8a^2 + 6a - 9 = 0$ e $4x^2 + 6x = 0$ f $9n^2 = 25$

g $x^2 = x$ h $(3x + 1)(2x - 1) = 4$ i $a(a + 3) = 10$

j $\frac{a}{5} - 5a^2 = 0$

Solving quadratic equations using the quadratic formula

Another method for solving quadratic equations is to use the **quadratic formula**. The quadratic formula for the solution of the equation $ax^2 + bx + c = 0$ is

$$x = \frac{-b \pm \sqrt{b^2 - 4ac}}{2a}$$

The answers will be exact if they are left in terms of surds or, if required, they can be calculated to a suitable degree of accuracy.

Whilst this method works for *all* quadratic equations, it should only be used when factorisation has already been tried but has been unsatisfactory, or when the a, b and c values are simply so big or awkward that factorisation could prove very difficult.

The first of the examples below demonstrates the method, using a quadratic equation which does, in fact, factorise (see Example 3).

EXAMPLE 7

Solve the equation $2x^2 + 11x + 12 = 0$.

SOLUTION

$a = 2$, $b = 11$ and $c = 12$.   Determine the values of a, b and c.

$x = \dfrac{-11 \pm \sqrt{112 - 4 \times 2 \times 12}}{2 \times 2}$ Substitute the values of a, b and c into the formula.

$$x = \frac{-11 \pm \sqrt{121 - 96}}{4}$$

$$x = \frac{-11 \pm \sqrt{25}}{4}$$

$$x = \frac{-11 + 5}{4} \quad \text{or} \quad x = \frac{-11 - 5}{4}$$

$$x = -\frac{6}{4} \quad \text{or} \quad x = -\frac{16}{4}$$

$$x = -1\frac{1}{2} \quad \text{or} \quad x = -4$$

> Note that these solutions are the same as achieved by factorisation – proving the guaranteed success of the quadratic formula. Remember, though, that if a quadratic *does* factorise, the factorisation method of solution should be used.

EXAMPLE 8

Solve the equation $2x^2 - 7x + 4 = 0$.

Give your answers correct to 2 decimal places.

SOLUTION

$a = 2$, $b = -7$ and $c = 4$.

$$x = \frac{-(-7) \pm \sqrt{(-7)^2 - 4 \times 2 \times 4}}{2 \times 2}$$

$$x = \frac{7 \pm \sqrt{49 - 32}}{4}$$

$$x = \frac{7 \pm \sqrt{17}}{4}$$

$$x = 2.78 \quad \text{or} \quad x = 0.72 \text{ (to 2 d.p.)}$$

> Note that $-(-7)$ means $-1 \times -7 = +7$ by the rules of multiplying negative numbers (see Chapter 4). Similarly, b^2 is $(-7)^2 = -7 \times -7 = +49$.

EXAMPLE 9

Solve the equation $3x^2 + 2x - 6 = 0$.

Give your answers in surd form.

SOLUTION

$a = 3$, $b = 2$ and $c = -6$.

$$x = \frac{-2 \pm \sqrt{2^2 - 4 \times 3 \times (-6)}}{2 \times 3}$$

$$x = \frac{-2 \pm \sqrt{4 - (-72)}}{6}$$

$$x = \frac{-2 \pm \sqrt{4 + 72}}{6}$$

$$x = \frac{-2 \pm \sqrt{76}}{6}$$

$$x = \frac{-2 \pm 2\sqrt{19}}{6}$$

$$x = \frac{-1 \pm \sqrt{19}}{3}$$

> Remember the rules of adding and subtracting negative numbers.

> Simplify the surd using the techniques from Chapter 13.
> $\sqrt{76} = \sqrt{4 \times 19} = 2\sqrt{19}$.

> Using surds gives an exact answer rather than an answer rounded to a certain degree of accuracy. Always simplify the answer as far as possible.

EXAMPLE 10

Solve the equation $3.4x^2 - 5.2x - 1.9 = 0$.

Give your answers correct to 3 significant figures.

SOLUTION

$a = 3.4$, $b = -5.2$ and $c = -1.9$.

> Do not try to factorise an equation involving decimals – use the formula straight away.

$$x = \frac{-(-5.2) \pm \sqrt{(-5.2)^2 - 4 \times 3.4 \times (-1.9)}}{2 \times 3.4}$$

$$x = \frac{5.2 \pm \sqrt{27.04 + 25.84}}{6.8}$$

$$x = \frac{5.2 \pm \sqrt{52.88}}{6.8}$$

$x = 1.83$ or $x = -0.30$ (to 3 s.f.)

EXAMPLE 11

Solve the equation $(k - 3)^2 = 10$.

Give your answers in surd form.

SOLUTION

$$(k - 3)^2 = 10$$

> Expand the brackets.

$$k^2 - 6k + 9 = 10$$

> Rearrange the equation so the right-hand side is zero ...

$$k^2 - 6k - 1 = 0$$

$a = 1$, $b = -6$ and $c = -1$.

> ... then identify a, b and c.

$$k = \frac{-(-6) \pm \sqrt{(-6)^2 - 4 \times 1 \times (-1)}}{2 \times 1}$$

> Note that the variable is k here rather than x but the formula is the same.

$$k = \frac{6 \pm \sqrt{36 + 4}}{2}$$

$$k = \frac{6 \pm \sqrt{40}}{2}$$

$$k = \frac{6 \pm 2\sqrt{10}}{2}$$

$$k = 3 \pm \sqrt{10}$$

Exercise 24.2

1 Solve each of these equations, giving your answers correct to 2 decimal places.

   a $x^2 - 4x + 1 = 0$ b $2x^2 + 6x - 3 = 0$ c $3x^2 + x - 3 = 0$

   d $2x^2 + 11x + 6 = 0$ e $3y^2 - 5y + 1 = 0$ f $4x^2 - x - 4 = 0$

   g $8x^2 + 9x - 7 = 0$ h $-3x^2 + 10x + 3 = 0$ i $2.2x^2 + 0.8x - 1.4 = 0$

   j $3y^2 - 5y - 3 = 0$

2 Solve each of these equations, giving the exact answers in surd form.

  a $x^2 - 2x - 5 = 0$ b $2x^2 - 6x + 1 = 0$ c $y^2 - 12y + 5 = 0$

  d $2x^2 + 6x + 3 = 0$ e $2k^2 + 5k - 1 = 0$ f $x^2 + 6x + 1 = 0$

  g $7x^2 - 12x + 3 = 0$ h $y^2 - 4y - 7 = 0$ i $t^2 - 6t + 6 = 0$

  j $8a^2 + 10a + 1 = 0$

3 Solve each of these equations, giving your answers correct to 3 significant figures.

  a $2x^2 = 5x + 2$ b $x(x + 2) = 5$ c $(x - 2)(x + 1) = 12$

  d $10y(2 - y) = 7$ e $2x(x + 1) = 10 - x$ f $3x^2 = 7x + 1$

  g $(y + 4)^2 = 2$ h $5a - 7 = \dfrac{2}{a}$ i $\dfrac{x + 1}{x} = 8$

  j $2a(a - 1) = (a + 1)^2 - 3$

Solving quadratic equations involving algebraic fractions

In Chapter 17 you learnt how to solve a linear equation involving algebraic fractions. In Chapter 23 you learnt how to simplify an algebraic fraction. You can combine this knowledge to solve quadratic equations involving algebraic fractions.

EXAMPLE 12

Solve the equation $\dfrac{2}{x} + \dfrac{2}{x + 1} = 3$.

SOLUTION

$$\dfrac{2}{x} + \dfrac{2}{x + 1} = 3$$

Rewrite the left-hand side using the common denominator $x(x + 1)$.

$$\dfrac{2(x + 1) + 2x}{x(x + 1)} = 3$$

Expand the bracket in the numerator.

$$\dfrac{4x + 2}{x(x + 1)} = 3$$

Multiply both sides by $x(x + 1)$ to eliminate the fractions.

$$4x + 2 = 3x(x + 1)$$

$$4x + 2 = 3x^2 + 3x$$

You can now see that the equation is a quadratic equation.

$$3x^2 + 3x - 4x - 2 = 0$$

$$3x^2 - x - 2 = 0$$

$$(3x + 2)(x - 1) = 0$$

This quadratic expression factorises.

$$3x + 2 = 0 \quad \text{or} \quad x - 1 = 0$$

$$x = -\dfrac{2}{3} \quad \text{or} \quad x = 1$$

EXAMPLE 13

Solve the equation $\dfrac{2}{x + 1} - \dfrac{3}{2x + 3} = \dfrac{1}{2}$.

$$\frac{4x + 6 - 3x + 3}{x + 3}$$

SOLUTION

$$\frac{2}{x + 1} - \frac{3}{2x + 3} = \frac{1}{2}$$

> Rewrite the left-hand side using the common denominator $(x + 1)(2x + 3)$.

$$\frac{2(2x + 3) - 3(x + 1)}{(x + 1)(2x + 3)} = \frac{1}{2}$$

> Expand the brackets.

$$\frac{x + 3}{2x^2 + 5x + 3} = \frac{1}{2}$$

$$2x^2 + 5x + 3 = 2(x + 3)$$

$$2x^2 + 5x + 3 = 2x + 6$$

$$2x^2 + 3x - 3 = 0$$

> Cross-multiply to eliminate the fractions. Multiply $(x + 3)$ by 2 and multiply 1 by $(2x^2 + 5x + 3)$. Note that you can write the result as $2(x + 3) = 2x^2 + 5x + 3$ or as $2x^2 + 5x + 3 = 2(x + 3)$, whichever is more convenient.

$a = 2$, $b = 3$ and $c = -3$.

$$x = \frac{-3 \pm \sqrt{3^2 - 4 \times 2 \times (-3)}}{2 \times 2}$$

> Since this quadratic does not factorise, you need to use the quadratic formula.

$$x = \frac{-3 \pm \sqrt{9 - (-24)}}{4}$$

$$x = \frac{-3 \pm \sqrt{33}}{4}$$

$$x = 0.7 \qquad \text{or} \qquad x = -2.2 \text{ (to 1 d.p.)}$$

EXAMPLE 14

Solve the equation $\dfrac{2a + 1}{a + 4} = \dfrac{a + 3}{a - 2}$ exactly.

SOLUTION

$$\frac{2a + 1}{a + 4} = \frac{a + 3}{a - 2}$$

$$(2a + 1)(a - 2) = (a + 3)(a + 4)$$

$$2a^2 - 3a - 2 = a^2 + 7a + 12$$

$$a^2 - 10a - 14 = 0$$

> The first step here is to cross-multiply to eliminate the fractions.

> This quadratic does not factorise, so use the formula.

$a = 1$, $b = -10$ and $c = -14$.

$$a = \frac{-(-10) \pm \sqrt{(-10)^2 - 4 \times 1 \times (-14)}}{2 \times 1}$$

> Try not to be confused by the fact that the letter a is used both as the variable in the quadratic equation and also to represent the coefficient of the squared term.

$$a = \frac{10 \pm \sqrt{100 - (-56)}}{2}$$

$$a = \frac{10 \pm \sqrt{156}}{2}$$

$$a = \frac{10 \pm 2\sqrt{39}}{2}$$

$$a = 5 \pm \sqrt{39}$$

> The question asks for an exact solution, so leave your answers in surd form, simplified as far as possible.

Exercise 24.3

Solve each of these equations.

Give your answers either exact or correct to 2 decimal places.

1 $3x - \dfrac{x}{5} = \dfrac{2}{3}$

2 $\dfrac{4(a - 2)}{5} + 1 = \dfrac{a}{2}$

3 $\dfrac{3x}{x - 1} - \dfrac{6}{x + 1} = 3$

4   $\dfrac{1}{a - 2} + \dfrac{2}{a + 4} = \dfrac{1}{3}$ 5 $\dfrac{4p}{3p - 2} - \dfrac{p - 1}{2p - 3} = 1$ 6 $\dfrac{2a + 3}{a} = \dfrac{a - 1}{a - 4}$

7   $\dfrac{15}{x + 3} + \dfrac{21}{x + 5} = 6$ 8 $\dfrac{8}{p + 3} = 6 - p$ 9 $\dfrac{2}{x - 2} + \dfrac{4}{x + 1} = 3$

10   $\dfrac{5}{2x - 5} - \dfrac{3}{x + 1} = \dfrac{1}{2}$ 11 $\dfrac{3}{y - 2} - \dfrac{4}{y + 1} = 5$ 12 $\dfrac{3}{a} - \dfrac{2}{a + 2} = 4$

Using quadratic equations to solve problems

Quadratic equations can be used to solve many problems. As with linear equations (see Chapter 17), you should use a suitable letter to represent the unknown quantity. Then write the given mathematical information in the form of an equation and solve it by one of the methods for quadratic equations. In some cases, the equation may not look like a quadratic equation when it is initially set up, but it evolves into one by various algebraic techniques.

You must always give an appropriate answer to the problem. In some cases, only one of the solutions to the quadratic may in fact be an appropriate answer, depending on the context of the question. Again, the answer should be checked against the original information.

Quadratic equations can be used to solve a wide variety of mathematical problems, including those from other areas of the Higher GCSE course such as compound measures, Pythagoras' theorem and probability, as illustrated in some of the examples below.

EXAMPLE 15

Find two consecutive integers such that the sum of their squares is 1201.

SOLUTION

Use n to represent the first integer.

Then the second integer is $n + 1$.

$$n^2 + (n + 1)^2 = 1201$$

$$n^2 + n^2 + 2n + 1 = 1201$$

$$2n^2 + 2n + 1 - 1201 = 0$$

$$2n^2 + 2n - 1200 = 0 \quad \longleftarrow$$

Divide the whole equation through by 2 here to make the factorisation easier.

$$n^2 + n - 600 = 0$$

$$(n - 24)(n + 25) = 0$$

$$n - 24 = 0 \quad \text{or} \quad n + 25 = 0$$

$$n = 24 \quad \text{or} \quad n = -25$$

So the first integer is 24 and the second is 25, or the first is -25 and the second is -24. $\longleftarrow$

Check
$24^2 + 25^2 = 576 + 625 = 1201$
$(-25)^2 + (-24)^2 = 625 + 576 = 1201$

EXAMPLE 16

A 40 cm by 40 cm picture is surrounded by a frame of width x cm, such that the total area of the framed picture is twice the area of the unframed picture.
Find the width of the frame to the nearest tenth of a millimetre.

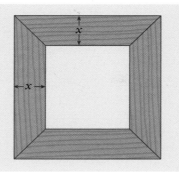

SOLUTION

Area of framed picture $= (40 + 2x)(40 + 2x) = 1600 + 160x + 4x^2$
Area of unframed picture $= 40 \times 40 = 1600$
$$1600 + 160x + 4x^2 = 2 \times 1600$$
$$1600 + 160x + 4x^2 - 3200 = 0$$
$$4x^2 + 160x - 1600 = 0$$
$$x^2 + 40x - 400 = 0$$

> Divide the whole equation through by 4.

> This quadratic does not factorise, so use the formula.

$a = 1, b = 40$ and $c = -400$.

$$x = \frac{-40 \pm \sqrt{40^2 - 4 \times 1 \times (-400)}}{2 \times 1}$$

$$x = \frac{-40 \pm \sqrt{1600 - (-1600)}}{2}$$

$$x = \frac{-40 \pm \sqrt{3200}}{2}$$

$$x = 8.28 \text{ cm} \quad \text{or} \quad x = -48.2 \text{ cm}$$

Since the width of the frame cannot be negative, the correct solution is 8.28 cm (to the nearest tenth of a millimetre).

> **Check**
> $56.56 \times 56.56 = 3199.0336$, which is approximately twice the area of the unframed picture.

EXAMPLE 17

A girl completes a journey of 420 km at x km/h.
If she were to increase her speed by 10 km/h, she could complete the journey in $\frac{3}{4}$ hour less.
Find her original speed x.

SOLUTION

$$\text{Speed} = \frac{\text{distance}}{\text{time}}$$

$$\text{so time} = \frac{\text{distance}}{\text{speed}}$$

So original time $= \frac{420}{x}$

Time at increased speed $= \frac{420}{x + 10}$

> You are told that the difference in the journey times is $\frac{3}{4}$ hour. Use this to write an equation.

$$\frac{420}{x} - \frac{420}{x + 10} = \frac{3}{4}$$

$$\frac{420(x + 10) - 420x}{x(x + 10)} = \frac{3}{4}$$

$$\frac{420x + 4200 - 420x}{x(x + 10)} = \frac{3}{4}$$

$$\frac{4200}{x(x + 10)} = \frac{3}{4}$$

$$3x(x + 10) = 16\,800$$
$$3x^2 + 30x - 16\,800 = 0$$
$$x^2 + 10x - 5600 = 0$$
$$(x + 80)(x - 70) = 0$$
$$x = -80 \quad \text{or} \quad x = 70$$

The speed cannot be negative, so the appropriate solution is 70 km/h.

> Cross-multiply to eliminate the fractions.

> **Check**
> At 70 km/h the journey takes $\frac{420}{70}$ = 6 hours.
> At 80 km/h the journey takes $\frac{420}{80}$ = 5 hours 15 minutes.
> Difference between the times = $\frac{3}{4}$ hour, as required.

EXAMPLE 18

A right-angled triangle has a perimeter of 43 cm, and the length of its hypotenuse is 19 cm. Find the length of each of the shorter sides, giving your answers to 2 decimal places.

SOLUTION

Since the perimeter is 43 cm and the hypotenuse is 19 cm, the lengths of the remaining two sides total 24 cm.

Use x to represent the length of one of these sides.

Then the second side has length $24 - x$.

By Pythagoras' theorem,
$$x^2 + (24 - x)^2 = 19^2$$
$$x^2 + 576 - 48x + x^2 - 361 = 0$$
$$2x^2 - 48x + 215 = 0$$

> This quadratic does not factorise, so use the formula.

$a = 2$, $b = -48$ and $c = 215$.

$$x = \frac{-(-48) \pm \sqrt{(-48)^2 - 4 \times 2 \times 215}}{2 \times 2}$$

$$x = \frac{48 \pm \sqrt{2304 - 1720}}{4}$$

$$x = \frac{48 \pm \sqrt{584}}{4}$$

$$x = 18.04 \quad \text{or} \quad x = 5.96$$

The lengths of the shorter sides are 18.04 cm and 5.96 cm.

> **Check**
> $18.04^2 + 5.96^2 = 360.963$ and $19^2 = 361$
> Perimeter = 19 + 18.04 + 5.96 = 43 cm.

Exercise 24.4

Solve each of these problems by forming and solving a suitable quadratic equation.

1 Two positive whole numbers have a difference of 3 and a product of 1120. Find the numbers.

2 When the price of apples rose by 6p an apple, I could buy three fewer for £3.60 than before. Find the original price of an apple.

3   The area of the square shown exceeds the
    area of the rectangle shown by 35 cm².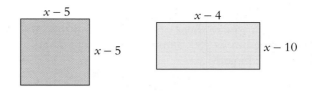
    Find the dimensions of the rectangle.

4   The numerator of a positive fraction is 1 less than the denominator.
    When both the numerator and the denominator are increased by 3,
    the value of the fraction is increased by $\frac{3}{40}$.
    Find the original fraction.

5   The product of two consecutive odd numbers is 899.
    Find the numbers.

6   A bag contains five blue discs, three green discs and a number of
    red discs. Two discs are taken from the bag without replacement.
    The probability that both discs are red is $\frac{1}{45}$.
    How many red discs are in the bag?

7   A man can travel to work either by train or by car. The journey is
    90 km. The train travels 15 km/h faster than the car, and completes
    the journey in half an hour less time. Find the speed of the car on
    its journey.

8   A stone is thrown upwards from the top of a cliff and lands in the
    sea some time later. Its height, h metres, above sea-level at any time
    t seconds is given by the formula $h = 40 + 3t - 5t^2$.
    After how many seconds will the stone reach the sea?

9   One term of the sequence $1 \times 5, 2 \times 6, 3 \times 7, \ldots$ is equivalent to
    396. Which term is it?

10 The sum of the ages of people in a group is 330. When a new
    member, aged 38, joins the group, the average age increases by one
    year. How many people were originally in the group?

11 Which triangular number has a value of 300?

12 A circular lawn of radius r metres is surrounded by a path
    1.5 m wide. If the area of the path is one-tenth the area of the lawn,
    find the radius of the lawn.

13 The formula $\frac{1}{f} = \frac{1}{u} + \frac{1}{v}$ gives the focal length f of a spherical
    mirror.
    u is the distance of the object from the mirror and v is the distance
    of the image from the mirror.
    Given that an object is 12 cm nearer to a mirror than the image is,
    and that the focal length of the mirror is 20 cm, find the distance of
    the object from the mirror.
    Give your answer to the nearest centimetre.

14 An 80 cm length of wire is cut into two parts, and each part is bent
    to form a square.
    The area of the large square is 20 cm² less than six times the area of
    the small square.
    What two lengths was the wire cut into?

15 An open box is made by cutting a 6 cm square from each corner of a square sheet of cardboard and then folding. The volume of the box is 253.5 cm³. Find the side length of the original piece of cardboard.

16 The current in a river flows at 1 km/h. A man can row at x km/h in still water. He rows up the river with the current for a distance of 12 km, and then back against the current. The total time it takes him is 5 hours. Find the speed at which he is rowing.

> **You should now:**
>
> - be able to solve a quadratic equation by factorisation
> - be able to solve a quadratic equation using the general formula
> - be able to solve algebraic fractional equations (including those with algebraic denominators)
> - be able to solve a variety of problems involving quadratic equations, by choosing an appropriate form of solution.

Summary exercise 24

1 Solve each of these equations by factorisation.

   a $(3a + 4)(2a - 3) = 0$ **b** $x^2 - 5x = 0$ **c** $a^2 + a - 12 = 0$

   d $(x + 3)^2 = 25$ **e** $4x^2 - 10x - 6 = 0$ **f** $49x^2 - 9 = 0$

   g $13x - x^2 = 12$ **h** $3t^2 - 13t + 4 = 0$ **i** $y(y - 3) = 10$

   j $5x^2 = \dfrac{1}{5}$

2 Solve each of these equations using the quadratic formula, giving your answers correct to 2 decimal places.

   a $2a^2 + 2a - 1 = 0$ **b** $4x^2 = 3x + 2$

   c $2x + \dfrac{1}{x} = 6$ **d** $5 - 2x - 4x^2 = 0$

3 Solve each of these equations using the quadratic formula, giving the exact answers in surd form.

   a $a^2 - 2a - 19 = 0$ **b** $3y^2 = 6y - 1$

   c $4a(a - 1) = 9$ **d** $1.5x^2 = 3x + 11$

4 Solve each of these equations by factorisation.

   a $\dfrac{6}{y + 1} - \dfrac{2}{y} = 1$ **b** $\dfrac{3}{1 - x} = 4(x + 1)$

5 Solve each of these equations using the quadratic formula. Give your answers correct to 2 decimal places.

   a $\dfrac{a}{a - 1} - \dfrac{1}{2a} = 4$ **b** $\dfrac{8}{x - 1} - \dfrac{8}{x + 2} = 2$

6 The length of a rectangle exceeds the width by 3 cm. Given that the area of the rectangle is 180 cm², find its length.

7 A tennis coach buys a number of tennis balls for £12. If each ball had cost 50p less, she could have bought four more balls for the same amount. How many tennis balls did the coach buy?

8 Two numbers have a difference of 2, and the sum of their reciprocals is $\frac{5}{12}$. Find the numbers.

9 When each edge of a cube is decreased by 2 cm, the volume of the cube decreases by $339\frac{1}{2}$ cm³.
Find the side length of the original cube.

10 A magnet is shaped as shown.

Given that the volume of metal used is 50 cm³, find the value of x, correct to 3 significant figures.

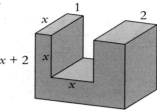

Examination questions

Use 'Topic Tracker' at www.ccea.org.uk to find more exam questions.

Questions **1** to **3** are from examination papers where you may not use a calculator.

1 Solve $x^2 + 14x - 15 = 0$.

2 Solve the equation $\dfrac{4}{(x-3)} + \dfrac{9}{(2x-1)} = 3$.

3 Expressions, in terms of x, for the sides of the quadrilateral ABCD are shown on the diagram.

The angles DAB and BCD are each 90°.
Calculate the value of x.
Show your working.
A solution by trial and improvement will not be accepted.

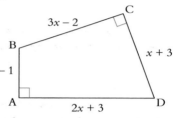

Questions **4** to **7** are from examination papers where you may use a calculator.

4 Solve $6x^2 - 7x - 3 = 0$.
A solution by trial and improvement will not be accepted.
Show your working clearly.

5 Solve $\dfrac{2}{x+1} - \dfrac{3}{2x+3} = 1$.

A solution by trial and improvement will not be accepted.
Show your working clearly.

6 The area of a rectangle is 6 cm² and the perimeter is 20 cm.
  a If x is the length of one side of the rectangle, show that $x^2 - 10x + 6 = 0$.

  b Find the lengths of the sides of the rectangle. You may give your answers correct to two decimal places.

7 **a** Find an expression, in its simplest form, for the perimeter of the shape shown.

  b Find an expression, in its simplest form, for the area of the shape shown.

  c Given that the area of the shape is 60 square units, find the perimeter of the shape.
Show your working.
A solution by trial and improvement will not be accepted.

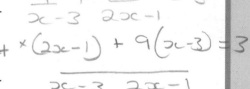

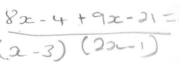

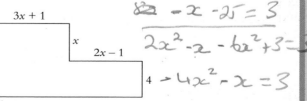

CHAPTER 25

Straight lines and linear graphs

This chapter is about:

- drawing straight-line graphs
- finding the midpoint of a line
- finding the length of a line
- finding the gradient of a line
- lines with positive and negative gradients
- interpreting the equation of a straight line
- finding the equation of a line
- horizontal, vertical, parallel and perpendicular lines
- recognising and drawing graphs of linear functions.

You should already know:

- how to work with positive and negative numbers
- the meaning of the terms *horizontal, vertical, parallel* and *perpendicular*
- how to find the reciprocal of a number
- how to substitute numbers into an algebraic expression
- how to solve linear equations
- how to change the subject of a formula
- how to plot and read co-ordinates in all four quadrants
- the meaning of the term *perpendicular bisector*.

Linear graphs

A **linear function** is one of the form $y = ax + b$ where a and b are constants and the x and y values vary. (A **constant** is a value which does not vary — a number such as $2, -3, 0.25$ or $\frac{1}{2}$.)

The graph of a linear function is a straight-line graph. One method for drawing a straight-line graph accurately is to make a table of values for x and y. Whilst it is only necessary to have two points in order to draw a straight line, it is good practice to choose at least *three* points, the third point acting as a check. Substitute the x values into the equation of the straight line to find the corresponding y values, and then plot the resulting set of co-ordinates.

EXAMPLE 1

Draw the straight-line graph of $y = 2x + 3$.

SOLUTION

First draw up a table of values for x and y.

x	-2	-1	0	1	2	3
y	-1	1	3	5	7	9

> The line can be extended beyond the points in the table.

> When the coefficient of x is positive, the line slopes upwards.

> Each y co-ordinate is found by substituting a value of x into the equation. For example, when $x = -2$, $y = 2 \times (-2) + 3 = -4 + 3 = -1$.

Now plot the set of co-ordinates (x, y) on a graph and join them with a straight line.

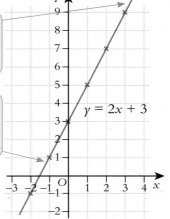

$y = 2x + 3$

EXAMPLE 2

Draw the straight-line graph of $y = 5 - 3x$ for x values from -2 to $+4$.

SOLUTION

x	-2	-1	0	1	2	3	4
y	11	8	5	2	-1	-4	-7

> When the coefficient of x is negative, the line slopes downwards.

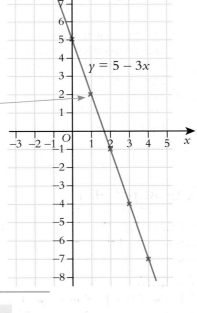

$y = 5 - 3x$

EXAMPLE 3

Draw the straight-line graph of $y = \frac{1}{2}x + 2$ for $-1 \leqslant x \leqslant 3$.

SOLUTION

x	-1	0	1	2	3
y	$1\frac{1}{2}$	2	$2\frac{1}{2}$	3	$3\frac{1}{2}$

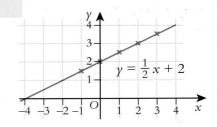

$y = \frac{1}{2}x + 2$

In Chapter 18 you saw that the rule for the nth term of a linear sequence was of the form $an + b$ where a was the common difference. It was called a *linear* sequence because if the terms of the sequence were plotted on a graph they would form a straight line.

There is much similarity between the rule for the nth term of a linear sequence and the equation of a straight line. The b term corresponds to the y co-ordinate when $x = 0$, and the a term corresponds to the differences in the y co-ordinates. Hence, once the first pair of co-ordinates $(0, y)$ has been determined, the difference method can be used to find subsequent pairs of co-ordinates.

For example, to draw the straight-line graph of $y = 6x - 2$, it is only necessary to find y when $x = 0$ (in this case -2) to find the first pair of co-ordinates $(0, -2)$, and then the subsequent y co-ordinates will have a difference of 6. So the line passes through $(0, -2)$, $(1, 4)$, $(2, 10)$, $(3, 16)$, etc.

Similarly, $y = 2 - 3x$ will pass through $(0, 2)$ and subsequent y co-ordinates will have a difference of -3, so the line passes through $(1, -1)$, $(2, -4)$, $(3, -7)$, etc.

Exercise 25.1

1 For each of these functions make a table of values for x from -3 to 4 and draw the straight-line graph.

   a $y = 2x - 1$ b $y = 3x + 2$ c $y = 4x$

   d $y = -x + 1$ e $y = 5x - 2$ f $y = -2x + 1$

   g $y = \frac{1}{2}x + 4$ h $y = 4 - x$ i $y = 10 - 2x$

   j $y = 8 - \frac{1}{2}x$ k $y = -3x$ l $y = \dfrac{x + 6}{2}$

2 Draw the graph of $p = 2q - 4$ for values of q from -3 to $+3$.

3 a Draw the straight-line graph of $y = 3x - 6$ for $-3 \leqslant x \leqslant 3$.

   b Write down the co-ordinates of the point where this line crosses the x-axis.

   c Write down the co-ordinates of the point where this line crosses the y-axis.

4 a Does the point $(1, 3)$ lie on the line $y = x + 4$?

   b Does the point $(5, 13)$ lie on the line $y = 2x - 3$?

   c Does the point $(-1, 3)$ lie on the line $x + y = 2$?

5 Without drawing the graphs, find on which of the following lines the point $(-2, 1)$ lies.

   $y = x + 3$ $y = 2x + 5$ $x + y = 1$

   $y = \frac{1}{2}x + 2$ $x + 2y = 0$

6 Which of these points do *not* lie on the line $y = 5 - 2x$?

   $(0, 5)$ $(1, 3)$ $(\frac{1}{2}, 4)$ $(-1, 7)$ $(2\frac{1}{2}, 0)$ $(-2\frac{1}{2}, 0)$

7 The point $(x, 7)$ lies on the line $y = 3x + 1$. What is the value of x?

8 The following points all lie on the line $y = 4x - 1$. Find the missing co-ordinate in each of them.

   a $(2, y)$ b $(x, -3)$ c $(-3, y)$

Length of a line

The length of a line joining two points can be found by forming a right-angled triangle between the points and applying Pythagoras' theorem. Consider the points A(2, 3) and B(5, 7).

By Pythagoras' theorem

$$AB^2 = 3^2 + 4^2$$
$$AB^2 = 9 + 16$$
$$AB^2 = 25$$
$$AB = \sqrt{25}$$
$$AB = 5$$

In general, the length of the straight line joining any two points with co-ordinates (x_1, y_1) and (x_2, y_2) is given by:

$$L = \sqrt{(x_2 - x_1)^2 + (y_2 - y_1)^2}$$

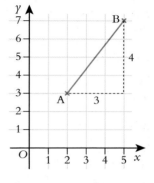

EXAMPLE 4

For each of these pairs of points, find the length of the line that joins them.

   a   A(1, 1) and B(6, 13)

   b   X(1, −5) and Y(9, 1)

   c   P(−3, 7) and Q(−5, 1)

SOLUTION

  a $AB = \sqrt{(6-1)^2 + (13-1)^2}$

       $AB = \sqrt{5^2 + 12^2}$

       $AB = \sqrt{25 + 144}$

       $AB = \sqrt{169}$

       $AB = 13$

  b $XY = \sqrt{(9-1)^2 + (1+5)^2}$

       $XY = \sqrt{8^2 + 6^2}$

       $XY = \sqrt{64 + 36}$

       $XY = \sqrt{100}$

       $XY = 10$

> Note, the difference between the y co-ordinates becomes $1 - (-5)$ which becomes $1 + 5$ using the rules of negative numbers.

  c $PQ = \sqrt{(-5+3)^2 + (1-7)^2}$

       $PQ = \sqrt{(-2)^2 + (-6)^2}$

       $PQ = \sqrt{4 + 36}$

       $PQ = \sqrt{40}$

       $PQ = 2\sqrt{10}$

> In many cases the length will not be an integer value and so its **exact** value is often given in surd form.

Midpoint of a line

The midpoint of a line joining two points can be found by plotting the two points and locating the co-ordinates of the midpoint. Consider the points A(1, 7) and B(6, 3).

A to B is a translation of 4 down and 5 units to the right. To move half the distance would be a translation of 2 units down and $2\frac{1}{2}$ units to the right, which leads to the midpoint at $(3\frac{1}{2}, 5)$.

These co-ordinates can also be determined from

$$\tfrac{1}{2}(1 + 6) = 3\tfrac{1}{2} \qquad \text{and} \qquad \tfrac{1}{2}(7 + 3) = 5$$

In general, the midpoint of a line joining any two points with co-ordinates (x_1, y_1) and (x_2, y_2) is given by:

$$M = \left(\tfrac{1}{2}(x_1 + x_2), \tfrac{1}{2}(y_1 + y_2)\right)$$

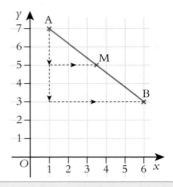

Alternatively for any pair of co-ordinates A and B

$$M = \frac{A + B}{2}$$

The reverse of this is useful if the midpoint M is given, and only one pair of co-ordinates identified. By changing the subject, A = 2M − B or B = 2M − A.

EXAMPLE 5

For each of these pairs of points, find the co-ordinates of the midpoint of the line that joins them.

  a   C(1, 2) and D(5, 7)   b   P(−3, 6) and R(5, −10)

SOLUTION

  a $M = (\tfrac{1}{2}(1 + 5), \tfrac{1}{2}(2 + 7))$ b $M = (\tfrac{1}{2}(−3 + 5), \tfrac{1}{2}(6 − 10))$

   $M = (\tfrac{1}{2}(6), \tfrac{1}{2}(9))$ $M = (\tfrac{1}{2}(2), \tfrac{1}{2}(−4))$

   $M = (3, 4\tfrac{1}{2})$ $M = (1, −2)$

EXAMPLE 6

The midpoint of the line joining the points A and B has co-ordinates (2, 1). A has the co-ordinates (−2, 6). Find the co-ordinates of B.

SOLUTION

$(2, 1) = (\tfrac{1}{2}(−2 + x_2), \tfrac{1}{2}(6 + y_2))$

Inspecting the x co-ordinates gives

$\tfrac{1}{2}(−2 + x_2) = 2$
$\quad −2 + x_2 = 4$
$\qquad x_2 = 4 + 2$
$\qquad x_2 = 6$

Inspecting the y co-ordinates gives

$\tfrac{1}{2}(6 + y_2) = 1$
$\quad 6 + y_2 = 2$
$\qquad y_2 = 2 − 6$
$\qquad y_2 = −4$

So, B has co-ordinates (6, − 4)

> Here we equate the expression for the x co-ordinate with its value, 2.

> Here we equate the expression for the y co-ordinate with its value, 1.

> Alternatively:
> B = 2M − A
> B = 2(2, 1) − (−2, 6)
> B = (4, 2) − (−2, 6)
> B = (6, −4)

Exercise 25.2

1. Find the length of the line joining each of these pairs of points:
   a. A(0, 10) and B(12, 4)
   b. X(−2, 5) and Y(3, 10)
   c. P(0, −2) and Q(4, 10)
   d. M(10, 4) and N(3, −1)
   e. D(−6, −8) and E(−2, −4)

2. Find the midpoint of the line joining each of these pairs of points:
   a. P(5, 2) and Q(3, 5)
   b. A(−2, 0) and B(6, 8)
   c. C(−2, −3) and D(−4, −5)
   d. M(0, −6) and N(−2, −8)
   e. J(−2, −1) and K(3, −1)

3. The midpoint of a line joining the points A(5, 0) and B is M(1, 3). Find the co-ordinates of the point B.

4. A circle has centre (1, 1) and radius 5. Does the point with co-ordinates (−3, 4) lie on the circumference of the circle?

5. A triangle has co-ordinates (2, 2), (2, 6) and (5, 1). By finding the lengths of the three sides determine the type of triangle.

6. A triangle has co-ordinates (−4, 3), (−4, 5) and (1, 5). Prove that the triangle is right-angled.

The gradient of a line

The **gradient** of a line is a measure of how steep the line is. It can be found using the formula:

$$\text{gradient} = \frac{\text{difference in } y \text{ co-ordinates}}{\text{difference in } x \text{ co-ordinates}}$$

EXAMPLE 7

Find the gradient of the line which passes through the points A(2, 1) and B(6, 3).

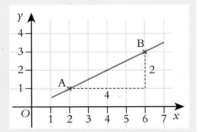

SOLUTION

The difference between the y co-ordinates is 2 and the difference between the x co-ordinates is 4.

Therefore gradient of AB $= \frac{2}{4}$

$= \frac{1}{2}$

> The differences in the x and y co-ordinates can by found by counting the squares on the graph.

In general, for any two points with co-ordinates (x_1, y_1) and (x_2, y_2), the gradient can be found using the formula:

$$\text{gradient} = \frac{y_2 - y_1}{x_2 - x_1}$$

The properties of gradients

1. All lines that slope upwards (when moving from left to right) have a **positive** gradient.

   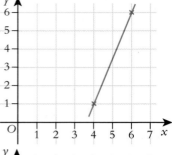

   For example, the gradient of the line joining the points (4, 1) and (6, 6) is

   $$\frac{6-1}{6-4} = \frac{5}{2}$$

   > Note that gradients are usually given as whole numbers or as fractions.

2. All lines that slope downwards (when moving from left to right) have a **negative** gradient.

   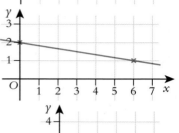

   For example, the gradient of the line joining the points (0, 2) and (6, 1) is

   $$\frac{1-2}{6-0} = -\frac{1}{6}$$

3. Horizontal lines have a gradient of **zero** − they have no slope.

   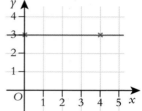

   For example, the gradient of the line joining the points (0, 3) and (4, 3) is

   $$\frac{3-3}{4-0} = \frac{0}{4} = 0$$

4. Vertical lines have an **undefined** gradient because they are so steep.

   For example, the gradient of the line joining the points (2, 1) and (2, 6) is

   $$\frac{6-1}{2-2} = \frac{5}{0}$$

   which is undefined.

5. Parallel lines have **equal** gradients − they have the same slope.

   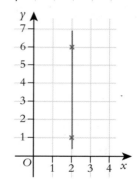

   For example, look at the gradient of the line joining A(1, 1) and B(3, 5) and the gradient of the line joining P(3, −1) and Q(4, 1).

   Gradient of AB $= \dfrac{5-1}{3-1} = \dfrac{4}{2} = 2$

   Gradient of PQ $= \dfrac{1-(-1)}{4-3} = \dfrac{2}{1} = 2$

6. The product of the gradients of perpendicular lines is −1.

   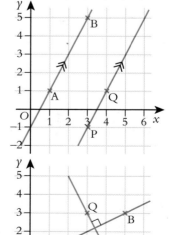

   For example, look at the gradient of the line joining the points A(1, 1) and B(5, 3) and the gradient of the line joining the points P(4, 1) and Q(3, 3).

   gradient of AB $= \dfrac{3-1}{5-1} = \dfrac{2}{4} = \dfrac{1}{2}$

   gradient of PQ $= \dfrac{3-1}{3-4} = \dfrac{2}{-1} = -2$

   The gradient of a perpendicular line can be found by taking the negative reciprocal of the gradient of the original line or by using the formula $m_1 m_2 = -1$, where m_1 is the gradient of the original line and m_2 is the gradient of a line perpendicular to it.

EXAMPLE 8

Find the gradient of each of the
lines shown.

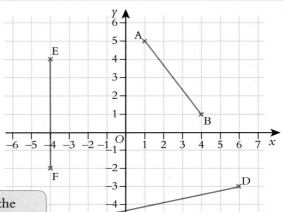

SOLUTION

Gradient of AB $= -\dfrac{4}{3}$

Gradient of CD $= \dfrac{2}{9}$

Gradient of EF $= \dfrac{6}{0}$ which is undefined

> The change in y and the change in x for each of the
> lines can be found by counting the squares on the graph.

EXAMPLE 9

Find the gradient of the line joining the points $(-6, -1)$ and $(4, 2)$.

SOLUTION

Gradient $= \dfrac{y_2 - y_1}{x_2 - x_1}$

> You do not need to draw a graph — you can
> use the formula to find the gradient of the line
> joining the points (x_1, y_1) and (x_2, y_2).

$\quad = \dfrac{2 - (-1)}{4 - (-6)} = \dfrac{3}{10}$

EXAMPLE 10

Find the value of n if the line joining the points $(3n, 4)$ and $(n, -8)$ has
gradient 2.

SOLUTION

Gradient $= \dfrac{-8 - 4}{n - 3n} = \dfrac{-12}{-2n} = 2$

So $\quad -4n = -12$

$\qquad n = 3$

EXAMPLE 11

Find the value of q if the line joining the points $(2p, q)$ and $(4, -6)$ is
parallel to the x-axis.

SOLUTION

Gradient $= \dfrac{-6 - q}{4 - 2p} = 0$

> The line is parallel to the x-axis — a horizontal
> line — so the gradient is zero.

So $\quad -6 - q = 0$

$\qquad q = -6$

EXAMPLE 12

Find the gradient of a line which is perpendicular to the line joining the points (1, 1) and (7, 5).

SOLUTION

Method 1

The gradient of the line joining the points (1, 1) and (7, 5) is

$$\frac{5-1}{7-1} = \frac{4}{6} = \frac{2}{3}$$

So, gradient of perpendicular line $= -\frac{3}{2}$

> Take the negative reciprocal of the gradient of the original line.

Method 2

Alternatively, using the formula $m_1 m_2 = -1$,

$$\frac{2}{3} \times m_2 = -1$$
$$m_2 = -1 \div \frac{2}{3}$$
$$= -1 \times \frac{3}{2}$$
$$= -\frac{3}{2}$$

> Substitute the gradient of the original line, $\frac{2}{3}$, for m_1.

The gradient of a line perpendicular to the original line is $-\frac{3}{2}$.

Exercise 25.3

1 Find the gradient of each of the lines L_1 to L_7.

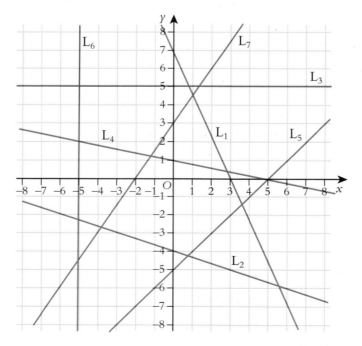

2 Find the gradient of each of the lines PQ, QR, RS and SP.

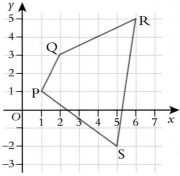

3 Find the gradient of the line joining each of these pairs of points.
   a (2, 3) and (8, 5)   b (1, −6) and (2, −4)
   c (−5, 0) and (−2, 5)   d (−6, −5) and (−8, 0)

4 A line joins the points with co-ordinates $(3p, q)$ and $(6, -8)$.
   a Find the value of q if the line is parallel to the x-axis.
   b Find the value of p if the line is parallel to the y-axis.

5 The line joining the points with co-ordinates (5, 1) and
   (8, 6) is parallel to the line joining the points with co-ordinates
   (2, −3) and (a, b).
   Find a set of possible values for a and b. Is there more than one
   answer? Explain your reasoning.

6 The gradient of a road is shown on the sign. For every 250 m
   horizontally, how high does the road rise?

7 What is the gradient of any line which is perpendicular to the line
   joining the points (−8, 4) and (2, 0)?

8 LMN is a triangle, with a right angle at M.
   L has co-ordinates (3, 1), M has co-ordinates (6, 4) and N has
   co-ordinates $(10, y)$. Find y.

The equation of a straight line, $y = mx + c$

Earlier in this chapter you learnt how to plot a straight-line graph by
making a table of values for x and y. You will now learn an alternative and
much quicker approach to plotting a straight-line graph. This involves an
understanding of the equation of a straight line.

Any straight-line graph will have an equation of the form $y = mx + c$,
where m represents the gradient of the line and c represents the intercept
on the y-axis. This is the point at which the line cuts the y-axis; it has the
co-ordinates $(0, c)$.

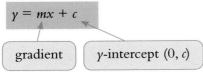

gradient y-intercept $(0, c)$

It is important to realise that whilst some linear equations may not at first
be of the form $y = mx + c$, they can be rearranged into this form by using
the same methods as for changing the subject of a formula (see Chapter 20).

For example, $2y + 3x = 1$ is the equation of a straight line; it can be
rearranged to give $y = -\frac{3}{2}x + \frac{1}{2}$. Rearranging the equation of a straight
line into the form $y = mx + c$ allows you to determine the gradient and
the y-intercept directly.

EXAMPLE 13

Find the gradient and y-intercept of the straight line with equation $y = 4x - 1$.

SOLUTION

Gradient $= 4$ y-intercept $= (0, -1)$

EXAMPLE 14

Find the gradient and y-intercept of the straight line with equation $4x + 3y = -2$.

SOLUTION

$$3y = -4x - 2$$
$$y = -\frac{4}{3}x - \frac{2}{3}$$

Gradient $= -\frac{4}{3}$

y-intercept $= (0, -\frac{2}{3})$

> Rearrange the equation into the form $y = mx + c$.

EXAMPLE 15

Which of the following lines are   a parallel?   b perpendicular?

$y = 2x - 1$ $y = 3x + 1$ $y = -2x + 5$ $y = -\frac{1}{2}x + 1$

$2y + x = 4$ $3y + x = -4$ $2y + x = 3$ $y = 2x$

SOLUTION

$y = 2x - 1$

> You are only interested in the gradients. For this line $m = 2$.

$y = 3x + 1$

> $m = 3$

$y = -2x + 5$

> $m = -2$

$y = -\frac{1}{2}x + 1$

> $m = -\frac{1}{2}$

$2y + x = 4$

> Rearranging this gives $y = -\frac{1}{2}x + 2$ so $m = -\frac{1}{2}$

$3y + x = -4$

> Rearranging this gives $y = -\frac{1}{3}x - \frac{4}{3}$ so $m = -\frac{1}{3}$

$2y + x = 3$

> Rearranging this gives $y = -\frac{1}{2}x + \frac{3}{2}$ so $m = -\frac{1}{2}$

$y = 2x$

> $m = 2$

a $y = 2x - 1$ and $y = 2x$ are parallel.

> Parallel lines have equal gradients. These two lines have $m = 2$.

   $y = -\frac{1}{2}x + 1$, $2y + x = 4$ and $2y + x = 3$ are also parallel.

b $y = 2x - 1$ and $y = 2x$ will be perpendicular to each of the lines:

> The product of the gradients of perpendicular lines equals -1. For these lines $m_1 = 2$ and $m_2 = -\frac{1}{2}$.

   $y = -\frac{1}{2}x + 1$, $2y + x = 4$ and $2y + x = 3$.

   $y = 3x + 1$ will be perpendicular to $3y + x = -4$.

Drawing straight-line graphs

Once the gradient and y-intercept have been identified these can quickly be used to sketch or draw the straight-line graph. You plot the y-intercept first, and then interpret the gradient as a fraction of the form:

$$\frac{\text{difference in } y}{\text{difference in } x}$$

EXAMPLE 16

Draw the straight-line graph $y = 3x - 2$.

SOLUTION

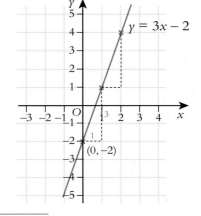

y-intercept $= (0, -2)$

gradient $= 3 = \frac{3}{1}$

For every 1 unit to the right on the x-axis, move 3 units up the y-axis.

EXAMPLE 17

Draw the straight-line graph of $4x - 2y = 3$.

SOLUTION

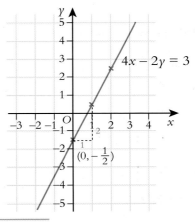

$$4x - 2y = 3$$
$$2y = 4x - 3$$
$$y = 2x - \frac{3}{2}$$

y-intercept $= (0, -1\frac{1}{2})$

gradient $= 2 = \frac{2}{1}$

Rearrange the equation into the form $y = mx + c$.

For every 1 unit to the right on the x-axis, move 2 units up the y-axis.

EXAMPLE 18

Sketch the straight-line graph of $y = -\frac{1}{2}x + 1$.

SOLUTION

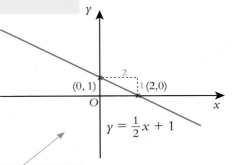

y-intercept $= (0, 1)$

The x-intercept is when $y = 0$.

$$0 = -\frac{1}{2}x + 1$$

So $x = 2$

Substitute $y = 0$ into the equation.

x-intercept $= (2, 0)$

A **sketch** requires the *main features* of the graph only. For a straight line these are the x- and y-intercepts. Plot these points and draw a straight line through them. Check that the gradient equals $-\frac{1}{2}$.

Horizontal lines

You have already seen that horizontal lines have a gradient of zero. As a result, the equation of a horizontal line will be of the form $y = 0x + c$, or simply $y = c$, where c is the intercept on the y-axis.

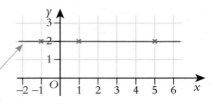

All the points on this line have y co-ordinate equal to 2, for example $(-1, 2)$, $(1, 2)$, $(5, 2)$, etc.
Therefore the equation of the line is $y = 2$.

EXAMPLE 19

Draw the graph of $y = 5$.

SOLUTION

This will simply be a horizontal line passing through the point $(0, 5)$.

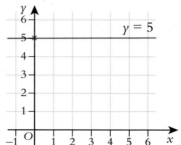

Vertical lines

You have already seen that vertical lines have an undefined gradient.

Since they are vertical they will not cross the y-axis at any point. Rather they will simply cross the x-axis at some point. As a result, the equation of a vertical line will be of the form $x = a$, where $(a, 0)$ is the point at which it crosses the x-axis.

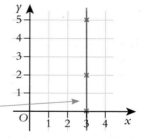

All the points on this line have x co-ordinate equal to 3, for example $(3, 0)$, $(3, 2)$, $(3, 5)$, etc. Therefore the equation of the line is $x = 3$.

EXAMPLE 20

Draw the graph of $x = -1$.

SOLUTION

This will simply be a vertical line passing through the point $(-1, 0)$.

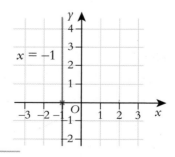

Exercise 25.4

1   Find the gradient and y-intercept of each of these lines.

   a $y = 2x - 7$ b $y = \frac{1}{3}x - 1$ c $y = 6x$

   d $2y = 4x - 6$ e $3y + x = 9$ f $4x - 2y = 1$

   g $x + 2y - 4 = 0$ h $3y = -2x + 1$

2   By finding the gradient and y-intercept, sketch each of these straight lines.

   a $y = x + 4$ b $y = x - 3$ c $y = 3x + 1$

   d $y = 2x - 5$ e $y = \frac{1}{2}x + 1$ f $y = -x + 4$

g $2y = 5x - 2$

h $y = -\frac{1}{3}x$

i $2y - x = 4$

j $4x - 2y + 1 = 0$

k $3x - 2y = -6$

l $2x + 5y = 10$

3 The lines $y = kx + 6$ and $ky = 4x - 2$ are parallel. Find the possible values of k.

4 What is the *equation* of the x-axis?

5 Here are the equations of several straight lines:

$y = -x + 6$ $2y = x - 4$ $4x + 12y = 6$ $x + 3y = 6$ $y = x - 1$

$y = 4 - 5x$ $5x + y = 10$ $y = 5 - 2x$ $y = 2x$

a Choose any pair of lines which would be parallel.

b Choose any pair of lines which would be perpendicular.

6 The lines $y = 2x + 6$ and $y = ax - 2$ are perpendicular.
Find the value of a.

Finding the equation of a straight line

There are several situations in which you might be asked to find the
equation of a straight line.

Finding the equation of a straight line given the graph

If you are given the graph, it is only necessary to read off the y-intercept
and calculate the gradient. You can then simply substitute these into the
equation $y = mx + c$.

EXAMPLE 21

Find the equation of each of the straight lines A and B.

SOLUTION

Line A

gradient $= \frac{1}{4}$

y-intercept $= (0, 1)$

$y = \frac{1}{4}x + 1$

> It is common practice to adjust the equation to
> eliminate any fractions. Here you would multiply
> through by 4 to give $4y = x + 4$.

Line B

gradient $= -\frac{3}{2}$

y-intercept $= (0, -3)$

$y = -\frac{3}{2}x - 3$

> It is also usual to rearrange the
> equation to avoid negative values,
> particularly as coefficients of the
> variables. In this case you would give
> the equation as $2y + 3x = -6$ or
> $2y + 3x + 6 = 0$.

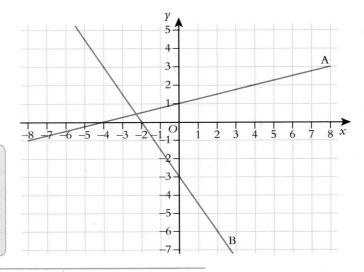

EXAMPLE 22

Find the equation of each of the lines L_1, L_2 and L_3.

SOLUTION

Line L_1

This is a vertical line with equation $x = 6$.

Line L_2

gradient $= -1$

y-intercept $= (0, 5)$

The equation is $y = -x + 5$ or $y + x = 5$.

Line L_3

gradient $= 3$

y-intercept $= (0, 6)$

The equation is $y = 3x + 6$.

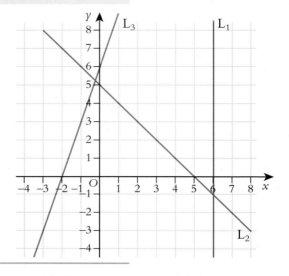

Finding the equation given the gradient and one point

If you are given the gradient, then this provides the m value. To find the value of c, substitute the given gradient and the x and y co-ordinates of the given point into the general equation $y = mx + c$ and rearrange it. You can then substitute the values of m and c into the general equation of a straight line to find the required equation.

EXAMPLE 23

Find the equation of the straight line with gradient 2 and y-intercept $(0, 6)$.

SOLUTION

$$y = mx + c$$
$$y = 2x + 6$$

In this case you have been given the intercept on the y-axis in co-ordinate form $(0, 6)$ and you can substitute directly for c.

EXAMPLE 24

Find the equation of the straight line with gradient 4 which passes through the point $(-2, 6)$.

SOLUTION

$$y = mx + c$$
$$y = 4x + c$$
$$6 = 4 \times -2 + c$$
$$6 = -8 + c$$
$$c = 6 + 8 = 14$$

Substitute for m.

The line passes through $(-2, 6)$ so those values of x and y satisfy the equation. So substitute $x = -2$ and $y = 6$.

The equation of the straight line with gradient 4 which passes through the point $(-2, 6)$ is $y = 4x + 14$.

EXAMPLE 25

Find the equation of the straight line with gradient $\frac{1}{2}$ which passes through the point $(2, -1)$.

SOLUTION

$$y = mx + c$$
$$y = \frac{1}{2} x + c$$
$$-1 = \frac{1}{2} \times 2 + c$$
$$-1 = 1 + c$$
$$c = -1 - 1 = -2$$

The line passes through $(2, -1)$ so substitute $x = 2$ and $y = -1$.

The equation of the straight line with gradient $\frac{1}{2}$ which passes through the point $(2, -1)$ is $y = \frac{1}{2}x - 2$.

Finding the equation of a line given two points on the line

If you know two points on a line then you can find the gradient of the line. You can use this gradient and substitute one of the points on the line into the general equation $y = mx + c$ to establish the c value.

EXAMPLE 26

Find the equation of the line joining the points $(3, 0)$ and $(0, 6)$.

SOLUTION

$$\text{gradient} = \frac{6 - 0}{0 - 3} = \frac{6}{-3} = -2$$
$$y = -2x + c$$
$$y = -2x + 6$$

Here the co-ordinates $(0, 6)$ provide the y-intercept so you can substitute directly for c.

EXAMPLE 27

Find the equation of the straight line passing through the points $(2, -3)$ and $(6, 1)$.

SOLUTION

$$\text{gradient} = \frac{1 - (-3)}{6 - 2} = \frac{4}{4} = 1$$
$$y = 1x + c$$

Substituting for the point $(6, 1)$,
$$1 = 1 \times 6 + c$$
$$1 = 6 + c$$
$$c = 1 - 6 = -5$$

Note that substituting for the point $(2, -3)$ would produce the same c value. It doesn't matter which point you choose for the substitution.

The equation of the straight line passing through the points $(2, -3)$ and $(6, 1)$ is $y = x - 5$.

EXAMPLE 28

Find the equation of the straight line passing through the points
(4, 2) and (−4, 8).

SOLUTION

gradient $= \dfrac{8 - 2}{-4 - 4} = \dfrac{6}{-8} = -\dfrac{3}{4}$

Substituting for the point (−4, 8),

$8 = -\dfrac{3}{4} \times (-4) + c = 3 + c$

$c = 8 - 3 = 5$

The equation of the straight line passing through the points (4, 2) and
(−4, 8) is $y = -\dfrac{3}{4}x + 5$.

EXAMPLE 29

Find the equation of the perpendicular bisector of the line joining the
points (−1, 6) and (5, −2).

> The perpendicular bisector is the straight line which is at right angles to another line and which passes through its midpoint.

SOLUTION

Gradient of the line joining these points $= \dfrac{-2 - 6}{5 - (-1)} = \dfrac{-8}{6} = \dfrac{-4}{3}$

So gradient of perpendicular line $= \dfrac{3}{4}$

The bisector passes through the midpoint, which has co-ordinates

$(\frac{1}{2}(-1 + 5), \frac{1}{2}(6 - 2)) = (2, 2)$

$y = mx + c$

$2 = \dfrac{3}{4} \times 2 + c$ ← Substitute for the gradient and the midpoint.

$2 = 1\frac{1}{2} + c$

$c = \dfrac{1}{2}$

The equation of the perpendicular bisector is $y = \dfrac{3}{4}x + \dfrac{1}{2}$ or $4y = 3x + 2$.

Exercise 25.5

1 Find the equation of each of the lines L_1 to L_6.

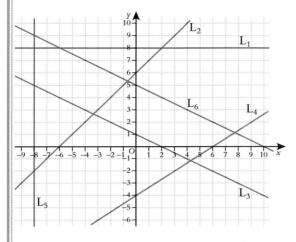

2 Write down the equation of each of the lines A to F.

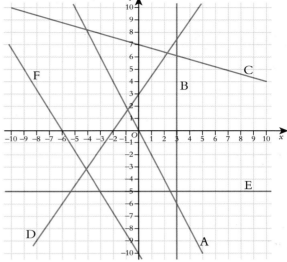

3 Find the equation of the line with gradient -2 which passes through the point $(0, 3)$.

4 Find the equation of the line with gradient -3 which passes through the point $(0, -2)$.

5 Find the equation of the line with gradient $-\frac{1}{2}$ which passes through the origin.

6 Find the equation of the line parallel to the line $y = 3x - 1$ which passes through the point $(1, -2)$.

7 Find the equation of the line with gradient $-\frac{1}{2}$ which passes through the point $(4, -3)$.

8 Find the equation of the line which passes through the points $(1, 1)$ and $(-2, -8)$.

9 Find the equation of the line which passes through the points $(-3, 5)$ and $(6, 2)$.

10 Find the equation of the line which is perpendicular to the line $y = 4x + 1$ and which passes through the point $(0, -2)$.

11 Find the equation of the line which passes through the point $(0, 4)$ and is perpendicular to the line joining the points $(0, 4)$ and $(9, 10)$.

12 Find the equation of the perpendicular bisector of the line joining the points $(-1, 4)$ and $(5, 12)$.

You should now:

- **be able to recognise and draw a linear graph**
- **be able to find the length of a line joining two points**
- **be able to find the midpoint of a line joining two points**
- **be able to find the gradient of a line**
- **know the properties of gradients, including the gradients of parallel and perpendicular lines**
- **understand and use the equation $y = mx + c$**
- **be able to draw a straight line using the gradient and crossing point (including lines not given in the form $y = mx + c$)**
- **be able to find the equation of a straight line given the graph**
- **be able to find the equation of a straight line given the gradient and one point on the line**
- **be able to find the equation of a straight line given two points on the line.**

Summary exercise 25

1 Draw each of these straight-line graphs.

    a $y = 4x - 3$ **b** $2y + x = 6$

    c $3y - 2x + 7 = 0$ **d** $x = 4$

2 Which of the following points lie on the line $y = 4x - 3$?

    $(2, 11)$ $(0, -3)$ $(-1, -7)$ $(-3, -12)$ $(3, 9)$

3 Which of the following lines does the point $(4, -1)$ lie on?

    $y = 2x - 9$ $y = x + 3$ $x + y = 5$ $y = 3 - x$

4 Find **i** the length and **ii** the midpoint of the lines joining each of the following pairs of co-ordinates:

    a P(2, 4) and Q(5, 9)   **b** A(−1, 6) and B(3, 4)

5 The points P(1, −2) and Q(5, 6) lie on the circumference of a circle, and join to form a diameter.
    Find **a** the centre and **b** the radius of the circle.

6 Find the gradient of the line joining each of these pairs of points:

    a P(0, −3) and Q(5, −4)   **b** W(−6, 2) and X(2, −1)

7 The gradient of a line is −2 and the point P with co-ordinates (4, 6) is on the line.
    Find the co-ordinates of any other point on the line.

8 The straight line $2x + 4y = 10$ cuts the x-axis at the point A and the y-axis at the point B.
    Find the co-ordinates of the points A and B.

9 Find the equation of each of the lines L_1 to L_5.

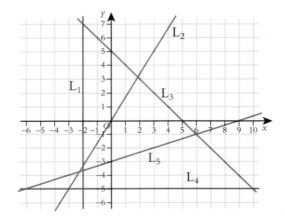

10 Find the equation of the line with gradient −3 which passes through the point (1, 5).

11 Find the equation of the line which passes through the points (2, −5) and $(3, -5\frac{1}{2})$.

12 Two variables P and Q are thought to be connected by an equation of the form $P = aQ + b$. The table shows some of the values of P and Q.

Q	10	12	15	18	20
P	10.4	12	14.4	16.8	18.4

   a Draw a straight-line graph to determine the relationship between P and Q.

   b **i** Find P when Q is 24.   **ii** Find Q when P is 28.

13 The line joining P and Q is perpendicular to the line joining L and M. L has co-ordinates $(2, -1)$, M has co-ordinates $(-4, -2)$ and P has co-ordinates $(-1, 4)$. Find a possible set of co-ordinates for the point Q.

14 Find the equation of the line which is perpendicular to the line $y = 4x - 3$ and which passes through the point $(4, -1)$.

15 Find the equation of the perpendicular bisector of the line joining the points $(2, 7)$ and $(-4, 1)$.

Examination questions

These questions are from examination papers where you may use a calculator.

1 A is the point $(0, 5)$ and B is the point $(4, 13)$.

   a Calculate the length of the line AB in surd form.

   b Find the equation of the line through A and B.

   c Find the equation of the line through A, perpendicular to AB.

2 The line AB has an equation $y = 3x + 7$.
Find the equation of the line which passes through $(0, 1)$ and is parallel to AB.

3 A is $(3, 3)$, B is $(-2, -3)$. Find the co-ordinates of the midpoint of AB.

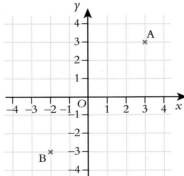

4 M and N have co-ordinates $(-3, 4)$ and $(3, -2)$, respectively. Find the midpoint of the line MN.

5 Calculate the length of the line joining the points A$(2, -2)$ and B$(-6, 4)$.

CHAPTER 26

Non-linear graphs

This chapter is about:

- recognising and drawing graphs of quadratic and cubic functions
- recognising and drawing graphs of reciprocal functions
- recognising and drawing graphs of exponential functions
- recognising and drawing graphs of trigonometric functions.

You should already know:

- how to plot and read points in all four quadrants
- how to substitute numbers in a formula
- how to calculate the speed of an object
- how to work with indices.

Quadratic graphs

A **quadratic function** involves an x^2 term and is of the form $y = ax^2 + bx + c$ where a ($a \neq 0$), b and c are constants.

The graph of a quadratic function takes the form of a curve, known as a **parabola**. When the x^2 term is positive ($a > 0$), the curve is $\cup$ shaped and has a minimum turning point.

When the x^2 term is negative ($a < 0$), the curve is $\cap$ shaped and has a maximum turning point.

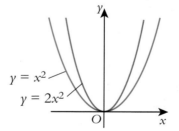

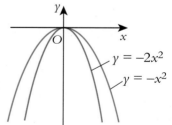

The larger the value of a, the narrower the curve.

A quadratic curve will cross the y-axis at the point $(0, c)$.

Quadratic curves are symmetrical about the turning point.

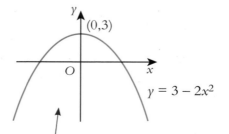

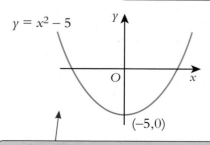

For this graph $a = -2$ and $c = 3$. The curve has a maximum turning point and it crosses the y-axis at $(0, 3)$.

For this curve $a = 1$ and $c = -5$. The curve has a minimum turning point and it crosses the y-axis at $(0, -5)$.

The graph of a quadratic function can be drawn by making a table of values for x and finding the corresponding values for y. The table can be constructed in stages as illustrated in the examples below.

EXAMPLE 1

Draw the graph of $y = x^2 + x - 6$.

SOLUTION

First draw up a table of values for x and y.

Now plot the set of co-ordinates (x, y) on a graph and join them with a smooth curve.

x	−4	−3	−2	−1	0	1	2	3
x^2	16	9	4	1	0	1	4	9
x	−4	−3	−2	−1	0	1	2	3
−6	−6	−6	−6	−6	−6	−6	−6	−6
$y = x^2 + x - 6$	6	0	−4	−6	−6	−4	0	6

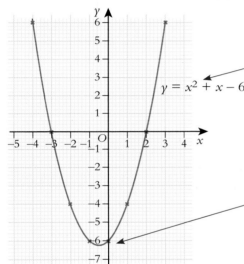

$y = x^2 + x - 6$

The x^2 term is positive ($a = +1$) so the turning point of the curve is at the *minimum* value of y.

$c = -6$ so the curve crosses the y-axis at $(0, -6)$.

The minimum point will occur halfway between $x = -1$ and $x = 0$ since these points have equal values of y and they are the minimum y values in the table.

When $x = -0.5$, $y = (-0.5)^2 + (-0.5) - 6 = -6.25$.

The minimum point is at $(-0.5, -6.25)$.

A quadratic graph crosses the x-axis when $y = 0$. The x co-ordinates of these points are the solutions of the associated quadratic equation, as met in Chapter 24. Here the crossing points on the x-axis are at $x = -3$ and $x = 2$ and are the solutions of the quadratic equation $x^2 + 3x - 6 = 0$.

In Chapter 24 you solved quadratic equations by factorising.
$x^2 + 3x - 6 = (x + 3)(x - 2) = 0$
The solutions are when $x = -3$ and $x = 2$, just as we see on the graph.

EXAMPLE 2

Draw the graph of $y = 3x^2 - 5x - 6$.

SOLUTION

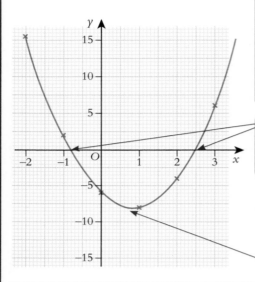

x	−2	−1	0	1	2	3
$3x^2$	12	3	0	3	12	27
$-5x$	10	5	0	−5	−10	−15
-6	−6	−6	−6	−6	−6	−6
$y = 3x^2 - 5x - 6$	16	2	−6	−8	−4	6

The solutions are at approximately $x = -0.8$ and $x = 2.5$. Note that it is generally not possible to give very accurate solutions using a graphical method.

For this graph, the minimum point is not easy to locate. Draw a smooth symmetrical curve joining the points you have calculated. The minimum point is just to the left of $x = 1$.

EXAMPLE 3

Draw the graph of $y = 4 - 3x - 2x^2$.

SOLUTION

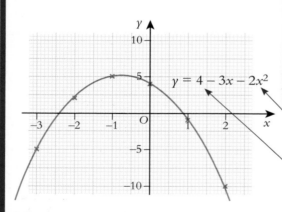

x	−3	−2	−1	0	1	2
4	4	4	4	4	4	4
$-3x$	9	6	3	0	−3	−6
$-2x^2$	−18	−8	−2	0	−2	−8
$y = 4 - 3x - 2x^2$	−5	2	5	4	−1	−10

Here the x^2 term is negative ($a = -2$) so the curve has a *maximum* point.

$c = 4$ so the curve crosses the y-axis at $(0, 4)$.

The maximum point is not easy to locate. Again, draw a smooth symmetrical curve joining the points you have plotted. The maximum point is just to the right of $x = -1$.

Exercise 26.1

Draw each of these quadratic curves.

1   $y = x^2 + 3x$ for $-4 \leqslant x \leqslant 2$

2   $y = x^2 - 2x$ for $-3 \leqslant x \leqslant 3$

3   $y = x^2 - 3x - 4$ for $-2 \leqslant x \leqslant 4$

4   $y = 2x^2 + 3x - 6$ for $-4 \leqslant x \leqslant 2$

5   $y = x^2 - 8x + 15$ for $0 \leqslant x \leqslant 6$

6   $y = 1 - 3x - x^2$ for $-5 \leqslant x \leqslant 2$

7   $y = 6 + x - 2x^2$ for $-3 \leqslant x \leqslant 3$

8   $y = 3x^2 - 5x + 4$ for $-1 \leqslant x \leqslant 3$

9   $y = x(5 - x)$ for $-1 \leqslant x \leqslant 5$

10   $y = (x + 1)(2x - 3)$ for $-2 \leqslant x \leqslant 3$

Cubic graphs

A cubic graph involves an x^3 term and is of the form
$y = ax^3 + bx^2 + cx + d$, where a ($\neq 0$), b, c and d are constants. The
simplest cubic function is $y = ax^3$, which passes through the origin. If a is
positive ($a > 0$) then the curve goes up from bottom left to top right, but
if a is negative ($a < 0$), then the curve goes down from top left to bottom
right.

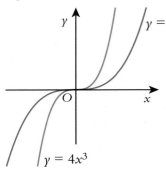

> The larger the value
> of a, the steeper the
> curve.

To draw the graph of a cubic function you can draw up a table of values,
just as for a quadratic function.

EXAMPLE 4

Draw the graph of the function $y = x^3 - x$.

SOLUTION

Draw up the table of values.

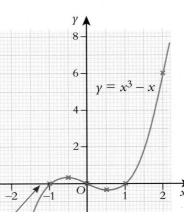

x	-2	-1	0	1	2	$-\frac{1}{2}$	$\frac{1}{2}$
x^3	-8	-1	0	1	8	$-\frac{1}{8}$	$\frac{1}{8}$
$-x$	2	1	0	-1	-2	$\frac{1}{2}$	$-\frac{1}{2}$
$y = x^3 - x$	-6	0	0	0	6	$\frac{3}{8}$	$-\frac{3}{8}$

> Using whole number values for x gave three values of 0.
> To get a better idea of what the curve looks like we
> need to try values in-between.

Now plot the set of co-ordinates (x, y) on a graph
and join them with a smooth curve.

> The curve cuts the x-axis at three points. This shows
> there are three roots to the equation $y = x^3 - x$.

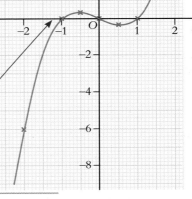

EXAMPLE 5

Draw the graph of the function $y = 4x - x^3 - 9$.

SOLUTION

x	−4	−3	−2	−1	0	1	2	3	4
4x	−16	−12	−8	−4	0	4	8	12	16
−x^3	64	27	8	1	0	−1	−8	−27	−64
−9	−9	−9	−9	−9	−9	−9	−9	−9	−9
$y = 4x - x^3 - 9$	39	6	−9	−12	−9	−6	−9	−24	−57

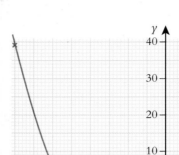

This equation only has one root.

The curve cuts the y-axis at $(0, d)$, so here it cuts at $(0, -9)$.

$y = 4x - x^3 - 9$

Exercise 26.2

Draw each of these cubic functions.

1   $6 - x^3$ for $-3 \leqslant x \leqslant 3$

2   $2x^3 + 3$ for $-3 \leqslant x \leqslant 3$

3   $x^3 - 4$ for $-3 \leqslant x \leqslant 3$

4   $x^3 - 9x$ for $-4 \leqslant x \leqslant 4$

5   $x^3 + x - 3$ for $-3 \leqslant x \leqslant 3$

Reciprocal graphs

A **reciprocal function** is one of the form $y = \dfrac{a}{x}$ where a is a constant.

The graph of a reciprocal function has a very distinctive shape. Since you cannot divide by zero, there will be a break in the graph at $x = 0$. The x- and y-axes become **asymptotes** as the graph will get very close to them but will never actually cross them.

EXAMPLE 6

Draw the graph of $y = \dfrac{10}{x}$ for $-5 \leqslant x \leqslant 5$.

SOLUTION

x	−5	−4	−3	−2	−1	0	1	2	3	4	5
$y = \dfrac{10}{x}$	−2	−2.5	$-3\frac{1}{3}$	−5	−10	—	10	5	$3\frac{1}{3}$	2.5	2

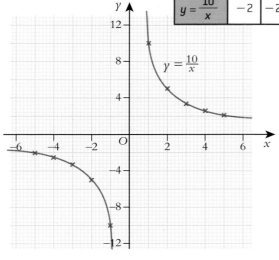

EXAMPLE 7

Draw the graph of $y = \dfrac{-4}{x}$ for $-4 \leqslant x \leqslant 4$.

SOLUTION

x	−4	−3	−2	−1	0	1	2	3	4
$y = \dfrac{-4}{x}$	1	$1\frac{1}{3}$	2	4	—	−4	−2	$-1\frac{1}{3}$	−1

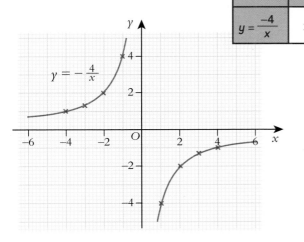

EXAMPLE 8

Draw the graph of $y = \dfrac{12}{x-3}$ for $-5 \leqslant x \leqslant 7$.

SOLUTION

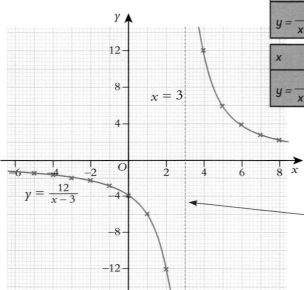

x	−5	−4	−3	−2	−1	0
$y = \dfrac{12}{x-3}$	−1.5	−1.7	−2	−2.4	−3	−4

x	1	2	3	4	5	6	7
$y = \dfrac{12}{x-3}$	−6	−12	—	12	6	4	3

Here the asymptote is when $x = 3$ as this is when the denominator will be zero. Hence this graph will never cross the line $x = 3$.

Exercise 26.3

1 Draw the graph of $y = \dfrac{6}{x}$ for $-6 \leqslant x \leqslant 6$.

2 Draw the graph of $y = \dfrac{20}{x}$. Choose suitable values of x for plotting.

3 Draw the graph of $y = \dfrac{-3}{x}$ for values of x from -3 to $+3$.

4 If the graph of $y = \dfrac{16}{x+2}$ were drawn, where would there be a vertical asymptote?

Exponential graphs

An **exponential function** is one of the form $y = a^x$ where a is a constant and x is the **exponent** (or power).

The graph of an exponential function has a very distinctive shape. In Chapter 15 you saw that $a^0 = 1$ and so exponential graphs will always pass through the point $(0, 1)$. They will never cross the x-axis, and hence the x-axis is an asymptote for such graphs.

EXAMPLE 9

Draw the graph of $y = 3^x$ for $-2 \leqslant x \leqslant 2$.

SOLUTION

The values in this table are calculated using the rules of indices from Chapter 15. For example when $x = -2$,

$$y = 3^{-2} = \frac{1}{3^2} = \frac{1}{9}$$

x	−2	−1	0	1	2
y	$\frac{1}{9}$	$\frac{1}{3}$	1	3	9

When the exponent is positive, the curve slopes upwards.
This type of curve is known as an **exponential growth curve**. You will learn more about this in Chapter 27.

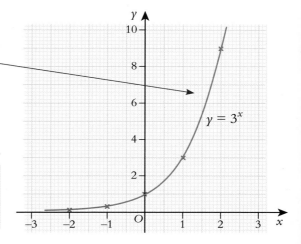

$y = 3^x$

EXAMPLE 10

Draw the graph of $y = 2^{-x}$ for $-3 \leqslant x \leqslant 3$.

SOLUTION

x	-3	-2	-1	0	1	2	3
y	8	4	2	1	$\frac{1}{2}$	$\frac{1}{4}$	$\frac{1}{8}$

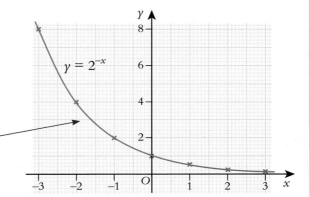

$y = 2^{-x}$

When the exponent is negative, the curve slopes downwards.
This type of curve is called an **exponential decay curve**. You will learn more about this in Chapter 27.

Exercise 26.4

1 a Draw the graph of $y = 2^x$ for values of x from -3 to 3.
   b From the graph, estimate the value of x for which $2^x = 5$.

2 a Draw the graph of $y = 1 + 3^{-x}$ for values of x from -2 to 2.
   b What is the value of the asymptote to this graph?

Graphs of the trig functions

The sine function

$y = \sin x$ for $0° \leqslant x \leqslant 360°$

This function is a smooth curve. To draw it we need to find the values of some of the points that will be on the sine graph. We can write these in a table like that below.

x [°]	0	30	60	90	120	150	180	210	240	270	300	330	360
$\sin x$	0	0.5	0.866	1	0.866	0.5	0	-0.5	-0.866	-1	-0.866	-0.5	0

A smooth curve can now be drawn through these points.

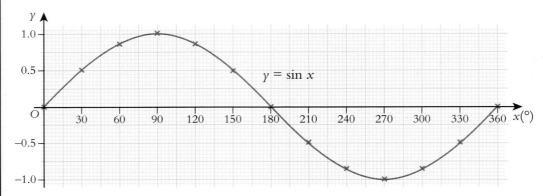

This graph can be used to answer various questions.

EXAMPLE 11

a   Find sin 45°.
b   Solve sin $x = 0.25$ for $0° \leqslant x \leqslant 360°$.

SOLUTION

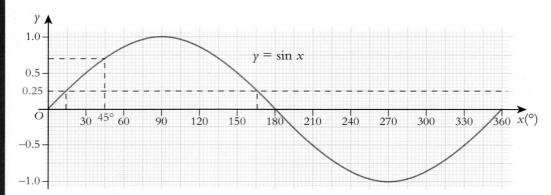

a   Go to 45° on the horizontal x-axis and draw vertically up to the graph and then across to the y-axis. (See the dashed blue lines on the graph.)

Read off the value as accurately as possible.

Answer: sin 45° = 0.7 approximately.

b   Go to 0.25 on the vertical y-axis.

Draw horizontally across to the graph and then down to the x-axis. (See the dashed green lines on the graph.)

Answers: $x = 15°$ or $165°$ approximately.

Remember to give all the answers in the specified region.

The cosine function

$$y = \cos x \quad \text{for} \quad 0° \leqslant x \leqslant 360°$$

Like the sine function, the cosine function is a smooth curve.

To draw the graph we need to find the values of some of the points that will be on it. We can write these in a table and then use the values to draw the graph.

x (°)	0	30	60	90	120	150	180	210	240	270	300	330	360
cos x	1	0.866	0.5	0	−0.5	−0.866	−1	−0.866	−0.5	0	0.5	0.866	1

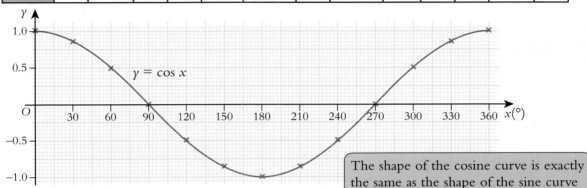

The shape of the cosine curve is exactly the same as the shape of the sine curve – it is just shifted to the left by 90°.

The tangent function

$$y = \tan x \quad \text{for} \quad 0° \leqslant x \leqslant 360°$$

This function has a very different graph from either sine or cosine. It is made up of separate sections which are all smooth curves – not a long continuous curve.

To draw the graph we need to find the values of some of the points that will be on it.

x (°)	0	45	90	135	180	225	270	315	360
tan x	0	1	not defined	1	0	−1	not defined	−1	0

The values of tan x for both 90° and 270° are not defined.

To find the shape of the tangent graph around $x = 90°$ we must consider values of x immediately before and after 90°.

x (°)	89.9	89.95	89.99	90.01	90.05	90.1
tan x	573	1146	5730	−5730	−1146	−5730

If we had found tan 89.999 99° using a calculator we would get 5729 577.951 (i.e. the value is getting very much larger as we approach 90°). We can say that as x approaches 90° from 89° then tan x approaches $+\infty$.

Similarly tan 90.000 01° = −5729 577.951 (i.e. the value is becoming a very much larger negative number as we approach 90°). So we can say that as x approaches 90° from 91° then tan x approaches $-\infty$.

By considering 270° similarly we can produce a table of values for $\tan x$ for $0° \leqslant x \leqslant 360°$.

269.99° is the same as −90.01°.

x (°)	0	45	89.99	90.01	135	180	225	269.99	315	360
tan x	0	1	5730	−5730	−1	0	1	5730	−5730	−1

We can now draw a smooth curve through these points. We will not label the y-axis as the curve tends to $+\infty$ and $-\infty$ at both 90° and 270°.

We can draw the two straight lines $x = 90°$ and $x = -270°$. The graph will never touch or cross these lines. These lines are the asymptotes to the tangent function.

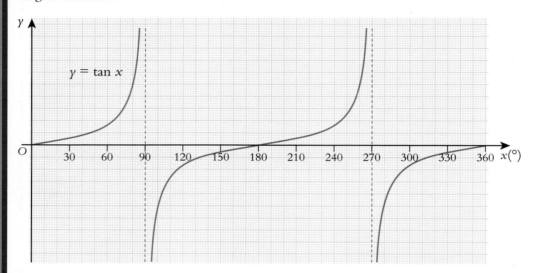

Exercise 26.5

Sketch these graphs.

1 $y = \sin x$ for $-180° \leqslant x \leqslant 180°$ 2 $y = \cos x$ for $0° \leqslant x \leqslant 360°$

3 $y = \tan x$ for $0° \leqslant x \leqslant 360°$ 4 $y = 2\sin x$ for $-180° \leqslant x \leqslant 180°$

5 $y = 3\cos x$ for $0° \leqslant x \leqslant 360°$ 6 $y = \tan x$ for $-360° \leqslant x \leqslant 0°$

Draw these graphs on 2 mm squared paper.

7 $y = \sin x$ for $0° \leqslant x \leqslant 360°$.
  a Use your graph to find these.
    i sin 40°   ii sin 100°   iii sin 200°   iv sin 310°
  b In the range $0° \leqslant x \leqslant 60°$, solve for
    i $\sin x = 0.8$ ii $\sin x = -0.6$.

8 $y = \cos x$ for $0° \leqslant x \leqslant 360°$.
  a Use your graph to find these.
    i cos 50°   ii cos 130°   iii cos 250°   iv cos 310°
  b In the range $0° \leqslant x \leqslant 360°$, solve for
    i $\cos x = 0.3$ ii $\cos x = -0.7$.

Summary of non-linear graphs

Here is a summary of the shapes and equations of the different types of graph described in this chapter.

Type of graph	Characteristic shape	
quadratic	$y = ax^2 + bx + c$ where $a > 0$	$y = ax^2 + bx + c$ where $a < 0$
cubic	$y = ax^3 + bx^2 + cx + d$ where $a > 0$	$y = ax^3 + bx^2 + cx + d$ where $a < 0$
reciprocal	$y = \dfrac{a}{x}$ where $a > 0$	$y = \dfrac{a}{x}$ where $a < 0$
exponential	$y = a^x$ where $x > 0$	$y = a^x$ where $x < 0$
trigonometric	$y = \sin x$ for $0° \leqslant x \leqslant 360°$	$y = \cos x$ for $0° \leqslant x \leqslant 360°$ $y = \tan x$ for $0° \leqslant x \leqslant 360°$

Recognising non-linear graphs

Rather than being asked to draw such graphs, sometimes you will be asked to recognise them or to match functions to their graphs.

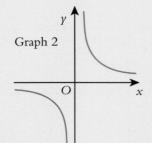
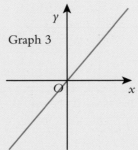
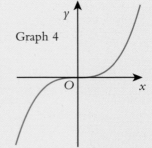
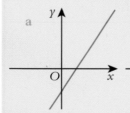
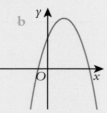
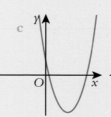
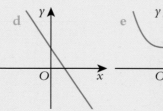

d This is a linear graph with a negative coefficient of x.
    The most suitable equation is $y = 2 - 3x$.

e This is a cubic graph with a negative coefficient of x.
    The most suitable equation is $y = 4 - 2x^3$.

You should now:

- be able to recognise and draw quadratic and cubic graphs
- be able to recognise and draw a reciprocal graph
- be able to recognise and draw an exponential graph
- be able to recognise and draw graphs of the trig functions sin, cos and tan
- be able to match a variety of functions with the appropriate graphical form.

Summary exercise 26

1 Draw the quadratic curve for each of these.
   a $y = x^2 - 7x + 10$ for $0 \leqslant x \leqslant 6$
   b $y = 2x^2 + 3x - 4$ for $-3 \leqslant x \leqslant 2$
   c $y = 5 + 3x - x^2$ for $-2 \leqslant x \leqslant 4$

2 Draw the graph for each of these cubic functions.
   a $y = 2 - x^3 - 9x$
   b $y = x^3 + 2x^2$

3 Draw the graph of $y = \dfrac{12}{x} + 4$ for $-6 \leqslant x \leqslant 6$.

4 If the graph of $y = \dfrac{8}{x - 4}$ were drawn, where would there be a vertical asymptote?

5 Sketch the graphs of these trig functions.
   a $y = 5\sin x$ for $0° \leqslant x \leqslant 360°$.
   b $y = 8\cos x$ for $0° \leqslant x \leqslant 360°$.
   c $y = \tan x$ for $0° \leqslant x \leqslant 360°$.

6 Use 2 mm squared paper to draw the graph of $y = \cos x$ for
   $0° \leqslant x \leqslant 360°$.
   a Use your graph to find **i** $\cos 20°$ **ii** $\cos 330°$.
   b In the range $0° \leqslant x \leqslant 360°$ solve for
      i $\cos x = 0.7$ **ii** $\cos x = -0.4$.

7 Match each of these graphs with the correct equation.

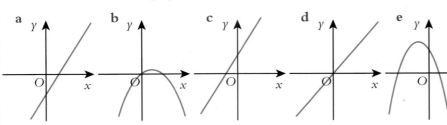

Equations:
$y = \frac{1}{2}x$ $y = 2^x$ $y = -2x^2 - 3x + 8$

$y = 2x + 4$ $y = 3x - 2x^2$ $y = x - 2$

8 Match each of these graphs with one of the given equations.

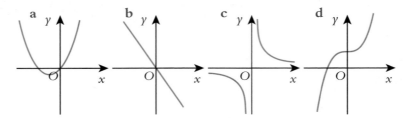

Equations:

$y = -x$ $y = -x^2 - x + 6$ $y = \dfrac{2}{x}$ $y = x^2 + 3x$ $y = x^3 + 5$

e Sketch the form of the remaining equation.

Examination questions

Use 'Topic Tracker' at www.ccea.org.uk to find more exam questions.

These questions are from examination papers where you may use a calculator.

1 From the list choose the most appropriate equation for each graph shown.

$y = \dfrac{4}{x}$ $y = 4 + x^2$ $y = 4 - x$ $y = x - 4$

a 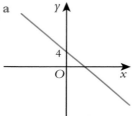 **b** 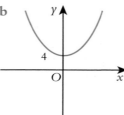 **c**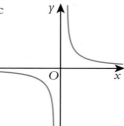

2 The graph of $y = \sin x$ is shown for $-360° \leqslant x \leqslant 360°$.

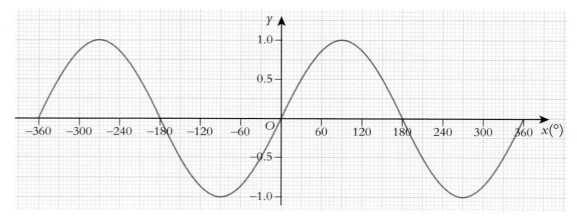

a Given that $\sin 30° = 0.5$, find the values of x in the range of $0° \leqslant x \leqslant 360°$ for which $2 \sin x = -1$.

b Sketch the graph of $y = \cos x$ for $-360° \leqslant x \leqslant 360°$.

3 Sketch the graph of $y = \tan x$ for $0° \leqslant x \leqslant 180°$.

CHAPTER 27

Real-life graphs

This chapter is about:

- drawing and interpreting graphs arising from real-life situations, including conversion graphs and travel graphs.

You should already know:

- how to plot and read points in all four quadrants
- how to substitute numbers in a formula
- how to calculate the speed of an object
- how to work with indices.

Straight-line graphs in context

In real life, recorded data often takes the form of a straight-line graph and so can be expressed in the form of a linear equation. The variables used may not be x and y, but the general equation for a straight line, $y = mx + c$, can be adapted to suit the particular data. This is illustrated in the examples below.

EXAMPLE 1

In an experiment, the variables A and B are thought to be connected by an equation of the form $B = kA + n$.

Some values of A and B are recorded in the table.

A	1	2	3.5	4.2	6.8
B	5.4	8.4	12.9	15	22.8

Find the values for k and n, and hence the equation of the graph.

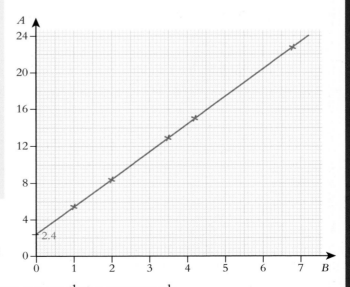

SOLUTION

The first step is to plot the values on a graph, with A on the horizontal axis and B on the vertical axis.

Comparing $B = kA + n$ with $y = mx + c$, you can see that n corresponds to c, and so to the intercept on the vertical axis. Here $n = 2.4$.

Similarly, k corresponds to m, the gradient. The gradient can be found by calculating the differences in x and y between two points, for example $(1, 5.4)$ and $(2, 8.4)$.

$$\text{Gradient} = \frac{8.4 - 5.4}{2 - 1} = \frac{3}{1} = 3$$

So $k = 3$

Hence the equation of this graph is $B = 3A + 2.4$.

> **Check**
> Substitute in a set of co-ordinates from the table, for example $(3.5, 12.9)$.
> $B = 3A + 2.4$
> $B = 3 \times 3.5 + 2.4 = 12.9$
> as required.

EXAMPLE 2

The table shows the largest quantity of salt, k grams, which can be dissolved in a beaker of water at different temperatures, $t\,^\circ C$.

$t\,(^\circ C)$	10	20	30	40	50	60
k (grams)	55	56	64	66	70	73

The data is thought to satisfy a law of the form $k = at + b$.

  a Find the values of a and b.

  b Calculate the temperature needed to dissolve 85 g of salt.

> For some sets of data, the points may not form an exact straight line since the data is experimental and subject to some inaccuracies of measurement. In these cases it is appropriate to draw a 'line of best fit'.

SOLUTION

Start by plotting the values on a graph.

  a a represents the gradient here.

$$\text{Gradient} = \frac{70 - 66}{50 - 40} = \frac{4}{10} = 0.4$$

So $a = 0.4$

b represents the intercept on the y-axis (the k-axis in this example). From the graph, $b = 50$.

  b The equation is $k = 0.4t + 50$.
Substituting in for $k = 85$,
$$85 = 0.4t + 50$$
$$0.4t = 85 - 50$$
$$= 35$$
$$t = \frac{35}{0.4} = 87.5\,^\circ C$$

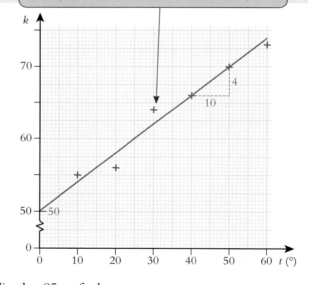

A temperature of $87.5\,^\circ C$ is needed to dissolve 85 g of salt.

EXAMPLE 3

The charges depend on the time t taken to repair the TV.

  a Find the equation connecting the charge C with the time t.

  b What does the gradient of the line represent?

  c A man is charged £84.
What is the maximum time spent repairing his TV?

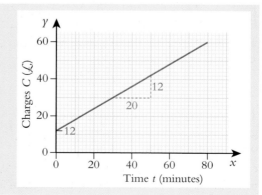

SOLUTION

a   Intercept on vertical axis = 12

gradient $= \dfrac{12}{20} = 0.6$

The equation is $C = 0.6t + 12$.

b   The gradient represents a charge of 60 pence per minute after a call-out charge of £12.

c   Substituting in for $C = 84$,

$$84 = 0.6t + 12$$
$$0.6t = 84 - 12 = 72$$
$$t = \dfrac{72}{0.6} = 120$$

The maximum time spent on the repair is 120 minutes or 2 hours.

Exercise 27.1

1   A stone is dropped from the top of a tall tower. Its speed, v m/s, at any time t seconds is given by the formula $v = u + at$. Some of the values for v and t are shown on the graph.

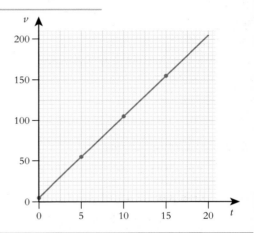

a   Find the values of u and a.

b   Hence find the time taken for the stone to reach a speed of 225 m/s.

2   The length, L mm, of the mercury column in a thermometer depends on the temperature, T °C. The relationship between L and T is thought to be linear. A number of readings were taken and are recorded in the table.

a   Plot the points on a graph.

b   Do they form a linear relationship? If so, find a formula connecting L and T.

c   What would the length of the mercury column be at a temperature of 75 °C?

Temperature, T (°C)	10	15	22	35	50
Length, L (mm)	21	21.4	22.1	23.5	25

3   A liquid was heated to 30 °C. The heating was then stopped and the temperature was recorded every 30 seconds. The results were as shown on the graph.

a   Find a linear relationship connecting the temperature T with the time in minutes, m.

b   Use your formula to estimate the time taken for the temperature to reach 5 °C.

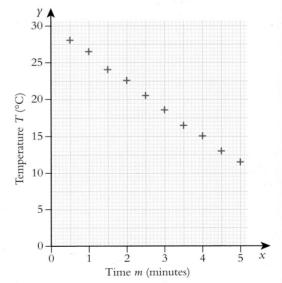

Straight-line graphs can also be used to represent real-life situations such as conversion rates, costs and distance.

Conversion graphs

Conversion graphs always pass through the origin. They are of the form $y = mx$.

EXAMPLE 4

5 miles is approximately 8 kilometres.

   a   Draw a conversion graph to convert distances of up to 50 miles into kilometres.

   b   Use your graph to find

      i   approximately how many kilometres 28 miles is.

      ii   approximately how many miles 37 kilometres is.

   c   The distance from Belfast to Derry is 73 miles.
      Use your graph to find approximately how many kilometres this is.

SOLUTION

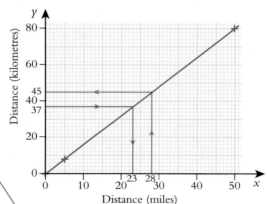

   a   The graph must go through $(0, 0)$.
The information given tells you that it goes through $(5, 8)$.
You want to convert distances of up to 50 miles.
50 is 5×10 so 50 miles is equal to $8 \times 10 = 80$ kilometres, so the graph also goes through $(50, 80)$.
Plot these three points and join them with a straight line.

   b   i   Look at the red lines on the graph.
Find 28 miles on the horizontal axis.
Draw a line vertically up to the graph line.
Then draw a line horizontally to the vertical axis. Read off the y value.
28 miles is approximately 45 kilometres.

You only need two points to draw a straight line, but it is good practice to use at least *three* points when plotting a linear graph, as a check.

      ii   Look at the blue lines on the graph.
Find 37 kilometres on the vertical axis.
Draw a line horizontally to the graph line.
Then draw a line vertically down to the horizontal axis.
Read off the x value.
37 kilometres is approximately 23 miles.

The graph does not extend up to 73 miles but you can find the kilometre equivalent by splitting the distance into $50 + 23$ miles.
You found the kilometre equivalent of 23 miles in part **b ii**.

   c   73 miles is approximately $80 + 37$
      $= 117$ kilometres.

Costs

If a graph is used to represent costs there is often a fixed charge plus a charge per unit. These graphs are of the form $y = mx + c$ where c is the fixed cost, m is the cost per unit and x is the number of units.

EXAMPLE 5

A plumber uses this graph to work out how much to charge for the jobs she does.

a   How much does she charge for a job taking 6 hours?

b   She charges £92 for a job.
    How long did it take?

c   What is the call-out charge?

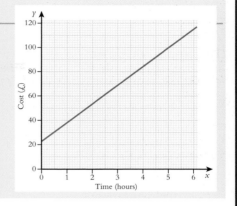

SOLUTION

a   Look at the red lines on the graph.
    She charges £115 for a job taking 6 hours.

b   Look at the blue lines on the graph.
    A job costing £92 takes $4\frac{1}{2}$ hours.

c   The call-out charge is £23.

> The call-out charge is the cost of the plumber attending a job before the cost of the work done is added. You read off the value when the time is zero.

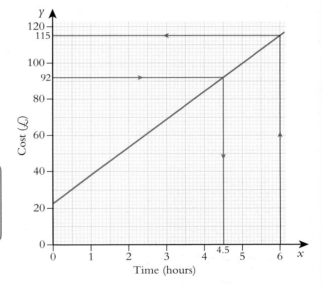

Travel graphs

A **distance–time graph** or **travel graph** can be used to represent a journey. It shows the distance travelled during a period of time. Time is always plotted on the horizontal axis. The distance travelled is plotted on the vertical axis.

A journey may consist of several stages. Each stage is shown with a different line.

The slope of the line indicates the **speed** at which the object is travelling. A steep line shows that the object is travelling quickly. A less steep line means the object is travelling more slowly. A horizontal line indicates that *no* distance has been travelled – in other words, the object has stopped.

The speed at which the object is travelling can be calculated by reading from the graph the distance travelled and the time taken, and using the formula

$$\text{speed} = \frac{\text{distance}}{\text{time}}$$

The **average speed** for the total journey is calculated by dividing the *total* distance travelled by the *total* time taken, including any stops.

EXAMPLE 6

A bus begins its journey from Coleraine at 10.00a.m. It arrives at Portstewart, 10 km away, at 10.40a.m. It stops there for 10 minutes and then continues for a further 6 km to Portrush. It arrives at Portrush at 11.50a.m. The bus stops there for 10 minutes before returning to Coleraine without stopping. It arrives back in Coleraine at 12.40p.m.

a Draw a travel graph to show this journey.
b Was the bus travelling more quickly between Coleraine and Portstewart or between Portstewart and Portrush?
c How long does the return journey take?
d What was the speed for the return journey? (Do not include the time spent at Portrush.)
e What was the average speed for the outward journey? (Include the time spent at Portrush.)

SOLUTION

a Choose scales for your graph.
Here you need to be able to plot distances from 0 to at least 16 km on the vertical axis and times from 10.00 to 12.40 on the horizontal axis.

Use the information given to plot each stage of the journey.

> Make sure you choose sensible scales, especially for the time axis, as you may need to read off values for parts of a unit on either of the axes.
> In the graph a scale of 1 unit = 10 minutes has been used on the time axis, but only every third unit is labelled.

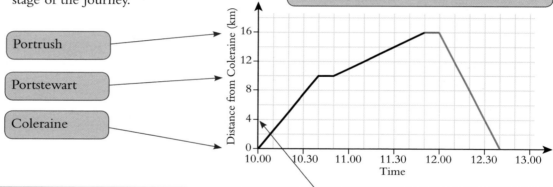

Portrush

Portstewart

Coleraine

> Notice that the vertical axis represents distance from the origin, in this case Coleraine, so that for the outward journey (shown in black) the lines slope upwards and for the return journey (shown in red) the line slopes downwards, indicating that the bus is travelling back towards Coleraine.

b The bus was travelling more quickly between Coleraine and Portstewart.

> The line is steeper for the journey between Coleraine and Portstewart than for the journey between Portstewart and Portrush.

c 40 minutes

> You can calculate this either from the information given in the question or by reading the values from your graph.

d The return journey is the journey from the destination back to the origin, in this case from Portrush back to Coleraine.

$$\text{speed} = \frac{\text{distance}}{\text{time}}$$

$$= \frac{16 \text{ kilometres}}{40 \text{ minutes}}$$

> Portrush is 16 km from Coleraine.

> Use your answer from part **c**.

$$= \frac{24 \text{ kilometres}}{1 \text{ hour}}$$

$$= 24 \text{ km/h}$$

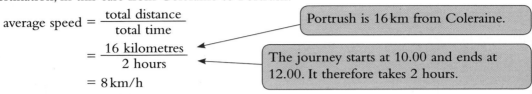

Speeds for vehicles are usually given per *hour*.
40 is $\frac{2}{3}$ of an hour so divide 16 by 2 and multiply the result by 3 to find the distance travelled in 1 hour. Alternatively, if you are using a calculator, you can divide 16 by 40 to find the distance travelled in 1 minute and then multiply by 60 to find the distance travelled in 1 hour.

e   The outward journey is the journey from the origin to the destination, in this case from Coleraine to Portrush.

$$\text{average speed} = \frac{\text{total distance}}{\text{total time}}$$

Portrush is 16 km from Coleraine.

$$= \frac{16 \text{ kilometres}}{2 \text{ hours}}$$

The journey starts at 10.00 and ends at 12.00. It therefore takes 2 hours.

$$= 8 \text{ km/h}$$

Several journeys may be shown on a single travel graph. Sometimes, the lines representing the different journeys cross. This tells you that the people meet or pass each other.

EXAMPLE 7

The travel graph shows Anne's journey to her Grandma's house.

a   Describe her journey.

Anne's brother Ben left home half an hour later and travelled to their Grandma's house at a constant speed of 15 km/h.

b   Copy the graph and add his journey to it.

c   At what time does Ben pass Anne?

d   How far from home are they when Ben passes Anne?

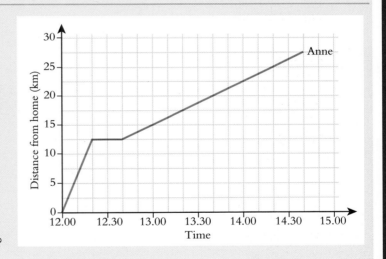

SOLUTION

a   Anne travels 12.5 km between 12.00 and 12.20.
She stops for 20 minutes.
She then travels a further 15 km between 12.40 and 14.40.

b   Ben leaves home half an hour after Anne, at 12.30.
He travels at a constant speed, meaning that he doesn't stop and he doesn't change speed.
The graph representing Anne's journey tells you that Grandma's house is 27.5 km from home.

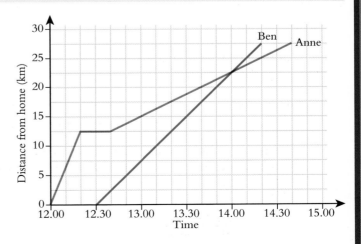

A speed of 15 km/h tells you that Ben travels 15 km in 1 hour.

You are given the speed but you need to plot *distance* against time.
Draw a line from (12.30, 0) to (13.30, 15) and continue it until it reaches a
point with a *y* co-ordinate of 27.5.

c   Ben passes Anne at 14.00.   ← Read off the time where the lines cross.
d   They are 22.5 km from home when
    Ben passes Anne.   ← Read off the distance where the lines cross.

Exercise 27.2

1   The cooking time, *t* hours, required to cook a roast of mass *m* kg is
    given by the formula $t = \frac{3m + 1}{2}$.

    a   Draw a graph of cooking time for $0 \leqslant m \leqslant 4$.
    b   From the graph, estimate the cooking time for a roast of 2.7 kg.
    c   From the graph, estimate the mass of a roast which requires
        $2\frac{3}{4}$ hours' cooking time.

2   The table shows the taxi fare for journeys of varying length.

Distance (miles)	2	5	8	10	15
Fare (£)	5.50	10	14.50	17.50	25

    a   Plot these values on a graph.
    b   From the graph, determine the length of journey for which the
        fare is £11.50.
    c   Determine the call-out charge for the taxi.

3   The graph shows the journeys
    of Claire and Dermot.
    a   Who travels further?
    b   Calculate the average speed
        at which each of them
        is travelling.
    c   At what time do they pass
        each other?
    d   Who is further from their
        destination when they pass?

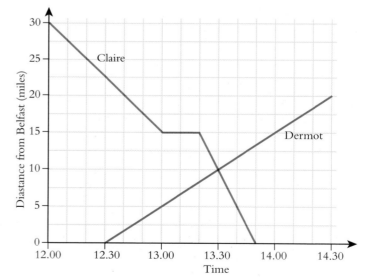

Quadratic graphs in context

As with linear graphs, quadratic graphs can be used to represent real-life situations. This is illustrated in the next examples.

EXAMPLE 8

A cricket ball is thrown over level ground so that after t seconds its height, h metres, is given by the formula $h = 20t - 5t^2$.

a   Copy and complete the table.
b   Draw the graph of h against t.
c   What is the greatest height reached by the ball?
d   How long does it take to reach this height?
e   How long does it take before it hits the ground?

t	0	1	2	3	4
$20t$					
$-5t^2$					
h					

SOLUTION

a

t	0	1	2	3	4
$20t$	0	20	40	60	80
$-5t^2$	0	-5	-20	-45	-80
h	0	15	20	15	0

b   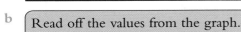 Read off the values from the graph.

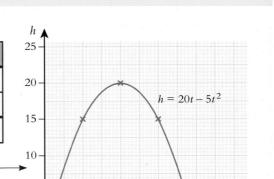

c   20 m
d   2 seconds
e   4 seconds

EXAMPLE 9

A man has 40 metres of wire fencing which he wants to use to make a rectangular pen for some animals. He uses a wall as one side of the pen so that the wire is only used for the other three sides of the pen. The width of the pen is x metres.

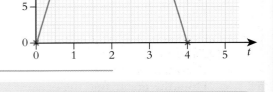

a   Write down an expression for the length of the pen.
b   Write down an expression for the area A of the pen.
c   Set up a table of values for x and A, and hence draw the graph.
d   What are the dimensions of the pen such that the largest possible area is enclosed?

SOLUTION

a $40 - 2x$
b $A = \text{length} \times \text{width}$
   $= (40 - 2x)x$
   $= 40x - 2x^2$

c

x	0	5	10	15	20
40x	0	200	400	600	800
$-2x^2$	0	-50	-200	-450	-800
A	0	150	200	150	0

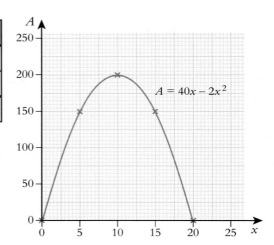

d   The largest possible area is $200\,\text{m}^2$.
This occurs when the width is $10\,\text{m}$, and
hence the length is $20\,\text{m}$.

Exercise 27.3

1   A mortar fires a firework so that its height, y metres, is given by the
formula $y = 10x - x^2$, where x is the horizontal distance travelled
by the firework (in hundreds of metres).
  a   Copy and complete the table of values
      for x and y.
  b   Draw the graph of y against x.
  c   What is the maximum height reached
      by the firework?

x	0	2	4	6	8	10
10x						
$-x^2$						
y						

2   A ball is thrown in the air so that t seconds after it is thrown, its
height, h metres, above its starting point is given by
$h = 30t - 5t^2$.
  a   Draw the graph of h against t for $0 \leqslant t \leqslant 5$.
  b   From the graph, find the time when the ball is at its greatest
      height.
  c   From the graph, find the greatest height reached by the ball.
  d   From the graph, find for how long the ball is at a height of
      more than $30\,\text{m}$.

3   In a science experiment, the temperature of an object is lowered
from room temperature to below freezing over a period of 6 hours.
If t is the time from the start of the experiment (in hours),
then the temperature P (in degrees Celsius) is given by
$P = t^2 - 9t + 10$.
  a   Copy and complete the table of values.
  b   Plot P against t.
  c   What was the room temperature at the start
      of the experiment?
  d   What was the object's temperature after
      $2\frac{1}{2}$ hours?
  e   How long did it take for the temperature to
      fall to freezing point ($0\,°\text{C}$)?

t	0	1	2	3	4	5	6
t^2							
$-9t$							
10							
P							

Exponential graphs in context

Exponential graphs represent many real–life situations, in particular situations of growth, for example population growth, or decay, for example radioactive decay.

A yeast mixture doubles in volume every hour. Initially there is $10\,cm^3$ of the mixture.

a   Complete the table to show the volume of yeast present for the first 5 hours.

Time (hours)	0	1	2	3	4	5
Volume of yeast (cm³)	10					

b   Draw the graph showing the volume of yeast against time.

c   Estimate the volume of yeast present after $2\frac{1}{2}$ hours.

SOLUTION

a

Time (hours)	0	1	2	3	4	5
Volume of yeast (cm³)	10	20	40	80	160	320

b

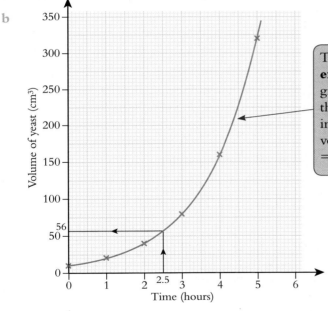

This type of curve is known as an **exponential growth curve**. The growth of the yeast could be given by the formula 10×2^t where t is the time in hours. For example, after 3 hours, the volume of yeast
$= 10 \times 2^3 = 10 \times 8 = 80\,cm^3$.

c   After $2\frac{1}{2}$ hours there is approximately $56\,cm^3$ of yeast.

A particular drug has a half-life in a patient's body of 24 hours. 120 mg of the drug is injected.

a   Draw a graph to show the amount of drug remaining in the patient's body over a period of 6 days.

b   After how long will there be 40 mg of the drug remaining?

SOLUTION

First draw up a table of values. The amount of drug remaining halves every 24 hours. So after 1 day there is half of 120 mg = 60 mg remaining, and after 2 days there is half of 60 mg = 30 mg remaining.

a

Time (days)	0	1	2	3	4	5	6
Amount of drug (mg)	120	60	30	15	7.5	3.75	1.875

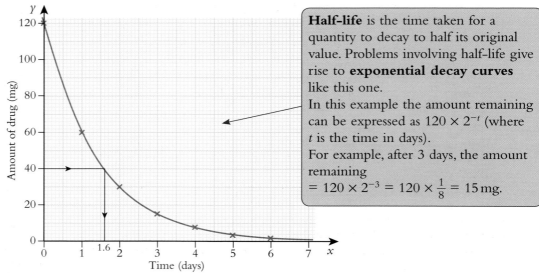

Half–life is the time taken for a quantity to decay to half its original value. Problems involving half-life give rise to **exponential decay curves** like this one.

In this example the amount remaining can be expressed as 120×2^{-t} (where t is the time in days).

For example, after 3 days, the amount remaining
$= 120 \times 2^{-3} = 120 \times \frac{1}{8} = 15$ mg.

b It takes approximately 1.6 days for amount of drug to fall to 40 mg.

Exercise 27.4

1   An economist estimates that the population of a country will increase by 20% every 10 years.
    The population is 30 million in the year 2000.
    a   Draw a graph showing the estimated population for the next 60 years.
    b   Estimate when the population will first exceed 45 million.

2   The value of a car originally costing £12 000 decreases by 15% each year.
    a   What is its value after 1 year?
    b   What is its value after 2 years?
    c   Write an expression in terms of t for its value after t years.

3   A radioactive substance has a half-life of 5 years.
    If there is 40 mg of the substance initially, how long will it take for it to decay to 1.25 mg?

You should now:

* be able to use graphs to represent real-life functions
* understand and use the terms exponential growth, exponential decay and half-life.

Summary exercise 27

1 Vale Taxis charges £3.00 plus £1.20 per mile while Acorn Cars charges £3.40 plus £1.15 per mile.
   a Draw a graph to show the fares for both taxi companies for journeys up to 10 miles.
   b Use your graph to find the distance for which the fare is the same for both taxi companies.

2 In an experiment, masses are added to a spring and the length of the spring is measured. The length of the spring L mm is given by the formula $L = \frac{1}{20}M + 9$, where M is the mass in grams.
   Complete the table of values:

Mass M (grams)	10	25	30	50	75	100
Length L (mm)	9.5			11.5		

   a Plot the straight-line graph.
   b Estimate the mass needed to stretch the spring to a length of 10.8 mm.
   c What is the length of the unstretched spring?

3 A girl on roller blades, travelling at 10 m/s passes a line as she skates up a slope. She slows down until she stops, turns and skates down the slope. Her distance, d metres from the line at any time t seconds is given by $d = 10t - 2t^2$.
   a Draw a graph of d against t for $0 \leqslant t \leqslant 6$.
   b At what time does she stop?
   c How far does she travel in the first 6 seconds?

4 On 1 September bacteria were introduced into a lake. The bacteria grew and spread so that after t days the volume of water containing bacteria, V m^3, was given by the formula $V = 2^t$.
   a Draw a graph to show the volume of bacteria in the lake for the first 6 days.

   At the same time on 1 September, the lake was contaminated by a pollutant. The pollutant spread so that after t days the volume of water containing pollutant, P m^3, was given by the formula $P = 30 + 4t$.

   b On the same axes draw the graph of $P = 30 + 4t$.
   c After how many days was the volume of water containing bacteria equal to the volume of water containing pollutant? (Give your answer to 1 decimal place.)

Examination questions

Use 'Topic Tracker' at www.ccea.org.uk to find more exam questions.

These questions are from examination papers where you may use a calculator.

1 This is the distance–time graph for Gareth's cycle race.

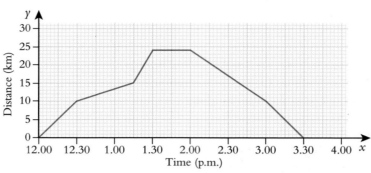

a What was happening between 1.30 and 2.00?

b How far had Gareth travelled in the first 15 minutes?

2 The values of P and R, recorded from an experiment and plotted below, are thought to satisfy a law of the form
$P = aR + b$.

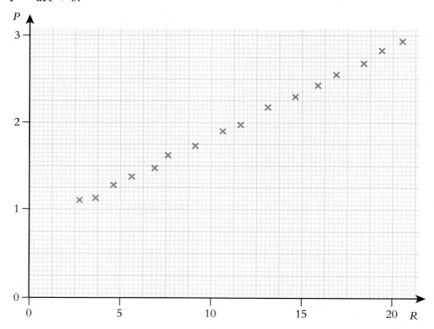

Find the values of a and b.

CHAPTER 28

Simultaneous equations

This chapter is about:

- solving simultaneous linear equations graphically
- solving simultaneous linear equations by substitution
- solving simultaneous linear equations by elimination
- solving problems involving simultaneous linear equations
- solving simultaneous equations algebraically when one is quadratic and the other is linear.

You should already know:

- how to work with positive and negative numbers
- how to round numbers to a given degree of accuracy
- how to solve linear equations
- how to change the subject of a formula
- how to solve quadratic equations by factorisation or by using the quadratic formula
- how to find the perimeter of rectangles and triangles
- how to find the equation of a straight line
- the properties of angles associated with parallel lines
- the sum of the angles of a triangle.

Simultaneous equations are pairs of equations that have the same solution. You may be asked to solve two linear equations, or one linear and one quadratic. In either case, the same set of solutions must satisfy both equations. This chapter describes the various methods used to solve simultaneous equations.

Solving simultaneous linear equations graphically

Simultaneous equations can be solved graphically by drawing the lines of both equations on the same axes. The point of intersection of the two lines gives the only values for x and y which satisfy both equations.

EXAMPLE 1

The graph shows the lines given by various equations. Use the graph to solve each of these pairs of simultaneous equations.

a $\quad y = 2x$
$\quad\quad y = x + 4$

b $\quad 3y + 4x = 24$
$\quad\quad y = 4$

c $\quad x + y = 10$
$\quad\quad y = x + 4$

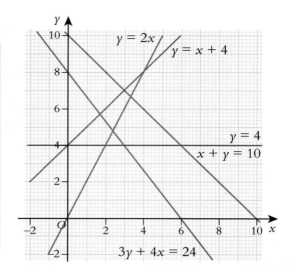

SOLUTION

a The lines for $y = 2x$ and $y = x + 4$ meet at the point (4, 8).
Solution: $x = 4$, $y = 8$

Check
$y = 2 \times 4 = 8$ and $y = 4 + 4 = 8$
Note that the solution must be checked in both equations.

b The lines for $3y + 4x = 24$ and $y = 4$ meet at the point (3, 4).
Solution: $x = 3$, $y = 4$

Check
$3 \times 4 + 4 \times 3 = 12 + 12 = 24$ and $y = 4$

c The lines for $x + y = 10$ and $y = x + 4$ meet at the point (3, 7).
Solution: $x = 3$, $y = 7$

Check
$3 + 7 = 10$ and $y = 3 + 4 = 7$

EXAMPLE 2

Solve graphically these simultaneous equations.

$$y = 3 + 2x \quad y = x + 5$$

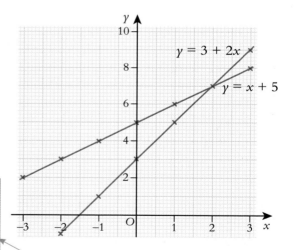

SOLUTION

Draw up a table of values, as you learnt in Chapter 25, to find various values of y for both equations.

x	−3	−2	−1	0	1	2	3
y = 3 + 2x	−3	−1	1	3	5	7	9
y = x + 5	2	3	4	5	6	7	8

Now plot both these sets of co-ordinates (x, y) on the same axes and join them with straight lines.

The lines meet at the point (2, 7).

Solution: $x = 2$, $y = 7$

Here integer values of x from −3 to 3 have been used. In fact it is only necessary to plot three points for each line, as the lines can be extended as required.

Check
$y = 3 + 2 \times 2 = 3 + 4 = 7$ and
$y = 2 + 5 = 7$

EXAMPLE 3

Solve graphically these simultaneous equations.

$$y + 4x + 6 = 0$$
$$y - x = 4$$

The equation is now in the form $y = mx + c$ where m is the gradient and c is the y-intercept (see Chapter 25) and these values can be used to draw the line. In general this method is much quicker, but if you prefer to set up tables of values for each equation, that method is equally acceptable.

SOLUTION

The first equation can be rearranged as $y = -4x - 6$.

So the line will go through $(0, -6)$ and have gradient -4.

Extend the lines for as far as is necessary for them to intersect.

Similarly, the second equation can be rearranged as $y = x + 4$.

So the line will go through $(0, 4)$ and have gradient 1.

The lines meet at $(-2, 2)$.

Solution: $x = -2$, $y = 2$

Check
$2 + 4 \times (-2) + 6$
$= 2 - 8 + 6 = 0$

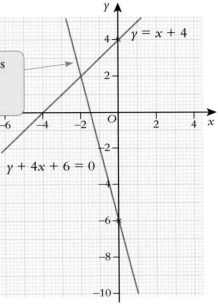

EXAMPLE 4

The equations for the sides of a triangle are
$3y + x = 9$,
$3y = -8x - 12$ and
$y = 2x - 4$.
Find the vertices of the triangle.

SOLUTION

Draw the lines represented by the equations on the same axes.

The points of intersection give the vertices of the triangle.

So the vertices are at $(-3, 4)$, $(3, 2)$ and $(0, -4)$.

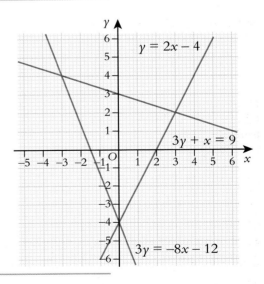

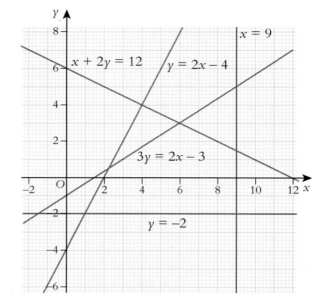

1 The graph shows the lines given by various equations. Use the graph to write down the solution to each of these pairs of simultaneous equations.

a $y = 2x - 4$
      $x + 2y = 12$

b $3y = 2x - 3$
      $x = 9$

c $y = 2x - 4$
      $y = -2$

2 By drawing suitable graphs, solve these pairs of simultaneous equations.

a $y = x + 1$ b $y = 2x - 1$
   $y = 5 - x$ $y = \frac{1}{2}x + 2$

c $y = 3 - 2x$ d $y = 2x + 2$
   $y = 1 - x$ $y = 4 - 2x$

3 By drawing suitable graphs, solve these pairs of simultaneous equations.

a $3x + y = 9$ b $x - 2y = 4$
      $x + 2y = 8$ $x + y = 7$

c $2y = x + 5$ d $x + 2y + 4 = 0$
   $y = 2x - 5$ $2x + y - 1 = 0$

4 A quadrilateral is defined by the lines

$y = x + 3$, $y = 5$, $y - 2x + 5 = 0$ and $3y = -2x + 9$.

By drawing a suitable graph, locate the vertices of the quadrilateral.

Solving simultaneous linear equations by substitution

This method involves substituting a variable from one of the equations directly into the second equation. The resulting equation is then in terms of only one variable, and can be solved using the methods for solving a linear equation from Chapter 17. Once this variable is known, it can be substituted back into the first equation in order to find the second variable.

Whilst this method can be used to solve any pair of simultaneous equations, *it is particularly suitable for those which have a variable with a coefficient of 1.* When there is no coefficient equal to 1, some rearrangement needs to take place first, and the resulting equation can be quite tedious to solve. In such cases, the elimination method proves more suitable.

EXAMPLE 5

Solve these simultaneous equations.

$$y = 1 - 2x$$
$$3x + 4y = -6$$

SOLUTION

$$3x + 4y = -6$$
$$3x + 4(1 - 2x) = -6$$
$$3x + 4 - 8x = -6$$
$$4 + 6 = 8x - 3x$$
$$10 = 5x$$
$$x = \frac{10}{5}$$
$$x = 2$$
$$y = 1 - 2 \times 2 = 1 - 4 = -3$$

Solution: $x = 2$, $y = -3$

Since the coefficient of y in the first equation is 1, $y = 1 - 2x$ can be substituted directly into the second equation.

Expand the brackets, simplify and solve.

The result for x is then substituted back into the first equation, $y = 1 - 2x$, to find y.

Check
$1 - 2 \times 2 = 1 - 4 = -3$ and
$3 \times 2 + 4 \times (-3) = -6$

EXAMPLE 6

Solve these simultaneous equations.

$$a - 2b = -10$$
$$3a + 4b = -5$$

SOLUTION

$$3a + 4b = -5$$
$$3(2b - 10) + 4b = -5$$
$$6b - 30 + 4b = -5$$
$$10b = -5 + 30$$
$$10b = 25$$
$$b = \frac{25}{10}$$
$$b = 2\frac{1}{2}$$
$$a = 2 \times 2\frac{1}{2} - 10 = -5$$

Solution: $a = -5$, $b = 2\frac{1}{2}$

The first equation can be rearranged to give $a = 2b - 10$ and this can then be substituted into the second equation.

The result for b can then be substituted back into the first equation, $a = 2b - 10$.

Check
$-5 - 2 \times 2\frac{1}{2} = -5 - 5 = -10$ and
$3 \times (-5) + 4 \times 2\frac{1}{2} = -15 + 10 = -5$

EXAMPLE 7

Solve these simultaneous equations.

$$2x + 3y = 4$$
$$3x - 4y = 6$$

SOLUTION

$$3x - 4y = 6$$
$$3\left(\frac{4 - 3y}{2}\right) - 4y = 6$$
$$3(4 - 3y) - 8y = 12$$
$$12 - 9y - 8y = 12$$
$$12 - 12 = 9y + 8y$$
$$17y = 0$$
$$y = 0$$
$$x = \frac{4 - 3y}{2} = \frac{4 - 3 \times 0}{2} = \frac{4}{2} = 2$$

Solution: $x = 2$, $y = 0$

Rearranging the first equation gives $2x = 4 - 3y$. Changing the subject of the formula in order to find x in terms of y, this gives $x = \dfrac{4 - 3y}{2}$, which can then be substituted into the second equation.

Multiply both sides by 2 to eliminate the fraction from the equation.

The result for y can then be substituted back into the equation $x = \dfrac{4 - 3y}{2}$.

In a case like this, elimination would be a more appropriate form of solution – substitution will work but the working is more difficult.

Check
$2 \times 2 + 3 \times 0 = 4 + 0 = 4$ and
$3 \times 2 - 4 \times 0 = 6 - 0 = 6$

Exercise 28.2

Solve each of these pairs of simultaneous equations by substitution.

1    $x = 4 + 5y$
     $3x - y = 26$

2    $2a + 3b = 1$
     $3a - b = 7$

3    $5p + q = 5$
     $7p = 13 + q$

4    $e = 27 + 2f$
     $7e + f = 9$

5    $y = x + 2$
     $3x + y = 18$

6    $x = 2 - y$
     $y + 2x = 1$

7    $y = 8x - 6$
     $7x + 5y = 17$

8    $m - 3n = 7$
     $m + n = 3$

9    $4x + y = 5$
     $2x - 3y = 20$

10    $x + y = 4$
      $2x + y = 5$

11    $4x + 3y = 11$
      $3x + 2y = 9$

12    $2x + 3y = 2$
      $3x + 2y = -7$

Solving simultaneous linear equations by elimination

In this method you aim to eliminate one of the variables from the equations, either by addition or by subtraction. The resulting equation is a linear equation in terms of only one variable, which can be solved using the methods covered in Chapter 17. Once this variable is known, it is substituted back into one of the original equations to find the second variable.

In some pairs of equations, one variable can be eliminated straight away.
In other cases, the equations may need to be rearranged first before
any elimination is done or may need to be adapted as illustrated in the
examples below.

EXAMPLE 8

Solve these simultaneous equations.

$$5x + 4y = 8$$
$$3x + 4y = 4$$

SOLUTION

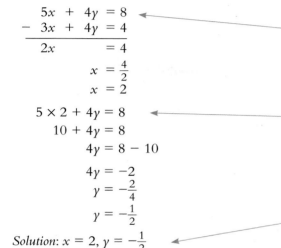

$$5x + 4y = 8$$
$$-\ 3x + 4y = 4$$
$$2x \qquad = 4$$
$$x = \frac{4}{2}$$
$$x = 2$$

Since the coefficients of y are the same in both
equations, the terms in y can be eliminated
straight away by subtraction.

$$5 \times 2 + 4y = 8$$
$$10 + 4y = 8$$
$$4y = 8 - 10$$

$$4y = -2$$
$$y = -\frac{2}{4}$$
$$y = -\frac{1}{2}$$

Solution: $x = 2$, $y = -\frac{1}{2}$

The result for x is then substituted
back into the first equation,
$5x + 4y = 8$, to find y.

Check
$5 \times 2 + 4 \times (-\frac{1}{2}) = 10 - 2 = 8$ and
$3 \times 2 + 4 \times (-\frac{1}{2}) = 6 - 2 = 4$

EXAMPLE 9

Solve these simultaneous equations.

$$5a + b = 8$$
$$a - b = 4$$

SOLUTION

$$5a + b = 8$$
$$+\ a - b = 4$$
$$6a \qquad = 12$$
$$a = \frac{12}{6}$$
$$a = 2$$

Since the coefficients of b are the same in both
equations, the b terms can be eliminated straight
away, in this case by addition.

$$5 \times 2 + b = 8$$
$$10 + b = 8$$
$$b = 8 - 10$$
$$b = -2$$

Solution: $a = 2$, $b = -2$

Substitute $a = 2$ back into the first
equation, $5a + b = 8$.

Check
$5 \times 2 + (-2) = 10 - 2 = 8$ and
$2 - (-2) = 2 + 2 = 4$

EXAMPLE 10

Solve these simultaneous equations.

$$5x + y = 22$$
$$2x - 5y = 25$$

SOLUTION

$$5x + y = 22$$
$$2x - 5y = 25$$

Since neither the x nor the y coefficients are the same, it is necessary to multiply one or both of the equations by a constant value. In this case, multiplying the first equation through by 5 will make the coefficients of y the same in both equations.

$$5(5x + y = 22)$$
$$25x + 5y = 110$$

$25x$	$+ 5y$	$= 110$
$+ 2x$	$- 5y$	$= 25$
$27x$		$= 135$

The y terms can now be eliminated by addition.

$$x = \frac{135}{27}$$
$$x = 5$$

$$5 \times 5 + y = 22$$
$$25 + y = 22$$
$$y = 22 - 25$$
$$y = -3$$

Solution: $x = 5, y = -3$

Substitute $x = 5$ back into the first equation, $5x + y = 22$.

Check
$5 \times 5 + (-3) = 25 - 3 = 22$ and
$2 \times 5 - 5 \times (-3) = 10 + 15 = 25$

EXAMPLE 11

Solve these simultaneous equations.

$$2x + 3y = 4$$
$$3x - 4y = 6$$

SOLUTION

As in Example 10, neither the x nor the y coefficients are the same, so it is necessary to multiply one or both equations by a constant value. In this case, multiplying the first equation by 4 and the second equation by 3 will leave the y coefficients the same, and these can then be eliminated by addition.

Alternatively, these equations could be solved by multiplying the first equation by 3 and the second by 2. This would leave the x coefficients the same, and the x terms could be eliminated by subtraction.

$8x$	$+ 12y$	$= 16$
$+ 9x$	$- 12y$	$= 18$
$17x$		$= 34$

$$x = \frac{34}{17}$$
$$x = 2$$

$$2 \times 2 + 3y = 4$$
$$4 + 3y = 4$$
$$3y = 4 - 4$$
$$y = 0$$

Solution: $x = 2$, $y = 0$

> Substitute $x = 2$ back into the first equation, $2x + 3y = 4$.

> **Check**
> $2 \times 2 + 3 \times 0 = 4 + 0 = 4$ and
> $3 \times 2 - 4 \times 0 = 6 - 0 = 6$

Notice that the equations in Example 11 are the same as those in Example 7. In Example 7 they were solved by substitution, but it was suggested that elimination would be the more appropriate method. This shows that no matter which method is selected, the solution will be the same.

EXAMPLE 12

Solve these simultaneous equations.

$$y = 6x + 17$$
$$5x = 10 - 4y$$

SOLUTION

Here the equations are not in the correct format for elimination. They must be rearranged first, so that all the variables are on one side and all the numbers are on the other side.

The first equation becomes $\quad -6x + y = 17$

and the second becomes $\quad 5x + 4y = 10.$

> The y coefficients can be made the same by multiplying the first equation through by 4. Then the y terms can be eliminated by subtraction.

$$
\begin{array}{r}
-24x + 4y = 68 \\
- \quad 5x + 4y = 10 \\
\hline
-29x = 58
\end{array}
$$

$$x = \frac{58}{-29}$$
$$x = -2$$

> Substitute $x = -2$ back into the first equation, $y = 6x + 17$.

$$y = 6 \times (-2) + 17 = -12 + 17 = 5$$

Solution: $x = -2$, $y = 5$

> **Check**
> $6 \times (-2) + 17 = -12 + 17 = 5 = y \quad$ and
> $10 - 4 \times 5 = 10 - 20 = -10 = 5 \times (-2) = 5x$

Notice that the equations in Example 12 could have been solved more simply using the method of substitution, since the coefficient of y in the first equation is 1.

Exercise 28.3

1 Solve each of these pairs of simultaneous equations by elimination.

a $5x + y = 5$
   $7x - y = 13$

b $5a + 2b = 53$
   $3a - 2b = 19$

c $c + 7d = 20$
   $c + 2d = 5$

d $2p + q = 1$
   $4p + q = 5$

e $x - 6y = 1$
   $4x - 6y = 22$

f $2a - 3b = 22$
   $2a + 3b = -2$

2   Solve each of these pairs of simultaneous equations by elimination.

   a $5x - 3y = 3$ b $3a - b = 26$ c $5p + 4q = 10$
       $7x - y = 1$ $a - 5b = 4$ $6p - q = -17$

   d $2a - 3b = 47$ e $2x - y = 5$ f $2p + 10q = 7$
       $4a + b = 45$ $3x - 2y = 7$ $p + 3q = 1$

3   Solve each of these pairs of simultaneous equations by elimination.

   a $2x + 3y = 12$ b $3a - 2b = 1$ c $5x - 2y = 9$
       $3x + 5y = 19$ $5a - 3b = 3$ $2x + 5y = 21$

   d $5p - 3q = 29$ e $2a + 3b = 5$ f $7p + 5q = 6$
       $4p - 2q = 24$ $3a - 8b = -35$ $3p - 4q = 21$

4   Solve each of these pairs of simultaneous equations by elimination.

   a $x + 3y = 5$ b $2x = 9 - 2y$ c $3 - 5a + 3b = 0$
       $x = 3 - y$ $y = 4x - 12$ $3a = 1 + 2b$

   d $5x + y = 8$ e $3x + 5y + 14 = 0$ f $y = 4x - 10$
       $y = x - 4$ $3x - 2y - 14 = 0$ $3x = 19 - 5y$

Solving problems using simultaneous equations

As with linear equations (see Chapter 17), simultaneous equations can be used to solve a wide variety of problems. The following steps should be taken.

- Use two different letters to represent the unknown quantities.
- Write the given mathematical information in the form of two equations.
- Solve the equations simultaneously.
- Check that your two solutions fit the *original mathematical information*.
- Use your solutions to answer the original question.

> The methods of elimination or substitution generally work best with problem-type questions.

EXAMPLE 13

The sum of two numbers is 32 and their difference is 4. Find the two numbers.

SOLUTION

Use x to represent the first number and y to represent the second number.

Then $x + y = 32$
and $x - y = 4$

> Build up the equations using the information you are given.

$$x + y = 32$$
$$-x - y = 4$$
$$2y = 28$$
$$y = \frac{28}{2}$$
$$y = 14$$
$$x + 14 = 32$$
$$x = 32 - 14 = 18$$

> The coefficients of x are the same so the x terms can be eliminated by subtraction.

> Substitute $y = 14$ back into the first equation, $x + y = 32$.

So the first number is 18 and the second number is 14.

> **Check**
> $18 + 14 = 32$ and $18 - 14 = 4$

EXAMPLE 14

Three bars of chocolate and five packets of crisps cost £1.70.
Five bars of the same chocolate and three packets of the same crisps cost £1.66.
Find the cost of a bar of chocolate and the cost of a packet of crisps.

SOLUTION

Use b to represent the cost of a bar of chocolate and c to represent the cost of a packet of crisps.

> You can use *any* letters to represent the unknown quantities, but sometimes it is easier to use letters that are related to the unknowns – in this case b for bars and c for crisps.

$$3b + 5c = 170$$
$$5b + 3c = 166$$

> Build up the equations using the information you are given. Changing pounds to pence makes the equations easier to solve, as there are no decimals.

$$9b + 15c = 510$$
$$- 25b + 15c = 830$$
$$\overline{- 16b \qquad = -320}$$

> Multiply the first equation by 3 and the second equation by 5 to make the coefficients of c the same. Then the terms in c can be eliminated by subtraction.

$$16b = 320$$
$$b = \frac{320}{16}$$
$$b = 20$$

$$3 \times 20 + 5c = 170$$
$$60 + 5c = 170$$
$$5c = 170 - 60$$
$$5c = 110$$
$$c = \frac{110}{5}$$
$$c = 22$$

> Substitute $b = 20$ back into the first equation, $3b + 5c = 170$.

So the cost of a bar of chocolate is 20p and the cost of a packet of crisps is 22p.

> **Check**
> $3 \times 20p + 5 \times 22p = £1.70$ and
> $5 \times 20p + 3 \times 22p = £1.66$

EXAMPLE 15

A woman is three times as old as her daughter. In 15 years' time she will be twice as old as her daughter. What are their present ages?

SOLUTION

Use w to represent the woman's present age and d to represent the daughter's present age.

> Build up the equations using the information you are given. These equations are easier to solve by substitution as the first equation gives w in terms of d and can be substituted directly into the second equation.

$$w = 3d$$
$$w + 15 = 2(d + 15) \qquad \text{or} \qquad w + 15 = 2d + 30$$
$$3d + 15 = 2d + 30$$
$$3d - 2d = 30 - 15$$
$$d = 15$$
$$w = 3 \times 15 = 45$$

> Expand the bracket.

> Substitute $d = 15$ back into $w = 3d$.

> **Check**
> Present ages: $45 = 3 \times 15$
> In 15 years: $60 = 2 \times 30$

So the woman's present age is 45 and the daughter's present age is 15.

EXAMPLE 16

At a charity sale, items are sold at either 50 pence or £1. At the end of the sale 229 articles have been sold and £140 raised. How many articles were sold at 50 pence and how many articles were sold at £1?

SOLUTION

Use x to represent the number of articles sold at 50 pence and y to represent the number of articles sold at £1.

229 articles were sold altogether so $x + y = 229$.

£140 was raised altogether so $\quad 0.5x + y = 140$.

Since all other quantities are in pounds, the 50 pence needs to be written in terms of pounds within the equations.

$$
\begin{array}{r}
x + y = 229 \\
- \quad 0.5x + y = 140 \\
\hline
0.5x \qquad = 89
\end{array}
$$

> Since the y coefficients are the same the y terms can be eliminated by subtraction.

$$x = \frac{89}{0.5}$$
$$x = 178$$
$$178 + y = 229$$

> Substitute $x = 178$ back into the first equation, $x + y = 229$.

$$y = 229 - 178$$
$$y = 51$$

So 178 articles were sold at 50 pence and 51 articles were sold at £1.

> **Check**
> $178 + 51 = 229$ articles
> $178 \times 50p + 51 \times £1 = £140$

Exercise 28.4

1 Twice a number added to five times another number gives 29. The difference between the two numbers is four. Find the numbers.

2 Three rubbers and two protractors cost 68p. Two rubbers and five protractors cost £1.37. Find the total cost of one rubber and one protractor.

3 A newspaper and a magazine together cost £2.12. The difference in their cost is 68 pence, with the magazine being the more expensive. Find the cost of each.

4 The perimeter of a rectangle is 40 cm. The difference between the length and the width is 4 cm. Find the length and the width.

5 Six adults and three children pay a total of £141 for a train journey. One adult and two children pay £41.50. Find the cost per adult and the cost per child.

6 The ages of a man and his son total 44. In 23 years' time the man will be twice as old as his son. What are their present ages?

7 A year ago a mother was four times as old as her daughter. Three years ago she was five times as old as her daughter. How old will the daughter be in two years' time?

8 Two numbers are such that if 11 is added to the first number, the answer is twice the second number. Also, if 25 is subtracted from the first number, the answer is half the second number. What are the two numbers?

9　Maths textbooks cost £7 each in a promotion, which ends on 31 May, or £8 each after 31 May.

5000 of these textbooks were sold and the total income from the sales was £38 500. How many books were bought during the promotion and how many books were bought after the promotion?

10　A child has 50 coins in her moneybox, totalling £8.20. Each coin is either a 20p coin or a 10p coin.

What is the total value of her 20p coins?

11　The average of two numbers is 33. Twice their difference is 36. Find the two numbers.

12　The line $y = mx + c$ passes through the two points with co-ordinates $(-1, 8)$ and $(2, -1)$. Find the equation of the line.

13　The diagram shows an equilateral triangle. Find its perimeter.

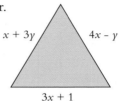

$x + 3y$　　$4x - y$

$3x + 1$

Solving simultaneous equations when one is quadratic

When the pair of simultaneous equations has one which is linear and the other quadratic, the substitution method *must* be used to solve them. One variable from the linear equation is substituted into the quadratic one. The resulting equation is quadratic and can be solved by one of the methods covered in Chapter 24. There are generally two sets of solutions, corresponding to the two points where the straight line and the curve intersect.

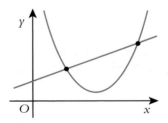

EXAMPLE 17

Solve these simultaneous equations.

$$y = x + 2$$
$$x^2 - 2y = 4$$

The first equation gives y in terms of x so substitute $y = x + 2$ directly into the second equation.

SOLUTION

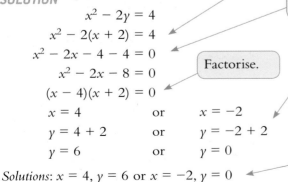

$$x^2 - 2y = 4$$
$$x^2 - 2(x + 2) = 4$$
$$x^2 - 2x - 4 - 4 = 0$$
$$x^2 - 2x - 8 = 0$$
$$(x - 4)(x + 2) = 0$$

$x = 4$	or	$x = -2$
$y = 4 + 2$	or	$y = -2 + 2$
$y = 6$	or	$y = 0$

Expand the bracket and rearrange.

Factorise.

Substitute each of these back into the first equation, $y = x + 2$.

Check
Both sets of solutions should be checked in both equations.
$4 + 2 = 6 = y$　　$-2 + 2 = 0 = y$
and　$4^2 - 2 \times 6 = 16 - 12 = 4$
$(-2)^2 - 2 \times 0 = 4 - 0 = 4$

Solutions: $x = 4$, $y = 6$ or $x = -2$, $y = 0$

EXAMPLE 18

Solve these simultaneous equations.

$$3y - x = 9$$
$$x^2 - 3y = 3$$

The first equation can be rearranged to give x in terms of y as $x = 3y - 9$, which can then can be substituted directly into the second equation.

SOLUTION

$$x^2 - 3y = 3$$
$$(3y - 9)^2 - 3y = 3$$
$$9y^2 - 54y + 81 - 3y - 3 = 0$$
$$9y^2 - 57y + 78 = 0$$
$$3y^2 - 19y + 26 = 0$$
$$(3y - 13)(y - 2) = 0$$

Divide through by 3 here to make the quadratic easier to factorise.

Substitute each y value back into the equation, $x = 3y - 9$.

$3y - 13 = 0$	or	$y - 2 = 0$
$3y = 13$	or	$y = 2$
$y = 4\frac{1}{3}$	or	$y = 2$
$x = 3 \times 4\frac{1}{3} - 9$	or	$x = 3 \times 2 - 9$
$x = 4$		$x = -3$

Solutions: $x = 4$, $y = 4\frac{1}{3}$ or $x = -3$, $y = 2$

Check
$3 \times 4\frac{1}{3} - 4 = 9$
$3 \times 2 - (-3) = 6 + 3 = 9$
and
$4^2 - 3 \times 4\frac{1}{3} = 3$
$(-3)^2 - 3 \times 2 = 9 - 6 = 3$

EXAMPLE 19

Solve these simultaneous equations.

$$x^2 + y^2 = 4$$
$$y + 2x = 3$$

The second equation can be rearranged as $y = 3 - 2x$ and then this can be substituted directly into the first equation.

SOLUTION

$$x^2 + y^2 = 4$$
$$x^2 + (3 - 2x)^2 = 4$$
$$x^2 + 9 - 12x + 4x^2 - 4 = 0$$
$$5x^2 - 12x + 5 = 0$$

This does not factorise, so use the quadratic formula with $a = 5$, $b = -12$ and $c = 5$.

$$x = \frac{12 \pm \sqrt{144 - 4 \times 5 \times 5}}{10}$$

$$x = \frac{12 \pm \sqrt{44}}{10} = \frac{12 \pm 2\sqrt{11}}{10} = \frac{6 \pm \sqrt{11}}{5}$$

Substitute each of these values back into $y = 3 - 2x$.
To make your answers as accurate as possible, you should store the *unrounded* values of x in your calculator and use these in subsequent calculations.

$x = 1.86$	or	$x = 0.54$ (both to 2 d.p.)
$y = 3 - 2 \times 1.86...$	or	$y = 3 - 2 \times 0.54...$
$y = -0.73$	or	$y = 1.93$ (both to 2 d.p.)

Solutions (to 2 d.p.):
$x = 1.86$, $y = -0.73$ or $x = 0.54$, $y = 1.93$

Check the solutions with a calculator.

EXAMPLE 20

Solve these simultaneous equations.

$$y = x^2 + 3x - 2$$
$$2x - y = -1$$

SOLUTION

$$y = x^2 + 3x - 2$$
$$2x + 1 = x^2 + 3x - 2$$
$$x^2 + 3x - 2 - 2x - 1 = 0$$
$$x^2 + x - 3 = 0$$
$$x = \frac{-1 \pm \sqrt{1 - 4 \times 1 \times (-3)}}{2}$$
$$x = \frac{-1 \pm \sqrt{13}}{2}$$

> The second equation can be rearranged to give y in terms of x as $y = 2x + 1$ and this is then substituted into the first equation.

> This does not factorise, so use the quadratic formula with $a = 1$, $b = 1$ and $c = -3$

$x = 1.30$	or	$x = -2.30$ (both to 2 d.p.)
$y = 2 \times 1.30... + 1$	or	$y = 2 \times (-2.30...) + 1$
$y = 3.60$	or	$y = -3.60$ (both to 2 d.p.)

> Substitute each of these values back into $y = 2x + 1$.

Solutions (to 2 d.p.):

$$x = 1.30, y = 3.60 \qquad \text{or} \qquad x = -2.30, y = -3.60$$

> Check the solutions with a calculator.

Exercise 28.5

Solve the pairs of simultaneous equations in questions **1** to **10**.
Give your answers in surd form where appropriate.

1 $y = x^2$
   $y = 2x - 1$

2 $3y - x = 9$
   $x^2 - 3y = 3$

3 $x - 2y = 3$
   $x^2 - y^2 = 24$

4 $x - 2y = 2$
   $xy = 12$

5 $y = x + 3$
   $y = x^2 - 9$

6 $y = x^2 + x$
   $y = 3x + 2$

7 $y = 2x - 1$
   $y = 4 - x^2$

8 $y = 3x + 2$
   $x^2 + y^2 = 28$

9 $y = x + 2$
   $x^2 + x + y^2 = 8$

10 $2y + 3x = 3$
    $x^2 + 2y^2 = 11$

11 Find the points of intersection of the line $x + y = 2$ and the curve $y = (x - 2)(x - 4)$.

12 Find the points of intersection of the line $2x = 12 - y$ and the curve $y = 2x^2 - 3x - 9$.

You should now:

- be able to solve two simultaneous linear equations graphically
- be able to solve two simultaneous linear equations algebraically
- be able to solve problems by forming and solving simultaneous equations
- be able to solve two simultaneous equations where one is linear and the other is quadratic
- understand the geometrical significance of simultaneous equations.

Summary exercise 28

1   The graph shows the lines given by various equations.

Use the graph to write down the solution to each of these pairs of simultaneous equations.

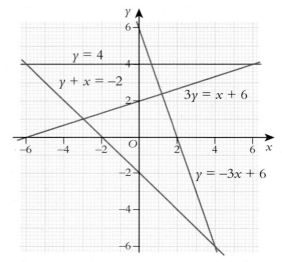

   a $y = -3x + 6$
              $y + x = -2$

   b $y = 4$
           $3y = x + 6$

   c $3y = x + 6$
              $y + x = -2$

2   By drawing suitable graphs, solve each of these pairs of simultaneous equations. Give your answers correct to 1 decimal place.

   a $y = 3x + 4$ **b** $y + 1 = 2x$
           $y = x + 2$ $y = 6 - 1\frac{1}{2}x$

   c $4x + 3y = 2$ **d** $5x + 4y = 20$
           $8x + 2y = 4$ $y = 2x$

3   Solve each of these pairs of simultaneous equations by substitution.

   a $a - 6b = 5$ **b** $x = 2y + 1$
           $2a - 4b = 14$ $2x - 3y = 3$

   c $2y = 3x - 10$ **d** $2y = x + 4$
           $y = 5 - x$ $2x + y = 2$

   e $x + 3y = 15$ **f** $2p - 5q = 3$
           $x - 2y = 0$ $3p + 10q = 22$

4   Solve each of these pairs of simultaneous equations by elimination.

   a $a - 2b = -4$ **b** $6x + 2y = 11$
           $3a + b = 9$ $9x + 2y = 28$

   c $5p - 4q = 8$ **d** $2a + 3b - 19 = 0$
           $7p + 3q = 37$ $a + 2.5b = 4.5$

   e $5x - y = 11$ **f** $4a - 2b = 10$
           $4x + 3y - 5 = 0$ $\dfrac{a}{4} + \dfrac{b}{3} = 2$

5   Write down a pair of simultaneous equations which would have the solution $x = 4$ and $y = -1$.

6   Two adult tickets and three child tickets for a flight cost £710. The difference between an adult fare and a child fare is £55. Find the price of each.

7 Use simultaneous equations to find the size of angle
   ABC in the diagram on the right.

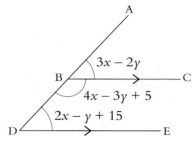

8 Joan and her mother share the same birthday.
   Joan's mother was 34 when Joan was born.
   Today, when Joan adds her mother's age to her own
   age the total is 100.
   How old is Joan today?

9 The height, h metres, of a particle above the ground t seconds after
   projection is given by the formula $h = at + bt^2$.
   After 1 second the particle is 19 m above the ground and after
   2 seconds the particle is 28 m above the ground.
   Find the height of the particle above the ground after 4 seconds.

You may use your calculator for this question.

10 Solve each of these pairs of simultaneous equations.
    a $y = 9x - 4$ b $y - x = 1$
        $y = 2x^2$ $2x^2 - 3y = 6$

    c $2x + y = 3$
          $x^2 - 2xy + y^2 = 8$

    Give your answers correct to 2 decimal places.

11 The line $y = 3x - 1$ intersects the curve
    $2x^2 + 2y^2 - x + y - 11 = 0$ at A and B.
    Find the co-ordinates of A and B.

12 The sum of two positive integers is 39 and their product is 360.
    Find the two numbers.

Examination questions

Questions **1** to **3** are from examination papers where you may not use a
calculator.

Use 'Topic Tracker'
at www.ccea.org.uk
to find more exam
questions.

1 a On the same axes draw the graphs of $y = -3x + 2$ and
      $y = 2x + 7$.
   b Using the graphs, solve the simultaneous equations
      $y = -3x + 2$ and $y = 2x + 7$.
   c Which one of the following lines is parallel to
      $y = -3x + 2$?
      $y = 2x - 3$ $y = 3x - 2$ $y = 3 - 2x$
      $y = -3x$ $y = 3x$ $y = 3x + 2$

2 Five times Carrie's age added to four times Deana's age equals
   150 years.
   Carrie is older than Deana and the difference between their ages is
   3 years.
   Use simultaneous equations to find Carrie's age and Deana's age.
   A solution by trial and improvement will not be accepted.
   Show your working clearly.

3   Mark buys 4 bags of crisps and 3 cans of lemonade.
    He pays a total of £2.20.
    Jake buys 3 bags of crisps and 6 cans of lemonade.
    He pays a total of £3.15.
    Kevin buys 1 bag of crisps and 1 can of lemonade.
    Use simultaneous equations to find how much Kevin pays.
    Show your working.
    A solution by trial and improvement will not be accepted.

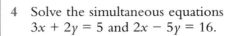

Questions 4 to 6 are from examination papers where you may use a
calculator.

4   Solve the simultaneous equations
    $3x + 2y = 5$ and $2x - 5y = 16$.

5   Solve the simultaneous equations $y = 3x + 5$ and $y = x^2$, giving
    your answers correct to 2 decimal places.

6   The line $y = 5 - 2x$ cuts the curve
    $y = 3x^2 + 4$ at two points.

    Find the co-ordinates of the two
    points.
    A graphical solution will not be
    accepted.
    A solution by trial and
    improvement will not be accepted.
    Show your working clearly.

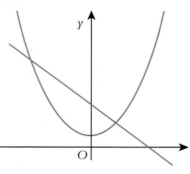

CHAPTER 29

Graphical solution of equations

This chapter is about:

- the significance of points of intersection of graphs in the context of solving equations
- solving a variety of equations using a particular graph
- determining the equation whose solutions are represented by the points of intersection of a particular pair of graphs.

You should already know:

- how to solve simultaneous linear equations graphically
- how to draw the graphs of linear, quadratic, cubic, reciprocal and exponential functions
- how to rearrange formulae
- how to substitute numbers in algebraic expressions.

Using points of intersection to solve equations

In Chapter 28 you saw how simultaneous linear equations could be solved graphically. For example, the solution of the two simultaneous linear equations $y = x + 4$ and $y = 10 - 5x$ can be found by drawing the two straight lines on a single graph and finding the point of intersection. Similarly, the solution of the linear and quadratic simultaneous equations $y = 2x - 3$ and $y = 2x^2 - 3x - 6$ can be found by drawing the straight line $y = 2x - 3$ and the curve $y = 2x^2 - 3x - 6$ on the same graph and finding the points of intersection.

The idea of solving equations graphically can be extended to many other types of equations. While it is a valid method for the solution of equations, owing to the nature of curve drawing and reading the points of intersection, it is not the most accurate. However, in some cases it may be the only possible method of solution at this level.

Once you have drawn a particular function on a graph, it is possible to solve a range of equations by rearranging them so that the left-hand side matches the function already drawn, then drawing additional lines on the graph and finding the points of intersection.

EXAMPLE 1

Solve the equation $x^2 + x - 6 = 0$ graphically.

SOLUTION

By drawing the curve $y = x^2 + x - 6$ and the straight line $y = 0$ (which is in fact the y-axis) and reading the points of intersection, the solutions to the equation $x^2 + x - 6 = 0$ can be found.

> Draw the graph by first making a table of values, as shown in Chapter 26.

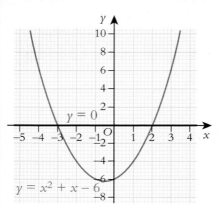

$y = 0$

$y = x^2 + x - 6$

From the graph it can be seen that the points of intersection are at

$x = 2$ and $x = -3$.

> These solutions can be checked by substituting them into the equation $x^2 + x - 6 = 0$. It is important to realise here that $x^2 + x - 6 = 0$ is much more easily solved by factorisation (see Chapter 24); however, this example illustrates that the same solutions can be achieved graphically.

EXAMPLE 2

Solve the equation $2x^2 - x - 3 = 8$ graphically.

SOLUTION

By drawing the curve $y = 2x^2 - x - 3$ and the straight line $y = 8$ and reading the points of intersection, the solutions to the equation $2x^2 - x - 3 = 8$ can be found.

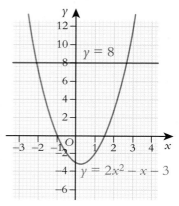

$y = 8$

$y = 2x^2 - x - 3$

From the graph it can be seen that the points of intersection are at approximately $x = 2.6$ and $x = -2.1$.

> Where the solutions are not integers, it is usual to give them to 1 decimal place when you are using a graphical method.

To obtain a more accurate solution you would solve the equation using the quadratic formula (see Chapter 24).

Note that this equation could also have been solved graphically by rearranging it as:

$$2x^2 - x - 3 = 8$$
$$2x^2 - x - 3 - 8 = 0$$
$$2x^2 - x - 11 = 0$$

and hence drawing $y = 2x^2 - x - 11$ and $y = 0$ to find the points of intersection.

In many cases you will need to rearrange the equation to be solved, so that the left-hand side matches the function already drawn. You then draw the graph of the function now on the right-hand side in order to find the solution.

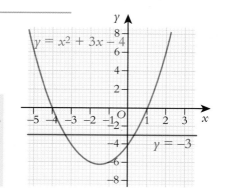

$y = x^2 + 3x - 4$

$y = -3$

EXAMPLE 3

Given the graph of $y = x^2 + 3x - 4$ (shown in red on the diagram opposite), use it to solve the equation $x^2 + 3x - 1 = 0$.

SOLUTION

Method 1

$$x^2 + 3x - 1 = 0$$
$$x^2 + 3x - 4 = -3$$

> Rearrange the equation to be solved, so that the left–hand side matches the function given in the diagram. To do this we subtract 3 from both sides.

Hence the equation $x^2 + 3x - 1 = 0$ can be solved by drawing the line $y = -3$ on the original graph and finding the points of intersection.

Solutions: $x = 0.3$ and $x = -3.3$

Method 2

An alternative approach is to equate the required function to zero, and subtract it from the function drawn. The resulting function gives the straight line which needs to be drawn.

$$\begin{array}{r} x^2 + 3x - 4 \\ - \quad x^2 + 3x - 1 \\ \hline -3 \end{array}$$

Hence draw the straight line $y = -3$.

EXAMPLE 4

a Draw the graph of $y = x^3 - 6x$ for values of x from -3 to 3.
b Use your graph to solve the equation $x^3 - 6x = 0$.
c Use your graph to solve the equation $x^3 - 8x + 5 = 0$.

SOLUTION

a Draw the graph of a cubic function using a table of values, as described in Chapter 26.

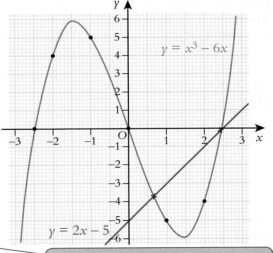

$y = x^3 - 6x$

$y = 2x - 5$

x	−3	−2	−1	0	1	2	3
x³	−27	−8	−1	0	1	8	27
−6x	18	12	6	0	−6	−12	−18
y = x³ − 6x	−9	4	5	0	−5	−4	9

b The solutions to the equation $x^3 - 6x = 0$ are where the curve crosses the x-axis.

   Solutions: $x = -2.5$, $x = 0$ and $x = 2.5$

> Notice that a cubic equation may have up to three solutions.

c $x^3 - 8x + 5 = 0$

Method 1

Rearrange the equation to be solved, so that the left-hand side becomes the function you have drawn.

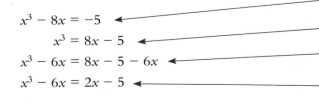

$$x^3 - 8x = -5$$
$$x^3 = 8x - 5$$
$$x^3 - 6x = 8x - 5 - 6x$$
$$x^3 - 6x = 2x - 5$$

> First subtract 5 from both sides.

> Add 8x to both sides.

> Subtract 6x from both sides.

> Simplify the right-hand side.

Hence the equation $x^3 - 8x + 5 = 0$ can be solved by drawing the line $y = 2x - 5$ on the graph (shown in green on the graph on page 301) and finding the points of intersection.

Solutions: $x = 0.7$ and $x = 2.4$

From the graph you can see that the line will cross the curve again somewhere to the left of $x = -3$. However, this solution is outside the range specified in the question so you are not expected to include it.

Method 2

Alternatively,

$$\begin{array}{r} x^3 - 6x \\ - \quad x^3 - 8x + 5 \\ \hline 2x - 5 \end{array}$$

Hence draw the straight line $y = 2x - 5$.

EXAMPLE 5

Given the graph of $y = 2x^2 - 3x - 5$, what straight line would you need to draw to solve each of these equations?

   a $2x^2 - 3x - 5 = 0$ b $2x^2 - x - 10 = 0$ c $2x^2 = x + 4$

SOLUTION

  a $y = 2x^2 - 3x - 5$ is already drawn, so draw the line $y = 0$ (the x-axis).

Rearrange the equation to make the left-hand side the same as the function whose graph you are given.

  b $2x^2 - x - 10 = 0$
$$2x^2 = x + 10$$
$$2x^2 - 3x - 5 = x + 10 - 3x - 5$$
$$2x^2 - 3x - 5 = 5 - 2x$$

Simplify the right-hand side.

Hence the line $y = 5 - 2x$ needs to be drawn.

  c $$2x^2 = x + 4$$
$$2x^2 - 3x - 5 = x + 4 - 3x - 5$$
$$2x^2 - 3x - 5 = -2x - 1$$

Hence the line $y = -2x - 1$ needs to be drawn.

EXAMPLE 6

The curve $y = x^2 - 4x - 2$ and the straight line $y = 2x - 7$ are drawn on the same axes and the points of intersection are found. Which quadratic equation is solved by these points of intersection?

SOLUTION

$$x^2 - 4x - 2 = 2x - 7$$
$$x^2 - 4x - 2x - 2 + 7 = 0$$
$$x^2 - 6x + 5 = 0$$

At the intersections, the y values of both functions are the same, so the two functions can be equated.

EXAMPLE 7

Given the graph of $y = x^2 - 4x - 3$, what line would you need to draw in order to solve each of these equations?

a $\quad x - 4 = \dfrac{3}{x}$ b $\quad 2x^2 = 8x - 3$ c $\quad x = \dfrac{8}{x - 3}$

SOLUTION

a
$$x - 4 = \frac{3}{x}$$
$$x^2 - 4x = 3 \quad \longleftarrow \quad \boxed{\text{Multiply both sides by } x \text{ to eliminate the fraction.}}$$
$$x^2 - 4x - 3 = 3 - 3$$
$$x^2 - 4x - 3 = 0$$

Hence the line $y = 0$ (the x-axis) needs to be drawn.

b
$$2x^2 = 8x - 3$$
$$x^2 = 4x - 1\tfrac{1}{2} \quad \longleftarrow \quad \boxed{\text{Divide both sides by 2.}}$$
$$x^2 - 4x - 3 = 4x - 1\tfrac{1}{2} - 4x - 3$$
$$x^2 - 4x - 3 = -4\tfrac{1}{2}$$

Hence the line $y = -4\tfrac{1}{2}$ needs to be drawn.

c
$$x = \frac{8}{x - 3}$$
$$x^2 - 3x = 8 \quad \longleftarrow \quad \boxed{\text{Multiply both sides by } (x - 3) \text{ to eliminate the fraction.}}$$
$$x^2 = 8 + 3x$$
$$x^2 - 4x - 3 = 8 + 3x - 4x - 3$$
$$x^2 - 4x - 3 = 5 - x$$

Hence the line $y = 5 - x$ needs to be drawn.

Exercise 29.1

1   a   Draw the graph of $y = x^3$ for values of x from -3 to 3.
    b   On the same set of axes draw the graph of $y = x^2 - 4$.
    c   Use your graph to find the approximate solution to the equation $x^3 = x^2 - 4$.

2   By drawing an appropriate curve and straight line, find approximate values for the two solutions of the equation
$x^2 - 2x = 9$.

3   The graphs of $y = x^2 - 3$, $y = 3x$ and $y = 3 - x$ are shown.

Use the graphs to solve each of these equations.
    a $x^2 - 3 = 3 - x$
    b $x^2 - 3 = 3x$

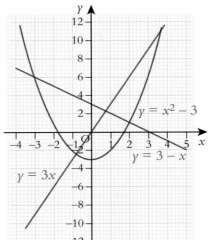

4 Here is the curve $y = x^2$.

Use it to solve each of these equations.
a $x^2 = 7$
b $x^2 = x + 5$
c $x^2 + 2x = 1$

$y = x^2$

5 a Copy and complete the table of values for the function

$$y = \frac{1}{x^2}$$

and hence draw the graph of $y = \frac{1}{x^2}$.

x	-3	-2	-1	-0.5	-0.25	0	0.25	0.5	1	2	3
$y = \dfrac{1}{x^2}$		0.25				—			1		

b What line needs to be added to your graph in order to solve the equation $\frac{1}{x^2} - 2x - 4 = 0$?

c Use your graph to find approximate values for the solution of the equation $\frac{1}{x^2} - 2x - 4 = 0$.

6 a Draw the graph of $y = x^2 - 4x$ for values of x from -2 to 6.
b By drawing additional lines on the same axes, find approximate solutions to each of these equations.
  i $x^2 - 4x = 0$ ii $x^2 - 4x = 6$
  iii $x^2 - 4x + 3 = 0$ iv $x^2 - 3x + 1 = 0$

7 a Draw the graph of $y = x^2 + 4x + 5$ for values of x from -6 to 2.
b By drawing additional lines on the same axes, find approximate solutions to each of these equations.
  i $x^2 + 3x - 1 = 0$ ii $x^2 + 5x + 2 = 0$

8 Given the graph of $y = 4x^3 - 9x$, what line would you need to draw in order to solve each of these equations?
a $4x^3 - 9x = 3$ b $4x^3 - 9x - 2 = 0$
c $4x^3 - 6x = 0$ d $4x^3 - 10x = 6$

9 Given the graph of $y = x^2 - 6x - 5$, what line would you need to draw in order to solve each of these equations?
a $x = 6 + \dfrac{5}{x}$ b $2x^2 = 12x + 9$
c $x^2 = 5$ d $2x - 3 = \dfrac{10}{x}$

10 In each part below, the equations of two graphs are given. In each case find, in its simplest form, an equation that has as its roots the x co-ordinates of the points of intersection of the two graphs.

a $y = 2 - x$ and $y = x^2 + 5x$ b $y = x^2 - 4$ and $y = \dfrac{1}{x}$
c $y = 6 - x$ and $y = \dfrac{6}{x}$ d $y = 2x^2 - 3x - 5$ and $y = x - 5$

11 a Draw the graph of $y = \dfrac{20}{x}$ for $1 \leqslant x \leqslant 10$, using a scale of 1 cm for 1 unit on each axis.
    b Use your graph to find approximate solutions to each of these equations.
       i $\dfrac{20}{x} = 2 + x$ ii $\dfrac{20}{x} + x = 10$

       iii $x^2 = 20$

12 a Draw the graph of $y = 2^x$ for $-4 \leqslant x \leqslant 4$, using a scale of 2 cm for 1 unit on the x-axis and 1 cm for 1 unit on the y-axis.
    b Use your graph to find approximate solutions to each of these equations.
       i $2^x = 7$ ii $2^x = 2x$ iii $x2^x = 2$
    c Find also the approximate value of $2^{1.5}$.

13 a Copy and complete the table of values for the function $y = 3^{-x}$, rounding each y value to 1 decimal place.

x	-3	-2.5	-2	-1.5	-1	-0.5	0	0.5	1	1.5	2
y											

    b Hence draw the graph of $y = 3^{-x}$.
    c Use your graph to solve each of these equations.

       i $3^{-x} = 5$ ii $\dfrac{1}{3^x} = 8$ iii $3^{2-x} = 189$

14 Given the graph of $y = x^3 - 6x^2 + 8x + 7$, find how many solutions each of these equations would have.
    a $x^3 - 6x^2 + 8x + 5 = 0$
    b $x^3 - 6x^2 + 8x + 7 = 6$
    c $x^3 - 6x^2 + 7x + 3 = 0$
    d $x^3 - 6x^2 + 8x = -4$

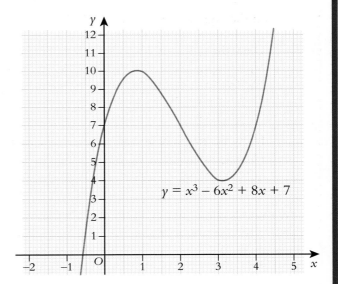

$y = x^3 - 6x^2 + 8x + 7$

You should now:

- understand the significance of points of intersection of graphs in the context of solving equations
- be able to determine the lines that need to be drawn on a graph in order to solve a particular equation
- be able to solve a variety of equations using a particular graph
- be able to determine the equation of a function represented by a particular point of intersection.

Summary exercise 29

1 The graphs of $y = x^2 + x - 1$, $y = 3$,
  $y = x + 1$ and $y = -x$ are shown.
  a Use the graphs to find approximate
  solutions for each of these equations.
  i $x^2 + x - 1 = 3$
  ii $x^2 - 2 = 0$
  b Find, in its simplest form, an equation
  that has as its roots the x co-ordinates of
  the points of intersection of the graphs
  of $y = x^2 + x - 1$ and $y = -x$.

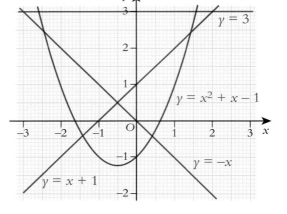

2 By drawing the graph of $y = x^2 - 5x$, find
  approximate solutions to each of these
  equations.
  a $x^2 - 5x = 4$
  b $x^2 - 6x = 0$
  c $x^2 - 4x + 1 = 0$

3 Given the graph of $y = x^3 - 3x^2$, what line would you need to
  draw in order to solve each of these equations?
  a $x^3 - 3x^2 - 2 = 0$ **b** $x^3 - 3x^2 - x + 2 = 0$
  c $x^3 - 3x^2 + 4x = 1$

4 Given the graph of $y = x + \dfrac{4}{x}$, what line would you need to draw
  in order to solve each of these equations?

  a $x + \dfrac{4}{x} - 3 = 0$ **b** $\dfrac{4}{x} - x = 0$

  c $x^2 - 5x + 4 = 0$ **d** $\dfrac{4}{x} - x - 1 = 0$

5 Here are sketches of five graphs.

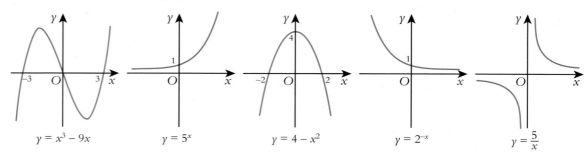

$y = x^3 - 9x$ $y = 5^x$ $y = 4 - x^2$ $y = 2^{-x}$ $y = \dfrac{5}{x}$

Use these sketches to find the number of solutions to each of these
equations.

a $\dfrac{5}{x} = 5^x$ **b** $4 - x^2 = 5^x$

c $x^3 - 9x = \dfrac{5}{x}$ **d** $2^{-x} = 4 - x^2$

e $x(x - 3)(x + 3) = 0$

Examination questions

Use 'Topic Tracker' at www.ccea.org.uk to find more exam questions.

Question **1** is from an examination paper where you may not use a calculator.

1 The graph of $y = x^3 - 4x + 1$ for $-2 \leqslant x \leqslant 2$ is shown.

  a Use a table of values for $y = x^3 - 4x + 1$ to make a copy of the graph below. Use your graph to find solutions of $x^3 - 4x + 1 = 0$ in the range $-2 \leqslant x \leqslant 2$.

  b By drawing a suitable straight line on your graph, solve the equation $x^3 - 3x = 0$.

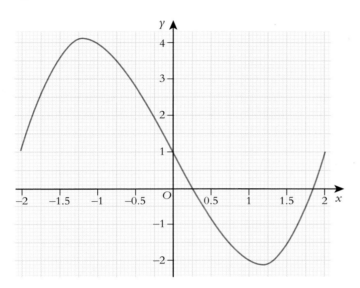

Question **2** is from an examination paper where you may use a calculator.

2 **a** Use the table of values for $y = x^2 + 2x - 2$ to draw the graph.

x	-4	-3	-2	-1	0	1	2
$y = x^2 + 2x - 2$	6	1	-2	-3	-2	1	6

  b By drawing a suitable straight line on your graph, find solutions to the equation $x^2 + 3x - 1 = 0$.

CHAPTER 30

Inequalities

This chapter is about:

- reading and writing inequalities
- showing inequalities on a number line
- solving linear inequalities algebraically
- using straight lines to locate regions represented by several inequalities
- determining inequalities from a graph
- determining the maximum and minimum values of a function subject to the constraints of a given set of inequalities.

You should already know:

- how to work with negative numbers
- how to solve linear equations
- how to draw the graph of a linear function
- how to solve simultaneous linear equations graphically
- how to find and interpret the equation of a straight line, $y = mx + c$
- how to find the perimeter of a rectangle
- how to find the area of a triangle
- the properties of parallel and perpendicular lines.

Inequalities on a number line

An **equation** states that one expression is equal to another. An **inequality** states that one expression may be different from another. There are four symbols which are used to describe inequalities:

- $<$ means *less than*. For example, $x < 4$ means 'x is less than 4'. So it implies that the integer values of x could be 3, 2, 1, 0, −1, ... In addition, x could also be any fraction or decimal less than 4, for example 3.5 or $2\frac{1}{2}$.

- $>$ means *greater than*. For example, $x > 3$ implies that the integer values of x could be 4, 5, 6, 7, ...

- $\leqslant$ means *less than or equal to*. For example, $x \leqslant 2$ implies that the integer values of x could be 2, 1, 0, −1, ...

- $\geqslant$ means *greater than or equal to*. For example, $x \geqslant -1$ implies that the integer values of x could be −1, 0, 1, 2 ... .

A double inequality such as $-3 \leqslant x < 5$ is read as 'x is less than 5 but greater than or equal to −3'. Hence the integer values of x could be 4, 3, 2, 1, 0, −1, −2 or −3.

Inequalities can be displayed on a number line. Care must be taken when displaying inequalities. It is important to read whether the solutions required are **integer** solutions or **real** solutions. The notation used on the number line differs according to the type of solution being shown.

Integer solutions are the possible positive or negative whole numbers which satisfy the inequality. They are represented on the number line by a solid dot •.

EXAMPLE 1

Illustrate each of these inequalities on a number line from $x = -6$ to $x = 8$, showing integer solutions only.

    a $x > 3$ b $x \leqslant -2$ c $2 \leqslant x < 6$

SOLUTION

    a $x > 3$

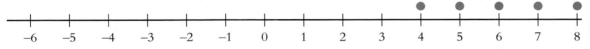

    b $x \leqslant -2$

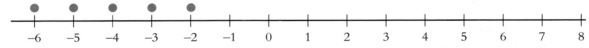

    c $2 \leqslant x < 6$

Real solutions include whole numbers, fractions and decimals. A line is used to denote the values included in the inequality. For the end points, a *solid* dot • indicates that the value *is* included in the inequality, whereas an *open* dot ○ indicates that the value is *not* included in the inequality.

EXAMPLE 2

Illustrate each of these inequalities on a number line, showing all real solutions.

    a $x > 2$ b $x \leqslant 3$ c $-2 \leqslant x < 2$

SOLUTION

    a $x > 2$

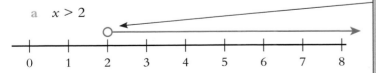

There is an open dot at 2, since 2 does not satisfy the inequality (although anything bigger does). You use an arrowhead to indicate that the solution continues to infinity.

b $x \leqslant 3$

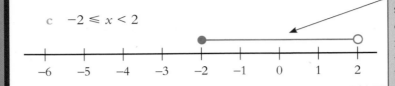

> There is a solid dot at 3, since 3 satisfies the inequality (as does anything smaller).

c $-2 \leqslant x < 2$

> There is a solid dot at −2 as it satisfies the inequality, an open dot at 2 as it does not satisfy the inequality, and a line for all other values included in the inequality in between.

Exercise 30.1

1 Is each of these statements true or false?

  a $6 < 9$ **b** $-2 > 2$ **c** $2.5 \geqslant 2$

  d $13 < 13$ **e** $-7 \geqslant -1$ **f** $\frac{1}{2} < 1$

  g $0.3 < \frac{1}{3}$ **h** $0 \geqslant -4$ **i** $2 \times 3 > 2 \times (-3)$

2 Write down one integer value for n which would satisfy each of these inequalities.

  a $n < 6$ **b** $n \leqslant -2$ **c** $n \geqslant -4$

  d $n - 2 > 7$ **e** $\dfrac{n}{2} \leqslant 10$ **f** $-6 \leqslant n \leqslant -4$

  g $4 < n \leqslant 7$ **h** $n + 3 < -1$ **i** $2n > -6$

3 **a** List the first five integer solutions for n which satisfy each of these inequalities.

     i $n > 6$ **ii** $n \leqslant -2$ **iii** $n \geqslant -4$ **iv** $n \leqslant 0$

  b List all the integer solutions for n which satisfy each of these inequalities.

     i $-3 \leqslant n < 3$ **ii** $0 \leqslant n \leqslant 5$

     iii $-6 < n < -4$ **iv** $-3 < n \leqslant 1$

4 I have an amount of money, £a.
Write each of these statements as an inequality involving a.

  a I have less than £12.   **b** I have no more than £4.

  c I cannot buy a book that costs £6.   **d** I have at least £3.

  e I have between £4 and £8.

5 Display each of these inequalities on a number line from $n = -6$ to $n = 8$, showing integer solutions only.

  a $n > 2$ **b** $n \leqslant 6$ **c** $n \geqslant -1$

  d $n \leqslant 0$ **e** $-4 \leqslant n \leqslant 1$ **f** $2 < n \leqslant 5$

6 Display each of these inequalities on a number line, showing all real solutions.

  a $x > -3$ **b** $x \leqslant -2$ **c** $x > 0$

  d $x \leqslant 6$ **e** $-3 < x \leqslant 2$ **f** $-4 \leqslant x \leqslant 0$

7   Write down the inequality that represents the possible values of x shown
    by each of these number lines.

a
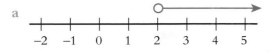

b
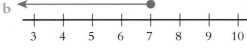

c

d
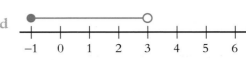

e
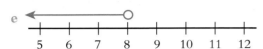

f
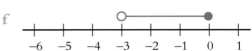

8   a   What is the highest integer which satisfies the inequality $n \leqslant 6$?
    b   What is the lowest integer which satisfies the inequality $n > 3$?
    c   What is the highest integer which satisfies the inequality $n \leqslant 2\frac{1}{2}$?
    d   What is the lowest integer which satisfies the inequality $-2 \leqslant n < 4$?
    e   What is the highest integer which satisfies the inequality $2 \leqslant n < 3\frac{1}{2}$?

9   Write down two different inequalities involving x which are satisfied by
    the integers 2, 3, 4, 5 and 6.

10 Write down *one* inequality which shows the values of x which satisfy
    these three inequalities.

    $x < 4$ $0 < x < 8$ $2 \leqslant x < 10$

Solving inequalities

Inequalities can be solved using the same algebraic processes as were
used for solving linear equations in Chapter 17. There is one important
exception, however, which needs some attention.

Look at this inequality:

$$4 < 10$$

Adding 2 to both sides of the inequality gives:

$$4 + 2 < 10 + 2$$
$$6 < 12$$

This inequality is still true and so *adding a positive number to both sides does
not affect the inequality*.

Subtracting 2 from both sides of the inequality gives:

$$4 - 2 < 10 - 2$$
$$2 < 8$$

This inequality is still true and so *subtracting a positive number from both sides
does not affect the inequality*.

Remember the rules of negative numbers. Adding a negative number gives
the same result as subtracting a positive number and subtracting a negative
number gives the same result as adding a positive number; for example,
$4 + (-2) = 2$ and $4 - (-2) = 6$. So *adding any number to or subtracting any
number from both sides of an inequality does not affect the inequality*.

Multiplying both sides of the inequality by 2 gives:

$$4 \times 2 < 10 \times 2$$
$$8 < 20$$

This inequality is still true and so *multiplying both sides by a positive number does not affect the inequality*.

Multiplying both sides of the inequality by -2 gives:

$$4 \times (-2) < 10 \times (-2)$$
$$-8 < -20$$

This inequality is in fact *not* true. Instead, $-8 > -20$ and so *multiplying both sides by a negative number reverses the inequality sign*.

Dividing both sides of the inequality by 2 gives:

$$4 \div 2 < 10 \div 2$$
$$2 < 5$$

This inequality is still true and so *dividing both sides by a positive number does not affect the inequality*.

Dividing both sides of the inequality by -2 gives:

$$4 \div (-2) < 10 \div (-2)$$
$$-2 < -5$$

This inequality is in fact *not* true. Instead, $-2 > -5$ and so *dividing both sides by a negative number reverses the inequality sign*.

Multiplying or dividing an inequality by a negative number reverses the inequality.

You can avoid this problem by making the variable term *positive* when solving an inequality, as shown in Examples 5 and 7 below. If you do multiply or divide by a negative number, you must remember to take this sign reversal into account.

EXAMPLE 3

Solve the inequality $3x - 1 < 11$.

> You solve inequalities as you do equations, by performing the same operation on both sides, except that there is an inequality sign rather than an equals sign.

SOLUTION

$$3x - 1 < 11$$
$$3x < 11 + 1$$
$$3x < 12$$
$$x < \frac{12}{3}$$
$$x < 4$$

> It is good practice to substitute a value back into the original inequality to check its validity. For example, given the solution $x < 4$, choose any value of x that satisfies this, e.g. $x = 2$, and substitute it into $3x - 1$. Is the value less than 11?
> $3 \times 2 - 1 = 6 - 1 = 5$ $5 < 11$ is true.

EXAMPLE 4

Solve the inequality $\dfrac{2x}{3} \geqslant 6$.

$$\frac{2x}{3} \geqslant 6$$

$$2x \geqslant 6 \times 3$$

$$2x \geqslant 18$$

$$x \geqslant \frac{18}{2}$$

$$x \geqslant 9$$

EXAMPLE 5

Solve the inequality $5 - 2x > -7$.

SOLUTION

Method 1

$$5 - 2x > -7$$

$$5 > 2x - 7$$

$$5 + 7 > 2x$$

$$12 > 2x$$

$$\frac{12}{2} > x$$

$$x < 6$$

> Add $2x$ to both sides of the inequality so that the variable term is positive.

> It is good practice to write the final inequality with the variable on the left-hand side. Notice that you need to reverse the inequality sign at this stage. Think about whether the point of the sign is nearer the variable term or the numerical term.

Method 2

$$5 - 2x > -7$$

$$-2x > -7 - 5$$

$$-2x > -12$$

$$x < \frac{-12}{-2}$$

$$x < 6$$

> Dividing by -2 reverses the inequality.

EXAMPLE 6

Solve the inequality $2(3x + 2) < 10$.

SOLUTION

$$2(3x + 2) < 10$$

$$6x + 4 < 10$$

$$6x < 10 - 4$$

$$6x < 6$$

$$x < \frac{6}{6}$$

$$x < 1$$

> Like linear equations, inequalities may involve more complicated expressions. Use the same techniques as you did for linear equations. In this case, expand the brackets first.

EXAMPLE 7

Solve the inequality $2x - 7 \geqslant 5x - 9$.

SOLUTION

Method 1

$$2x - 7 \geqslant 5x - 9$$
$$-7 + 9 \geqslant 5x - 2x$$
$$2 \geqslant 3x$$
$$\frac{2}{3} \geqslant x$$
$$x \leqslant \frac{2}{3}$$

When rearranging the inequality, aim for the variable term to be positive.

Method 2

$$2x - 7 \geqslant 5x - 9$$
$$2x - 5x \geqslant -9 + 7$$
$$-3x \geqslant -2$$
$$x \leqslant \frac{-2}{-3}$$
$$x \leqslant \frac{2}{3}$$

Dividing by -3 reverses the inequality.

Double inequalities

These involve *two* inequality signs. The best approach is to solve the two inequalities separately and then combine the two resulting inequalities, if possible, into one final inequality. This final inequality will have two inequality signs and result in a limited range of solutions, so you will often be asked to list the integer solutions.

EXAMPLE 8

Solve the inequality $-8 \leqslant 4x + 2 \leqslant 10$.

SOLUTION

$$-8 \leqslant 4x + 2 \qquad \text{and} \qquad 4x + 2 \leqslant 10$$
$$-8 - 2 \leqslant 4x \qquad\qquad\qquad 4x \leqslant 10 - 2$$
$$-10 \leqslant 4x \qquad\qquad\qquad 4x \leqslant 8$$
$$\frac{-10}{4} \leqslant x \qquad\qquad\qquad x \leqslant 2$$
$$-2\frac{1}{2} \leqslant x \qquad\qquad\qquad x \leqslant 2$$

$$-2\frac{1}{2} \leqslant x \leqslant 2$$

The solutions can be combined.

EXAMPLE 9

Solve the inequality $-3 < 4 - 2x \leqslant 12$.

SOLUTION

$$-3 < 4 - 2x \qquad \text{and} \qquad 4 - 2x \leqslant 12$$
$$2x < 4 + 3 \qquad\qquad\qquad 4 - 12 \leqslant 2x$$
$$2x < 7 \qquad\qquad\qquad\qquad -8 \leqslant 2x$$
$$x < \frac{7}{2} \qquad\qquad\qquad\qquad \frac{-8}{2} \leqslant x$$
$$x < 3\frac{1}{2} \qquad\qquad\qquad\qquad -4 \leqslant x$$

$$-4 \leqslant x < 3\frac{1}{2}$$

Note the arrangement of the final inequality here, with the most negative term appearing on the left-hand side of the variable.

EXAMPLE 10

Find the integer solutions to the inequality $-2 < \dfrac{2n}{3} + 1 < 7$.

SOLUTION

$$-2 < \dfrac{2n}{3} + 1 \qquad \text{and} \qquad \dfrac{2n}{3} + 1 < 7$$

$$-2 - 1 < \dfrac{2n}{3} \qquad\qquad \dfrac{2n}{3} < 7 - 1$$

$$-3 < \dfrac{2n}{3} \qquad\qquad \dfrac{2n}{3} < 6$$

$$-3 \times 3 < 2n \qquad\qquad 2n < 6 \times 3$$

$$-9 < 2n \qquad\qquad 2n < 18$$

$$-\dfrac{9}{2} < n \qquad\qquad n < \dfrac{18}{2}$$

$$-4\tfrac{1}{2} < n \qquad\qquad n < 9$$

$$-4\tfrac{1}{2} < n < 9$$

The integer solutions are $-4, -3, -2, -1, 0, 1, 2, 3, 4, 5, 6, 7$ and 8.

EXAMPLE 11

Solve the inequality $2 \leqslant 4 - 2x < x - 5$.

SOLUTION

$$2 \leqslant 4 - 2x \qquad \text{and} \qquad 4 - 2x < x - 5$$

$$2x \leqslant 4 - 2 \qquad\qquad 4 + 5 < x + 2x$$

$$2x \leqslant 2 \qquad\qquad 9 < 3x$$

$$x \leqslant \dfrac{2}{2} \qquad\qquad \dfrac{9}{3} < x$$

$$x \leqslant 1 \qquad\qquad x > 3$$

> Notice that it does not make sense to combine the final inequalities here, as the inequality signs are pointing towards opposite ends of the number line.

Like equations, inequalities can be used for solving problems. This will be developed in greater detail later in the chapter.

Exercise 30.2

Solve each of these inequalities.

1 $x + 4 > 9$

2 $3x - 5 < 7$

3 $\frac{1}{2}x \leqslant 6$

4 $3t - 7 > 11$

5 $a - 3 \leqslant -1$

6 $2 - 5x > -8$

7 $2(2n + 1) \leqslant -5$

8 $2p + 5 > 5p - 1$

9 $3x - 9 < 12 - 4x$

10 $4(1 - 2x) \geqslant -6$

11 $\dfrac{2 - x}{4} > 1$

12 $3 + \dfrac{2t}{5} < 10$

13 $5x - 8 \geqslant 2 - 3x$

14 $3(2a - 1) < 8a - 5$

15 $3 - 2m < 2(3 + 2m)$

16 $5(x - 3) > 2 + 3(x + 1)$

17 $\dfrac{6k}{5} - 1 > -2$

18 $9 > 3(2x - 1)$

19 $\frac{1}{2}(3a - 1) \leqslant 4 - \frac{1}{2}a$

20 $\frac{3}{4}x + 4 > \frac{1}{2}x - 2$

Solve each of these double inequalities.
For questions 21, 22 and 23, list the integer solutions.

21 $2 \leqslant 4n - 6 < 3n - 2$ 22 $4 - 2n < 8 + 2n < n + 9$ 23 $n - 10 < 2(n - 3) < n$

24 $6 \leqslant 4 - 2a < 1 + a$ 25 $2a + 3 \leqslant 3a - 1 \leqslant a + 5$

Solve each of these problems by forming and solving a suitable inequality.

26 The length of a rectangle is 4 cm greater than the width.
   If the perimeter is less than 30 cm, find the range of possible values for the width.

27 The area of the triangle must be greater
   than the area of the rectangle.

   Find the range of possible values for x.

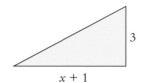

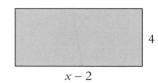

28 Eoin has exactly £12 more than John. They have less than £60 altogether.
   What is the maximum amount John can have?

Graphs of inequalities

Inequalities can also be displayed graphically. A graph can be drawn
to represent an inequality involving just one variable, but graphs are
particularly useful for displaying inequalities involving two variables.

When a line is drawn on a graph, it splits the graph into two regions.

For inequalities involving > or <, a *broken* line is used, as points on that
line do *not* satisfy the inequality.

For inequalities involving ⩾ or ⩽, a *solid* line is used, as points on that line
do satisfy the inequality.

Points on one side of the line will satisfy the inequality, whilst points
on the other side of the line will not. To decide which side satisfies the
inequality, choose a point (not a point that lies on the line) and test the
co-ordinates of that point in the inequality. The point (0, 0) is generally
easy to use, providing it does not lie on the line.

It is good practice to shade the side which does *not* satisfy the inequality
and leave the region which *does* satisfy the inequality clear. You often mark
the region with the letter R.

EXAMPLE 12

Draw a graph to show the region which satisfies the
inequality $x \geqslant 3$.

SOLUTION   A *solid* line is used as the inequality
          includes $x = 3$.

It is obvious that any point to the right of the
line has an x co-ordinate greater than 3, hence
shade the region to the *left* of it.

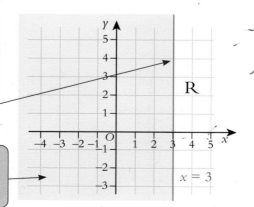

EXAMPLE 13

Draw a graph to show the region which satisfies the inequality $2 < y \le 5$.

SOLUTION

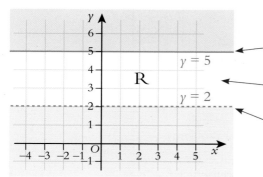

A *solid* line is used for the line $y = 5$.

Any point with y co-ordinate between 2 and 5 satisfies the inequality, so you shade the parts *below* the line $y = 2$ and *above* the line $y = 5$.

A *broken* line is used for the line $y = 2$.

EXAMPLE 14

Draw a graph to show the region which satisfies the inequality $x + 2y \ge 4$.

SOLUTION

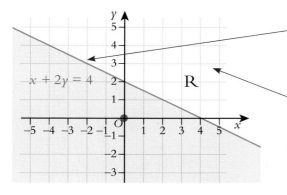

Draw the straight line using whichever of the methods from Chapter 25 you prefer.

The correct region is not so easy to identify when the line is sloping. To decide, choose a point which is not on the line (e.g. $(0, 0)$) and substitute its co-ordinates into the inequality. Is $0 + 2 \times 0 \ge 4$? No. This means that $(0, 0)$ is on the side of the line that you do *not* want, so this is the side that you shade.

EXAMPLE 15

Draw a graph to show the region which satisfies the inequality $2x - y < -1$.

SOLUTION

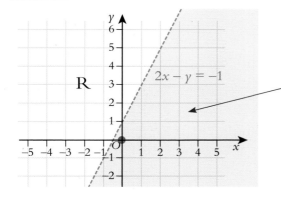

Test the point $(0, 0)$.
Is $2 \times 0 - 0 < -1$? No.
This means this side of the line does *not* satisfy the inequality, so you shade it out. Note that *any* point can be used as a test point. You could choose the point $(-1, 1)$ here, for example.
Is $2 \times (-1) - 1 < -1$? Yes.
This means you would leave the side on which $(-1, 1)$ lies *unshaded*, as it *does* satisfy the inequality. The resulting graph would be the same as here.

Draw graphs to show the region which satisfies each of these inequalities.

1 $x < 4$	2 $y \geqslant -2$	3 $x \leqslant 0$	4 $-1 \leqslant x \leqslant 3$
5 $x + y > 6$	6 $2x - y < 6$	7 $y \geqslant x$	8 $y - 3x < 1$
9 $2x + 3y \leqslant 12$	10 $5y - 2x > 10$	11 $3y - x \leqslant 9$	12 $y > 2x$
13 $x + 4y > -8$	14 $y \leqslant 3x - 4$	15 $4x + 5y \geqslant 20$	

Graphs of sets of inequalities

We will now look at displaying several inequalities together on a single graph. This is particularly useful when solving complex practical problems.

The procedure is the same as for graphing single inequalities, but extra care must be taken with the shading in order to locate the region which satisfies *all* the inequalities.

EXAMPLE 16

Draw a graph to show the region which satisfies the inequalities

$3x + 2y \leqslant 8$, $2x + 3y > 6$ and $x > -1$.

SOLUTION

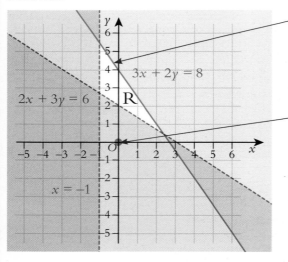

Remember to use solid or broken lines, as appropriate.

Here, the point $(0, 0)$ was used to determine which side of each line to shade.
For $3x + 2y \leqslant 8$:
Is $3 \times 0 + 2 \times 0 \leqslant 8$? Yes.
So shade the other side.
For $2x + 3y > 6$:
Is $2 \times 0 + 3 \times 0 > 6$? No.
So shade the $(0, 0)$ side.
For $x > -1$:
$(0, 0)$ lies to the right of the line $x = -1$.
So shade the other side.

EXAMPLE 17

Draw a graph to show the region which satisfies the inequalities

$x \geq 0$, $y \geq x - 2$ and $x + y < 10$.

SOLUTION

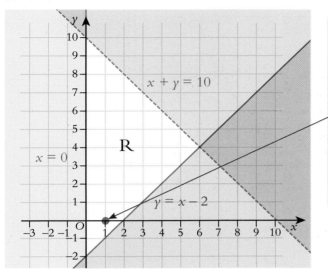

(1, 0) was used as the test point here, as (0, 0) lies on one of the lines.

For $x \geq 0$:

(1, 0) lies to the right of the line $x = 0$.

So shade the other side.

For $y \geq x - 2$:

Is $0 \geq 1 - 2$? Yes.

So shade the other side.

For $x + y < 10$:

Is $1 + 0 < 10$? Yes.

So shade the other side.

Exercise 30.4

Draw graphs to show the region which satisfies each of these sets of inequalities.

1. $3x + 2y \leq 12$, $x \geq 0$ and $y \geq 0$
2. $x < 6$ and $y \leq 3$
3. $x + y \leq 6$, $x \geq 0$ and $y \geq 0$
4. $3x + y > 6$, $y > 2$ and $x \leq 4$
5. $y < 2x + 1$, $y > x + 1$ and $x \leq 2$
6. $x + y > 2$ and $x \geq -1$
7. $2x + y > 6$, $y > x$ and $y < 4$
8. $y \geq \frac{1}{2}x - 2$, $y \leq -1$ and $x \geq -5$
9. $y > 1$, $y - 2x < 4$ and $x + y < 5$
10. $x < 3$, $2x + 3y \geq 6$ and $y < 3x$

Determining inequalities from a graph

We will now consider the reverse process, in which you are given the graph and need to work back to find the associated inequalities.

Taking each line in turn, first you determine the equation of the line using the techniques from Chapter 25. Then, by choosing a point, you decide which region has been left unshaded and so insert the correct inequality sign. Remember that a *solid* line represents $\geq$ or $\leq$, whilst a *broken* line represents $<$ or $>$.

EXAMPLE 18

Find the inequalities which define the region R.

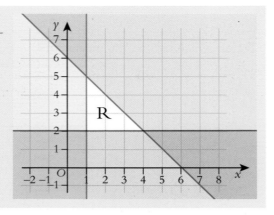

SOLUTION

Green line
This vertical line has equation $x = 1$.
R lies to the right of this line, so the inequality is $x \geqslant 1$.

Red line
This horizontal line has equation $y = 2$.
R lies above this line, so the inequality is $y \geqslant 2$.

Blue line
This sloping line has gradient -1 and y-intercept $(0, 6)$.
Hence it has equation $y = -x + 6$.

Choosing a point within the region R as a test point, for example $(2, 3)$, and substituting these co-ordinates into the equation:
$3 < -2 + 6$.
So the inequality is $y \leqslant -x + 6$.

> $\leqslant$ is used for all the inequalities because all the lines are solid.

EXAMPLE 19

Find the inequalities which define the region R.

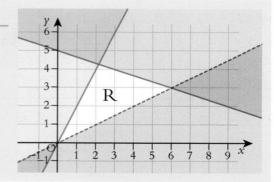

SOLUTION

Green line
Gradient $= 2$ and y-intercept $= (0, 0)$.
Therefore the equation is $y = 2x$.
Choosing the point $(3, 3)$ for substitution gives $3 < 6$.
The resulting inequality is $y \leqslant 2x$.

> The line on the graph is solid so $\leqslant$ is used in the inequality.

Red line

Gradient = $\frac{1}{2}$ and y–intercept = $(0, 0)$.

Therefore the equation is $y = \frac{1}{2}x$.

Choosing the point $(3, 3)$ for substitution gives $3 > 1\frac{1}{2}$.

The resulting inequality is $y > \frac{1}{2}x$ or $2y > x$.

> $>$ is used because the line is broken.

Blue line

Gradient = $-\frac{1}{3}$ and y–intercept = $(0, 5)$.

Therefore the equation is $y = -\frac{1}{3}x + 5$.

Choosing the point $(3, 3)$ for substitution gives $3 < -1 + 5$.

The resulting inequality is $y \leqslant -\frac{1}{3}x + 5$ or $3y + x \leqslant 5$.

Exercise 30.5

Find the set of inequalities which defines each of these regions R.

1
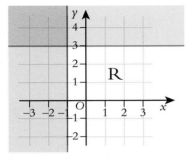

2
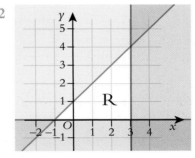

3
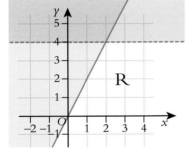

4
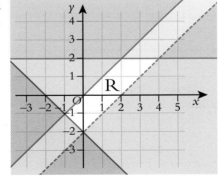

5
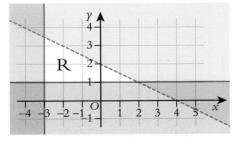

6
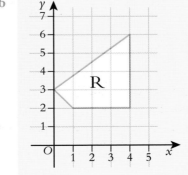

Maximising and minimising

Within the suitable region there are often a number of solutions which satisfy all the given inequalities. Sometimes it will be necessary to find the maximum or minimum value of a particular function subject to the constraints defined by the given inequalities. The maximum or minimum value will always occur at one of the vertices of the region, so it is only necessary to check the value of the function at the vertices of the suitable region.

EXAMPLE 20

Which values of x and y provide the maximum value of the function $x + 3y$ for the region shown?

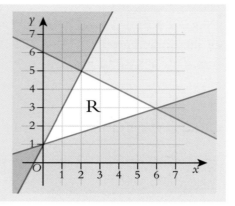

SOLUTION

The vertices of the suitable region are at $(0, 1)$, $(2, 5)$ and $(6, 3)$.
Substituting each of these into the function $x + 3y$ gives

$$0 + 3 \times 1 = 3$$
$$2 + 3 \times 5 = 17$$
or $\quad 6 + 3 \times 3 = 15.$

The maximum value of the function $x + 3y$ in this region is 17.
It occurs when $x = 2$ and $y = 5$.

EXAMPLE 21

Find the minimum value of the function $2x - y$ subject to the constraints $x \geqslant 1$, $y \geqslant 2$ and $3x + 2y \geqslant 13$.

SOLUTION

First draw a graph to show the inequalities and find the suitable region by shading.

The vertices of the suitable region are at $(3, 2)$ and $(1, 5)$.

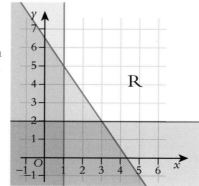

Substituting each of these into the function $2x - y$ gives

$$2 \times 3 - 2 = 4$$
or $\quad 2 \times 1 - 5 = -3.$

The minimum value of the function $2x - 3y$ subject to these constraints is -3. It occurs when $x = 1$ and $y = 5$.

Sometimes some or all of the vertices of the suitable region will have non–integer co-ordinates. In this case, you need to check whether the question asks for integer solutions or real solutions. The maximum and minimum values of the function will still occur at the vertices but, if you are asked for integer solutions, you must examine the points with integer co-ordinates that lie close to the vertices and within the suitable region, as illustrated in the next example.

EXAMPLE 22

Find the maximum value of the function $x + 2y$ subject to the constraints $y \geq 2$, $y \leq x + 2$ and $4y + 3x \leq 24$ and that x and y take integer values.

SOLUTION

Here two of the vertices of the suitable region do not have integer co-ordinates.

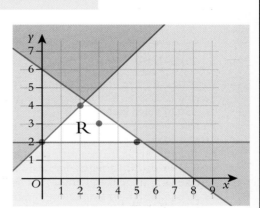

It is necessary to examine points *close to* the vertices and *within* the suitable region.

Suitable points for inspection here are $(0, 2)$, $(2, 4)$, $(3, 3)$ and $(5, 2)$.

Substituting each of these into the function $x + 2y$ gives:

$$0 + 2 \times 2 = 4$$
$$2 + 2 \times 4 = 10$$
$$3 + 2 \times 3 = 9$$
or $$5 + 2 \times 2 = 9.$$

The maximum value of the function $x + 2y$ subject to these constraints is 10. It occurs when $x = 2$ and $y = 4$.

Exercise 30.6

1 Find the point with integer co-ordinates which maximises the function $x + 2y$ for the region shown.

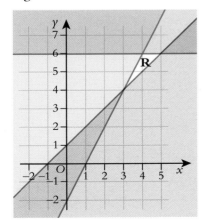

2 Find the point with integer co-ordinates which minimises the function $4x - y$ for the region shown.

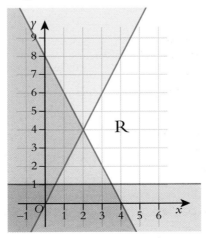

3 Find the point with integer co-ordinates which maximises the function $x + y$ subject to the constraints of these inequalities.

$$y \leqslant x + 3 \qquad y \geqslant 4 \qquad x \leqslant 4$$

4 Find the point with integer co-ordinates which minimises the function $x + 3y$ subject to the constraints of these inequalities.

$$2x + y \geqslant 6 \qquad x + y \geqslant 5 \qquad y \geqslant 2 \qquad x \geqslant 0$$

5 Find the point with integer co-ordinates which maximises the function $3x - y$ subject to the constraints of these inequalities.

$$x + y \geqslant 5 \qquad y \leqslant 5 \qquad 2y - x \geqslant 4$$

6 Find the point with integer co-ordinates which maximises the function $y - 2x$ subject to the constraints of these inequalities.

$$y \leqslant 3x \qquad 2y \geqslant x \qquad x \leqslant 6 \quad y \leqslant 6$$

You should now:

- know how to read and write inequalities
- be able to display and interpret inequalities on a number line
- be able to solve inequalities
- be able to solve double inequalities
- be able to solve problems involving inequalities
- be able to display inequalities graphically
- be able to identify a region satisfied by a number of inequalities
- be able to find the inequalities that define a region
- be able to find the maximum or minimum value of a function subject to the constraints of a given set of inequalities.

Summary exercise 30

1 Write down all the integer solutions for n that satisfy the inequality $-3 \leqslant n < 4$.

2 Display each of these inequalities on a number line.
   a $x > -4$ (real solutions)   b $-2 \leqslant n \leqslant 1$ (integer solutions)

3 Write down the inequality that represents the possible values of x shown by each of these number lines.

a

```
      ○----------------→
 +   +   +   +   +   +   +
-10  -9  -8  -7  -6  -5  -4
```

b

```
 ●----------------○
 +   +   +   +   +   +   +   +   +
-1   0   1   2   3   4   5   6   7
```

4 Solve each of these inequalities.
   a $2x + 3 < 8$ b $3x - 2 > 5x - 9$
   c $3(a - 4) \leqslant 5a + 3$ d $\dfrac{2p}{3} - 6 > -2$

5 Solve the inequality $2 + n \leqslant 1 + 2n \leqslant n + 5$, listing the integer solutions.

6 Solve the inequality $2k + 3 \leqslant 4k + 1 \leqslant 3k - 2$.

7 Ken has four times as much money as Jake has.
   Even if Ken gave Jake £360, Ken would still be the richer.
   What is the least amount of money (a whole number of pounds) that Jake can have?

8   Display each of these inequalities on a separate graph.
    a $y \leqslant -1$ **b** $2x - 3y > 8$ **c** $4y - x < -4$

9   Draw a graph to show the region which satisfies this set of inequalities.
    $$y \leqslant 2x + 10 \qquad y \geqslant 10 \qquad x \leqslant 3$$

10 Draw a graph to show the region which satisfies this set of inequalities.
    $$x \geqslant 0 \qquad x \leqslant y \qquad y \leqslant 2x + 1 \qquad y \leqslant 8 - x$$

11 Find the set of inequalities which defines the region R shown below.

12 Find the point with integer co-ordinates which maximises the function $x + y$ for the region shown.

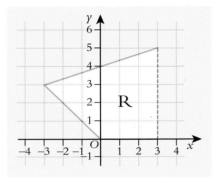

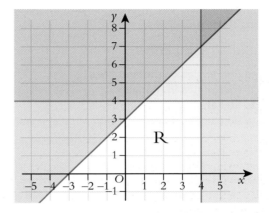

13 Find the point with integer co-ordinates which minimises the function $2x + y$ subject to the constraints of these inequalities.
    $$x + y \geqslant 6 \qquad 2y \geqslant 8 - x \qquad x \geqslant 2 \qquad y \geqslant 1$$

Examination questions

Questions **1** and **2** are from examination papers where you may not use a calculator.

1   Solve the inequality $8 < 2n < 17$ where n is an integer.

2   Illustrate on a number line from $x = -8$ to $x = 13$ the values of x which satisfy
    $-8 < 3x + 4 \leqslant 13$
    where x is a real number.

Question **3** is from an examination paper where you may use a calculator.

3   **a** Draw the graph of $y = 2x + 1$.
    b On your graph, show the region satisfying the three inequalities
    $x \geqslant 6, \quad y \geqslant 2, \ y \leqslant 2x + 1$
    Indicate the region with the letter R.

Use 'Topic Tracker' at www.ccea.org.uk to find more exam questions.

CHAPTER 31

Angles in circles

This chapter is about:

- learning and using language associated with circles
- learning and using the different angle properties of circles
- learning and using the different tangent properties of circles
- proving these properties.

You should already know:

- how to find angles on straight lines
- how to find angles in triangles
- how to find angles in quadrilaterals
- how to find angles associated with parallel lines.

Parts of a circle

The parts of a circle have special names.

Circumference

This is the special name given to the perimeter of the circle.

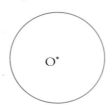

Radius

The **radius** is any straight line joining the centre O to the circumference of the circle. OA is a radius. *All radii are equal in length.*

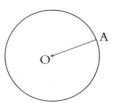

Diameter

The **diameter** is any straight line joining any two points on the circumference passing through the centre. BA = 2 OA

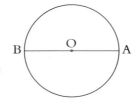

Tangent

A **tangent** to a circle is a straight line which touches the circle at one point only. This point is called the **point of contact**. TC is a tangent.

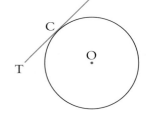

Chord

A **chord** is a straight line which cuts the circumference in two places but does *not* pass through the centre.

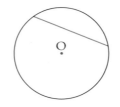

Arc

The **arc** of a circle is the curved line joining two points on the circumference. PQ is an arc.

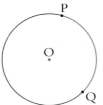

Note that the larger arc is called the major arc and the smaller arc is called the minor arc. We assume the arc to be the minor arc unless told explicitly otherwise.

Sector

A **sector** is the area between two radii and an arc.

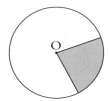

Segment

A **segment** is the area between a chord and an arc.

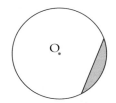

Exercise 31.1

Use compasses to draw a circle centre O for each question below.

1   Draw and label **a** a radius and **b** an arc.

2   Draw and label **a** a diameter and **b** a tangent to the circle.

3   Draw and label **a** a chord and **b** a segment.

4   Draw and label a sector.

5   **a**   Draw and label a chord PQ.
    b   Join O to the midpoint of PQ. Measure the angle OMP.

6   **a**   Draw the radii OP and OQ.   **b**   Mark any point R on the major arc PQ.
    c   Join RP and RQ.   **d**   Measure the angles POQ and PRQ.
    e   What do you notice about your answers?

7   **a**   Draw an arc PQ.
    b   Mark any three points T, R and S on the major arc PQ.
    c   Join TP, TQ and RP, RQ and SP, SQ.
    d   Measure the angles PTQ, PRQ and PSQ.
    e   What do you notice about your answers?

8   **a**   Draw a diameter BA.
    b   Mark two points N and M, one on the circumference of one semicircle and the other on the circumference of the other semicircle.
    c   Measure the angles BNA and BMA
    d   What do you notice about your answers?

9   **a**   Mark four points W, X, Y and Z anywhere on the circumference.
    b   Join WY, YZ, ZW and WX.
    c   **i**   Measure the angles YXW and WZY.   **ii**   Work out angle YXW + angle WZY.
    d   **i**   Measure the angles XYZ and XWZ.   **ii**   Work out angle XYZ + angle XWZ.
    e   What do you notice about your answers?

10   **a**   Mark any point C on the circumference.   **b** Join OC.
     c   Draw the tangent to the circle at C from a point T.   **d** Measure the angle TCO.

11   **a**   Draw a chord AB.   **b**   Draw a tangent at A from a point T.
     c   Mark any point N on the major arc AB.   **d**   Measure the angles TAB and ANB.
     e   What do you notice about your answers?

Angle properties of circles

THEOREM

The angle at the centre of a circle is twice the angle at the circumference when they are both subtended by the same two points,
i.e. angle AOB = 2 × angle ACB

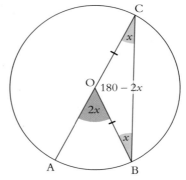

PROOF

Let angle AOB = $2x$

Then angle BOC = $180° - 2x$ *(angles on a straight line add up to 180°)*

angle OBC + angle OCB = $180° - (180 - 2x) = 2x$
                                    (angles in a triangle add up to 180°)

But BOC is an isosceles triangle   *(two radii are equal)*

So   angle OBC = angle OCB

So   angle OBC = $\frac{1}{2}(2x) = x$

Look back at your answer to question **6** in Exercise 31.1.

THEOREM

Angles on the circumference in the same segment, subtended by the same two points, are equal.

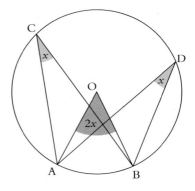

PROOF

Let angle AOB = $2x$

Then   angle ACB = x *(angle at the centre is twice the angle at the circumference)*

But   angle ADB = x *(angle at the centre is twice the angle at the circumference)*

So   angle ACB = angle ADB

Look back at your answer to question **7** in Exercise 31.1.

THEOREM

Every angle on the circumference of a semicircle is 90°.

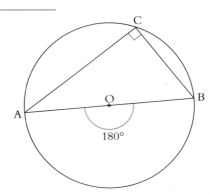

PROOF

Angle AOB = $180°$ *(angle on a straight line)*

Angle ACB = $\frac{1}{2}(180°) = 90°$ *(angle at the centre is twice the angle at the circumference)*

Look back at your answer to question **8** in Exercise 31.1.

We can use these properties to calculate angles in a circle.

EXAMPLE 1

What are the values of angles x and y?

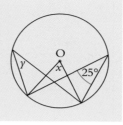

SOLUTION

$x = 25 \times 2 = 50°$ (*angle at the centre is twice the angle at the circumference*)

$y = 25°$ (*angles on the circumference in the same segment are equal*)

EXAMPLE 2

What is the value of x?

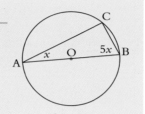

SOLUTION

Angle ACB $= 90°$ (*angle in a semicircle*)

$x + 5x = 90°$ (*angles in a triangle add up to 180°*)

$6x = 90°$

$x = \dfrac{90}{6} = 15°$

Since angle ACB is 90°, $x + 5x$ must sum to
$180° - 90° = 90°$.

EXAMPLE 3

What is the value of y?

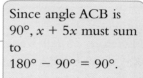

SOLUTION

$y = 240 \div 2 = 120°$ (*angle at the centre is twice the angle at the circumference*)

Exercise 31.2

Calculate the missing angles below where O is the centre of each circle.

1
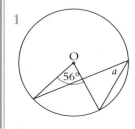

2
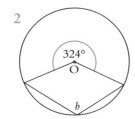

3
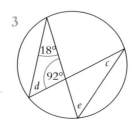

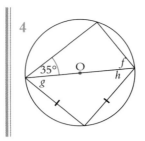

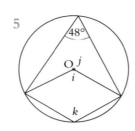

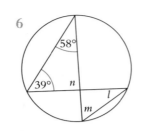

Cyclic quadrilaterals

A cyclic quadrilateral is a quadrilateral whose vertices all lie on the circumference of a circle.

THEOREM

Opposite angles of a cyclic quadrilateral add up to 180°.

PROOF

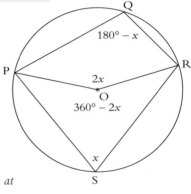

Let PSR = x

Then   obtuse angle POR = $2x$ *(angle at centre is twice angle at circumference)*

Therefore   reflex angle POR = $(360° - 2x)$

(angles at a point add to 360°)

Angle PQR = $\frac{1}{2}$ reflex POR = $\frac{1}{2}(360° - 2x) = 180° - x$

(angle at centre is twice angle at circumference)

So   angle PSR + angle PQR = $x + 180° - x = 180°$.

EXAMPLE 4

Find the values of x and y.

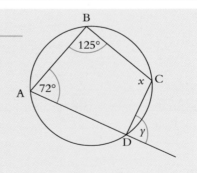

SOLUTION

$x = 180° - 72° = 108°$ *(opposite angles in a cyclic quadrilateral add up to 180°)*

$y = 125°$ *(angle ADC adjacent to $y = 180° - 125°$*
= 55°
and so $y = 180° - 55° = 125°$)

> ADC and ABC are opposite angles in the cyclic quadrilateral.

Exercise 31.3

Calculate the missing angles below where O is the centre of the circle.

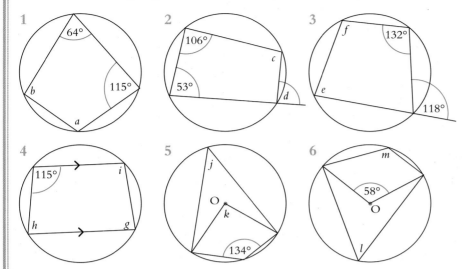

Tangent properties of a circle

There are some further properties of circles relating to tangents.

- The angle between a tangent and a radius at the point of contact is 90°.
- Both tangents drawn from the same point to a circle are equal in length.

Using the tangent properties above, and the theorems we have already looked at, we can work out angles.

EXAMPLE 5

CD is a tangent to the circle centre O.

The angle BCD = 35°.

Find the following angles:

   a OCB b COB c CAB

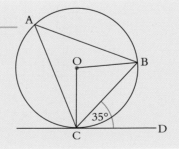

SOLUTION

a   Angle OCD = 90°   *(angle between the tangent and the radius = 90°)*

    So   angle OCB = 90° − BCD
         Angle OCB = 90° − 35° = 55°

b The triangle OBC is isosceles   *(two radii are equal)*
    So   angle OBC = angle OCB = 55°
         55° + 55° =110°
         Angle COB = 180° − 110° = 70° *(angles in a triangle add to 180°)*

c   Angle CAB = $\frac{1}{2}$ angle COB   *(angle at centre is twice the angle at the circumference)*

      Angle CAB = $\frac{70}{2}$ = 35°

Tangent kite

A tangent kite is the special quadrilateral formed by the two radii and the two tangents. The following example uses circle properties to find angles in a tangent kite.

PT and QT are tangents to a circle centre O. The angle PRQ is 28°.

Find angle PTQ.

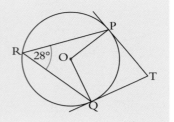

SOLUTION

Angle POQ = 56°	(angle at centre is twice the angle at the circumference)
Angle OPT = angle OQT = 90°	(angle between the tangent and the radius)
56° + 90° + 90° = 236° ←	
So angle PTQ = 360° − 236° = 124°	(angles in a quadrilateral add up to 360°)

This is the sum of the angles we now know in the quadrilateral POQT.

Exercise 31.4

Calculate the missing angles below where O is the centre of each circle.

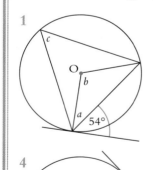

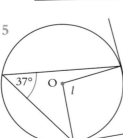
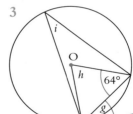
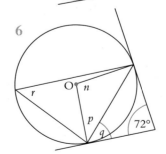

Alternate segment theorem

We now know that the angle between a tangent and a radius is always 90°. The angle between a tangent and a chord will not be 90° – and it will be different for every different chord. However, there is a special relationship between the angles which is explained in the following alternate segment theorem.

THEOREM

The angle between a tangent and a chord equals the angle on the circumference in the exact opposite segment

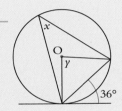

PROOF

Let   angle TAB = x

Then   angle BAO = $90 - x$ *(angle between the tangent and the radius)*

But the triangle AOB is isosceles and so angle ABO = $90° - x$

      Angle AOB = $180° - (90° - x) - (90° - x)$

               $= 180° - 90° + x - 90° + x = 2x$

               (angles in a triangle add to 180°)

So   angle ACB = $\frac{1}{2}(2x) = x$ *(angle at centre is twice the angle at the circumference)*

So   angle TAB = angle ACB

EXAMPLE 7

Find the values of angles x and y.

SOLUTION

    $x = 36°$ *(alternate segment theorem)*

    $y = 36° \times 2 = 72°$ *(angle at centre is twice the angle at the circumference)*

Exercise 31.5

Calculate the missing angles below. Where shown, O is the centre of the circle.

1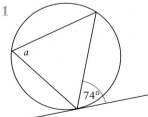

2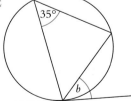

3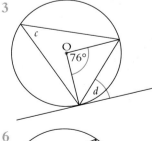

4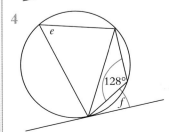

5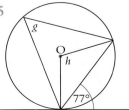

6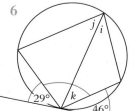

The exercise that follows brings together all the circle properties in this chapter.

Exercise 31.6

In questions 1 to 5, find the missing angles. C is the centre of the circle.

1

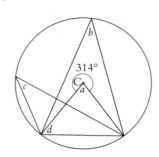

2 Find the following angles:
   a AED   b CAD   c DAB
   d ABC   e ADB

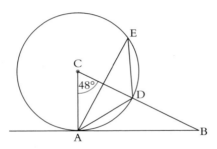

3 Angle DEA = 14°. Find the following angles:
   a DCA   b CAD   c DAB
   d ADB   e ABD

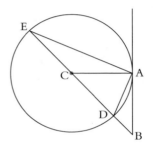

4 Angle CDA = 73°. Find the following angles:
   a CAD   b ACD   c AED
   d DAB   e DBA

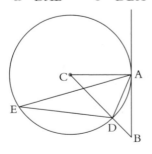

5 Angle DAB = 21°. Find the following angles:
   a CAD   b ACD   c AED
   d ADB   e ABD

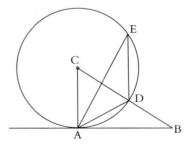

For questions 6 and 7 use the diagram on the right.

6 Angle ADB = 71°. Find the following angles:
   a ACB   b CAB   c BAT
   d ATB   e CBD

7 Angle ACB = 116°. Find the following angles:
   a ADB   b CAB   c BAT
   d ATB   e CBD

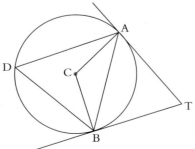

For questions 8 and 9 use the diagram on the right.

8 Angle EAB = 54°. Find the following angles:
   a BDE   b ECB   c CEB

9 Angle BDE = 132°. Find the following angles:
   a EAB   b ECB   c CEB

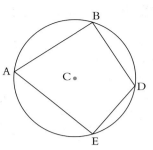

For questions 10 and 11 use the diagram on the right.

10 Angle TAB = 24°. Find the following angles:
   a ADB   b ACB   c CAB

11 Angle ADB = 32°. Find the following angles:
   a TAB   b ACB   c CAB

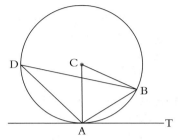

You should now:

- know the names of the different parts of a circle
- know the properties of circles
- be able to prove the properties of circles
- be able to use the properties of circles to calculate angles.

Summary exercise 31

1 Draw a circle centre O radius 4 cm. On your circle identify:
   a a sector   b a segment   c a tangent.

For questions 2 to 8, calculate the missing angles where O is the centre of each circle.

2
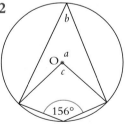

3
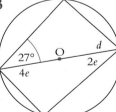

4
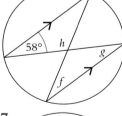

5
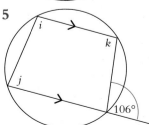

6
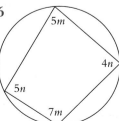

7
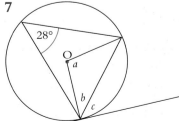

8

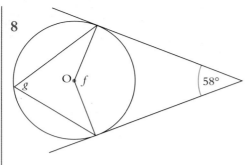

9 Prove that angle TRS = angle QPS.

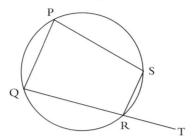

Examination questions

These questions are from examination papers where you may not use a calculator.

1 By considering the angles at the centre, O, of the circle, prove that opposite angles in a cyclic quadrilateral add up to 180°.

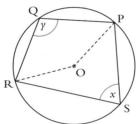

2 TA and TB are tangents to a circle centre O. Angle BAT = 53°.
   Find:

   a angle OAB

   b angle ATB.

   Angle SBC = 59°

   c Find angle CAO.

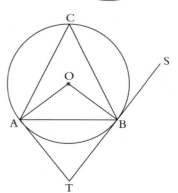

CHAPTER 32

Polygons

This chapter is about:

- calculating angles in regular polygons
- calculating angles in irregular polygons

You should already know:

- how to find angles on straight lines
- the sum of the angles in a triangle
- how to remove brackets in algebraic equations
- how to solve algebraic equations
- how to share within a ratio.

Polygons

A polygon can be defined as a closed shape with straight sides. The names of the more common polygons with five or more sides are shown below.

Number of sides	5	6	7	8	9	10
Name	pentagon	hexagon	heptagon	octagon	nonagon	decagon

Interior and exterior angles

An **interior angle** is each angle *inside* the shape (usually referred to as the angle).

An **exterior angle** is each angle *outside* the shape (between each side of the shape produced and the next side).

Some important facts about polygons are listed below.

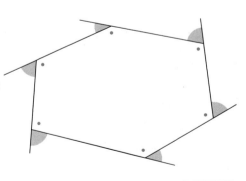

- The sum of an interior angle and an exterior angle at a vertex is 180° (because they make a straight line).

interior angle + exterior angle = 180°

> Exterior angles are shown in blue. Interior angles are shown in red.

- The sum of *all* the exterior angles in a polygon is 360° (because if we start at one vertex we go through a complete turn as we add up all the exterior angles).
- The sum of all the angles (or interior angles) in an *n*-sided polygon is 180° × (*n* − 2).

The last point can be proved easily, as shown here.

PROOF

Consider a pentagon.

We can split the pentagon up into three triangles using two of its sides to form the first triangle (i.e. 5 − 2 = 3). The sum of the angles in a triangle is 180° and so the sum of all the angles in the pentagon is 180° × 3.

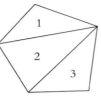

5 sides → 3 triangles

Now consider an *n*-sided polygon. We can split it up into (*n* − 2) triangles using two of its sides to form the first triangle. The sum of the angles in a triangle is 180° and so the sum of all the angles in the pentagon is 180° × (*n* − 2).

We can use these facts to work out the sizes of the angles in polygons.

EXAMPLE 1

Find the missing angles.

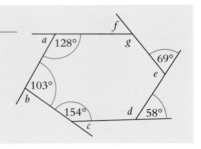

SOLUTION

$$a + 128° = 180° \qquad \text{(angles on a straight line)}$$

So $a = 180 − 128 = 52°$

Similarly $b = 180 − 103 = 77°$

$c = 180 − 154 = 26°$

$d = 180 − 58 = 122°$

$e = 180 − 69 = 111°$

To find *f* and *g* we must find *f* first. The sum of the exterior angles is 360°. So, adding up all the other exterior angles, we have:

$$52 + 77 + 26 + 58 + 69 = 282°$$

$$f = 360 − 282 = 78°$$

So $g = 180 − 78 = 102°$

Exercise 32.1

Find the missing angles in each of the polygons.

1

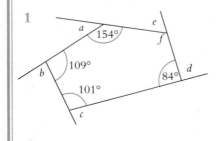

2

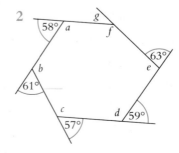

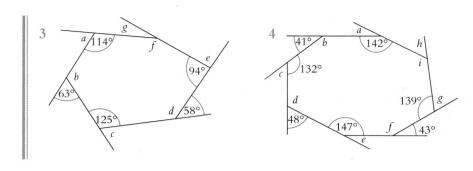

Regular polygons

A regular polygon has all sides equal and all angles equal.

This means we can find the number of sides, because we know that the sum of the exterior angles is always 360°. We can also find the size of each angle, because they are all equal.

EXAMPLE 2

Find the size of each angle in a regular 15-sided polygon.

SOLUTION

Sum of the exterior angles = 360°

So each exterior angle = $\frac{360}{15}$ = 24°

Sum of an exterior and an interior angle = 180°

So each angle = 180 − 24 = 156°

> Always work out the exterior angle first.

> Remember that the angle in a polygon is the *interior* angle.

EXAMPLE 3

Each angle in a regular polygon is 140°. How many sides has it?

SOLUTION

Each interior angle is 140°.

Each exterior angle = 180 − 140 = 40°

Number of sides = $\frac{360}{40}$ = 9

Exercise 32.2

1 Give the names of the polygons with:
   a   5 sides   b   8 sides   c   9 sides.

2 Find the size of each angle in a regular hexagon.

3 Find the size of each angle in a regular octagon.

4 Find the size of each angle in a regular 20–sided polygon.

5 Find the size of each angle in a regular 24–sided polygon.

6 Each angle in a regular polygon is 108°. How many sides has it?

7   Each angle in a regular polygon is 144°. How many sides has it?

8   Explain why a regular polygon cannot have angles of 166°.

9   A square and two identical regular polygons fit together exactly at a point. How many sides has the regular polygon?

10 Explain why a square, a hexagon and an octagon can't fit together at a point.

Irregular polygons

The sum of all the angles (or interior angles) in an n-sided polygon is $180° \times (n - 2)$. Because the angles in an irregular polygon are not equal, we can't work out the sizes of the angles just from the number of sides.

The examples below show how you can use extra information about the angles, together with the facts about angle sums, to find the angles and number of sides in irregular polygons.

EXAMPLE 4

Find the sum of the angles in an irregular 11-sided polygon.

SOLUTION

Sum of the angles = $180° \times (11 - 2) = 180° \times 9 = 1620°$ Substitute the number of sides into the equation.

EXAMPLE 5

The sum of the angles in a polygon is 7380°. How many sides has it?

SOLUTION

$180° \times (n - 2) = 7380$

$n - 2 = \frac{7380}{180} = 41$

$n = 41 + 2 = 43$

The polygon has 43 sides.

EXAMPLE 6

The angles in a pentagon are 113°, 127°, $2x$, $3x$ and $5x$. Find x.

SOLUTION

Sum of angles = $180° \times (5 - 2) = 180° \times 3 = 540°$ Find the sum of the angles in a pentagon and then set up an equation.

So $113° + 127° + 2x + 3x + 5x = 540°$

$240° + 10x = 540°$

$10x = 540 - 240 = 300°$

$x = 30°$

Exercise 32.3

1   Find the sum of the angles in a 7-sided polygon.

2   Find the sum of the angles in a 19-sided polygon.

3   The sum of the angles in a polygon is 1980°. How many sides has it?

4   The sum of the angles in a polygon is 6480°. How many sides has it?

5   The angles in a pentagon are 107°, 111°, 114°, 126° and x. Find x.

6   The angles in a hexagon are 115°, 119°, 122°, 126°, 127° and x. Find x.

7   The angles in a pentagon are $2x$, $4x$, $5x$, $9x$ and 80°. Find x.

8   Five of the angles in an octagon are 127°, 135°, 138°, 146° and 156°. The rest of the angles are equal. Find the size of each of the other angles.

9   The angles in a pentagon are in the ratio 1:2:2:2:3. Find the size of each angle.

10   The angles in a hexagon are $2x - 15$, $5x$, $4x + 27$, 118°, 126° and 134°. Find x.

Finding angles within polygons

We can use the facts about polygons to find angles within these shapes.

EXAMPLE 7

ABCDEFGH is a regular octagon whose diagonals cross at O. Find the sizes of:

   a   angle AOB   b   angle OAB.

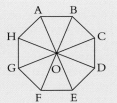

SOLUTION

   a   Because it is a regular octagon, the eight angles at O are equal. They add up to 360° (as they fit together at a point).
So angle AOB = $\frac{360}{8}$ = 45°

   b   Triangle AOB is isosceles because the diagonals of a regular octagon are equal.
180 − 45 = 135°
Angle OAB = 135 ÷ 2 = 67.5°

Exercise 32.4

1   PQRST is a regular pentagon. O is the centre of the pentagon. Find:
   a   angle POQ
   b   angle OPQ
   c   angle QRS.

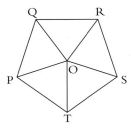

2   ABCDEF is a regular hexagon whose diagonals cross at O.

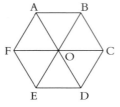

a   Find angle FOE.
b   Find angle FEO.
c   What type of triangle is FOE?
d   Find angle CBA.

3   Each angle at the centre of a regular polygon is 30°. How many sides has it?

4   Each angle at the centre of a regular polygon is 18°. How many sides has it?

5   Find the angle at the centre of a regular 15-sided polygon.

6   Find the angle at the centre of a regular 25-sided polygon.

7   A regular polygon has *n* sides. Find, in terms of *n*, the size of:
a   each angle at the centre   b   each exterior angle
c   each angle.

8   The angle at the centre of a regular polygon is *x*. Find, in terms of *x*, the size of:
a   each angle   b   each exterior angle.

You should now:

- know the names of polygons with 5, 6, 7, 8, 9 and 10 sides
- be able to differentiate between interior and exterior angles
- know that all the sides are equal in a regular polygon and that all the angles are equal
- know that an interior angle and an exterior angle at a vertex add up to 180°
- know that the sum of the exterior angles is 360°
- know that the sum of the angles of a *n*-sided polygon is 180° × (*n* − 2)
- be able to find the number of sides in a regular polygon if you know each angle
- be able to find the angles in a regular polygon if you know the number of sides
- be able to find the angle at the centre of a regular polygon
- be able to find the missing angles in an irregular polygon.

Summary exercise 32

1   Find the missing angles.

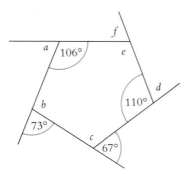

2   Find the missing angles.

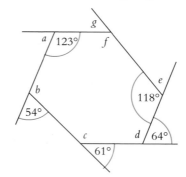

3 Give the name of:
  a a 6-sided polygon   **b** a 7-sided polygon   **c** a 10-sided polygon.

4 Find the size of each angle in a regular pentagon.

5 Find the size of each angle in a regular nonagon.

6 Find the size of each angle in a regular 15-sided polygon.

7 Each angle in a regular polygon is 135°. How many sides has it?

8 Each angle in a regular polygon is 170°. How many sides has it?

9 Each angle in a regular polygon is 162°. How many sides has it?

10 Explain why a regular polygon cannot have angles of 130°.

11 A square, a regular hexagon and another regular polygon fit together exactly at a point. How many sides has the regular polygon?

12 Find the sum of the angles in a 17-sided polygon.

13 Find the sum of the angles in a 20-sided polygon.

14 The sum of the angles in a polygon is 4500°. How many sides has it?

15 The sum of the angles in a polygon is 7380°. How many sides has it?

16 The angles in a hexagon are 117°, 121°, 124°, 126°, 129° and x. Find x.

17 The angles in a pentagon are $2x$, $3x$, $4x$, 117° and 135°. Find x.

18 The angles in an octagon are in the ratio $2:3:3:4:5:6:8:9$. Find the size of:
  a the smallest angle   **b** the largest angle.

19 The angles in a pentagon are $x + 16$, $x - 24$, $2x + 15$, $2x - 10$, and $3x + 12$. Find the size of each angle.

20 ABCDE is a regular pentagon. O is the centre of the pentagon. DC is produced (extended) to F.
  Find:
  a angle AOD
  b angle FCO.

21 Each angle at the centre of a regular polygon is 22.5°. How many sides has it?

22 Find the angle at the centre of a regular 50-sided polygon.

Use 'Topic Tracker' at www.ccea.org.uk to find more exam questions.

Examination questions

These questions are from examination papers where you may not use a calculator.

1 Each exterior angle of a regular polygon is 40°. How many sides has it?

2 **a** Calculate the interior angle of a regular pentagon.
  b Two identical regular pentagons are joined together as shown.

  A regular polygon fits against the pentagons as shown. How many sides has the regular polygon?

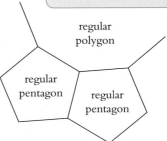

regular polygon

regular pentagon   regular pentagon

CHAPTER 33

Pythagoras and trigonometry

This chapter is about:

- understanding and applying Pythagoras' theorem in right-angled triangles in 2D
- understanding and applying trigonometry in right-angled triangles in 2D
- understanding and applying Pythagoras' theorem in right-angled triangles in 3D
- understanding and applying trigonometry in right-angled triangles in 3D.

You should already know:

- how to square numbers
- how to find the square root of numbers
- how to solve equations
- what is meant by a bearing
- what is meant by an angle of elevation and an angle of depression
- the properties of a cuboid and a regular pyramid.

Pythagoras' theorem

Consider the right-angled triangle on the right.

The side opposite the right angle in a right-angled triangle is called the **hypotenuse**. In this triangle the side AC is the hypotenuse.

A famous Greek mathematician named Pythagoras of Samos, who lived around 580–500 BC, discovered a relationship between the sides of **every right-angled triangle**.

This relationship is known as Pythagoras' theorem and it states that:

> In any right-angled triangle, the area of the square whose side is the hypotenuse is equal to the sum of the areas of the squares on the other two sides.

Pythagoras' theorem is more usefully remembered as follows:

> The square on the hypotenuse is equal to the sum of the squares on the other two sides.

This can be shown to be true for the triangle ABC above.

$AC^2 = 10^2 = 100$ $AB^2 = 8^2 = 64$ and $BC^2 = 6^2 = 36$

$100 = 64 + 36$

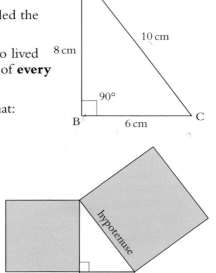

We can use Pythagoras' theorem to find the squares of the length of any side in a right-angled triangle in terms of the squares of the lengths of the other two sides.

For any triangle ABC we can write:

$$b^2 = a^2 + c^2$$
or $$a^2 = b^2 - c^2$$
or $$c^2 = b^2 - a^2$$

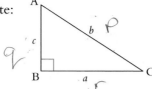

Exercise 33.1

Look at each of the diagrams and then write expressions for the squares of each of the lengths of the sides in turn.

1 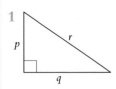   2   3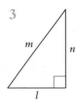

Calculating the hypotenuse given the other two sides

EXAMPLE 1

ABC is a right-angled triangle.
AB = 15 cm, BC = 36 cm and angle ABC = 90°.
Calculate the length of AC.

> Draw a sketch.
> Identify the hypotenuse.
> Use Pythagoras' theorem.

SOLUTION

We can use Pythagoras' theorem to calculate AC because this triangle is right-angled. If we call AC 'x' then we can write the equation:

$$x^2 = 36^2 + 15^2$$
$$x^2 = 1521$$
$$x = \sqrt{1521} = 39$$
$$AC = 39 \text{ cm}$$

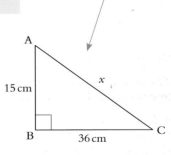

EXAMPLE 2

ABC is a right-angled triangle.
AB = 3.9 cm, BC = 5.7 cm and angle ABC = 90°.
Calculate the length of AC. Give your answer to 3 significant figures.

SOLUTION

If we call AC 'x' then we can write the equation:

$$x^2 = 5.7^2 + 3.9^2$$
$$x^2 = 47.7$$
$$x = \sqrt{47.7} = 6.906$$
$$x = 6.91 \text{ cm (to 3 s.f.).}$$

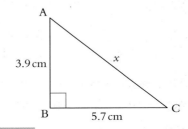

Exercise 33.2

Give your answers to 3 significant figures where appropriate.

1. ABC is a right-angled triangle. AB = 1.5 cm, BC = 2 cm and angle ABC = 90°. Calculate the length of AC.

2. ABC is a right-angled triangle. AB = 24.6 cm, BC = 32.8 cm and angle ABC = 90°. Calculate the length of AC.

3. ABC is a right-angled triangle. AB = 7.5 cm, BC = 18 cm and angle ABC = 90°. Calculate the length of AC.

4. ABC is a right-angled triangle. AB = 5 cm, BC = 7 cm and angle ABC = 90°. Calculate the length of AC.

5. ABC is a right-angled triangle. AB = 4.6 cm, BC = 7.2 cm and angle ABC = 90°. Calculate the length of AC.

6. ABC is a right-angled triangle. AB = 6.4 cm, BC = 12 cm and angle ABC = 90°. Calculate the length of AC.

Calculating one of the other two sides when the hypotenuse is given

EXAMPLE 3

Calculate the length AB in the right-angled triangle shown. Give the answer correct to 3 significant figures.

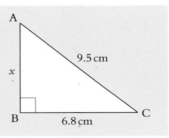

SOLUTION

Let AB = x cm

Then $x^2 = 9.5^2 - 6.8^2$

$x^2 = 44.01$

$x = \sqrt{44.01}$

$x = 6.634$

$x = 6.63$ cm (to 3 s.f.).

> Label the missing side x in the diagram.

EXAMPLE 4

Calculate the length BC in the right-angled triangle in the diagram.

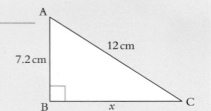

SOLUTION

Let $BC = x\,\text{cm}$ ⟵

Again, label the missing side x in the diagram.

Then $x^2 = 12^2 - 7.2^2$

$\qquad x^2 = 92.16$

$\qquad x = \sqrt{92.16}$

$\qquad x = 9.6\,\text{cm}$

Exercise 33.3

Give your answers to 3 significant figures where appropriate.

1 PQR is a right-angled triangle. PR = 2.5 cm, QR = 2 cm, angle PQR = 90°. Calculate the length of PQ.

2 PQR is a right-angled triangle. PR = 8.4 cm, PQ = 6.26 cm, angle PQR = 90°. Calculate the length of QR.

3 PQR is a right-angled triangle. PR = 26 cm, QR = 24 cm, angle PQR = 90°. Calculate the length of PQ.

4 PQR is a right-angled triangle. PR = 24 cm, PQ = 17.9 cm, angle PQR = 90°. Calculate the length of QR.

5 PQR is a right-angled triangle. PR = 3.8 cm, QR = 2.4 cm, angle PQR = 90°. Calculate the length of PQ.

6 PQR is a right-angled triangle. PR = 15.6 cm, PQ = 6 cm, angle PQR = 90°. Calculate the length of QR.

Solving problems using Pythagoras' theorem

We can use Pythagoras' theorem to solve problems involving the lengths of the sides of right-angled triangles.

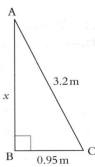

EXAMPLE 5

A ladder 3.2 m long is placed 0.95 m away from a wall.
How high up the wall will it reach ?

SOLUTION

Call the ladder AC.
Then x is the height that the ladder can reach up the wall.

Then $x^2 = 3.2^2 - 0.95^2$

$\qquad x^2 = 9.3375$

$\qquad x = \sqrt{9.3375}$

$\qquad x = 3.055\ldots$

$\qquad x = 3.06\,\text{m}$ (to 3 s.f.).

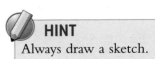

HINT
Always draw a sketch.

EXAMPLE 6

The diagonals of a rhombus are 31.2 cm and 13 cm long.
Calculate the length of each side in this rhombus.

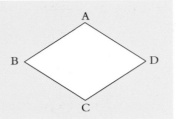

SOLUTION

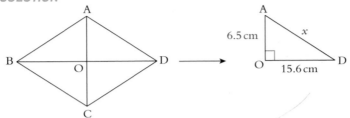

> Add the diagonals to the rhombus.
> Then draw out a right-angled triangle.

AC = 13 cm and BD = 31.2 cm, so AO = 6.5 cm and OD = 15.6 cm.

Then $x^2 = 6.5^2 + 15.6^2$

$x^2 = 285.61$

$x = \sqrt{285.61}$

$x = 16.9$

The length of the side is 16.9 cm.

Exercise 33.4

Give your answers to 3 significant figures where appropriate.

1   The length and breadth of a rectangle are 7.4 cm and 2.3 cm. Calculate the length of the diagonal.

2   A boat leaves a harbour H and travels 12 km due north and then 28.8 km due west before arriving at a port P. Calculate the distance HP.

3   A ladder is 2.4 m long. It is placed on horizontal ground and leans against a vertical wall. It reaches a height of 2.24 m up the wall. Calculate the distance from the foot of the ladder to the wall.

4   The diagonals of a rhombus are 18 cm and 8 cm long. Calculate the length of each side in this rhombus.

5   The length of each diagonal in a square is 4 cm. Calculate the length of each side in this square.

6   PQRS is a trapezium. Angles P and Q are right angles. PQ = 5 cm, PS = 4 cm and QR = 1.5 cm. Calculate the length of SR.

Trigonometry

There is a special relationship between the sides in a right-angled triangle and the angles that are not the right angle. Here we look at three of these relationships.

To define the relationships, we must first label the sides in relation to the angle x as follows:

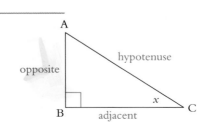

We can then define three different trigonometric functions.

$$\mathbf{S}\text{ine} \quad = \frac{\text{Opposite}}{\text{Hypotenuse}} \quad \text{(written as } \sin x\text{)}$$

$$\mathbf{C}\text{osine} \quad = \frac{\text{Adjacent}}{\text{Hypotenuse}} \quad \text{(written as } \cos x\text{)}$$

$$\mathbf{T}\text{angent} \quad = \frac{\text{Opposite}}{\text{Adjacent}} \quad \text{(written as } \tan x\text{)}$$

We can remember these using the mnemonic **SOHCAHTOA**.

> The first recorded use of trigonometry came from the Hellenistic mathematician Hipparchus around 150 BC, who compiled a trigonometric table using the sine for solving triangles.

Finding trig ratios

The following example shows how to find the trig ratios for different right-angled triangles.

EXAMPLE 7

Find the trig ratio connecting the given sides and angle x in the following diagrams.

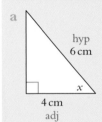
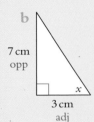
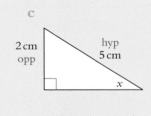

SOLUTION

a $\cos x = \dfrac{4}{6}$ b $\tan x = \dfrac{7}{3}$ c $\sin x = \dfrac{2}{5}$

> Label the sides.
> Use the mnemonic SOHCAHTOA to help you remember which ratio is which.

Exercise 33.5

Find the trig ratio connecting the given sides and angle x in the following diagrams.

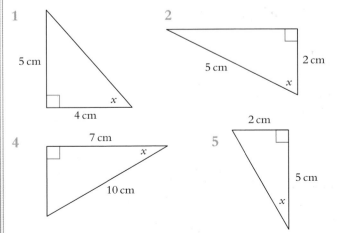
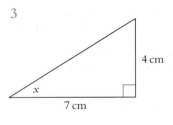

Using trigonometry to find missing sides

Once you know how to identify the ratios, you can use them to find missing sides in a right-angled triangle. The following examples show how this is done.

HINTS
Label the side you know and the side you are trying to find.
Choose the appropriate trig ratio.
Make sure your calculator is in **degree** mode.

EXAMPLE 8

Calculate the missing side in this right-angled triangle.

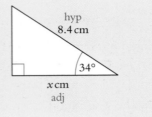

hyp
8.4 cm

34°

x cm
adj

SOLUTION

$$\cos 34° = \frac{x}{8.4}$$
$$x = 8.4\cos 34° = 6.963\ldots$$
$$x = 6.96 \text{ cm (to 3 s.f.)}.$$

Cross–multiply to separate the variable from the numbers. Always write the trig term last.

EXAMPLE 9

Find the length x in this triangle.

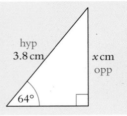

hyp
3.8 cm

x cm
opp

64°

SOLUTION

$$\sin 64° = \frac{x}{3.8}$$
$$x = 3.8\sin 64° = 3.415\ldots$$
$$x = 3.42 \text{ cm (to 3 s.f.)}.$$

EXAMPLE 10

Find the length x in this triangle.

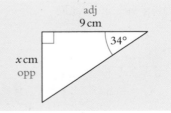

adj
9 cm

34°

x cm
opp

SOLUTION

$$\tan 34° = \frac{x}{9}$$
$$x = 9\tan 34° = 6.070\ldots$$
$$x = 6.07 \text{ cm (to 3 s.f.)}.$$

Exercise 33.6

Calculate the value of x in each triangle.
Give your answers to 3 significant figures.

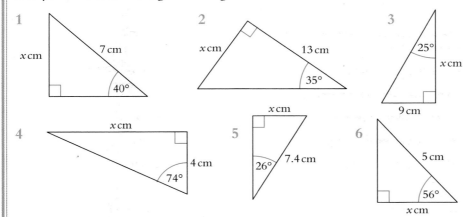

You can also use the trig ratios to find the length of the hypotenuse if you
know an angle and another side.

EXAMPLE 11

Calculate the length of x in this right-angled triangle.

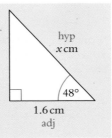

SOLUTION

$$\cos 48° = \frac{1.6}{x}$$

We need to use the cosine, but x is on the bottom of the ratio.

$$x \cos 48° = 1.6$$

Multiply both sides by x.

$$x = \frac{1.6}{\cos 48°} = 2.391\ldots$$

$$x = 2.39 \text{ cm (to 3 s.f.)}.$$

EXAMPLE 12

Find the length x in this right-angled
triangle.

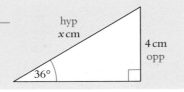

SOLUTION

$$\sin 36° = \frac{4}{x}$$

$$x \sin 36° = 4$$

$$x = \frac{4}{\sin 36°} = 6.805\ldots$$

$$x = 6.81 \text{ cm (to 3 s.f.)}.$$

EXAMPLE 13

Find the length x in this right–angled triangle.

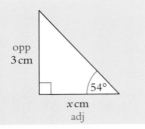

SOLUTION

$$\tan 54° = \frac{3}{x}$$

$$x\tan 54° = 3$$

$$x = \frac{3}{\tan 54°} = 2.179\ldots$$

$$x = 2.18\,\text{cm} \text{ (to 3 s.f.)}.$$

Exercise 33.7

Calculate the values of x in each of the right-angled triangles below.
Give your answers to 3 significant figures.

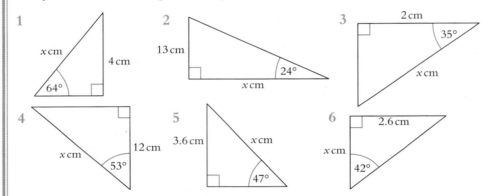

Using trigonometry to find missing angles

If you know two of the sides of a right-angled triangle, you can use these
to form one of the trig ratios for an angle. Then you can use this to find
the value of the angle.

For example, if you know the hypotenuse and the opposite side, you
can work out the sine of the angle. Then you can use the inverse sine
function on your calculator to work out the missing angle. This may be
labelled $\sin^{-1}$. On some calculators you press the SHIFT key to access this
function, while on others you use the 2nd F key.

EXAMPLE 14

Calculate the missing angle in this right-
angled triangle.

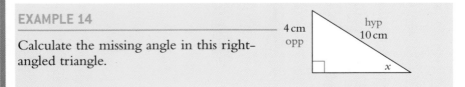

SOLUTION

$$\sin x = \frac{4}{10} = 0.4$$

$$x = 23.57\ldots$$

$$x = 23.6° \text{ (to 3 s.f.)}.$$

> We do **not** cross-multiply this time because the variable is already separated from the numbers.

> To find x press the 2nd F or SHIFT key on your calculator followed by sin (which gives the function $\sin^{-1}$).

EXAMPLE 15

What is the value of angle x?

SOLUTION

$$\cos x = \frac{3}{11}$$

$$x = 74.17\ldots$$

$$x = 74.2° \text{ (to 3 s.f.)}.$$

EXAMPLE 16

Find angle x in this right-angled triangle.

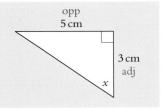

SOLUTION

$$\tan x = \frac{5}{3}$$

$$x = 59.03\ldots$$

$$x = 59.0° \text{ (to 3 s.f.)}.$$

Exercise 33.8

For questions **1** to **6** calculate the value of x in each of the right-angled triangles shown. Give your answers to 3 significant figures.

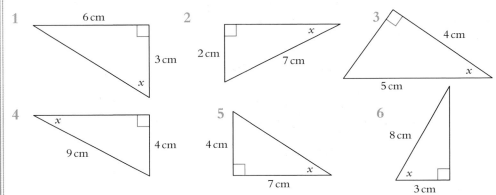

Give your answers to questions 7 to 16 to 3 significant figures.

7   PQR is a right-angled triangle in which angle PQR is 90°.
    Angle PRQ = 24°. PR = 2.6 cm. Calculate RQ.

8   PQR is a right-angled triangle in which angle PQR is 90°.
    Angle PRQ = 53°. RQ = 2.4 cm. Calculate PR.

9   PQR is a right-angled triangle in which angle PQR is 90°.
    PQ = 7 cm and RQ = 2 cm. Calculate angle PRQ.

10 PQR is a right-angled triangle in which angle PQR is 90°.
    Angle PRQ = 36°. PR = 5.4 cm. Calculate PQ.

11 PQR is a right-angled triangle in which angle PQR is 90°.
    Angle PRQ = 62°. RQ = 5.8 cm. Calculate PQ.

12 PQR is a right-angled triangle in which angle PQR is 90°.
    PR = 10 cm and RQ = 8 cm. Calculate angle PRQ.

13 PQR is a right-angled triangle in which angle PQR is 90°.
    Angle PRQ = 48°. PQ = 1.7 cm. Calculate PR.

14 PQR is a right-angled triangle in which angle PQR is 90°.
    Angle PRQ = 29°. PQ = 3.6 cm. Calculate RQ.

15 PQR is a right-angled triangle in which angle PQR is 90°.
    PR = 9 cm and PQ = 3 cm. Calculate angle PRQ.

16 PQR is a right-angled triangle in which angle PQR is 90.
    Angle PRQ = 32°. PR = 9.2 cm. Calculate PQ.

Solving problems using trig ratios

Problems involving distances, directions and angles of elevation or
depression can often be solved using trig ratios. Some examples of the
sorts of problems you will meet are given below.

EXAMPLE 17

A ship sailed 12.4 nautical miles on a bearing of 205° from
harbour H. How far **a** west and **b** south is it now from H?

Remember

Bearings are measured in
degrees from the **north** in
a **clockwise** direction.

SOLUTION

$205° - 180° = 25°$

So the angle in the right-angled
triangle is 25°.

a $\sin 25° = \dfrac{x}{12.4}$

$x = 12.4 \sin 25° = 5.240\ldots$

The ship is now
5.24 nautical miles west of H.

b   There are three different methods
to calculate y. It does not matter
which method you use.

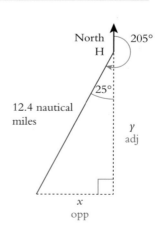

HINTS

Draw a sketch.
Draw the appropriate
right-angled triangle.
Call the unknowns x
and y.

Method 1

$$\cos 25° = \frac{y}{12.4}$$
$$y = 12.4 \cos 25° = 11.2 \text{ nautical miles}$$

Method 2

$$\tan 25° = \frac{5.24}{y}$$
$$y \tan 25° = 5.24$$
$$y = \frac{5.24}{\tan 25°} = 11.2$$

This uses the value for x you worked out in part **a**.

Method 3

$$y^2 = 12.4^2 - 5.24^2 = 126$$
$$y = \sqrt{126} = 11.2 \text{ nautical miles}$$

This uses Pythagoras' theorem using the value of x you worked out in part **a**.

The ship is now 11.2 nautical miles south of H.

EXAMPLE 18

The angle of elevation of the top of a statue ST from a point O 18 m horizontally from T is 24°. Calculate:

   a   the height of the statue ST   **b**   the length of OS.

Give your answers to an appropriate degree of accuracy.

Remember that the angle of elevation (and the angle of depression) is measured from the horizontal.

SOLUTION

   a $\tan 24° = \frac{x}{18}$

         $x = 18 \tan 24° = 8.01...$

         The statue is 8.0 m high.

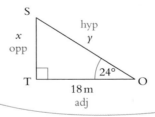

It would be appropriate to give the answers correct to 2 significant figures as that is the degree of accuracy of the numbers given in the question.

   b   There are three different methods to calculate y.
It does not matter which method you use.

Method 1

$$\cos 24° = \frac{18}{y}$$
$$y \cos 24° = 18$$
$$y = \frac{18}{\cos 24°} = 19.7 \text{ m}$$

Method 2

$$\sin 24° = \frac{8.0}{y}$$
$$y \sin 24° = 8.0$$
$$y = \frac{8.0}{\sin 24°} = 19.7 \text{ m}$$

Method 3

$$y^2 = 8.0^2 + 18^2 = 388$$
$$y = \sqrt{388} = 19.7 \text{ m}$$

The length OS is 20 m to 2 significant figures.

All three methods will give 20 to 2 significant figures.

Exercise 33.9

Give all your answers to an appropriate degree of accuracy.

1 A ship sailed 8 km due south from harbour H and then sailed 11 km due east, arriving at port P. Calculate:
   a   the distance HP   b   the bearing of P from H.

2 ABCD is a rectangle. The diagonal BD = 9.7 cm. Angle BDC = 25°. Calculate:
   a   BC   b   CD.

3 PQRS is a rhombus. The diagonal PR = 11.2 cm. Angle RSP = 78°. Calculate:
   a   PS   b   QS.

4 A girl stands at a point C on top of a vertical cliff which is 850 m high. She sees a boat at a point B at an angle of depression of 35° from C. Calculate:
   a   the horizontal distance between B and the foot of the cliff
   b   BC.

5 A boat sails 204 m on a bearing of 144° from a buoy at B to a buoy at C.
   a   How far east is it from B?   b   How far south is it from B?

6 A boy at X sees a tower YZ which is 24 m tall. X is 30 m horizontally from Z, the base of the tower.
   a   Calculate the angle of elevation of Y from X.
       The boy then walks towards the tower to a point T where the angle of elevation of Y from T is 52°.
   b   Calculate the distance XT.

Three-dimensional questions using Pythagoras and/or trigonometry

When solving any 3D question you should always

* draw out the appropriate 2D shape (preferably a right-angled triangle or a rectangle)
* choose whether to use Pythagoras (sides only) or trigonometry (sides/angle).

In many 3D problems you need to find the angle between a line and a plane. Draw a right-angled triangle by

* identifying the point **not** on the plane
* drawing a perpendicular from this point to the plane
* completing the right-angled triangle.

EXAMPLE 19

ABCDEFGH is a cuboid.
AB = 8 cm, BC = 2.5 cm
and CG = 4 cm. Calculate:

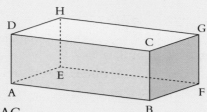

a   AC   b   AG

c   the angle between AC and AG.

SOLUTION

a   The appropriate 2D shape is the rectangle ABCD.

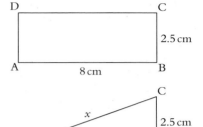

We can then select the right-angled triangle ABC.

$$x^2 = 8^2 + 2.5^2 = 70.25$$

$$x = \sqrt{70.25} = 8.38...$$

AC is 8.38 cm.

b   The appropriate 2D shape is the right-angled triangle ACG.

$$y^2 = 8.38...^2 + 4^2 = 70.25 + 16 = 86.25$$

$$y = \sqrt{86.25} = 9.287...$$

$$y = 9.29 \text{ cm}$$

AG is 9.29 cm.

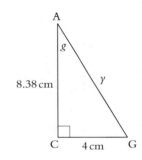

c $\tan g = \dfrac{4}{8.38}$

$$g = 25.5°$$

The angle between AC and AG is 25.5° (to 3 s.f.).

EXAMPLE 20

TQ is a vertical tower standing
at corner Q of a rectangular
yard PQRS. SR = 7.5 m and
PS = 2.5 m. The angle of
elevation of T from P is 26°.
Calculate:

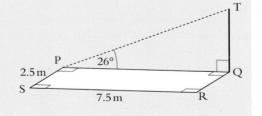

a   TQ   b   the angle of elevation of T from R

c   SQ   d   the angle of elevation of T from S.

SOLUTION

a $\tan 26° = \dfrac{h}{7.5}$ ⟵   PQ = SR = 7.5 m

$$h = 7.5 \tan 26° = 3.66 \text{ m}$$

So TQ is 3.66 m.

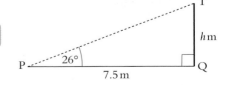

b $\tan x = \dfrac{3.66}{2.5}$

$x = 55.7°$

The angle of elevation of T from R is 55.7°.

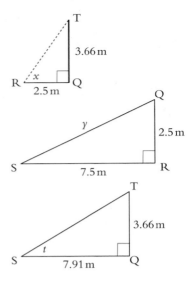

c $y^2 = 7.5^2 + 2.5^2 = 62.5$

$y = \sqrt{62.5} = 7.91\,\text{m}$

SQ = 7.91 m.

d $\tan t = \dfrac{3.66}{7.91}$

$t = 24.8°$

The angle of elevation of T from S is 24.8°.

Exercise 33.10

Give your answers to 3 significant figures where appropriate.

1 ABCDEFGH is a cuboid. AB = 4.6 cm, BC = 3.8 cm and CG = 1.9 cm. Calculate:
   a AC   **b** AG
   c the angle between AC and AG.

2 ABCDEFGH is a cuboid. AC = 65 cm and AB = 60 cm. The angle between AC and AG is 20°. Calculate:
   a BC   **b** CG   **c** AG.

3 ABCDEFGH is a cuboid. AG = 4.6 cm, GC = 2.8 cm and BC = 3.4 cm. Calculate:
   a the angle between AG and GC
   b AC   **c** AB.

4 TQ is a vertical statue where Q is on the ground. From a point A, 18.4 m from Q, the angle of elevation of T is 30°.
   Calculate:
   a TQ   **b** AT.

   B is another point on the ground, such that BQ = 12.5 m.
   c Calculate the angle of elevation of T from B.
   d Angle ABQ = 90°. Calculate AB.

5 VABCD is a regular rectangular pyramid. V is vertically above O, the centre of ABCD. VO = 18 cm. The angle between VA and ABCD is 25°. BC = 15 cm. Calculate:
   a VA   **b** AC   **c** AB.

6 VABCD is a regular rectangular pyramid. V is vertically above O, the centre of ABCD. VO = 5.8 cm. The angle between VA and ABCD is 17°. BC = 20.6 cm. Calculate:

   a VA   b AC   c AB.

7 VABCD is a regular rectangular pyramid. V is vertically above O, the centre of ABCD. AB = 56 cm, BC = 41 cm and VO = 28 cm. Calculate:

   a AO   b the angle between AV and ABCD

   c AV

8 VABCD is a regular rectangular pyramid. V is vertically above O, the centre of ABCD. VA = 19.5 cm. The angle between VA and ABCD is 54°. AB = 9.4 cm. Calculate:

   a VO   b AC   c BC.

You should now:

- know Pythagoras' theorem
- be able to use Pythagoras' theorem to find missing sides
- be able to apply Pythagoras' theorem to solving problems in 2D
- know the three trig ratios: sin, cos and tan
- be able to use trigonometry to find missing sides
- be able to use trigonometry to find missing angles
- be able to apply trigonometry to solving problems in 2D
- be able to apply Pythagoras' theorem and trigonometry to solving problems in 3D.

Summary exercise 33

Give your answers to an appropriate degree of accuracy where relevant.

1 ABC is a right-angled triangle. AB = 2.4 cm and BC = 3.2 cm. Angle ABC = 90°.
Calculate the length of AC.

2 PQR is a right-angled triangle. PR = 83.2 cm and QR = 32 cm. Angle PQR = 90°.
Calculate the length of PQ.

3 A boat leaves a harbour H and travels 44.8 km due west and then 153.6 km due south before arriving at a port P.
Calculate the distance HP.

4 A ladder is 1.9 m long.
It is placed on horizontal ground and leans against a vertical wall. It reaches a height of 1.65 m up the wall.
Calculate the distance from the foot of the ladder to the wall.

5 PQR is a right-angled triangle in which angle PQR is 90°.
Angle PRQ is 73°. RQ = 8.5 cm.
Calculate PQ.

6 PQR is a right-angled triangle in which angle PQR is 90°. PQ = 3.6 cm and RP = 4 cm. Calculate angle PRQ.

7 PQRS is a rhombus. The diagonal PR = 42 cm. Angle RSP is 36°. Calculate:
   a PS   **b** QS.

8 A boat sails 5.6 km on a bearing of 310° from a buoy at B to a buoy at C.
Calculate how far **a** west and **b** north it is from B.

9 ABCDEFGH is a cuboid. AC = 43 cm and AB = 25.8 cm. The angle between AC and AG is 37°. Calculate:
   a BC   **b** CG   **c** AG

10 VABCD is a regular rectangular pyramid. V is vertically above O, the centre of ABCD. VO = 7 cm. The angle between VA and ABCD is 24°. BC = 15 cm. Calculate:
   a VA   **b** AC   **c** AB

Examination questions

Question **1** is from an examination paper where you may not use a calculator.

Use 'Topic Tracker' at www.ccea.org.uk to find more exam questions.

1 Find the area of the triangle. (Give your answer in m².)

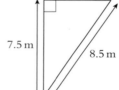

Questions **2** and **3** are from examination papers where you may use a calculator.

2 a A ramp AB, 4 metres long, is attached to the back of a lorry at a point, B, 1.2 metres above the ground.

   i Calculate the distance AC.

   ii Calculate the angle that the ramp makes with the ground.

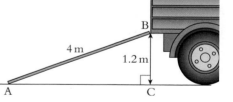

  b The ramp is moved and placed against a vertical fence. The ramp makes an angle of 65° with the fence.

   Calculate the height, above the ground, of the top of the ramp.

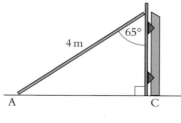

3 ABCDH is a square based pyramid. AB = 9.6 cm. The vertical height, OH, of the pyramid is 14.5 cm. Find the angle that the sloping edge HB makes with the base ABCD of the pyramid.

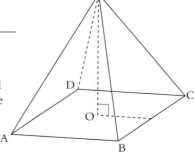

CHAPTER 34

Similarity

This chapter is about:

- proving that shapes are similar
- calculating lengths of sides in similar shapes
- using the ratio of lengths to work out the ratio of areas and the ratio of volumes
- calculating areas and volumes of similar shapes.

You should already know:

- how to simplify ratios
- the sum of the angles in triangles and quadrilaterals
- the angle properties associated with parallel and intersecting lines
- how to solve equations by cross-multiplying
- how to use Pythagoras' theorem.

Similar figures

Similar figures have the same shape but are of different sizes. Two shapes are similar when:

- **all** the angles in one shape equal **all** the corresponding angles in the other shape

and

- all the **corresponding** sides in each shape are in the same ratio.

EXAMPLE 1

Prove that quadrilaterals ABCD and PQRS are similar.

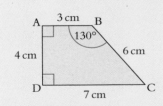
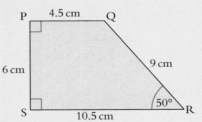

SOLUTION

We need to find angles C and Q first. Remember that the sum of the angles in a quadrilateral is 360°.

| ABCD | A + D = 180° | so | C = 180 − 130 = 50° |
| PQRS | P + S = 180° | so | Q = 180 − 50 = 130° |

To prove similarity we have to prove that corresponding angles are equal and that corresponding sides are in the same ratio.

Angles

A = P = 90°

D = S = 90°

B = Q = 130°

C = R = 50°

Sides

$\dfrac{PS}{AD} = \dfrac{6}{4} = 1.5$

$\dfrac{PQ}{AB} = \dfrac{4.5}{3} = 1.5$

$\dfrac{QR}{BC} = \dfrac{9}{6} = 1.5$

$\dfrac{SR}{DC} = \dfrac{10.5}{7} = 1.5$

Therefore ABCD and PQRS are similar.

Exercise 34.1

For questions 1 to 7, prove that the pairs of shapes are similar.

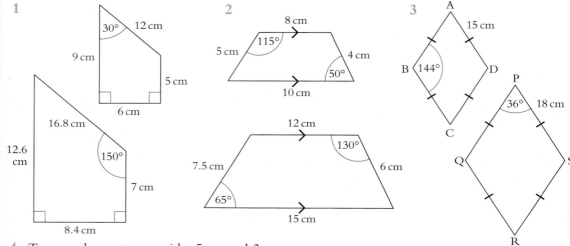

4 Two regular pentagons sides 5 cm and 3 cm.

5 Rectangle R_1 with length and breadth 8 cm and 5 cm and rectangle R_2 with length and breadth 20 cm and 12.5 cm.

6 Two squares with sides 4 cm and 5.6 cm.

7 Kite ABCD where AB = BC = 4 cm, AD = CD = 14 cm, angle B = 85° and angle D = 35° and kite PQRS, where PQ = QR = 3.2 cm, PS = RS = 11.2 cm, angle P = 120° and angle S = 35°.

8 Explain why any two circles must be similar.

9 a Explain why any two squares must be similar.
  b Explain why two rectangles will not always be similar.

Enlargements

When any shape is enlarged, then the original shape and its enlargement will be similar.

Let us consider enlarging a rectangle length 4 cm and breadth 3 cm by a scale factor of 2.5.

The enlargement will be a larger rectangle length 4×2.5 ($= 10$ cm) and breadth 3×2.5 ($= 7.5$ cm).

These two rectangles will be similar because:

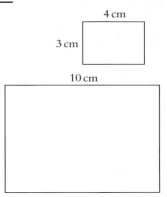

- all the angles in one rectangle equal all the corresponding angles in the other rectangle (all 90°)

and

- all the corresponding sides in both rectangles are in the same ratio (i.e. 2.5 : 1).

EXAMPLE 2

A regular pentagon with sides of length 6 cm is enlarged by a scale factor of $\frac{1}{2}$. Show that the original pentagon and its enlargement are similar.

SOLUTION

The enlargement will be a smaller regular pentagon with sides of length 6×0.5 ($= 3$ cm).

These two regular pentagons will be similar because:

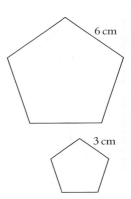

- all the angles in one regular pentagon equal all the corresponding angles in the other regular pentagon (all 108°)

and

- all the corresponding sides in each regular pentagon are in the same ratio (i.e. 1 : 2).

Finding sides in similar shapes

We can use the rules of similarity to find missing sides in similar shapes.

EXAMPLE 3

The trapezia ABCD and PQRS are similar.
Find a PS and b DC.

Because the trapezia are similar we know that the corresponding sides are in the same ratio. We can then set up an equation by matching up the corresponding sides.

$$\frac{AB}{PQ} = \frac{AD}{PS} = \frac{DC}{SR}$$

We know sides AB and PQ, so we know the ratio $\dfrac{AB}{PQ} = \dfrac{8}{12.8}$.

Let PS = x and DC = y.

a   Substituting for x in the ratio that contains PS, we have:

$$\frac{8}{12.8} = \frac{5.4}{x}$$

$$8x = 5.4 \times 12.8$$

$$x = \frac{5.4 \times 12.8}{8} = 8.64\,\text{cm}$$

> Remember that we must cross–multiply to solve this equation.

b   Substituting for y in the ratio that contains DC, we have:

$$\frac{8}{12.8} = \frac{y}{21.12}$$

$$12.8y = 8 \times 21.12$$

$$y = \frac{8 \times 21.12}{12.8} = 13.2\,\text{cm}$$

Exercise 34.2

Calculate the missing lengths in the following pairs of similar shapes.

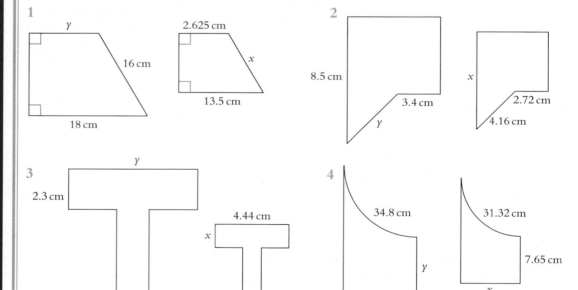

1

y

16 cm

18 cm

2.625 cm

x

13.5 cm

2

8.5 cm

3.4 cm

y

x

2.72 cm

4.16 cm

3

y

2.3 cm

1.6 cm

4.44 cm

x

0.96 cm

4

34.8 cm

y

24 cm

31.32 cm

7.65 cm

x

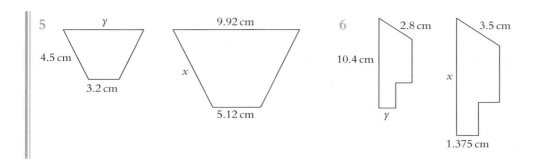

5

y

4.5 cm

3.2 cm

9.92 cm

x

5.12 cm

6

2.8 cm

10.4 cm

y

3.5 cm

x

1.375 cm

Similar triangles

Similar triangles are special shapes. To prove that triangles are similar we need **only** prove that either:

- **all** the angles in each triangle are equal

or

- **all** the corresponding sides in each triangle are in the same ratio.

Equal angles

Triangles ABC and PQR illustrate how to find if two triangles are similar when you are given the angles.

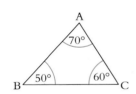

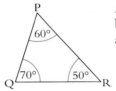

ABC and PQR are similar because A = Q and B = R and C = P.

> If you rotate triangle PQR so Q is at the top, the angles correspond to those in triangle ABC.

Sides in the same ratio

Triangles DEF and GHI illustrate how to find if two triangles are similar when you are given the lengths of the sides.

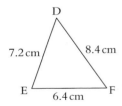

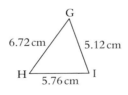

We must match up the sides in the correct order of lengths (i.e. the largest sides in each triangle first, and so on). Then write the ratio of the sides.

$\dfrac{DF}{GH}$ (largest) $\dfrac{ED}{HI}$ $\dfrac{EF}{IG}$ (smallest)

Substituting the values from the question:

$\dfrac{DF}{GH} = \dfrac{8.4}{6.72} = 1.25$ and $\dfrac{ED}{HI} = \dfrac{7.2}{5.76} = 1.25$ and $\dfrac{EF}{IG} = \dfrac{6.4}{5.12} = 1.25$

> The ratios of corresponding sides are all equal.

Therefore EDF and IHG are similar.
The pairs of equal angles are E, I and F, G and D, H.

Exercise 34.3

Prove that the triangles in each question are similar. State the ratios of the corresponding sides or the pairs of equal angles as appropriate.

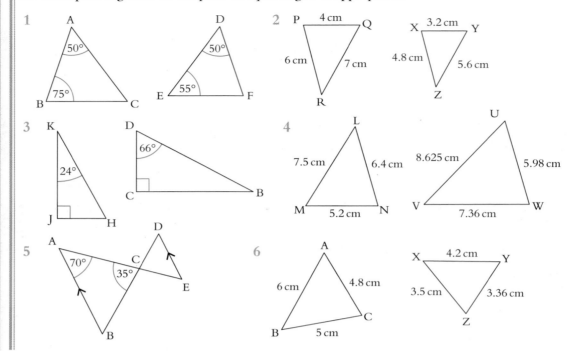

Now we will look at some more complex cases, where you need to use other facts about geometry or Pythagoras' theorem to find a missing side.

EXAMPLE 4

AB is parallel to DE in the diagram.
Prove that the triangles ABC and DEC are similar.

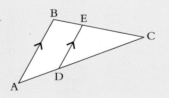

SOLUTION

Look at each triangle and identify equal angles.

> Give reasons why the angles are equal.

Triangle ABC		Triangle DEC	
A	=	D	*(corresponding angles are equal)*
B	=	E	*(corresponding angles are equal)*
C	=	C	*(common angles)*

Three angles are equal and so the triangles are similar.

EXAMPLE 5

Prove that the triangles PQR and SPR are similar.

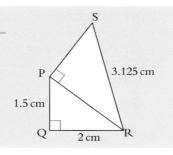

SOLUTION

To prove these triangles are similar we must find the missing sides (using Pythagoras' theorem) and then calculate the ratio of corresponding sides.

Triangle PQR $\quad$ $PR^2 = 2^2 + 1.5^2 = 6.25$

$\quad\quad\quad\quad\quad\quad$ $PR = 2.5\,cm$

Triangle SPR $\quad$ $PS^2 = 3.125^2 - 2.5^2 = 3.515625$

$\quad\quad\quad\quad\quad\quad$ $PS = 1.875\,cm$

Then $\dfrac{SR}{PR} = \dfrac{3.125}{2.5} = 1.25$ and $\dfrac{PR}{QR} = \dfrac{2.5}{2} = 1.25$

and $\dfrac{PS}{PQ} = \dfrac{1.875}{1.5} = 1.25.$

Therefore the triangles are similar.

> Use the value of PR to calculate the missing side in triangle SPR.

Exercise 34.4

1 Prove triangle PTS is similar to triangle PRQ.

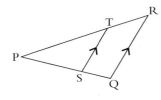

2 Prove that the triangles POQ and YOX are similar.

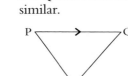

3 ABCD is a rectangle whose diagonals cross at O. Prove that the triangles AOD and BOC are similar.

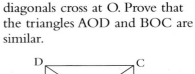

4 Prove that the triangles COD and FOE are similar.

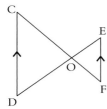

5 Prove that the triangles ABC and ACD are similar.

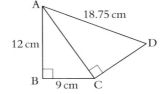

6 Prove that the triangles ABC and BDC are similar.

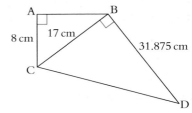

Finding sides in similar triangles

We can use the properties of similar triangles to find missing sides.

EXAMPLE 6

a Prove that ABC and EDC are similar triangles.

b Hence calculate

  i CE, ii CB and iii DB.

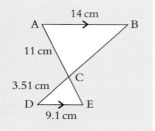

SOLUTION

a We must first identify which angles are equal.

  Triangle ABC   Triangle EDC

A	=	E	(alternate angles are equal)
B	=	D	(alternate angles are equal)
C	=	C	(vertically opposite angles are equal)

  The triangles have three angles the same, so they are similar.

b Since the triangles are similar, by matching the angles and sides we know that

  $$\frac{AB}{ED} = \frac{AC}{EC} = \frac{BC}{DC}$$

  Let EC = x and BC = y

  i Substituting the values from the question in the ratio that contains EC:

  $$\frac{14}{9.1} = \frac{11}{x}$$

  > We know AB and ED, so this tells us the ratio between the other pairs of corresponding sides.

  $$14x = 11 \times 9.1$$

  $$x = \frac{11 \times 9.1}{14} = 7.15 \text{ cm}$$

  So CE = 7.15 cm

  > EC = CE

  ii Now use the ratio that contains BC (which equals CB).

  $$\frac{14}{9.1} = \frac{y}{3.51}$$

  $$9.1y = 14 \times 3.51$$

  $$y = \frac{14 \times 3.51}{9.1} = 5.4 \text{ cm}$$

  So CB = 5.4 cm

  iii DB = DC + CB

  > Use the value for CB calculated in part b ii.

  $$= 3.51 + 5.4$$

  $$= 8.91 \text{ cm}$$

Exercise 34.5

1 Calculate:
a PT and **b** QR.

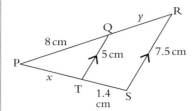

2 Calculate:
a XO and **b** YZ.

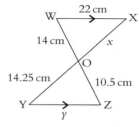

3 Calculate:
a FH and **b** EF.

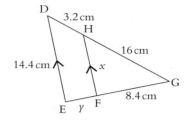

4 Calculate:
a ON and **b** OW.

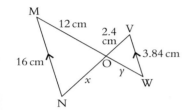

5 Calculate:
a BC and **b** BD.

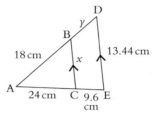

6 Calculate:
a PO and **b** SR.

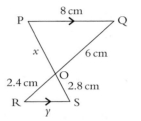

7 ABC is a triangle in which AB = 7.2 cm and BC = 5.6 cm.
The angles A and C equal 58° and 72°.

EFD is a triangle in which DE = 6.72 cm and EF = 10.08 cm.
The angles E and F equal 58° and 50°.
a Prove that triangles ABC and EFD are similar.
b Hence calculate: **i** AC **ii** DF.

8 GHI is a triangle in which GH = 6.5 cm and HI = 5.2 cm.
The angles H and I equal 40° and 86°.

LJK is a triangle in which JK = 4.368 cm and KL = 4.872 cm.
The angles K and L equal 86° and 54°.
a Prove that triangles GHI and LJK are similar.
b Hence calculate: **i** GI **ii** JL.

Surface areas and volumes of similar 3D shapes

If two 3D shapes X and Y are similar, then the ratio of the lengths of
their corresponding sides will be the same.

Let us define this ratio as $a:b$.

Then the ratio of the surface areas of the two similar shapes will be $a^2:b^2$
and the ratio of their volumes will be $a^3:b^3$.

Therefore if we know the ratio of the lengths, then we:

• square the numbers to get the ratio of the areas
• cube the numbers to get the ratio of the volumes.

If we know the ratio of the areas, then we:

• take the square root of the numbers to get the ratio of the lengths.

If we know the ratio of the volumes, then we:

- take the cube root of the numbers to get the ratio of the lengths.

Consider two similar cubes A and B of sides 2 cm and 3 cm.

Then the ratio of the side lengths of A and B is 2 : 3.

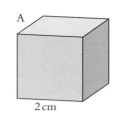

Surface area

A   the area of each side is $2 \times 2 = 4\,cm^2$
       the total surface area is $6 \times 4 = 24\,cm^2$

B   the area of each side is $3 \times 3 = 9\,cm^2$
       the total surface area is $6 \times 9 = 54\,cm^2$

The ratio of the surface areas is then $24 : 54$ which cancels to $4 : 9 = 2^2 : 3^2$.

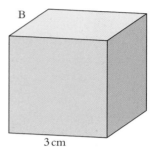

Volume

A   volume $= 2 \times 2 \times 2 = 8\,cm^3$
B   volume $= 3 \times 3 \times 3 = 27\,cm^3$

The ratio of the volumes is then $8 : 27$ which equals $2^3 : 3^3$.

EXAMPLE 7

Two solids P and Q are similar. The height of P is 3.6 cm and the height of Q is 6.48 cm. The base area of P is $24\,cm^2$. The volume of Q is $8398.08\,cm^3$. Calculate:

   a   the ratio of the lengths of P and Q in its simplest form

   b   the base area of Q

   c   the volume of P.

SOLUTION

   a   The ratio of the heights of P and Q is $3.6 : 6.48$.
       So this is the ratio of the lengths.

       Remember that a ratio in its simplest form must have only whole numbers, so we have to multiply by 100.

$$3.6 : 6.48 = 360 : 648$$
$$= 180 : 324 \quad \textit{(dividing by 2)}$$
$$= 90 : 162 \quad \textit{(dividing by 2)}$$
$$= 45 : 81 \quad \textit{(dividing by 2)}$$
$$= 5 : 9 \quad \textit{(dividing by 9)}$$

       The ratio of the lengths in simplest form is $5 : 9$.

   b   The ratio of lengths $= 5 : 9$, so the ratio of areas $= 5^2 : 9^2 = 25 : 81$.
       Let the base area of Q be A. Then we have:
$$\frac{25}{24} = \frac{81}{A}$$
$$A = \frac{24 \times 81}{25} = 77.76\,cm^2$$
       The base area of Q is $77.76\,cm^2$.

   c   The ratio of lengths $= 5 : 9$, so the ratio of volumes $= 5^3 : 9^3 = 125 : 729$.

Let the volume of P be V. Then we have:

$$\frac{125}{V} = \frac{729}{8398.08}$$

$729V = 125 \times 8398.08$

$V = 1440\,\text{cm}^3$

The volume of P is $1440\,\text{cm}^3$.

EXAMPLE 8

The capacities of two similar cylinders C and D are $216\,\text{cm}^3$ and $512\,\text{cm}^3$.

a The radius of C is 10.2 cm. Find the radius of D.

b The curved surface area of D is $115.2\,\text{cm}^2$. Find the curved surface area of C.

SOLUTION

a To find the radius we must first work out the ratio of the lengths.

> Remember that capacity is a measure of volume.

Ratio of volumes $= 216:512$

We must cancel this as far as possible.

$\quad 216:512 = 108:256$ *(dividing by 2)*

$\qquad\qquad = 54:128$ *(dividing by 2)*

$\qquad\qquad = 27:64$ *(dividing by 2)*

We then take the cube roots of these numbers to get the ratio of the lengths.

So the ratio of the lengths $= 3:4$

Let the radius of D be x. Then:

$$\frac{3}{10.2} = \frac{4}{x}$$

$3x = 4 \times 10.2$

$x = \dfrac{4 \times 10.2}{3} = 13.6\,\text{cm}$

b Ratio of lengths $= 3:4$, so the ratio of areas $= 3^2:4^2 = 9:16$.

Let the area of C be A. Then:

$$\frac{9}{A} = \frac{16}{115.2}$$

$16A = 9 \times 115.2$

$A = \dfrac{9 \times 115.2}{16} = 64.8\,\text{cm}^2$

Exercise 34.6

1 Two solids X and Y are similar. The lengths of X and Y are 12 cm and 30 cm.
Find the ratio of a their lengths and b their volumes.

2 Two solids V and W are similar. The base areas of V and W are $270\,\text{cm}^2$ and $1470\,\text{cm}^2$.
Find the ratio of a their lengths and b their volumes.

3 Two solids Q and R are similar. The volumes of Q and R are 512 cm³ and 1728 cm³.
Find the ratio of **a** their lengths and **b** their areas.

4 Two solids J and K are similar. The lengths of J and K are 28.8 cm and 76.8 cm.
Find the ratio of **a** their lengths and **b** their volumes.

5 Two solids X and Y are similar. The base areas of X and Y are 140.4 cm² and 62.4 cm².
Find the ratio of **a** their lengths and **b** their volumes.

6 The heights of two similar solids A and B are 8 cm and 12 cm.
  a The base area of A is 58 cm². Find the base area of B.
  b The volume of B is 256.5 cm³. Find the volume of A.

7 The volumes of two similar solids A and B are 205.2 cm³ and 60.8 cm³.
  a The length of A is 20.4 cm. Find the length of B.
  b The base area of B is 198 cm². Find the base area of A.

8 The base areas of two similar solids A and B are 112 cm² and 700 cm².
  a The length of A is 7.6 cm. Find the length of B.
  b The volume of B is 17 500 cm³. Find the volume of A.

9 The heights of two similar solids A and B are 65 cm and 39 cm.
  a The base area of A is 240 cm². Find the base area of B.
  b The volume of B is 864 cm³. Find the volume of A.

10 The volumes of two similar solids A and B are 216 cm³ and 64 cm³.
  a The length of A is 11.1 cm. Find the length of B.
  b The base area of B is 90 cm². Find the base area of A.

You should now:

- know the definition of similar figures
- be able to calculate missing lengths in similar figures
- be able to prove that two triangles are similar
- know the relationship between the ratios of length, area and volume of similar figures
- be able to use the relationship between the ratios of length, area and volume of similar figures to calculate lengths, areas and volumes.

Summary exercise 34

1 Prove that the following shapes are similar.

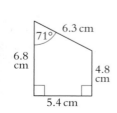

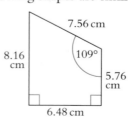

2 Find the missing lengths in the following pair of similar shapes.

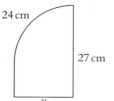

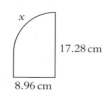

3 Prove that the triangles below are similar. List the ratios of the corresponding sides.

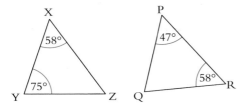

4 Prove that the triangles below are similar. List pairs of equal angles.

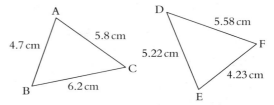

5 Prove that triangle LMN is similar to triangle QPN. List the ratios of the corresponding sides.

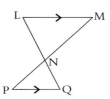

6 **a** Prove that triangle ABC is similar to triangle ZXY.
   b Find **i** AC and **ii** XY.

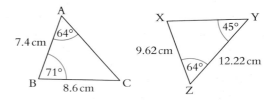

7 **a** Prove that triangle DHE is similar to triangle DGF.
   b Find **i** HG and **ii** DE.

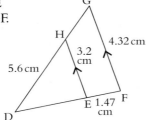

8 Two solids X and Y are similar. The lengths of X and Y are 102 cm and 136 cm.
   a The base area of X is 846 cm². Find the base area of Y.
   b The volume of Y is 16640 cm³. Find the volume of X.

9 The base areas of two similar solids A and B are 425 cm² and 68 cm².
   a The length of A is 3.8 cm. Find the length of B.
   b The volume of B is 3087 cm³. Find the volume of A.

10 The ratio of the volumes of two similar solids is 216 : 343.
   Find the ratio of **a** their lengths and **b** their areas.

Examination question

Use 'Topic Tracker' at www.ccea.org.uk to find more exam questions.

This question is from an examination paper where you may not use a calculator.

1 AB and CD are two parallel lines. AD and BC meet at X. The triangles AXB and DXC are similar.
   AB = 6.0 cm, CD = 10.0 cm, BX = 2.9 cm and DX = 8.5 cm.
   Calculate the length of AX.

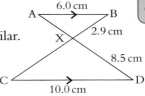

CHAPTER 35

Trig rules

> **This chapter is about:**
> - extending the rules of trigonometry to angles of any size
> - learning, using and knowing when to use the sine rule and cosine rule
> - calculating the areas of triangles that are not right-angled.
>
> **You should already know:**
> - how to use trigonometry in a right-angled triangle.

In Chapter 33 you used the rules of trigonometry with right-angled triangles to find angles and lengths of sides. When the triangle is **not** right-angled you must use one of two special rules – the **sine rule** or the **cosine rule**.

The sine rule

Triangle ABC is a general triangle with no right angle.
The sine rule states that for **every** triangle ABC:

$$\frac{a}{\sin A} = \frac{b}{\sin B} = \frac{c}{\sin C}$$

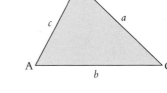

We use the sine rule when we know **two** angles and **one** side, and want to find a second side, or when we know **two** sides and **one** angle, and want to find another angle.

Finding a missing side using the sine rule

Examples 1 and 2 show how to use the sine rule to find a missing side.

EXAMPLE 1

Find the missing side x.

SOLUTION

$$\frac{x}{\sin 38°} = \frac{8}{\sin 64°}$$

$$x \sin 64° = 8 \sin 38° \quad \longleftarrow \quad \boxed{\text{Cross–multiply.}}$$

$$x = \frac{8\sin 38°}{\sin 64°}$$

$$x = 5.48\,\text{cm}$$

ABC is a triangle in which AC = 5.3 cm. Angle BAC = 77° and angle ACB = 42°. Calculate AB.

SOLUTION

Draw the triangle.

We must **first** find the size of angle ABC (the angle **opposite** AC).

77 + 42 = 119°

Angle ABC = 180 − 119 = 61°
The missing side AB is c in the sine formula.

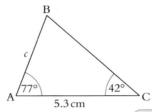

Subtract from 180° to find the missing angle.

So $\quad \dfrac{c}{\sin 42°} = \dfrac{5.3}{\sin 61°}$

$$c\sin 61° = 5.3\sin 42°$$

$$c = \frac{5.3\sin 42°}{\sin 61°}$$

$$c = 4.05\,\text{cm}$$

Side AB = 4.1 cm (to 1 decimal place).

Exercise 35.1

1   Calculate x.

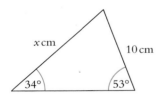

2   Calculate x.

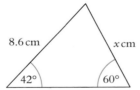

3   ABC is a triangle in which AC = 2.4 cm. Angle BAC = 102° and angle ACB = 54°. Calculate AB.

4   ABC is a triangle in which BC = 5 cm. Angle BAC = 113° and angle ABC = 41°. Calculate AC.

5   ABC is a triangle in which BC = 6.4 cm. Angle BAC = 50° and angle ABC = 71°. Calculate AB.

6   ABC is a triangle in which AB = 5.4 cm. Angle ABC = 34° and angle ACB = 56°. Calculate AC.

Finding a missing angle using the sine rule

Examples 3 and 4 show how to use the sine rule to find a missing angle, given one angle and two sides.

EXAMPLE 3

Find the missing angle x.

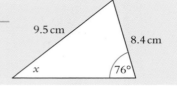

SOLUTION

$$\frac{\sin x}{8.4} = \frac{\sin 76°}{9.5}$$

$$9.5 \sin x = 8.4 \sin 76°$$

$$\sin x = \frac{8.4 \sin 76°}{9.5}$$

$$x = 59.1°$$

EXAMPLE 4

ABC is a triangle in which AB = 6.4 cm and BC = 7.2 cm.
Angle BAC = 124°.
Calculate angle ABC.

SOLUTION

Draw the triangle.

We must **first** find the size of angle ACB (the angle **opposite** AB).

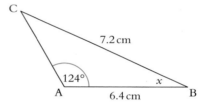

$$\frac{\sin C}{6.4} = \frac{\sin 124°}{7.2}$$

$$7.2 \sin C = 6.4 \sin 124°$$

$$\sin C = \frac{6.4 \sin 124°}{7.2}$$

$$C = 47.5°$$

$$47.5 + 124 = 171.5°$$ ◄ — Find the sum of the two angles BAC and ACB.

$$180 - 171.5 = 8.5°$$ ◄ — Subtract from 180° to find the missing angle.

Angle ABC = 8.5°

Exercise 35.2

1   Calculate x.

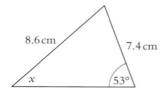

2   Calculate x.

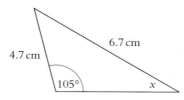

3   ABC is a triangle in which AB = 5.3 cm and BC = 4.2 cm.
Angle ACB = 62°. Calculate angle ABC.

4   ABC is a triangle in which AC = 6.8 cm and BC = 5.1 cm.
    Angle ABC = 73°. Calculate angle BAC.

5   ABC is a triangle in which AB = 4.3 cm and AC = 2.8 cm.
    Angle ACB = 54°. Calculate angle BAC.

6   ABC is a triangle in which AB = 7 cm and AC = 9 cm.
    Angle ABC = 84°. Calculate angle ACB.

The cosine rule

The cosine rule for **every** triangle states: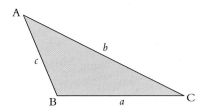

	$a^2 = b^2 + c^2 - 2bc\cos A$
or	$b^2 = a^2 + c^2 - 2ac\cos B$
or	$c^2 = a^2 + b^2 - 2ab\cos C$

We use the cosine rule when there are **three**
sides and **one** angle including the unknown.

You must always start the equation with the side **opposite** the angle
which you know or want to find.

Finding a missing side using the cosine rule

Examples 5 and 6 show how to use the cosine rule to find missing sides.

EXAMPLE 5

Find the missing side x in the triangle.

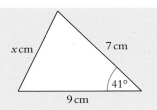

SOLUTION

$$x^2 = 7^2 + 9^2 - 2 \times 7 \times 9 \cos 41°$$
$$x^2 = 34.9$$
$$x = 5.91 \text{ cm}$$

EXAMPLE 6

PQR is a triangle in which the angle QPR = 114°, PQ = 6.4 cm and
PR = 5.8 cm.
Calculate QR.

SOLUTION

Draw the triangle.

$$QR^2 = 6.4^2 + 5.8^2 - 2 \times 6.4 \times 5.8 \cos 114°$$
$$QR^2 = 104.8$$
$$QR = 10.2 \text{ cm}$$

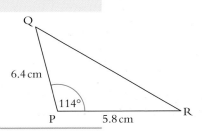

Exercise 35.3

1 Calculate x.

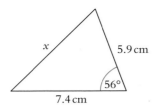

2 Calculate x.

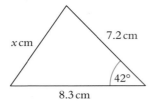

3 PQR is a triangle in which the angle QPR = 43°, PQ = 6.4 cm and PR = 7.2 cm. Calculate QR.

4 PQR is a triangle in which the angle PQR = 124°, PQ = 6.2 cm and QR = 5.3 cm. Calculate PR.

5 PQR is a triangle in which the angle QPR = 98°, PQ = 4.7 cm and PR = 5.3 cm. Calculate QR.

6 PQR is a triangle in which the angle QRP = 52°, QR = 3.6 cm and PR = 5.4 cm. Calculate PQ.

Finding a missing angle using the cosine rule

Examples 7 and 8 show how to use the cosine rule to find missing angles, when you know three sides.

EXAMPLE 7

Find the missing angle x.

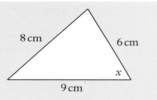

SOLUTION

$$8^2 = 6^2 + 9^2 - 2 \times 6 \times 9 \cos x$$
$$64 = 117 - 108 \cos x$$
$$108 \cos x = 53$$
$$\cos x = \frac{53}{108}$$
$$x = 60.6°$$

> Use the inverse cosine function on your calculator, labelled $\cos^{-1}$. You may need to press the SHIFT key or the 2ndF key.

EXAMPLE 8

ABC is a triangle in which AB = 3.5 cm, AC = 5.2 cm and BC = 2.7 cm. Calculate the size of angle ABC.

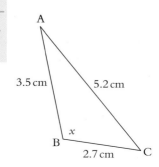

SOLUTION

Draw the triangle and identify the angle you have been asked to find.

$$5.2^2 = 2.7^2 + 3.5^2 - 2 \times 2.7 \times 3.5 \cos x$$
$$27.04 = 19.54 - 18.9 \cos x$$

$$18.9\cos x = 19.54 - 27.04$$
$$18.9\cos x = -7.5$$
$$\cos x = \frac{-7.5}{18.9}$$
$$x = 113.4°$$

Exercise 35.4

1 Calculate x.

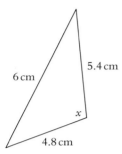

2 Calculate x.

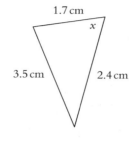

3 ABC is a triangle in which AB = 6 cm, AC = 5.3 cm and BC = 4 cm. Calculate the size of angle ABC

4 ABC is a triangle in which AB = 13 cm, AC = 11.5 cm and BC = 17 cm. Calculate the size of angle BAC.

5 ABC is a triangle in which AB = 4.7 cm, AC = 5.8 cm and BC = 6.4 cm. Calculate the size of angle ABC.

6 ABC is a triangle in which AB = 6.8 cm, AC = 7.2 cm and BC = 8.4 cm. Calculate the size of angle BAC.

Area of a triangle

You already know how to find the area of a triangle when you know the base and perpendicular height.

When you do not know the perpendicular height of a triangle an alternative method for working out the area is to use this formula:

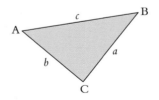

$$A = \frac{1}{2}\,bc\sin A$$

Rule
You multiply the lengths of two sides by the sine of the angle **between** them and divide by 2.

EXAMPLE 9

Find the area of this triangle.

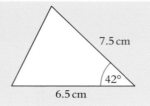

SOLUTION

$A = \frac{1}{2} \times 7.5 \times 6.5 \times \sin 42° = 16.3 \, \text{cm}^2$

EXAMPLE 10

Find the area of triangle XYZ.

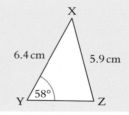

SOLUTION

We must first work out angle XZY using the sine rule:

$$\frac{\sin Z}{6.4} = \frac{\sin 58°}{5.9}$$

$$5.9 \sin Z = 6.4 \sin 58°$$

$$\sin Z = \frac{6.4 \sin 58°}{5.9}$$

$$Z = 66.9°$$

We can then find angle YXZ.

$$58 + 66.9 = 124.9°$$

$$180 - 124.9 = 55.1°$$

We can then use the area rule.

$$A = \frac{1}{2} \times 6.4 \times 5.9 \times \sin 55.1° = 15.5 \, \text{cm}^2$$

EXAMPLE 11

LMN is a triangle in which LM = 7.2 cm and angle LMN = 54°.
The area of LMN is 19 cm². Calculate MN.

SOLUTION

Draw the triangle.

$$A = \frac{1}{2} \times 7.2 \times MN \times \sin 54° = 19$$

$$2.91 \times MN = 19$$

$$MN = \frac{19}{2.91}$$

$$MN = 6.53 \, \text{cm}$$

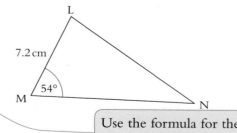

Use the formula for the area of the triangle.

Exercise 35.5

1 Calculate the area of this triangle.

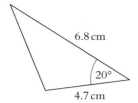

2 Calculate the area of this triangle.

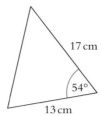

3 ABC is a triangle in which AB = 6.4 cm, BC = 7.5 cm and angle BAC = 46°. Calculate the area of ABC.

4 ABC is a triangle in which AB = 7.5 cm, AC = 8.2 cm and angle ACB = 65°. Calculate the area of ABC.

5 ABC is a triangle in which AB = 4.7 cm, BC = 6 cm and angle ABC = 84°. Calculate the area of ABC.

6 ABC is a triangle in which AB = 7 cm, BC = 9 cm and angle BAC = 54°. Calculate the area of ABC.

7 XYZ is a triangle in which XY = 6 cm and angle XYZ = 30°. The area of XYZ is 12 cm². Calculate YZ.

8 XYZ is a triangle in which XY = 6.4 cm and angle XYZ = 52°. The area of XYZ is 12 cm². Calculate YZ.

9 XYZ is a triangle in which XY = 9 cm and YZ = 4 cm. The area of XYZ is 15 cm². Calculate angle XYZ.

10 PQRS is a parallelogram in which PS = 6 cm and SR = 10 cm. The area of PQRS is 20 cm². Calculate angle PSR.

Exercise 35.6

1 PQR is an isosceles triangle in which PQ = PR = 8.4 cm. The angle QPR = 24°. Calculate:
   a QR   b the area of PQR.

2 ABC is a triangle in which AC = 6.4 cm, AB = 5.8 cm and angle ABC = 50°. Calculate:
   a angle BAC   b BC   c the area of ABC.

3 PQRS is a trapezium in which PQ is parallel to SR. Angle SPQ = 86°. SQ = 8 cm, QR = 9.2 cm and SR = 7.2 cm. Calculate:
   a angle QSR   b the area of PQRS.

4 A ship sails 6.4 km on a bearing of 052° from port P until it reaches position A. Another ship sails 9.5 km on a bearing of 135° from P until it reaches B. Calculate:
   a AB   b the bearing of B from A.

5 A person at a point A on the ground sees a vertical tower TQ of height 8 m where Q is on the ground. The angle of elevation of T from A is 27°. The angle of elevation of T from B, another point on the ground, is 36°. Angle AQB = 54°. Calculate AB.

6 LMNP is a rhombus of side 8 cm. Angle MLP = 54°. Calculate:
   a   MP   b   the area of LMNP.

7 WXYZ is a quadrilateral in which XW = 5.2 cm, WY = 6 cm and YZ = 3.6 cm. Angle XWY = 54° and angle WYZ = 68°. Calculate:
   a   the perimeter of WXYZ   b   the area of WXYZ.

You should now:

- know when to use the sine rule and the cosine rule
- be able to calculate missing sides and angles using either rule
- know when to use the area rule
- know the graphs of sine, cosine and tangent.

Summary exercise 35

1 ABC is a triangle in which BC = 8.3 cm, angle BAC = 64° and angle ABC = 57°. Calculate AB.

2 ABC is a triangle in which AB = 36 cm, angle ABC = 64° and angle ACB = 47°. Calculate AC.

3 ABC is a triangle in which AB = 5.8 cm and AC = 4.3 cm. Angle ACB = 48°. Calculate angle BAC.

4 ABC is a triangle in which AB = 15 cm and AC = 23 cm. Angle ABC = 72°. Calculate angle ACB.

5 ABC is a triangle in which AB = 9.6 cm, AC = 6.4 cm and angle ACB = 77°. Calculate the area of ABC.

6 XYZ is a triangle in which XY = 36 cm and YZ = 29 cm. The area of XYZ is 400 cm². Calculate angle XYZ.

7 PQRS is a parallelogram in which PS = 5.8 cm and SR = 9.3 cm. The area of PQRS is 18 cm². Calculate angle PSR.

8 A ship sails 7.8 km on a bearing of 073 from port P until it reaches position A. Another ship sails 8.2 km on a bearing of 129 from P until it reaches B. Calculate:
   a   AB   b   the bearing of B from A.

9 A person at a point A on the ground sees a vertical tower TQ of height 6.8 m where Q is on the ground. The angle of elevation of T from A is 34°. The angle of elevation of T from B, another point on the ground, is 41°. Angle AQB = 67°. Calculate AB.

10 LMNP is a rhombus of side 2.6 cm. Angle MLP = 73°. Calculate:
   a   MP   b   the area of LMNP.

Examination questions

Use 'Topic Tracker' at www.ccea.org.uk to find more exam questions.

These questions are from examination papers where you may use a calculator.

1 The top, T, of a hill can be seen from a point P with an angle of elevation 54°. T can also be seen from L with an angle of elevation 31°. L, P and B are on the same horizontal level.
The distance LP is 140 m.

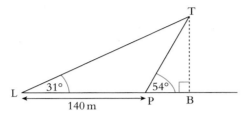

   a Calculate the distance LT.

   b Hence, find TB, the height of the hill.

2 Use the information given in the diagram to calculate the size of the angle DBC.

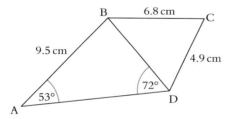

CHAPTER 36

Perimeter, area and volume 1

This chapter is about:

- finding the circumference and area of a circle
- finding the area of a parallelogram, a rhombus, a kite and a trapezium
- calculating the area and volume of regular and compound shapes including cylinders and right prisms
- calculating the surface areas of cubes, cuboids and cylinders

You should already know:

- how to find the perimeter of a square, a rectangle and a triangle
- how to find the area of a square, a rectangle and a triangle
- how to find the volume of a cube and cuboid
- how to solve equations
- how to manipulate fractions
- how to use Pythagoras' theorem
- how to use trigonometry
- how to find square roots and cube roots
- how to use the cosine rule
- how to find the area of a triangle that is not right-angled.

Perimeter and area of compound shapes

The perimeter is the distance around the outside of a shape.

The area is the space inside a shape.

EXAMPLE 1

For the shape shown, find:

a   the perimeter

b   the area.

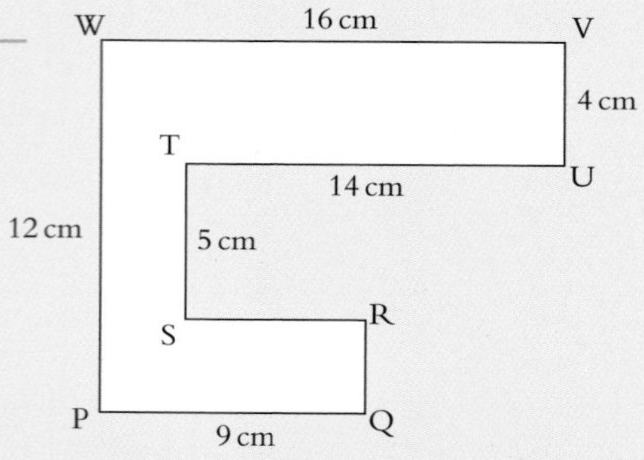

W ——— 16 cm ——— V
4 cm
T
14 cm
12 cm   5 cm   U
S
R
P ——— 9 cm ——— Q

SOLUTION

a   We must first work out the lengths of QR and SR.

WP = 12 cm

VU + ST = 4 + 5 = 9 cm and so QR = 3 cm

WV = 16 cm and TU = 14 cm and so the horizontal distance to the left of SR = 2 cm

PQ = 9 cm and so SR = 9 − 2 = 7 cm

We can now work out the perimeter by adding up all the lengths of the sides.

Perimeter = 12 + 9 + 3 + 7 + 5 + 14 + 4 + 16 = 70 cm

b   We can work out the area by either:

* splitting the compound shape into regular shapes and adding up their areas

or

* finding the area of the surrounding rectangle and subtracting the appropriate rectangles.

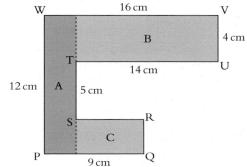

Method 1

Area of a rectangle = length × breadth

Area of A = 2 × 12 = 24 cm²

Area of B = 4 × 14 = 56 cm²

Area of C = 3 × 7 = 21 cm²

Total area = 24 + 56 + 21 = 101 cm²

Method 2

Area of the surrounding rectangle
= 16 × 12 = 192 cm²

Area of D = 5 × 14 = 70 cm²

Area of E = 3 × 7 = 21 cm²

Area of the compound shape
= 192 − 70 − 21 = 101 cm²

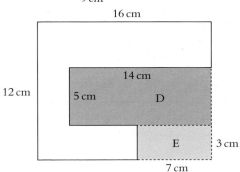

EXAMPLE 2

For the shape shown, find:

a   the perimeter

b   the area.

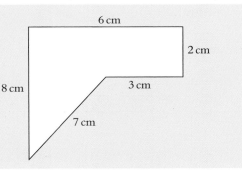

SOLUTION

a   Perimeter = 8 + 7 + 3 + 2 + 6 = 26 cm

b   Using Method 1 we have:

area of A = 6 × 2 = 12 cm²

B is a triangle and the area of a triangle is found using the formula $A = \frac{1}{2}$ base × height.

So   area of B = $\frac{1}{2}$ × 3 × 6 = 9 cm²

Total area = 12 + 9 = 21 cm²

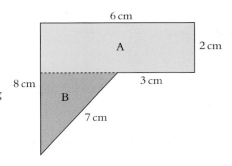

Exercise 36.1

For the shapes in questions **1** to **6** find:

a the perimeter   b the area.

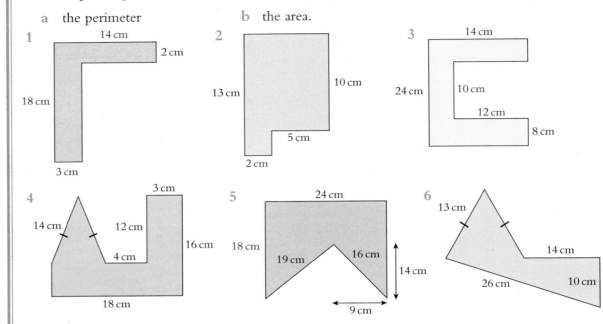

Circumference of a circle

The perimeter of a circle is called its **circumference**.

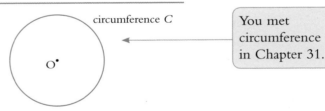

You met circumference in Chapter 31.

Calculating the circumference

We use the following formulae to calculate the circumference, C:

$$C = \pi d \qquad \text{or} \qquad C = 2\pi r$$

where d = the diameter, r = the radius and π is an irrational number which approximates to 3.14 when rounded to 3 significant figures. A more exact value (though still only approximate) can be obtained by using the π button on your calculator.

EXAMPLE 3

Find the circumference of a circle radius 8 cm. Give your answer in terms of π.

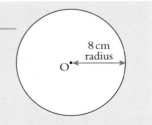

SOLUTION

$$C = 2\pi r = 2\pi \times 8 = 16\pi \text{ cm}$$

EXAMPLE 4

Find the circumference of a circle diameter 9.6 cm to 3 significant figures.

SOLUTION

$C = \pi d = \pi \times 9.6 = 30.15... = 30.2$ cm (to 3 s.f.).

EXAMPLE 5

The circumference of a circle is 56π cm.
Find its radius.

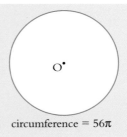

circumference = 56π

SOLUTION

$$2\pi r = C$$
$$2\pi r = 56\pi$$
$$r = \frac{56\pi}{2\pi} = 28 \text{ cm}$$

EXAMPLE 6

The circumference of a circle is 4.86 cm. Find its diameter.

SOLUTION

$$\pi d = 4.86$$
$$d = \frac{4.86}{\pi}$$
$$d = 1.55 \text{ cm (to 3 s.f.).}$$

Exercise 36.2

1 Find the circumference of each of the following circles. Give your
  answers in terms of π.

a
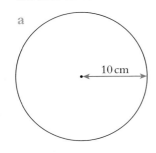
10 cm

b
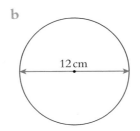
12 cm

c
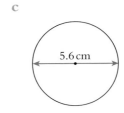
5.6 cm

d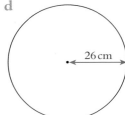
26 cm

e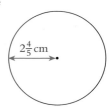
$2\frac{4}{5}$ cm

f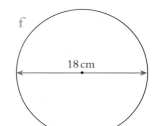
18 cm

2   Find the diameter of the circles with circumference:
   a 15π cm   b 28π cm   c 6.8π cm   d $3\frac{2}{3}\pi$ cm

3   Find the radius of the circles with circumference:
   a 36π cm   b 9π cm   c 8.4π cm   d $2\frac{3}{4}\pi$ cm

Exercise 36.3

1   Find the circumference of the circles with:
   a   radius 9 cm   b   diameter 34 cm   c   diameter 6.2 cm
   d   radius 1.56 cm   e   radius $2\frac{1}{2}$ cm   f   diameter 11 cm
   g   diameter 5.46 cm   h   radius 25 cm   i   radius 56 cm

2   Find the diameter of the circles with circumference:
   a   34 cm   b   9.6 cm   c   28 cm   d   50 cm   e   166 cm

3   Find the radius of the circles with circumference:
   a   48 cm   b   2.5 cm   c   8.4 cm   d   35 cm   e   90 cm

Perimeters of shapes involving parts of circles

We can extend this work to find the perimeter of a semicircle or the
perimeter of any composite shape involving part of a circle.

EXAMPLE 7

Find the perimeter of a semicircle of
radius 4.2 cm.

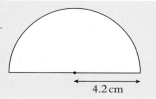
4.2 cm

SOLUTION

We need to find the lengths of the straight part and the curved part
separately. We will then add these together to get the perimeter.
Straight part = 4.2 × 2 = 8.4 cm
Curved part = $\frac{1}{2}C = \frac{1}{2} \times 2\pi r = \pi r = 4.2\pi = 13.2$ cm
Perimeter = 8.4 + 13.2 = 21.6 cm

EXAMPLE 8

Find the perimeter of this shape.

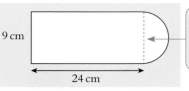

9 cm

24 cm

Add a line to show how the shape can be split.

SOLUTION

We need to split the shape into a rectangle and a semicircle.
Straight part = 9 + 24 + 24 = 57 cm
Curved part = $\frac{1}{2}C = \frac{1}{2} \times \pi d = \frac{1}{2}\pi \times 9 = 4.5\pi = 14$ cm
Perimeter = 57 + 14 = 71 cm

EXAMPLE 9

Find the perimeter of this shape.

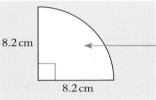

8.2 cm

8.2 cm

This shape is called a **quadrant** of a circle.

SOLUTION

Straight part = 8.2 × 2 = 16.4 cm
Curved part = $\frac{1}{4} \times 2\pi r = 12.9$ cm
Perimeter = 16.4 + 12.9 = 29.3 cm

Exercise 36.4

Give your answers correct to 3 significant figures.

1   Find the perimeter of a semicircle diameter 4.6 cm.

2   Find the perimeter of a semicircle radius 32 cm.

3   Find the perimeter of a semicircle radius 5.8 cm.

4   Find the perimeter of a semicircle diameter 90 cm.

5   Find the perimeter of a quadrant of a circle diameter 1.6 cm.

6   Find the perimeter of a quadrant of a circle radius 8 cm.

7   Find the perimeter of a quadrant of a circle radius 9.4 cm.

8   Find the perimeter of a quadrant of a circle diameter 40 cm.

9   Find the perimeter of the following shapes.

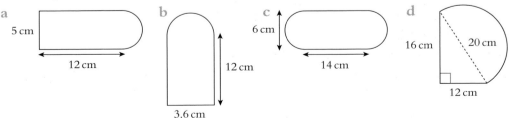

a 5 cm, 12 cm

b 12 cm, 3.6 cm

c 6 cm, 14 cm

d 16 cm, 20 cm, 12 cm

Area of a circle

We use the following formula to calculate the area of a circle:

$$A = \pi r^2$$

EXAMPLE 10

Find the area of a circle with radius 2.5 cm.

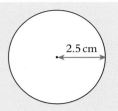

2.5 cm

SOLUTION

$A = \pi \times 2.5^2 = 19.6\,\text{cm}^2$

EXAMPLE 11

Find the area of a circle with diameter 4.7 cm.

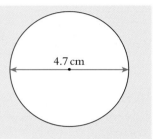

4.7 cm

SOLUTION

We must first find the radius.

$r = \dfrac{4.7}{2} = 2.35\,\text{cm}$

$A = \pi \times 2.35^2 = 17.3\,\text{cm}^2$

EXAMPLE 12

The area of a circle is 57 cm². Find **a** its radius and **b** its circumference.

SOLUTION

a $\quad \pi r^2 = A$

$\quad \pi r^2 = 57$

$\quad r^2 = \dfrac{57}{\pi} = 18.1$

$\quad r = \sqrt{18.1} = 4.26\,\text{cm}$

b $\quad C = 2\pi r = 2\pi \times 4.26 = 26.8\,\text{cm}$

> Use the value for r you found in part **a**.

Exercise 36.5

Give your answers correct to 3 significant figures.

1 Find the area of a circle with radius 6.4 cm.

2 Find the area of a circle with radius 6.9 cm.

3 Find the area of a circle with diameter 5.42 cm.

4 The area of a circle is 48 cm². Find its radius.

5 The area of a circle is 6 cm². Find its radius.

6 The area of a circle is 540 cm². Find its diameter.

7 The area of a circle is 9 cm². Find **a** its radius and
   b its circumference.

8 The area of a circle is 700 cm². Find **a** its radius and
   b its circumference.

9 The circumference of a circle is 3 cm. Find its area.

10 The circumference of a circle is 92.6 cm. Find its area.

Areas of shapes involving parts of circles

We can extend this work to find the area of a composite shape involving semicircles and quadrants.

EXAMPLE 13

Find the area of this shape.

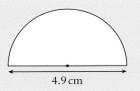

4.9 cm

SOLUTION

$r = \dfrac{4.9}{2} = 2.45$ cm

Area of a circle $= \pi r^2$

So the area of the semicircle $= \frac{1}{2}\pi r^2 = \frac{1}{2} \times \pi \times 2.45^2 = 9.43$ cm²

EXAMPLE 14

Find the area of this shape.

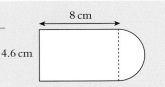

8 cm

4.6 cm

SOLUTION

We need to split the shape into a rectangle and a semicircle.

Area of the rectangle $= 8 \times 4.6 = 36.8$ cm²

Area of the semicircle $= \frac{1}{2} \times \pi \times 2.3^2 = 8.31$

Total area $= 36.8 + 8.31 = 45.11$ cm²

> The radius is half the diameter.
> $r = \dfrac{4.6}{2} = 2.3$ cm.

Exercise 36.6

Give your answers correct to 3 significant figures.

1 Find the area of a semicircle radius 11 cm.

2 Find the area of a semicircle diameter 4 cm.

3 Find the area of a semicircle diameter 74 cm.

4 Find the area of a semicircle radius 4.9 cm.

5 Find the area of a quadrant radius 27 cm.

6 Find the area of a quadrant radius 90 cm.

7 Find the area of a quadrant radius 5.4 cm.

8 Find the area of a quadrant radius 36 cm.

9 Find the area of these shapes.

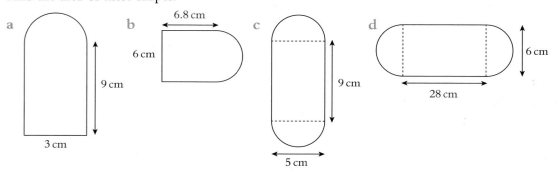

Areas of other shapes

Area of a parallelogram

A parallelogram is a shape with two pairs of parallel sides. The area is given by:

area = base × perpendicular height   or $A = bh$

EXAMPLE 15

Find the area of this parallelogram.

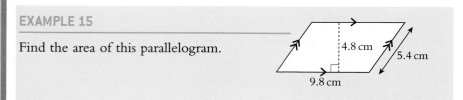

SOLUTION

We must choose the *perpendicular* height, i.e. 4.8 cm.
Area = $9.8 \times 4.8 = 47.04 \, cm^2$

Area of a trapezium

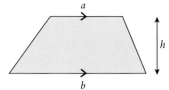

A trapezium is a quadrilateral with one pair of parallel sides.
The area is given by:

area = $\frac{1}{2}$(sum of the parallel sides) × perpendicular height

or

$A = \frac{1}{2}(a + b)h$

EXAMPLE 16

Find the area of this trapezium.

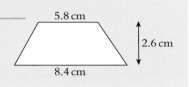

SOLUTION

Area = $\frac{1}{2}(8.4 + 5.8) \times 2.6 = 18.46\,\text{cm}^2$

Exercise 36.7

1 Find the area of the parallelograms shown.

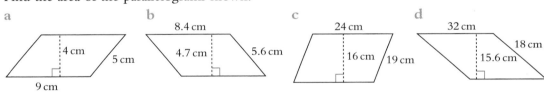

2 Find the area of each trapezium.

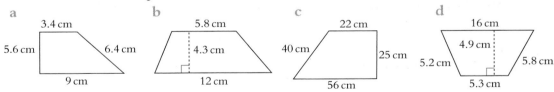

3 The base of a parallelogram of area 36 cm² is 8 cm long. Find the perpendicular height.

4 The parallel sides of a trapezium of area 68 cm² are 5.8 cm and 4.2 cm long. Find the perpendicular height.

5 The perpendicular height of a parallelogram of area 171 cm² is 18 cm. Find the length of the base.

6 The base of a parallelogram of area 84 cm² is 25 cm long. Find the perpendicular height.

Surface area and volume

Surface area and volume of a cuboid

A cuboid has six surfaces:

- the top and bottom (each of area *lb*).
- the front and back (each of area *lh*)
- the left and right sides (each of area *bh*).

Thus the total surface area is given by:

$$A = 2lb + 2lh + 2bh$$

The cuboid has a cross-sectional area of *lb* (the base) and its height is *h*.
So the volume is given by:

$$V = lbh$$

length *l*

height *h*

breadth *b*

EXAMPLE 17

A cuboid has length 6 cm, breadth 4 cm and height 3 cm.
Find **a** the surface area and **b** the volume.

SOLUTION

    a $l = 6\,cm$ $b = 4\,cm$ $h = 3\,cm$

        $A = 2 \times 6 \times 4 + 2 \times 6 \times 3 + 2 \times 4 \times 3$ ←   Substitute in the formula $A = 2lb + 2lh + 2bh$.

           $= 48 + 36 + 24$

           $= 108\,cm^2$

    b $V = lbh = 6 \times 4 \times 3 = 72\,cm^3$

EXAMPLE 18

A cuboid has volume 64.8 cm³. Its length and height are 9 cm and 5 cm.
Find **a** its breadth and **b** its total surface area.

SOLUTION

    a $lbh = V$

       So $9 \times b \times 5 = 64.8$

             $45b = 64.8$

               $b = \dfrac{64.8}{45} = 1.44\,cm$

       The breadth is 1.44 cm.

    b $A = 2 \times 9 \times 1.44 + 2 \times 9 \times 5 + 2 \times 1.44 \times 5$

           $= 25.92 + 90 + 14.4$

           $= 130.32\,cm^2$

       The total surface area is 130.32 cm² (to 2 d.p.).

Exercise 36.8

1 Find **a** the surface area and **b** the volume of a cuboid with length 8 cm, breadth 7 cm and height 4 cm.

2 Find **a** the surface area and **b** the volume of a cuboid with length 14 cm, breadth 11 cm and height 9 cm.

3 Find **a** the surface area and **b** the volume of a cuboid with length 7.6 cm, breadth 4.5 cm and height 3.9 cm.

4 A cuboid has volume 94 cm³. Its length and breadth are 5 cm and 4 cm. Find **a** its height and **b** its total surface area.

5 A cuboid has volume 512 cm³. Its length and height are 10 cm and 8 cm. Find **a** its breadth and **b** its total surface area.

6 A cuboid has volume 3136 cm³. Its length is 16 cm and the breadth and height are equal. Find **a** its breadth and **b** its total surface area.

7 The total surface area of a cuboid of length 4.5 cm and breadth 3.8 cm is 103.92 cm². Find **a** the height and **b** the volume.

8 The total surface area of a cuboid of length 35 cm and height 16 cm is 3262 cm². Find **a** the breadth and **b** the volume.

9 The total surface area of a cuboid is 550 cm².
The length is three times the height. The breadth is double the height. Find **a** the height and **b** the volume.

10 The length, breadth and height of a cuboid are 6x, 3x and 2x.
Show that the volume, V, and the total surface area, A, satisfy the equation $A = \dfrac{2V}{x}$.

Surface area and volume of a prism

A prism is a three-dimensional shape with a constant cross-section. A cuboid is a rectangular prism.
The wedge in the diagram is a triangular prism.
The volume of a prism is given by:

volume of any prism = cross-sectional area × length

or

$V = Al$

EXAMPLE 19

Find the volume of a prism of base area 68 cm² and length 7.5 cm.

SOLUTION

$V = Al$
$V = 68 \times 7.5 = 510 \text{ cm}^3$

EXAMPLE 20

Find **a** the volume and **b** the total surface area of the trapezoidal prism shown.

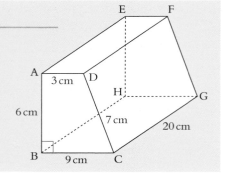

SOLUTION

a   The cross-sectional area is the trapezium ABCD.

$$\text{Area of ABCD} = \tfrac{1}{2}(3 + 9) \times 6 = 36 \text{ cm}^2$$
$$\text{Volume} = Al = 36 \times 20 = 720 \text{ cm}^3$$

b   To get the total surface area we must find the area of each side and add up all the answers:

Area of ABCD = 36 cm^2

Area of HGFE = 36 cm^2

BCGH, CGFD, DFEA and BHEA are all rectangles

Area of BCGH = 9 × 20 = 180 cm^2

Area of CGFD = 7 × 20 = 140 cm^2

Area of DFEA = 3 × 20 = 60 cm^2

Area of BHEA = 6 × 20 = 120 cm^2

So the total surface area is
36 + 36 +180 + 140 + 60 + 120 = 572 cm^2.

Exercise 36.9

1   Find the volume of a prism of cross-sectional area 264 cm^2 and length 75 cm.

2   Find the volume of a prism of cross-sectional area 35 cm^2 and length 8.4 cm.

3   Find the length of a prism of cross-sectional area 65 cm^2 and volume 1183 cm^3.

4   Find the cross-sectional area of a prism of length 7.2 cm and volume 93.6 cm^3.

5   Find the length of a prism of cross-sectional area 72.8 cm^2 and volume 698.88 cm^3.

6   Find the cross-sectional area of a prism of length 36 cm and volume 3168 cm^3.

For questions **7** to **10**, find **a** the volume and **b** the total surface area of each of the prisms.

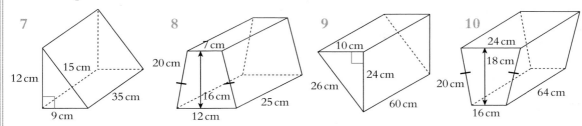

7   15 cm   12 cm   35 cm   9 cm

8   7 cm   20 cm   16 cm   25 cm   12 cm

9   10 cm   24 cm   26 cm   60 cm

10   24 cm   18 cm   20 cm   16 cm   64 cm

Surface area and volume of a cylinder

The top and bottom of a cylinder are circles and so their area is given by:

$$A = \pi r^2$$

where r is the base radius.

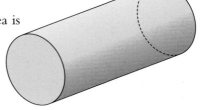

The curved surface area is given by:

$$\text{curved surface area} = 2\pi rh$$

where h is the height.

← This is the circumference of the base × the height.

So

• the total surface area of a cylinder closed at both ends is $2\pi rh + 2\pi r^2$
• the total surface area of a cylinder open at one end is $2\pi rh + \pi r^2$
• the total surface area of a cylinder open at both ends is $2\pi rh$.

A cylinder is a circular prism and so its volume is given by:

$$V = Ah = \pi r^2 h$$

EXAMPLE 21

A cylinder has a base radius of 18 cm and a height of 64 cm. It is open at one end. Find:

   a   the volume   **b**   the curved surface area

   c   the total surface area.

SOLUTION

   a $r = 18$ cm   and $h = 64$ cm

      So $V = \pi r^2 h = \pi \times 18^2 \times 64$

                $= 65\,100$ cm^3 (to 3 s.f.)

   b   Curved surface area $= 2\pi rh = 2\pi \times 18 \times 64$

                            $= 7240$ cm^2 (to 3 s.f.)

   c   The area of one end $= \pi r^2 = \pi \times 18^2 = 1020$ cm^2

      So the total surface area $= 7240 + 1020 = 8260$ cm^2.

EXAMPLE 22

The base diameter and curved surface area of a cylinder are 18 cm and 1700 cm². Find its volume.

SOLUTION

We must first find the cylinder's height.

$$d = 18\,\text{cm and so } r = \frac{18}{2} = 9\,\text{cm}$$

Curved surface area $= 2\pi rh = 2\pi \times 9 \times h = 56.55h = 1700\,\text{cm}^2$

$$h = \frac{1700}{56.55} = 30\,\text{cm}$$

So $\quad V = \pi r^2 h = \pi \times 9^2 \times 30 = 7630\,\text{cm}^3$.

EXAMPLE 23

For the semicircular prism shown, find:

a the volume

b the total surface area.

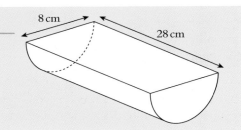

SOLUTION

a The cross-sectional area is a semicircle.

$d = 8\,\text{cm so } r = 4\,\text{cm}$

$A = \frac{1}{2}\pi r^2 = \frac{1}{2}\pi \times 4^2 = 25.13\,\text{cm}^2$

$l = 28\,\text{cm}$

So $V = 25.13 \times 28 = 704\,\text{cm}^3$

b The top is a rectangle with area $= 8 \times 28 = 224\,\text{cm}^2$

The curved surface area is half the curved surface area of a cylinder

$= \frac{1}{2}\,2\pi rh = \pi rh$

So the curved surface area $= \pi \times 4 \times 28 = 352\,\text{cm}^2$

The area of the two semicircular ends is the same as the area of the whole circle $= \pi \times 4^2 = 50.2 = 50\,\text{cm}^2$ to the nearest whole number.

The total surface area $= 224 + 352 + 50 = 626\,\text{cm}^2$.

Exercise 36.10

1 Find a the volume, b the curved surface area and c the total surface area of a cylinder with base radius 24 cm and height 50 cm if it is open at one end.

2 Find a the volume, b the curved surface area and c the total surface area of a cylinder with base radius 9.6 cm and height 16 cm if it is closed at both ends.

3 Find a the volume and b the total surface area of a cylinder with base diameter 8.4 cm and height 12.5 cm, open at both ends.

4 The base radius and curved surface area of a cylinder are 7 cm and 800 cm². Find its volume.

5 The height and curved surface area of a cylinder are 42 cm and 7000 cm². Find its volume.

6 The base diameter and curved surface area of a cylinder are 13 cm and 370 cm². Find its volume.

7 The height and volume of a cylinder are 4.5 cm and 120 cm³. Find its curved surface area.

For the semicircular prisms in questions 8 and 9, find **a** the volume and **b** the total surface area.

8
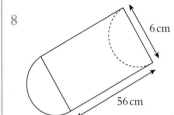
6 cm

56 cm

9
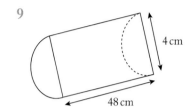
4 cm

48 cm

10 The curved surface area and volume of a cylinder are 6330 cm² and 88 700 cm³. Find **a** the base radius and **b** the height.

You should now:

- be able to calculate the perimeter and area of a circle and of shapes including circular sections
- be able to calculate the area of a parallelogram and a trapezium
- be able to calculate the surface area and volume of a prism and a cylinder.

Summary exercise 36

1 Find **a** the circumference and **b** the area of a circle radius 8.9 cm.

2 The circumference of a circle is 65 cm. Find its area.

3 Find **a** the perimeter and **b** the area of a semicircle diameter 2.7 cm.

4 Find the area of this parallelogram.
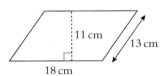
11 cm
13 cm
18 cm

5 Find the area of this trapezium.
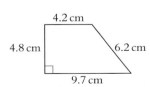
4.2 cm
4.8 cm
6.2 cm
9.7 cm

6 Find **a** the surface area and **b** the volume of a cuboid with length 3.6 cm, breadth 2.8 cm and height 1.5 cm.

7 Find **a** the surface area and
b the volume of the prism below.

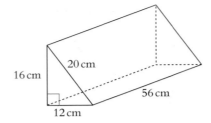

8 Find **a** the volume, **b** the curved surface area and **c** the total surface area of a cylinder with base radius 8.4 cm and height 13.2 cm if it is open at one end.

9 The base radius and curved surface area of a cylinder are 3.8 cm and 524 cm². Find its volume.

10 The curved surface area and volume of a cylinder are 374 cm² and 1265 cm³. Find **a** the base radius and **b** the height.

Examination questions

Question **1** is from an examination paper where you may not use a calculator.

> Use 'Topic Tracker' at www.ccea.org.uk to find more exam questions.

1 The diagram shows some of the measurements of one end of a child's climbing frame.
A bar, PQ, of length 0.8 metres, is 1.2 metres above the ground.
A cross bar, BC, fixing the frame to the ground is 2.4 metres.

a Calculate the area of the trapezium PBCQ.

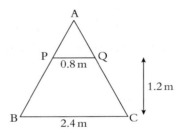

The climbing frame stands on horizontal ground and is 4 metres long. Horizontal bars, equal to PQ and each 1.2 metres from the ground, are fitted across the frame.

b Calculate the volume of space inside the frame, *underneath* the bars.

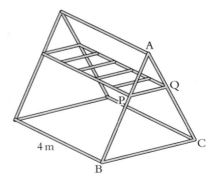

Questions **2** to **4** are from examination papers where you may use a calculator.

2 **a** Find the area of a circular flowerbed of radius 2.5 metres. Give the answer to an appropriate degree of accuracy.

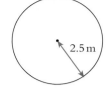

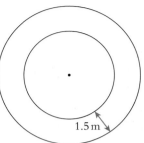

b A path 1.5 metres wide surrounds the flowerbed. Calculate the area of the path.

3 A cylindrical can of beans is shown.

A label completely covers the curved surface of the can. Calculate the area of the label.

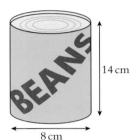

4 A cylindrical pond has radius 1.8 m.
a Find the area of the base of the pond.

The pond is filled with water to a depth of 0.45 m.
b Hence, find the volume of the water in the pond.

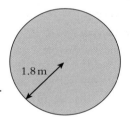

CHAPTER 37

Perimeter, area and volume 2

This chapter is about:

- calculating the area and volume of regular and compound shapes including cones and spheres
- calculating the lengths of arcs
- calculating the areas of sectors
- calculating the areas of segments
- calculating the surface areas of cones and spheres
- using dimensions to distinguish between length, area and volume.

You should already know:

- how to find the perimeter of a square, a rectangle and a triangle
- how to find the area of a square, a rectangle, a triangle, a parallelogram, a rhombus, a kite and a trapezium
- how to find the volume of a cube and a cuboid
- how to solve equations
- how to manipulate fractions
- the names of the different parts of circles
- how to use Pythagoras' theorem
- how to use trigonometry
- how to find square roots and cube roots
- how to use the cosine rule
- how to find the area of a triangle that is not right-angled
- the rules of indices.

Surface area and volume of a cone

An ice cream cone is a practical example of a cone.
It has a circular base and tapers to a point.
The curved surface area of a cone is given by:

$$\text{curved surface area} = \pi r l$$

The total surface area is given by:

$$\pi r l + \pi r^2$$

The volume is given by:

$$V = \frac{1}{3} \pi r^2 h$$

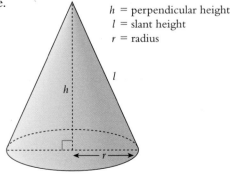

h = perpendicular height
l = slant height
r = radius

EXAMPLE 1

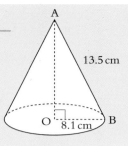

For this cone, calculate:

   a   the curved surface area

   b   the total surface area

   c   the volume.

SOLUTION

   a   OB = 8.1 cm and AB = 13.5 cm

      So r = 8.1 cm and l = 13.5 cm

      Curved surface area = $\pi \times 8.1 \times 13.5 = 344 \text{ cm}^2$

   b   The area of the circular base = $\pi r^2 = \pi \times 8.1^2 = 206 \text{ cm}^2$

      Total surface area = $344 + 206 = 550 \text{ cm}^2$

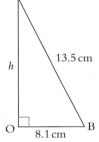

   c   To find the volume we must first work
out the perpendicular height.
We can do this by drawing out the right-angled
triangle AOB and using Pythagoras' theorem.

      $h^2 = 13.5^2 - 8.1^2 = 116.64$

      $h = \sqrt{116.64} = 10.8 \text{ cm}$

      So $V = \frac{1}{3}\pi \times 8.1^2 \times 10.8 = 742 \text{ cm}^3$

EXAMPLE 2

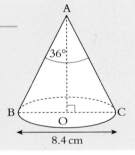

For this cone, calculate:

   a   the curved surface area

   b   the total surface area

   c   the volume.

SOLUTION

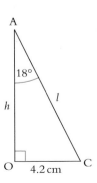

   a   We must first find r and l.

      d = 8.4 cm, so

      $r = \dfrac{8.4}{2} = 4.2 \text{ cm}$

      To find l we must draw out the right-angled
triangle AOC and use trigonometry.

      $\sin 18° = \dfrac{4.2}{l}$

      $l \sin 18° = 4.2$

      $l = \dfrac{4.2}{\sin 18°} = 13.6 \text{ cm}$

      So curved surface area = $\pi \times 4.2 \times 13.6 = 179 \text{ cm}^2$

b $\pi r^2 = \pi \times 4.2^2 = 55.4$

Total surface area $= 179 + 55.4 = 234.4\,\text{cm}^2$

c We must first work out h using the right-angled triangle AOC.

This time we use $\tan 18° = \dfrac{4.2}{h}$.

$h\tan 18° = 4.2$

$h = \dfrac{4.2}{\tan 18°} = 12.9\,\text{cm}$

So the volume is

$V = \frac{1}{3}\pi \times 4.2^2 \times 12.9 = 238\,\text{cm}^3$

Exercise 37.1

Calculate **a** the curved surface area, **b** the total surface area and **c** the volume of each of the following cones.

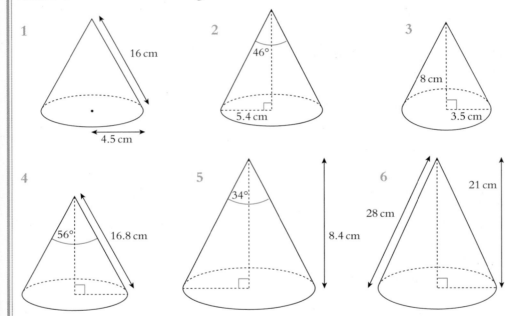

1 16 cm 4.5 cm

2 46° 5.4 cm

3 8 cm 3.5 cm

4 56° 16.8 cm

5 34° 8.4 cm

6 21 cm 28 cm

More complex problems

You may need to go through more steps to find the different lengths, areas or volume of a cone. The following examples show some of the different types of question you will meet.

EXAMPLE 3

The curved surface area of a cone of base radius 6.5 cm is 170 cm². Find its volume.

SOLUTION

We must first find its slant height by using the formula:

curved surface area $= \pi r l$

So $\pi r l = 170$

$$\pi \times 6.5 \times l = 170$$
$$20.4l = 170$$
$$l = \frac{170}{20.4} = 8.33 \, \text{cm}$$

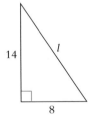

We can now use the radius and the slant
height to calculate the perpendicular height.
$$h^2 = 8.33^2 - 6.5^2 = 27.1389$$
$$h = \sqrt{27.1389} = 5.21$$
We can now calculate the volume using the formula $V = \frac{1}{3}\pi r^2 h$.
$$V = \frac{1}{3}\pi \times 6.5^2 \times 5.21 = 231 \, \text{cm}^3$$

EXAMPLE 4

The volume of a cone of perpendicular height 14 cm is 940 cm³. Find its
curved surface area.

SOLUTION

We must first find its base radius by using the formula $V = \frac{1}{3}\pi r^2 h$.
$$\frac{1}{3}\pi r^2 h = V$$
$$\frac{1}{3}\pi \times r^2 \times 14 = 940$$
$$14.66r^2 = 940$$
$$r^2 = \frac{940}{14.66} = 64.12$$
$$r = \sqrt{64.12} = 8 \, \text{cm}$$

We can now use the radius and the perpendicular
height to calculate the slant height.
$$l^2 = 14^2 + 8^2 = 260$$
$$l = \sqrt{260} = 16.12 \, \text{cm}$$
So curved surface area $= \pi rl = \pi \times 8 \times 16.12$
$$= 405 \, \text{cm}^2$$

Exercise 37.2

1   The curved surface area of a cone of base radius 12 cm is 942 cm².
    Find its volume.

2   The volume of a cone of perpendicular height 6 cm is 402 cm³.
    Find its curved surface area.

3   The curved surface area of a cone of slant height 28 cm is 170 cm².
    Find its volume.

4   The volume of a cone of radius 24 cm is 6032 cm³. Find its curved
    surface area.

5   The volume of a cone of perpendicular height 5 cm is 33.8 cm³.
    Find its curved surface area.

6   The curved surface area of a cone of perpendicular height 3.6 cm is
    90.5 cm². Find its volume.

7 The slant height of a cone is three times the radius, r. The total surface area is A, and the volume is V.

Show that $\dfrac{V}{A} = \dfrac{\sqrt{2}\,r}{6}$

Volume of a frustum of a cone

A frustum of a cone is made by removing the top part of the cone.

EXAMPLE 5

Work out the volume of this frustum.

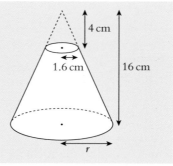

SOLUTION

We first need to work out the radius r of the original cone.
We can use the similarity of the two cones to find r:

$$\frac{4}{1.6} = \frac{16}{r}$$

Cross–multiplying gives:

$4r = 16 \times 1.6$

$4r = 25.6$

$r = 6.4$

Volume of the original cone

$V = \frac{1}{3}\pi r^2 h$

$V = \frac{1}{3}\pi \times (6.4)^2 \times 16$

$V = 686.3\,\text{cm}^3$

Volume of the top part of the cone

$V = \frac{1}{3}\pi r^2 h$

$V = \frac{1}{3}\pi \times (1.6)^2 \times 4$

$V = 10.72\,\text{cm}^3$

Rules for finding the volume of a frustum
- Work out the volume of the original cone.
- Work out the volume of the top part of the cone.
- Subtract the volumes.

Subtract the volumes

Volume of frustum $= 686.3 - 10.72 = 675.58$

So, the volume of the frustum is $676\,\text{cm}^3$.

EXAMPLE 6

Work out the volume of this frustum.

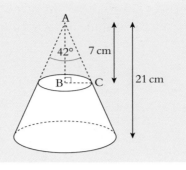

We first need to work out the radius r of the top part of the cone.
We do this by using trigonometry.
We draw out the right-angled triangle ABC.

We can now use $\tan 21° = \dfrac{r}{7}$

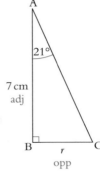

Cross-multiplying gives $r = 7 \tan 21°$
$$r = 2.687\ldots$$
$$r = 2.69\,\text{cm}$$

We can now work out the radius R of the original cone
as before.

$$\frac{21}{7} = \frac{R}{6.4}$$

Cross-multiplying gives
$$7R = 21 \times 6.4$$
$$7R = 134.4$$
$$R = 19.2\,\text{cm}$$

Volume of the original cone
$$V = \tfrac{1}{3}\pi R^2 h$$
$$V = \tfrac{1}{3}\pi \times (19.2)^2 \times 21$$
$$V = 8106.8\,\text{cm}^3$$

Volume of the top part of the cone
$$V = \tfrac{1}{3}\pi r^2 h$$
$$V = \tfrac{1}{3}\pi \times (2.69)^2 \times 7$$
$$V = 53.04\,\text{cm}^3$$

Subtract the volumes

Volume of frustum $= 8106.8 - 53.04 = 8053.76$
So, the volume of the frustum is $8054\,\text{cm}^3$.

Exercise 37.3

For questions **1** to **3**, work out the volume of each frustum, giving your
answer to the nearest integer.

1

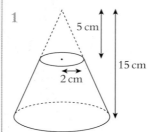

5 cm

2 cm

15 cm

2

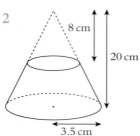

8 cm

20 cm

3.5 cm

3

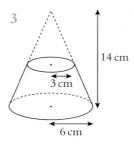

3 cm

14 cm

6 cm

4 The volume of the frustum
below is 288 cm³.
Find the volume of the top
part of the cone to 1 decimal
place.

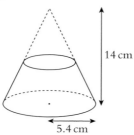

14 cm

5.4 cm

5 The volume of the frustum
below is 444 m³.
Find the volume of
the original cone to 1 decimal
place.

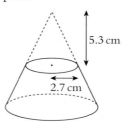

5.3 cm

2.7 cm

6 The volume of the frustum below is 92 cm³.
Find the volume of the top part of the cone to
1 decimal place.

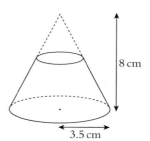

8 cm

3.5 cm

For questions **7** to **10**, work out the volume of each
frustum, giving your answer to the nearest integer.

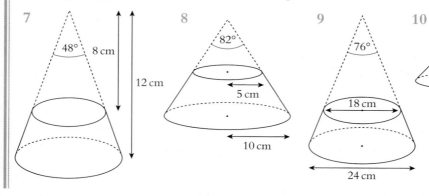

7

48°

8 cm

12 cm

8

82°

5 cm

10 cm

9

76°

18 cm

24 cm

10

114°

6 cm

4 cm

Surface area and volume of a sphere

A ball is an example of a sphere.
The curved surface area of a sphere is given by:

$$\text{Curved surface area} = 4\pi r^2$$

where r is the radius of the sphere.
The volume of a sphere is given by:

$$V = \tfrac{4}{3}\pi r^3$$

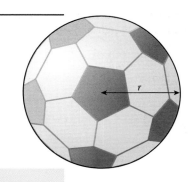

EXAMPLE 7

Calculate a the curved surface area and b the volume of a sphere of diameter 4.8 cm.

SOLUTION

The diameter is 4.8 cm so the radius $r = \dfrac{4.8}{2} = 2.4$ cm.

    a   Curved surface area $= 4\pi r^2 = 4\pi \times 2.4^2 = 72.4$ cm^2

    b   Volume $V = \tfrac{4}{3}\pi r^3 = \tfrac{4}{3}\pi \times 2.4^3 = 57.9$ cm^3

EXAMPLE 8

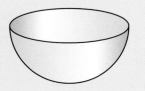

The total surface area of a hemisphere is 68 cm^2.
Calculate its volume.

SOLUTION

We must first find the radius.
The curved surface area of a hemisphere $= \tfrac{1}{2}$ of $4\pi r^2 = 2\pi r^2$
The top (or bottom) of a hemisphere is a circle of area πr^2.
So the total surface area of a hemisphere is $2\pi r^2 + \pi r^2 = 3\pi r^2$

So $3\pi r^2 = 68$

        $9.42 r^2 = 68$

          $r^2 = \dfrac{68}{9.42} = 7.219$

            $r = \sqrt{7.219} = 2.69$ cm

The volume of a hemisphere is given by $\tfrac{1}{2} \times \tfrac{4}{3}\pi r^3 = \tfrac{2}{3}\pi r^3$
So the volume $= \tfrac{2}{3}\pi \times 2.69^3 = 40.8$ cm^3

Exercise 37.4

1   Calculate a the curved surface area and b the volume of a sphere of radius 17 cm.

2   Calculate a the curved surface area and b the volume of a sphere of diameter 9.2 cm.

3   Calculate **a** the curved surface area and **b** the volume of a sphere of diameter 42 cm.

4   Calculate **a** the total surface area and **b** the volume of a hemisphere of radius 60 cm.

5   Calculate **a** the total surface area and **b** the volume of a hemisphere of diameter 12 cm.

6   The curved surface area of a sphere is 84 cm². Calculate its volume.

7   The volume of a sphere is 55 cm³. Calculate its curved surface area.

8   The volume of a sphere is 24 cm³. Calculate its curved surface area.

9   The total surface area of a hemisphere is 200 cm². Calculate its volume.

10   The volume of a hemisphere is 57 cm³. Calculate its total surface area.

Questions involving two solids

EXAMPLE 9

A test tube consists of a cylinder of height 6.8 cm on top of a hemisphere of base radius 1.2 cm. Calculate **a** its volume and **b** its total surface area.

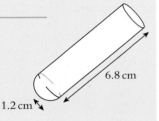

6.8 cm

1.2 cm

SOLUTION

a   *Cylinder*
   $h = 6.8$ and $r = 1.2$, so
   $V = \pi \times 1.2^2 \times 6.8 = 30.76 \text{ cm}^3$
   Hemisphere
   $r = 1.2$ so $V = \frac{2}{3} \pi \times 1.2^3 = 3.619 \text{ cm}^3$
   So the total volume is $30.76 + 3.619 = 34.4 \text{ cm}^3$

b   *Cylinder*
   Curved surface area $= 2\pi \times 1.2 \times 6.8 = 51.27 \text{ cm}^2$
   Hemisphere
   Curved surface area $= 2\pi \times 1.2^2 = 9.048 \text{ cm}^2$
   So the total surface area is $51.27 + 9.048 = 60.3 \text{ cm}^2$

> We find the volume of each solid separately and then add the answers together.

> Similarly for the surface area, we find the surface area of each solid separately and then add the answers together.

> The test tube is open at the top, so there is no flat surface area.

Exercise 37.5

1   A spinning top consists of a cone of perpendicular height 16 cm on top of a hemisphere of diameter 6 cm.

   Calculate **a** its volume and **b** its surface area.

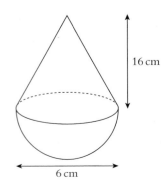

16 cm

6 cm

2. A test tube consists of a cylinder of height 11 cm on top of a hemisphere of base diameter 1.6 cm.

Calculate **a** its volume and **b** its total surface area.

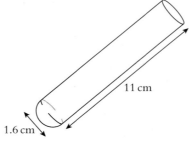

3. A metal cylinder of radius 8.4 cm and height 12 cm is to be melted down and recast as equal spheres of radius 24 mm. How many spheres can be made?

4. A frustum of a cone is formed by removing the top part of the cone.
AD = 10 cm, AB = 4 cm and angle BAC = 48°.
Calculate the volume of the shaded frustum.

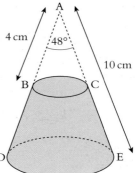

5. The diagram shows a cone of radius 2.3 cm and angle at the top of 56° joined to a hemisphere. Calculate **a** the volume and **b** the surface area of the combined shape.

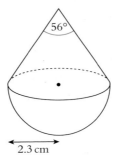

6. A cylindrical hole of diameter 3 cm is drilled from one side of a trapezoidal prism to the other.

PQ = 5 cm, PS = 6 cm, SR = 12 cm, RQ = 8 cm and RT = 20 cm.
Calculate the remaining volume.

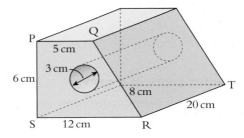

7. A cylindrical box radius 6 cm and height 48 cm is to be filled with spheres of radius 6 cm. Calculate the amount of space left inside the box.

Arcs and sectors

Length of an arc

The diagram shows an arc of a circle AB which subtends an angle of 40° at the centre O of a circle radius 5.8 cm.

We know what the circumference of the circle is, so we can use this to find the length of the arc.

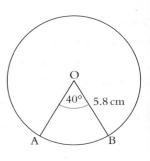

Since the arc subtends an angle of 40°, then the length of the arc is given by:

$$\frac{40}{360} \times 2\pi \times 5.8 = 4.05\,\text{cm}$$ ◄— Remember that the circumference of a circle is given by $2\pi r = 2\pi \times 5.8$.

Area of a sector

In a similar way we can find the area of the sector AOB in the diagram on page 411 as follows:

The area of the circle is given by $\pi r^2 = \pi \times 5.8^2$

So the area of the sector is given by:

$$\frac{40}{360} \times \pi \times 5.8^2 = 11.7\,\text{cm}^2$$

Exercise 37.6

Calculate **a** the length of the arc AB and **b** the area of the sector AOB in each of the following diagrams where O is the centre of the circle.

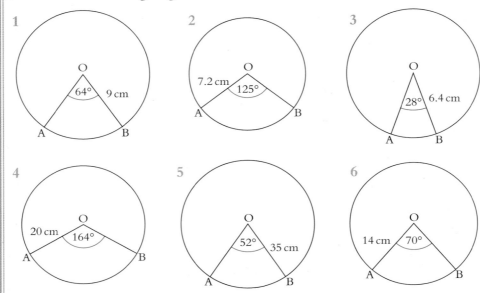

1. 64°, 9 cm
2. 7.2 cm, 125°
3. 28°, 6.4 cm
4. 20 cm, 164°
5. 52°, 35 cm
6. 14 cm, 70°

Calculating the angle in a sector

You can now use what you have learnt to work out more complex problems, such as finding the angle subtended by an arc of a given length, or the length of an arc when you know the area of the sector.

EXAMPLE 10

The length of the arc AB in the circle centre O and radius 8 cm is 4.2 cm. Calculate:

  a   angle AOB

  b   the area of the sector AOB.

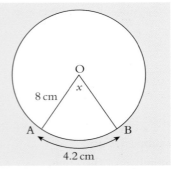

SOLUTION

a   Let angle AOB = x

We set up an equation and solve it to find x.
As before the length of the arc AB is given by:

$$\frac{x}{360} \times 2\pi \times 8 = 4.2$$
$$0.1396x = 4.2$$
$$x = \frac{4.2}{0.1396} = 30°$$

b   We can now find the area as before.

$$\text{Area} = \frac{30}{360} \times \pi \times 8^2 = 16.8\,\text{cm}^2$$

EXAMPLE 11

The area of the sector of a circle which subtends an angle of 84° at the centre is 52 cm². Calculate the length of the arc in this sector.

SOLUTION

We must first set up an equation using the area of the sector to find r.

$$\frac{84}{360} \times \pi \times r^2 = 52$$
$$0.733r^2 = 52$$
$$r^2 = \frac{52}{0.733} = 70.94$$
$$r = \sqrt{70.94} = 8.42\,\text{cm}$$

Length of the arc $= \dfrac{84}{360} \times 2\pi \times 8.42 = 12.3\,\text{cm}.$

Exercise 37.7

1   The length of the arc AB in the circle centre O and radius 4.9 cm is 4.2 cm. Calculate:
   a   angle AOB
   b   the area of the sector AOB.

2   The area of the sector AOB of a circle which subtends an angle of 75° at the centre is 27 cm². Calculate:
   a   angle AOB
   b   the length of the arc AB.

3   The length of the arc AB in the circle which subtends an angle of 87° at the centre O is 13 cm. Calculate:
   a   AO
   b   the area of the sector AOB.

4   The length of the arc AB in the circle centre O and radius 12 cm is 4.2 cm. Calculate:
   a   angle AOB
   b   the area of the sector AOB.

5   The area of the sector AOB of a circle radius 6.4 cm is 27 cm². Calculate:
    a   angle AOB
    b   the length of the arc AB.

6   The length of the arc AB in the circle centre O and radius 15 cm is 32 cm. Calculate the area of the sector AOB.

7   The area of the sector of a circle which subtends an angle of 72° at the centre of a circle is 8.9 cm². Calculate the length of the arc in this sector.

8   The length of the arc AB in the circle centre O is 4.2 cm and angle AOB = 55°. Calculate the area of the sector AOB.

9   The area of the sector of a circle of radius 6.3 cm is 52 cm². Calculate the length of the arc in this sector.

10 The radius of a circle is t cm. Show that the ratio of the length of the arc, L, which subtends angle $x°$ at the centre, to the area of the sector, A, is $2 : t$.

Finding the perimeter and area of a segment

The diagram shows a segment of a circle (coloured blue), where OP = 5 cm and angle POQ = 54°.

We want to find the perimeter and the area of the segment.

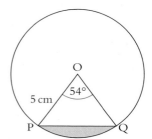

Perimeter
The perimeter consists of the arc PQ and the chord PQ.

The length of the arc PQ = $\dfrac{54}{360} \times 2\pi \times 5 = 4.71$ cm

We find the length of the chord PQ by using the cosine rule in the triangle POQ.

Then we have:

$$x^2 = 5^2 + 5^2 - 2 \times 5 \times 5 \cos 54°$$
$$x^2 = 20.61$$
$$x = \sqrt{20.61} = 4.54 \text{ cm}$$

So the perimeter = 4.71 + 4.54 = 9.25 cm

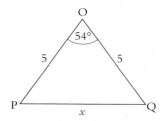

Area
We can find the area of the segment by finding the area of the sector POQ and the area of the triangle POQ and then subtracting them.

Area of sector

$$A = \dfrac{54}{360} \times \pi \times 5^2 = 11.8 \text{ cm}^2$$

Area of triangle
We can use the formula $A = \dfrac{1}{2} bc \sin A$ to get

$$A = \dfrac{1}{2} \times 5 \times 5 \sin 54° = 10.1 \text{ cm}^2$$

So the area of the segment = 11.8 − 10.1 = 1.7 cm²

Exercise 37.8

In questions **1** to **6**, find the perimeter and area of the shaded segments.

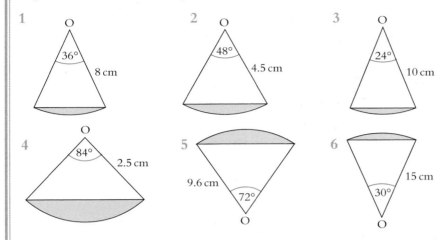

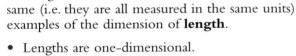

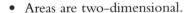

Dimensions

Consider a rectangle ABCD.

In this rectangle line AB = 4 cm, line BC = 3 cm and line AC = 5 cm.

Although each line is different in size, all the dimensions are the same (i.e. they are all measured in the same units). These are all examples of the dimension of **length**.

- Lengths are one-dimensional.

Consider a cuboid ABCDEFGH.

The area of ABFE = 4 × 3 = 12 cm², the area of BCGF = 2 × 3 = 6 cm² and the area of ABCD= 4 × 2 = 8 cm².

Although the area of each of these faces is different in size, all the dimensions are the same (i.e. they are all measured in the same units). These are all examples of the dimension of **area**.

- Areas are two–dimensional.

Similarly volumes of different solids could be 16 cm³ or 2616 cm³ where the dimensions are the same (the same units). These are examples of the dimension of **volume**.

- Volumes are three-dimensional.
- Numbers have no dimension.

A formula with only lengths added or subtracted represents a **length**.

A formula with two lengths multiplied together (or the sum or difference of two lengths multiplied together) represents an **area**.

A formula with three lengths multiplied together (or the sum or difference of three lengths multiplied together) represents a **volume**.

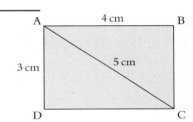

For example, the expression $a + 2b - 3c$ would represent a length.

For example, the expression $ab + 5b^2$ would represent an area.

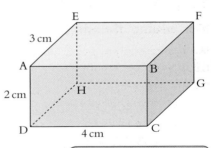

For example, the expression $\pi abc - b^2c + d^3$ would represent a volume.

Say whether the following expressions represent length, area or volume where p, q and r are all lengths.

1 $p + q$ 2 qr 3 p^2

4 q^3 5 $pq - 3rp$ 6 $3(p - q)$

7 $\pi p^3 - 2pqr$ 8 $p(q + r)$ 9 $4\pi pqr$

10 $3q(rq - p^2)$

Using dimension theory

We can represent a dimension of length by L, a dimension of area by L^2 and a dimension of volume by L^3.

We ignore any numbers or constants and only consider the dimensions to find out if an expression is a length, area, volume or none of these.

To combine the dimensions of the terms of an expression, we follow the same rules as for indices.

Adding and subtracting dimensions

We can only add or subtract *equal* dimensions and the answer has the same dimension.

For example:

$$L + L = L \quad \text{or} \quad L^2 - L^2 = L^2 \quad \text{or} \quad L^3 + L^3 - L^3 = L^3$$

but $L + L^3$ is impossible and therefore none of these dimensions.

Multiplying dimensions

We can multiply equal or different dimensions, adding the indices to get the answer. For example:

$L \times L = L^2$ which is a dimension of area

$L \times L^2 = L^3$ which is a dimension of volume

but $L^3 \times L^2 = L^5$ which is impossible and therefore none of these dimensions.

Dividing dimensions

We can divide equal or different dimensions, subtracting the indices to get the answer. For example:

$L^3 \div L = L^2$ which is a dimension of area

$L^3 \div L^2 = L$ which is a dimension of length

but $L \div L = L^0$ which is impossible and therefore none of these dimensions.

Squares of dimensions

We can square a dimension by multiplying the index by 2, i.e.

$(L)^2 = L^2$ which is a dimension of area

but $(L^2)^2 = L^4$ which is impossible and therefore none of these dimensions.

Square roots of dimensions

We can take a square root of a dimension by dividing the index by 2, i.e.

$$\sqrt{L^6} = L^3 \qquad \text{which is a dimension of volume}$$

but $\quad \sqrt{L} = L^{\frac{1}{2}} \qquad$ which is impossible and therefore none of these dimensions.

EXAMPLE 12

Say whether the following expressions are lengths, areas, volumes or none of these, where a, b and c are lengths.

a $\quad 4a - 6b + 2c$

b $\quad 6a - 5$

c $\quad 7ab - 4c^2$

d $\quad abc + cb$

e $\quad 3b(a - 2c)^2$

f $\quad \dfrac{4a^2(b - c)^3}{bc}$

g $\quad \dfrac{3\pi(c - a)^2}{b}$

h $\quad \sqrt{a(b - c)^2}$

SOLUTION

a $\quad 4a - 6b + 2c$
We can write these in their dimensions, remembering that numbers have no dimension.
So we have $L + L + L = L$
Therefore the answer is a length.

b $\quad 6a - 5$
We can only add equal dimensions and since 5 has no dimension then this expression is impossible and therefore none of these dimensions.

c $\quad 7ab - 4c^2$
We can write these in their dimensions, remembering that numbers have no dimension.
So we have $L^2 - L^2 = L^2$, which is a dimension of area.

d $\quad abc + cb$
We can write these in their dimensions.
So we have $L^3 + L^2$ which is impossible and therefore none of these dimensions.

e $\quad 3b(a - 2c)^2$
We can write these in their dimensions.
So we have $L(L - L)^2 = L \times (L)^2 = L \times L^2 = L^3$, which is a dimension of volume.

f $\quad \dfrac{4a^2(b - c)^3}{bc}$
Writing this expression as dimensions we get:
$$\frac{L^2(L - L)^3}{L \times L} = \frac{L^2 \, (L)^3}{L^2}$$
$$= \frac{L^5}{L^2}$$
$$= L^3$$
which is a dimension of volume.

g $\quad \dfrac{3\pi(c - a)^2}{b}$

Writing this expression as dimensions we get:
$$\dfrac{(L - L)^2}{L} = \dfrac{L^2}{L}$$
$$= L$$
which is a dimension of length.

h $\quad \sqrt{a(b - c)^2}$

Writing this expression as dimensions we get:
$$\sqrt{L(L - L)^2} = \sqrt{L \times L^2}$$
$$= \sqrt{L^3}$$
$$= L^{\frac{3}{2}}$$
which is impossible and therefore none of these dimensions.

Exercise 37.10

Work out whether the following expressions are lengths, areas, volumes or none of these, where m, n and p are lengths.

1 $\quad 2m - 5n$

2 $\quad 5mn$

3 $\quad 4n(mp - n^2)$

4 $\quad 6mn(p - n)$

5 $\quad mn(p - n)^2$

6 $\quad \dfrac{(m - n)^2}{p}$

7 $\quad \dfrac{mn^2}{n + p}$

8 $\quad (n - mp)^2$

9 $\quad \dfrac{\pi n(m - p)^2}{n - p}$

10 $\quad \pi n^2 - 3nmp$

11 $\quad \sqrt{\pi p(n + m)}$

12 $\quad \dfrac{\pi p}{n - m}$

13 $\quad \pi n^2(m - p)$

14 $\quad 6n(m - p)$

You should now be able to:

- calculate the perimeter and area of a circle or shapes including circular sections
- calculate the area of a parallelogram and a trapezium
- calculate the surface area and volume of a prism, cylinder, cone or sphere
- calculate the volume of a solid made up from two solids
- calculate the length of an arc of a circle
- calculate the area of a sector of a circle
- distinguish between formulae for length, area and volume by considering dimensions.

Summary exercise 37

1 Calculate **a** the curved surface area, **b** the total surface area and **c** the volume of the cone opposite.

2 The volume of a cone of perpendicular height 7.2 cm is 56 cm³. Find its curved surface area.

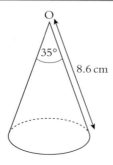

3 Calculate **a** the curved surface area and **b** the volume of a sphere of radius 4.9 cm.

4 The curved surface area of a sphere is 77 cm². Calculate its volume.

5 A test tube consists of a cylinder of height 5.8 cm on top of a hemisphere of base radius 1.7 cm. Calculate **a** its volume and **b** its total surface area.

6 A cone of radius 12 cm and slant height 32 cm is to be melted down and recast as equal spheres of radius 17 mm. How many spheres can be made?

7 In the diagram opposite, calculate:
  a the length of the arc AB
  b the area of the sector AOB.

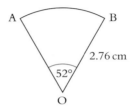

8 The area of the sector AOB of a circle radius 13 cm is 51 cm². Calculate:
  a angle AOB
  b the length of the arc AB.

9 Find the perimeter and area of the shaded segment opposite.

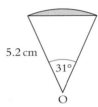

10 Copy and complete the table below by ticking the correct column each time where x, y and z are all lengths.

Expression	Length	Area	Volume	None of these
$7x - 4y$				
$\pi y(x + z)^2$				
$\frac{2}{3}\pi(x^3 - yz)$				
$\sqrt{y}(x - z)$				
$\dfrac{6x}{y - z}$				
$\pi z^3 - yz^2$				
$\sqrt{x^2}(y - z)^2$				

Examination questions

Use 'Topic Tracker' at www.ccea.org.uk to find more exam questions.

These questions are from examination papers where you may use a calculator.

1 The toy shown is made up of a cone attached to a hemisphere.
The cone has base radius 6 cm and perpendicular height 8 cm.
The hemisphere has the same radius as the cone.
Calculate the volume of the toy.

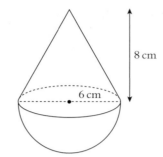

2 The shaded segment of the diagram shows a plan view of the shape of the interior window ledge of a bay window.

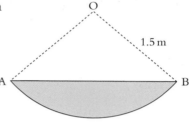

The straight edge AB is 2.4 metres long and the curved edge AB is an arc of a circle of radius 1.5 metres. The angle AOB is 106°.

a Calculate the area of the sector OAB.

b The window ledge is to be covered with a sheet of mahogany. Calculate the area of the mahogany.

3 A cone of radius r cm and vertical height 7 cm is removed from the top of a cone of radius 8 cm and vertical height 16 cm.

a Use similarity to find the length of DE.

b Find the volume of the remaining frustum of the cone.

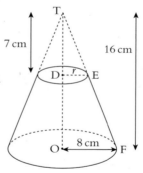

4 x, y, z are measured lengths. Decide whether each of the expressions represents length, area, volume or none of these. Copy and complete the table, ticking the correct column.

Formula	Length	Area	Volume	None of these
$\frac{1}{2}\pi z^2 x$				
$\pi(x + \; + z)$				
$\pi\sqrt{(x^2 + y^2)}z$				

CHAPTER 38

Constructions, loci, plans and elevations

> **This chapter is about:**
> - using a ruler and compasses to do standard constructions
> - drawing loci
> - drawing plans and elevations.
>
> **You should already know:**
> - the angle properties of triangles
> - how to draw bearings.

Constructions

Constructing triangles and scale drawings

A construction is different from a sketch. All measurements **must** be drawn exactly. You need to be able to construct triangles in different situations such as when you are given:

- two sides and one angle
- one side and two angles
- three sides.

> Here we have been given two sides and one angle.

EXAMPLE 1

Construct the triangle ABC where AB = 7.4 cm, AC = 6.8 cm and angle BAC = 40°.

SOLUTION

Rules
- Draw the base AB 7.4 cm long.
- Draw an angle of 40° at A.
- Measure 6.8 cm from A and mark C.
- Join BC.

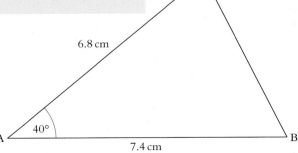

EXAMPLE 2

Construct the triangle ABC where AB = 6.5 cm, angle BAC = 65°
and angle ABC = 58°. ◄

Here we have been
given one side and
two angles.

SOLUTION

Rules

- Draw the base AB 6.5 cm long.
- Draw an angle of 65° at A.
- Draw an angle of 58° at B.
- C is where the two arms of
  the angles cross when drawn.

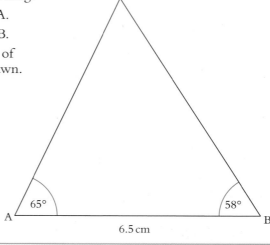

EXAMPLE 3

Construct the triangle ABC where AB = 6 cm, AC = 4.5 cm and
BC = 7.5 cm using compasses. ◄

Here we have been
given three sides.

SOLUTION

Rules

- Draw the base AB 6 cm long.
- Open up the compass to a radius of 4.5 cm.
  Put the compass at A and draw an arc.
- Open up the compass to a radius of 7.5 cm.
  Put the compass at B and draw an arc.
- C is where the arcs cross. Join AC and BC.

You **must** leave all construction arcs in your
construction diagram.

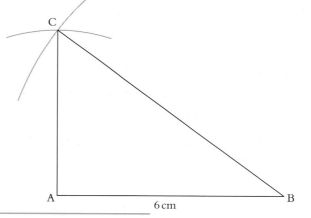

Bearings

You may be asked to solve problems involving bearings by constructing a
scale drawing.

EXAMPLE 4

A ship sails 57.6 km due north from harbour H to position P and then 70.2 km on a bearing of 132° from P to Q.

a Use a scale of 1 cm = 9 km to construct a scale drawing.

b Hence find:

  i   the direct distance from H to Q

  ii the bearing of Q from H.

SOLUTION

Rules

- Calculate the scaled distances:

$$\frac{57.6}{9} = 6.4 \text{ cm}$$

$$\frac{70.2}{9} = 7.8 \text{ cm}$$

- Draw P 6.4 cm due north of H.
- Draw a clockwise angle of 132° from P.
- Measure 7.8 cm from P to locate Q.
- Join PQ.
- Measure the scaled distance HQ (5.9 cm).
- Calculate the actual distance HQ:

  5.9 × 9 = 53.1 km

- Measure the bearing of Q from H (079°).

The bearing of Q from H is 079°.

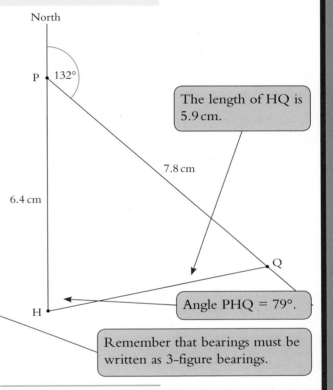

The length of HQ is 5.9 cm.

Angle PHQ = 79°.

Remember that bearings must be written as 3-figure bearings.

Exercise 38.1

Construct the following triangles.

1 PQR where PQ = 8.4 cm, PR = 7.5 cm and angle QPR = 48°.

2 PQR where PQ = 6.3 cm, angle QPR = 72° and angle PQR = 57°.

3 PQR where PQ = 6.4 cm, PR = 5.9 cm and QR = 7.1 cm.

4 PQR where PQ = 7.3 cm, QR = 7.5 cm and angle PQR = 52°.

5 PQR where PQ = 9.6 cm, angle QPR = 44° and angle PRQ = 98°.

6 PQR where PQR is isosceles with PQ = PR = 6.9 cm and QR = 4.6 cm.

7 PQR where PQ = 4.7 cm, PR = 5.4 cm and angle QPR = 118°.

8 PQR where PQR is an equilateral triangle with sides 5.8 cm.

9 A ship sails 43.5 km due north from harbour H to position P and then 46 km on a bearing of 072° from P to Q.
   a Use a scale of 1 cm = 5 km to construct a scale drawing.
   b Hence find:
      i the direct distance from P to Q
      ii the bearing of Q from P.

10 Make a scale drawing of this diagram using 1 cm = 20 m.

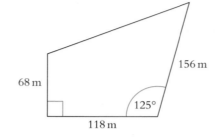

Special constructions

The following are standard constructions that you should be able to do using **only** a ruler and compasses.

When you draw constructions you **must** leave all the construction arcs in your answers.

Constructing the perpendicular bisector of a straight line

The following example shows how to construct the perpendicular bisector of a line using ruler and compasses.

EXAMPLE 5

Construct the perpendicular bisector of the line PQ which is 8.6 cm long.

SOLUTION

Rules

- With compass at P and a radius bigger than half of 8.6 cm draw an arc.
- With compass at Q and the **same** radius draw an arc to intersect the first arc at A and B.
- Draw a straight line joining AB.

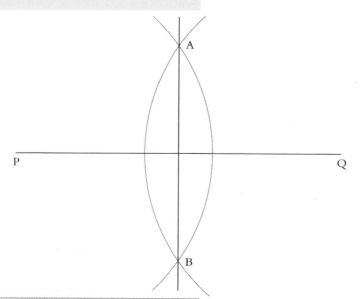

Constructing the bisector of an angle

The example below shows how to construct the bisector of an angle using ruler and compasses.

EXAMPLE 6

Construct the bisector of the angle XOY.

SOLUTION

Rules

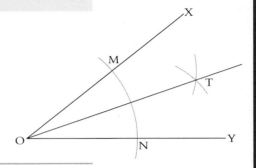

- With compass at O draw an arc cutting each arm of the angle at M and N.
- With compass at M (and then at N) and the **same** radius draw two arcs intersecting at T.
- Join OT.

Constructing a perpendicular from a point to a line

The following example shows how to construct the perpendicular from a point to a line using a ruler and compasses.

EXAMPLE 7

Construct the perpendicular from P to the line AB below it.

SOLUTION

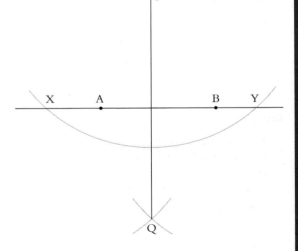

Rules

- Produce the line (i.e. make it longer).
- With compass at P draw an arc cutting the line at X and Y.
- With compass at X (and then Y) and the **same** radius draw two arcs intersecting at Q.
- Join PQ.

Exercise 38.2

1 Draw a line XY 6.7 cm long. Use compasses to construct the perpendicular bisector of this line.

2 Draw the angle LMN = 49°. Use compasses to construct the bisector of this angle.

3 Draw a line DE 7.8 cm long. Use compasses to construct the perpendicular at E.

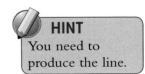

HINT
You need to produce the line.

4   Draw a line PQ 12 cm long. Use compasses to construct the perpendicular bisector of this line.

5   Draw the angle LMN = 153°. Use compasses to draw the bisector of this angle.

6   a   Construct the triangle ABC where AB = 5.9 cm, angle BAC = 35° and angle ABC = 52°.
    b   Construct the perpendicular from C to AB.

7   a   Construct the triangle PQR where PQ = 7 cm, PR = 6 cm and QR = 6.5 cm.
    b   Construct the perpendiculars of **i** PQ, **ii** PR.

8   a   Construct the parallelogram VWXY where VW = 7.2 cm, WX = 5.8 cm and angle VWX = 126°.
    b   Construct the bisectors of the angles at V and W.

9   a   Construct the equilateral triangle DEF where DE = 6.1 cm.
    b   Construct the perpendicular from F to DE.
    c   Construct the perpendicular at E.

10 a   Construct the rhombus GHIJ where GH = 4.8 cm and angle JGH = 54°.
    b   Construct the perpendicular bisector of GH.
    c   Construct the bisector of angle HIJ.

Loci

A **locus** describes the position of points which obey a certain rule. The locus can be the path traced out by a point as it moves subject to certain conditions. The plural of locus is **loci**.

Draw the locus of all points:

   a   1.5 cm from a fixed point O
   b   between 1.5 cm and 2.4 cm from O.

SOLUTION

a

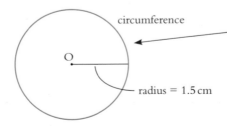

circumference

radius = 1.5 cm

The locus of all points a fixed distance from a point is the circumference of a **circle** whose centre is the fixed point and whose radius is the distance.

b   The locus will be the area between the two concentric circles centre O and radii 1.5 cm and 2.4 cm.

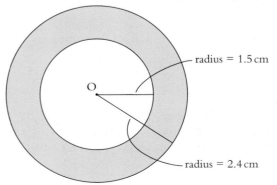

radius = 1.5 cm

radius = 2.4 cm

EXAMPLE 9

Draw the locus of all points 1.6 cm from a line AB 3.1 cm long.

SOLUTION

The locus of all points a fixed distance from a
line is the shape made up of two lines parallel
to the given line (above and below it) and
two semicircular arcs at each end.

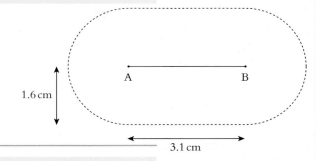

EXAMPLE 10

Two ports P and Q are 22.5 km apart. Q is due east of P.
A ship sails between P and Q subject to the conditions:

    a   It is always less than 16.2 km from P.
    b   It is always closer to Q than P.

Use a scale of 1 cm = 9 km to show the locus of its path.

SOLUTION

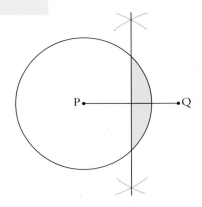

- We must first work out the scaled distances:

$$\frac{22.5}{9} = 2.5 \text{ cm}$$

$$\frac{16.2}{9} = 1.8 \text{ cm}$$

- Draw the line PQ (= 2.5 cm) with Q to the right of P.
- Construct a circle centre P radius 1.8 cm.
- Construct the perpendicular bisector of PQ.
- Shade the segment to the right of the perpendicular bisector.

Exercise 38.3

1 Construct the locus of all points:
    a   6.2 cm from a fixed point O
    b   less than 4.3 cm from O.

2 Construct the locus of all
   points equidistant from
   AB and AC below.

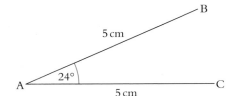

3 Construct the locus of all points 43 m from a point C using a scale
   of 1 cm = 5 m.

4 Construct the locus of all points 11 km from a line EF 15.6 km long
   where F is due west of E using a scale of 1 cm = 4 km.

5 Construct the locus of all points equidistant from P and Q where Q is 53.9 miles east of P using a scale of 1 cm = 7 miles.

6 Construct the locus of all points equidistant from two straight lines UV and VW which meet at V where angle UVW = 58°.

7 PQRS is a square side 4.7 cm.
   a Construct the square.
   b Construct the locus of all points closer to P than R and less than 3.4 cm from Q.

8 Construct the triangle HJK where HJ = 6.3 cm, HK = 5.8 cm and JK = 5.2 cm. Construct the locus of all points:
   a equidistant from H and J
   b equidistant from HJ and HK.

9 a Construct the rectangle PQRS where PQ = 8.3 cm and QR = 6.7 cm.
   b Construct the locus of all points inside the rectangle that are:
      i   nearer to P than R
      ii more than 5 cm from S.

10 Construct the locus of the point Q such that angle PQR = 90° where PR = 5.6 cm.

Plans and elevations

The view of an object looking down from above is called its **plan.**
Look at the cylinder below.

If you were to look down at it from above you would see a circle the same size as the top of the cylinder. This would be the **plan**.

The view of an object looking from the front is called its **front elevation** and the view from the side is called its **side elevation**.

If we looked at the cylinder from the front or the side we would see a rectangle the same height and width as the cylinder. This would be the front and side elevation.

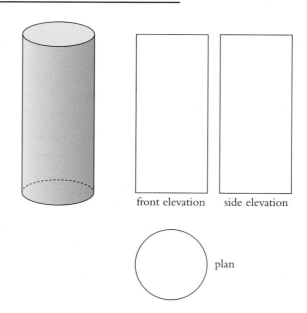

front elevation   side elevation

plan

EXAMPLE 11

The diagram shows a
3-dimensional object. The
object has a circular hole in
the middle of the top and
a rectangular hole in the
middle of the front.

Draw its:

a plan

b front elevation

c side elevation.

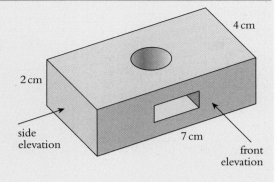

SOLUTION

The plan would be a rectangle 7 cm by 4 cm with a circle in the middle.

The front elevation would be a rectangle 7 cm by 2 cm with a rectangle in the middle.

The side elevation would be a rectangle 4 cm by 2 cm.

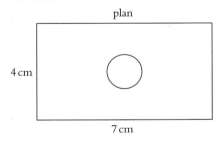

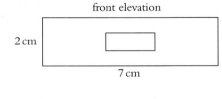

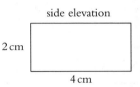

EXAMPLE 12

The diagram shows a solid wedge
with a circular hole through it.
Draw the plan, front and side
elevations.

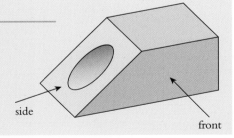

SOLUTION

The plan of the solid is a rectangle.

The front elevation is a trapezium.

The side elevation is a rectangle with a
circle in the middle.

Note that in an elevation drawing, we cannot represent the 3-dimensional slope of the solid. The view from the right-hand side of the solid is the same as that from the left-hand side.

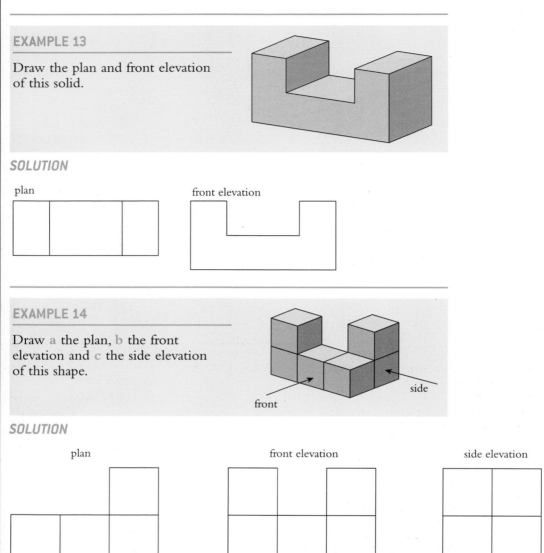

EXAMPLE 13

Draw the plan and front elevation of this solid.

SOLUTION

plan

front elevation

EXAMPLE 14

Draw **a** the plan, **b** the front elevation and **c** the side elevation of this shape.

front

side

SOLUTION

plan

front elevation

side elevation

Exercise 38.4

For the following shapes draw:

    a   the front elevation   b   the side elevation   c   the plan.

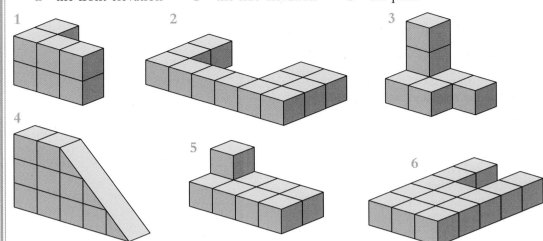

You should now:
• **be able to construct triangles**
• **know how to construct the perpendicular bisector of a straight line**
• **know how to construct the bisector of an angle**
• **know how to construct a perpendicular from a point to a straight line**
• **know the meaning of 'locus'**
• **be able to sketch loci**
• **know the meaning of plan and elevation**
• **be able to draw a plan and elevation.**

Summary exercise 38

1   Construct the triangle PQR where PQ = 6.8 cm, PR = 6.4 cm and angle QPR = 76°.

2   Construct the triangle PQR where PQ = 9.5 cm, angle QPR = 38° and angle PQR = 44°.

3   Construct the parallelogram PQRS where PQ = 5.2 cm, PS = 4.7 cm and angle QPS = 122°.

4   A ship sails 28.2 km due north from harbour H to position P and then 17.1 km on a bearing of 133° from P to Q.
    a Use a scale of 1 cm = 3 km to construct a scale drawing.
    b Hence find:
       i   the direct distance from P to Q
      ii the bearing of Q from P.

5   a Construct the triangle ABC where AB = 7.2 cm, angle BAC = 64° and angle ABC = 78°.
    b Construct the perpendicular from C to AB.

6 a Construct the triangle PQR where PQ = 5.3 cm, PR = 5.8 cm and QR = 5 cm.

  b Construct the perpendiculars **i** from R to PQ and **ii** from Q to PR.

7 a Construct the parallelogram VWXY where VW = 6.8 cm, WX = 5.3 cm and angle VWX = 119°.

  b Construct the bisectors of the angles at V and W.

8 PQRS is a square side 5.8 cm.

  a Construct the square.

  b Construct the locus of all points closer to R than to P and more than 2.7 cm from Q.

9 a Construct the triangle HJK where HJ = 5.7 cm, HK = 5.2 cm and JK = 6.1 cm.

  b Construct the locus of all points:

  i equidistant from H and K

  ii equidistant from KJ and HK.

10 The diagram shows a three-dimensional object. Draw its:

  a plan

  b front elevation

  c side elevation.

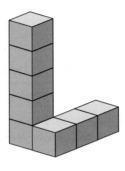

Examination questions

Use 'Topic Tracker' at www.ccea.org.uk to find more exam questions.

These questions are from examination papers where you may not use a calculator.

1 These are the front and side elevations of a tower block (cuboid) and a water tank (cylinder). Sketch the plan.

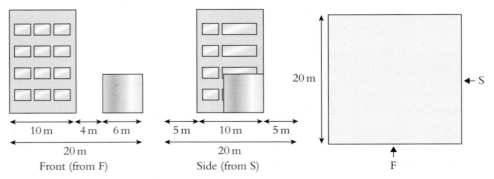

2 a Draw a horizontal line approximately 8 cm long. Label one end A and the other B. Construct the perpendicular bisector of the line AB.

  b Shade in the region such that the distance from A is less than 6 cm and the distance from A is greater than the distance from B.

CHAPTER 39

Compound measures

This chapter is about:
- working with distance, time and speed
- working with density, mass and volume.

You should already know:
- how to solve equations
- how to cancel fractions
- how to add and multiply fractions
- the relationship between metric units
- how to find the volume of a cube and a cuboid.

A **compound measure** is one made up of two or more other measures: speed and density are both compound measures.

Distance, time and speed

A body moving at a constant **speed** will cover a **distance** in a **time**. When the body travels at a **constant** speed we can use the following formulae to work out the unknown quantity:

$$\text{distance} = \text{speed} \times \text{time} \quad \left(D = ST\right)$$

$$\text{speed} = \frac{\text{distance}}{\text{time}} \quad \left(S = \frac{D}{T}\right)$$

$$\text{time} = \frac{\text{distance}}{\text{speed}} \quad \left(T = \frac{D}{S}\right)$$

An easy way to remember these formulae is to use this triangle. Cover up the letter that stands for the unknown quantity to find the equation you should use.

When using these formulae we must make sure that the units match up (i.e. if the speed is given in miles/hour the distance must be in miles and the time must be in hours).

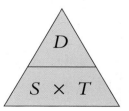

EXAMPLE 1

A car travels for 5 hours at an average speed of 36 mph (miles per hour). How far will it have gone?

SOLUTION

$D = ST = 36 \times 5 = 180$ miles

EXAMPLE 2

A van travels 468 km in 9 hours. Find its average speed.

SOLUTION

$S = \dfrac{D}{T} = \dfrac{468}{9} = 52$ km/h

EXAMPLE 3

A bus travels 140 km at an average speed of 40 km/h.
How long will it take?

SOLUTION

$T = \dfrac{D}{S} = \dfrac{140}{40} = \dfrac{14}{4} = \dfrac{7}{2} = 3.5$ hours

---

Exercise 39.1

1 A car travels for 7 hours at an average speed of 43 mph. How far will it have gone?

2 A bus travels 235 km in 5 hours. Find its average speed.

3 A van travels 180 km at an average speed of 36 km/h. How long will it take?

4 A cyclist travels 256 km at an average speed of 32 km/h. How long will he take?

5 A van travels 496 km in 8 hours. Find its average speed.

6 A car travels 400 km at an average speed of 50 km/h. How long will it take?

7 A van travels 448 km at an average speed of 56 km/h. How long will it take?

8 A car travels for 4 hours at an average speed of 54 mph. How far will it have gone?

9 A bus travels 448 km at an average speed of 64 km/h. How long will it take?

10 A motor bike travels 636 km in 12 hours. Find its average speed.

The time taken may not always be a whole number of hours. Sometimes it is easier to work in fractions of an hour, and sometimes in hours and minutes.
Examples 4 to 6 show how to deal with these types of question.

EXAMPLE 4

A car travels for 4 hours 24 minutes at an average speed of 45 mph. How far will it have gone?

SOLUTION

We need to either change the time to hours, or change the time into minutes.

Method 1: Change the time into hours

$$T = 4\frac{24}{60}\,\text{h}$$

$$\frac{24}{60} = \frac{4}{10} = 0.4$$

So $\quad T = 4.4$ hours

Then we have

$$D = ST = 45 \times 4.4$$

We can do this without a calculator by long multiplication of decimals.

```
        4   5
  ×     4 . 4
  ─────────────
      1 8   0
  1   8   0
  ─────────────
  1   9   8 . 0   = 198 km
```

Method 2: Change the time into minutes

$$4\,\text{h} = 4 \times 60\,\text{min}$$

So $\quad 4\frac{24}{60}\text{h} = 240 + 24 = 264\,\text{min}$

Then

$$D = ST = \frac{45 \times 264}{60}$$

We can then cancel this expression down.

$$\frac{\overset{3}{\cancel{45}} \times \cancel{264}^{66}}{\cancel{60}\cancel{20}_{1}} = 198\,\text{km}$$

> We have to divide by 60 here to change the time back into hours to match up with the speed.

EXAMPLE 5

A body travels 28 km in 35 minutes. Find its average speed in km/h.

SOLUTION

$$S = \frac{D}{T} = \frac{28}{35}$$

But this speed will be in km/min.
So, we must multiply by 60 to change it to km/h.

$$S = \frac{28 \times 60}{35}$$

which we can cancel as before.

$$S = \frac{\overset{4}{\cancel{28}} \times \cancel{60}^{12}}{\cancel{35}_{5}\,_{1}} = 48\,\text{km/h}$$

EXAMPLE 6

A body travels 96 km at an average speed of 36 km/h. How long will it take? Give your answer in hours and minutes.

SOLUTION

$$T = \frac{D}{S} = \frac{96}{36}\text{h}$$

This is the time in hours. We can simplify this by dividing by common factors.

$$\frac{96}{36} = \frac{16}{6} = \frac{8}{3} = 2\frac{2}{3}\text{h}$$

We must change the fractional part of an hour into minutes by multiplying by 60.

$$\frac{2}{3} \times 60 = 40$$

So, it will take 2 h 40 min

Exercise 39.2

1 A car travels for 2 hours 20 minutes at an average speed of 51 mph. How far will it have gone?

2 A moped travels 20 km in 40 minutes. Find its average speed in km/h.

3 A van travels 204 km at an average speed of 48 km/h. How long will it take? Give your answer in hours and minutes.

4 A bus travels for 5 hours 50 minutes at an average speed of 36 mph. How far will it have gone?

5 A car travels 209 km at an average speed of 57 km/h. How long will it take? Give your answer in hours and minutes.

6 A car travels 452 km at an average speed of 60 km/h. How long will it take? Give your answer in hours and minutes.

7 A van travels 156 km in 2 hours 24 minutes. Find its average speed in km/h.

8 A bus travels for 4 hours 24 minutes at an average speed of 45 mph. How far will it have gone?

9 A motor bike travels 291 km in 6 hours 28 minutes. Find its average speed in km/h.

10 A car travels for 4 hours 44 minutes at an average speed of 75 mph. How far will it have gone?

Calculations involving arrival times

Sometimes we either need to calculate the arrival time or we are given the arrival time.

EXAMPLE 7

A man left home at 09.45 and drove at an average speed of 48 mph for 176 miles. When did he arrive?

SOLUTION

We must first find the time taken to travel the 176 miles.

$$T = \frac{D}{S} = \frac{176}{48} = \frac{44}{12} = \frac{11}{3} = 3\tfrac{2}{3}\,\text{h} = 3\,\text{h}\ 40\,\text{min}$$

We can then add this on to the start time.

	h	min
	9	45
+	3	40
	12	85
+	1	− 60
	13	25

So, he arrived at 13.25.

EXAMPLE 8

A train leaves at 13.55 and travels 399 km, arriving at its destination at 18.40. Find its average speed.

SOLUTION

We must first find the time taken by subtracting the departure time from the arrival time.

$$
\begin{array}{r}
18.40 \\
-\ 13.55
\end{array}
\longrightarrow
\begin{array}{ccc}
\text{h} & \text{min} \\
17 & 100 \\
13 & 55 \\
\hline
4 & 45
\end{array}
= 4\,\text{h}\ 45\,\text{min} = 4\tfrac{3}{4}\,\text{h}
$$

> Here we have exchanged 1 hour for 60 minutes.

So $S = \dfrac{D}{T} = \dfrac{399}{4\tfrac{3}{4}} = 399 \div 4\tfrac{3}{4} = 399 \div \dfrac{19}{4} = 399 \times \dfrac{4}{19}$

Using long division, we can find $399 \div 19$.

$$
\begin{array}{r}
\,2\ \ 1 \\
19\,\overline{)\,3\ \ 9\ \ 9} \\
-\ \underline{3\ \ 8\ \ 0} \\
1\ \ 9 \\
-\ \underline{1\ \ 9} \\
0
\end{array}
$$

So, $S = 21 \times 4 = 84\,\text{km/h}$

Exercise 39.3

Copy and complete the following table.

Question	Departure time	Arrival time	Distance (miles)	Speed (mph)
1	08.35	11.10	154	
2	09.45	10.30		52
3	11.45		242	66
4	10.40	13.20		57
5	12.57	14.45	99	
6		15.10	153	36
7	16.37	17.21		75
8	18.36	21.12	169	
9	18.52		210	56
10	21.56	23.50		40

Average speed

The average speed is the *total* distance divided by the *total* time.

EXAMPLE 9

A car travels $4\frac{1}{2}$ miles in 6 minutes and then $2\frac{1}{4}$ miles in 4 minutes. Find its average speed.

SOLUTION

We must first find the *total* distance travelled and the *total* time taken. We can then find the average speed.

$$\text{Total distance} = 4\frac{1}{2} + 2\frac{1}{4} = 4\frac{2}{4} + 2\frac{1}{4} = 6\frac{3}{4} \text{ miles}$$

$$\text{Total time} = 6 + 4 = 10 \text{ min}$$

$$\text{Average speed} = \frac{6\frac{3}{4}}{10} \times 60$$

We multiply by 60 to get the speed in miles per hour.

$$\frac{6\frac{3}{4}}{10} \times 60 = \frac{27 \times 60^{6^3}}{{}_2 4 \times 10_1} = \frac{81}{2} = 40.5 \text{ mph}$$

Exercise 39.4

Find the average speed in the following journeys.

Question	First part of the journey	Second part of the journey
1	48 miles in 1 hour	66 miles in 2 hours
2	76 miles in 3 hours	54 miles in 2 hours
3	87 miles in 4 hours	143 miles in 6 hours
4	132 miles in $2\frac{1}{2}$ hours	192 miles in $4\frac{1}{4}$ hours
5	2 miles in 3 min	$1\frac{1}{2}$ miles in 2 min
6	4 miles in 8 min	6 miles in 7 min
7	8 miles in 30 min	7 miles in 45 min
8	11 miles in 48 min	10 miles in 36 min
9	132 miles in 3 h 20 min	84 miles in 2 h 40 min
10	223 miles in 5 h 54 min	312 miles in 6 h 36 min

Changing speeds

You may be given a speed in one set of units, and need to change it into a different set of units, for example changing a speed in m/s to km/h.

EXAMPLE 10

Convert these speeds:

   a 18 m/s to km/h   b 86.4 km/h to m/s.

SOLUTION

  a 18 m/s to km/h

     We need to change m to km by dividing by 1000 and seconds to hours by multiplying by $60 \times 60 = 3600$.

     Thus we get $\dfrac{18 \times 3600}{1000} = \dfrac{18 \times 36}{10} = \dfrac{648}{10} = 64.8$ km/h

$$\begin{array}{r} 1\;\;8 \\ \times\;\;\;\;\;3\;\;6 \\ \hline 1\;\;0\;\;8 \\ 5\;\;4\;\;0 \\ \hline 6\;\;4\;\;8 \\ \hline \end{array}$$

  b 86.4 km/h to m/s

     We need to change km to m by multiplying by 1000 and hours to seconds by dividing by 3600.

     Thus we get $\dfrac{86.4 \times 1000}{3600} = \dfrac{{}^{144}\!\cancel{864}}{\cancel{36}_6} = 24$ m/s

Exercise 39.5

Copy and complete the following table, changing between speeds in km/h and m/s.

Question	Speed (m/s)	Speed (km/h)
1	5	
2		54
3	20	
4		14.4
5	8	
6		25.2
7	45	
8		216
9	3	
10		126

Density

The density (D) of a substance is its mass (M) per unit volume (V). It is calculated using the formula:

$$\text{density} = \frac{\text{mass}}{\text{volume}} \qquad \left(D = \frac{M}{V} \right)$$

We can rearrange the formula to work out an unknown mass if we know the density and volume, or an unknown volume if we know the mass and density.

$$\text{mass} = \text{density} \times \text{volume} \qquad (M = DV)$$
$$\text{volume} = \frac{\text{mass}}{\text{density}} \qquad \left(V = \frac{M}{D} \right)$$

An easy way to remember these formulae is to use this triangle.

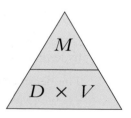

EXAMPLE 11

A block of mass 349.2 g has a volume of 36 cm³. Find its density.

SOLUTION

$$D = \frac{M}{V}$$

So $\qquad D = \dfrac{349.2}{36} = 9.7\,\text{g/cm}^3$ (using a calculator)

EXAMPLE 12

The density of a material is $2.4\,\text{g/cm}^3$. Find the mass of $5\,\text{cm}^3$ of the material.

SOLUTION

$$M = DV$$

So $\qquad M = 2.4 \times 5 = 12\,\text{g}$

EXAMPLE 13

A mass of $384\,\text{g}$ in the shape of a cube has a density of $6\,\text{g/cm}^3$.
Find the length of each side of the mass.

SOLUTION

We must find the volume first.

$$V = \frac{M}{D} = \frac{384}{6} = 64\,\text{cm}^3$$

But the volume of a cube of side l is given by l^3.

$$l^3 = 64\,\text{cm}^3$$

So $\qquad l = 4\,\text{cm}$

Exercise 39.6

1 A block of mass $84\,\text{g}$ has a volume of $15\,\text{cm}^3$. Find its density.

2 The density of a material is $3.8\,\text{g/cm}^3$. Find the mass of $9\,\text{cm}^3$ of the material.

3 A block of mass $120\,\text{g}$ has a density of $7.5\,\text{g/cm}^3$. Find its volume.

4 A block of mass $378\,\text{g}$ has a volume of $45\,\text{cm}^3$. Find its density.

5 The density of a material is $7.9\,\text{g/cm}^3$. Find the mass of $23\,\text{cm}^3$ of the material.

6 A block of mass $940.5\,\text{g}$ has a volume of $57\,\text{cm}^3$. Find its density.

7 A mass of $684\,\text{g}$ in the shape of a cuboid has a density of $1.5\,\text{g/cm}^3$. Its length and height are $9.5\,\text{cm}$ and $8\,\text{cm}$. Find its breadth.

8 The density of a material is $32\,\text{g/cm}^3$. Find the mass of $84.5\,\text{cm}^3$ of the material.

9 A block of mass $259.2\,\text{g}$ has a density of $4.8\,\text{g/cm}^3$. Find its volume.

10 A block of mass $252\,\text{g}$ has a volume of $18\,\text{cm}^3$. Find its density.

Other compound measures

There are many other situations where we use compound measures, such as prices per kg or per m^2, rates of flow, or populations in a given area.

EXAMPLE 14

The population of a country is 24 million. Its land area is 150 000 km². Find its population density in people/km².

SOLUTION

The units give a clue as to which order to divide.
Thus people/km² means we divide the number of people by the area.

$$\frac{24\,000\,000}{150\,000} = 160 \text{ people/km}^2$$

HINT
We divide to get density.

Exercise 39.7

1 A farmer grows raspberries in a rectangular field of length 125 m and breadth 84 m. He sells them making a profit of 17p per m². Find his total profit.

2 The population of a country is 32 million. Its land area is 250 000 km². Find its population density in people/km².

3 A shopkeeper sells 36 m² of carpet for £992.16. Find the selling price per m².

4 The population density of a country is 125 people/km². Its land area is 450 000 km². Find its population.

5 The selling price per kilogram of potatoes is £1.74. How many kilograms could be bought with £4.35?

6 The amount of concentrated juice in a drink is 175 ml/litre. How much concentrated juice would be in a drink of 840 ml?

7 The population of a country is 4.41 million. Its land area is 180 000 km². Find its population density in people/km².

8 A teacher buys 840 identical textbooks at a total cost of £7963.20. Find the cost per book.

9 A water tank has the shape of a cuboid. Its length is 5.6 m and its breadth is 4.5 m. It is completely filled with water in 48 minutes at an average rate of 107.1 m³/hour. Find its height.

10 The population of a country is 17.28 million. Its population density is 96 people/km². Find its land area.

You should now:
- know the formulae to find distance, speed and time
- be able to use the formulae to find distance, speed and time
- know the formulae to find mass, density and volume
- be able to use the formulae to find mass, density and volume
- be able to use other compound measures.

Summary exercise 39

1 A train travels 837 km in 9 hours. Find its average speed.

2 A van travels 171 km at an average speed of 45 km/h. How long will it take? Give your answer in hours and minutes.

3 A lorry travels for 6 hours 15 minutes at an average speed of 68 mph. How far will it have gone?

4 A man left home at 19.48 and drove at an average speed of 30 mph for 200 miles. When did he arrive?

5 A car travels 24 miles in 40 minutes and then 44 miles in 45 minutes. Find its average speed.

6 Convert these speeds:
   a   40 m/s to km/h
   b   9 km/h to m/s.

7 A bus leaves town A at 09.35 and arrives at town B at 11.15.
   a   If its average speed was 63 mph, find the distance AB.
   b   Another bus travels from B to A at an average speed of 50 mph, arriving at A at 15.00. When did it leave B?

8 A mass of 276.48 g in the shape of a cuboid has a density of 2.4 g/cm^3. Its length and height are 7.5 cm and 4.8 cm. Find its breadth.

9 The population of a country is 27 million. Its land area is 150 000 km^2. Find its population density in people/km^2.

10 The population of a country is 61.38 million. Its population density is 186 people/km^2. Find its land area.

Examination question

This question is from an examination paper where you may not use a calculator.

> Use 'Topic Tracker' at www.ccea.org.uk to find more exam questions.

1 The graph shows Adam's journey from home to Newton and back.
   a What was his average speed on the way to Newton?
   b Do you think Adam travelled on foot, on a bicycle or by train? Give a reason for your answer.

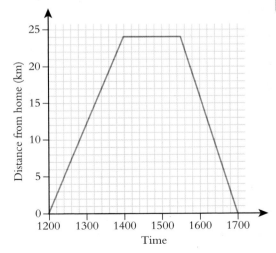

CHAPTER 40

Bounds

This chapter is about:

- understanding the continuous nature of measure
- understanding and calculating the upper and lower bounds of the values of expressions involving numbers, given to a stipulated degree of accuracy.

You should already know:

- how to approximate to a whole number
- how to approximate to a given number of decimal places
- how to approximate to a given number of significant figures
- how to use a calculator
- the relationship between time, distance and speed
- the relationship between mass, density and volume
- how to find the circumference and area of a circle
- how to find the volume of a cylinder and a sphere
- Pythagoras' theorem
- how to find the surface area of a solid.

Measurement

When we measure any quantity we can only give our measurement correct to the degree of accuracy of the measuring device we are using. All measurements are continuous (i.e. they can take any value). Thus a time of 6 seconds, 6.0 seconds or 6.000 seconds could all be three different times, depending on the accuracy of the measurement.

Let us call the time t seconds.

When we measure to the nearest second we have ..., 5, 6, 7, ...

Then 6 seconds measured to the nearest second could be anywhere in the interval $5.5 \leqslant t \leqslant 6.5$

When we measure to 1 decimal place we have ..., 5.9, 6.0, 6.1, ...

Then 6.0 seconds measured to 1 decimal place could be anywhere in the interval $5.95 \leqslant t \leqslant 6.05$

When we measure to 4 significant figures we have ..., 5.999, 6.000, 6.001, ...

Then 6 seconds measured to 4 significant figures could be anywhere in the interval $5.9995 \leqslant t \leqslant 6.0005$

Upper and lower bounds

The upper and lower bounds are the biggest and smallest possible values which a measurement may take.

Whenever measurements are given we must look at the degree of accuracy to determine the bounds.

We can put the results for measuring 6 seconds to different accuracies into a table.

Measurement	Accuracy	Lower bound	Upper bound
6 seconds	nearest second	5.5	6.5
6.0 seconds	1 decimal place	5.95	6.05
6.000 seconds	4 significant figures	5.995	6.005

EXAMPLE 1

Find the upper and lower bounds of:
   a   740 g measured to the nearest 10 g
   b   740 g measured to the nearest integer.

SOLUTION

   a   Measuring to the nearest 10 g would give us ..., 730, 740, 750, ...
       Halfway between 730 and 740 is 735 and halfway between 740 and 750 is 745.
       Thus the lower bound is 735 g and the upper bound is 745 g.
   b   Measuring to the nearest integer would give us ..., 739, 740, 741, ...
       Halfway between 739 and 740 is 739.5 and halfway between 740 and 741 is 740.5.
       Thus the lower bound is 739.5 g and the upper bound is 740.5 g.

Exercise 40.1

Copy and complete the table below.

	Measurement	Accuracy	Lower bound	Upper bound
1	48 kg	nearest integer		
2	5.3 cm	1 decimal place		
3	4.28 ml	3 significant figures		
4	40 s	nearest 10 seconds		
5	5000 mm	nearest 1000 mm		
6	58 cm^2	nearest cm^2		
7	400 ml	nearest 10 ml		
8	5000 mg	nearest 100 mg		
9	59 ml	nearest ml		
10	6.000 km	nearest m		

Combining measurements

We often need to combine measurements, for example when finding the area or perimeter of a rectangular shape we need to measure the length and the breadth. Both these measurements have upper and lower bounds. The accuracy to which we can give the area or perimeter depends on the accuracy of the measurements of length and breadth.

EXAMPLE 2

The length and breadth of a rectangle are measured as 8.4 cm and 5.6 cm each correct to 1 decimal place. Find:
- a the minimum possible perimeter
- b the maximum possible difference between the length and the breadth
- c the maximum possible area.

SOLUTION

Length: ..., 8.3, 8.4, 8.5, ...

Thus the lower bound is 8.35 and the upper bound is 8.45

Breadth: ..., 5.5, 5.6, 5.7, ...

Thus the lower bound is 5.55 and the upper bound is 5.65

- a Perimeter $P = 2(\text{length} + \text{breadth})$, i.e. $P = 2(l + b)$
  So $\min P = 2(\min l + \min b) = 2(8.35 + 5.55) = 27.8$ cm
- b Difference $D = l - b$
  So $\max D = \max l - \min b = 8.45 - 5.55 = 2.9$ cm
- c Area $A = lb$
  So $\max A = \max l \times \max b = 8.45 \times 5.65 = 47.7425$ cm^2

> **HINT**
>
> We must first find the upper and lower bounds of the length and breadth and then work out the minimum and maximum measurements.

EXAMPLE 3

The length and breadth of a cuboid were measured as 8 cm and 5 cm, each correct to the nearest integer. The volume was measured as 56 cm^3 correct to the nearest integer.

Find the range of values within which the height could lie, giving your answers to 3 significant figures.

SOLUTION

$V = lbh$ or $lbh = V$

Thus $h = \dfrac{V}{lb}$

Thus $\min h = \dfrac{\min V}{(\max l \times \max b)}$ and $\max h = \dfrac{\max V}{(\min l \times \min b)}$

We must find the lower and upper bounds for each measure first:

$l = 8$ cm	$b = 5$ cm	$V = 56$ cm^3
$\min l = 7.5$ cm	$\min b = 4.5$ cm	$\min V = 55.5$ cm^3
$\max l = 8.5$ cm	$\max b = 5.5$ cm	$\max V = 56.5$ cm^3

Thus $\min h = \dfrac{55.5}{(8.5 \times 5.5)} = \dfrac{55.5}{46.75} = 1.19$

And $\max h = \dfrac{56.5}{(7.5 \times 4.5)} = \dfrac{56.5}{33.75} = 1.67$

The height could lie between 1.19 and 1.67 cm.

Exercise 40.2

1 The length and breadth of a rectangle are measured as 4.8 cm and 6.2 cm, each correct to 1 decimal place. Find:
   a the minimum perimeter
   b the maximum area.

2 The area of a rectangle is measured as 56.5 cm² correct to 1 decimal place. The length is measured as 9.6 cm correct to 1 decimal place. Find the range within which the breadth could lie.

3 The radius of a circle is measured as 4.8 cm correct to 2 significant figures. Find:
   a the minimum circumference
   b the maximum area.

4 The length, breadth and height of a cuboid were measured as 30 cm, 20 cm and 40 cm, each correct to the nearest 10 cm. Find the range within which the volume could lie.

5 A car travels 150 miles in 2.8 hours, each measured to 2 significant figures. Find the range within which the speed in mph could lie.

6 The mass and volume of a solid are measured as 38 g and 7.8 cm³, each correct to 2 significant figures. Find the range within which the density could lie.

7 The base of a parallelogram is measured as 8.6 cm correct to 2 decimal places. The area of the parallelogram is measured as 40 cm² correct to the nearest 10 cm². Find the range within which the perpendicular height of the parallelogram could lie.

8 The two perpendicular sides of a right-angled triangle are measured as 7.2 cm and 5.8 cm, each correct to 1 decimal place Find:
   a the maximum length of the hypotenuse
   b the minimum area.

9 The diameter of a sphere is measured as 14 cm correct to the nearest integer. Find:
   a the minimum radius
   b the maximum volume.

10 The length of a prism is measured as 18 cm correct to the nearest integer. The volume of the prism is measured as 64 cm³ correct to the nearest integer. Find the range within which the cross-sectional area could lie.

Calculating the upper and lower bounds of the values of expressions

When calculating the upper and lower bounds of an expression, you should follow this procedure.

- Always find the upper and lower bound of each number first.
- Then use these rules:

$$\max (A + B) = \max A + \max B$$
$$\min (A + B) = \min A + \min B$$
$$\max (A - B) = \max A - \min B$$
$$\min (A - B) = \min A - \max B$$
$$\max (AB) = \max A \times \max B$$
$$\min (AB) = \min A \times \min B$$
$$\max \left(\frac{A}{B}\right) = \frac{\max A}{\min B}$$
$$\min \left(\frac{A}{B}\right) = \frac{\min A}{\max B}$$

EXAMPLE 4

The values P, Q and R were measured as 6.4, 4.7 and 5.3, each correct to 2 significant figures.

a Find the minimum value of: i $P + Q$ ii $\dfrac{P}{R}$ iii Q^2

b Find the maximum value of: i $R - Q$ ii PQ iii $\sqrt{R}$

SOLUTION

We should first write down the lower and upper bounds for P, Q and R.

	Lower bound	Value	Upper bound
P	6.35	6.4	6.45
Q	4.65	4.7	4.75
R	5.25	5.3	5.35

a   i $\min P + \min Q = 6.35 + 4.65 = 11.00$

    ii $\dfrac{\min P}{\max R} = \dfrac{6.35}{5.35} = 1.19$

    iii $(\min Q)^2 = 4.65^2 = 21.6225$

b   i $\max R - \min Q = 5.35 - 4.65 = 0.70$

    ii $\max P \times \max Q = 6.45 \times 4.75 = 30.6375$

    iii $\sqrt{\max R} = \sqrt{5.35} = 2.31$

Exercise 40.3

1 A and B were measured as 74 and 53, each correct to 2 decimal places.

    a Find the maximum value of: **i** $A + B$ **ii** $\dfrac{A}{B}$

    b Find the minimum value of: **i** AB **ii** $A - B$

2 C and D were measured as 5.16 and 4.58, each correct to 3 significant figures.

    a Find the maximum value of: **i** CD **ii** $C - D$

    b Find the minimum value of: **i** $C + D$ **ii** $\dfrac{C}{D}$

3 E and F were measured as 9.6 and 4.2, each correct to 1 decimal place.

    a Find the maximum value of: **i** $E + F$ **ii** $\dfrac{E}{F}$

    b Find the minimum value of:

      i EF **ii** $\sqrt{E}$ **iii** $E - F$

4 G was measured as 320 to the nearest 10 and H as 200 correct to the nearest 100.

    a Find the maximum value of:

      i GH **ii** $\sqrt{H}$ **iii** $G - H$

    b Find the minimum value of:

      i $G - H$ **ii** H^2 **iii** $\dfrac{G}{H}$ **iv** $\dfrac{H}{G}$

5 The values A, B and C were measured as 5.8, 2.6 and 1.3, each correct to 1 decimal place.

    a Find the maximum value of:

      i $A + B$ **ii** BC **iii** C^2 **iv** $\dfrac{A}{B}$

      v $B - C$ **vi** $\dfrac{(A + B)}{C}$ **vii** $\dfrac{(B - C)}{A}$

    b Find the minimum value of:

      i AC **ii** $B + C$ **iii** $\sqrt{B}$ **iv** $A - C$

      v $\dfrac{C}{B}$ **vi** $\dfrac{AB}{C}$ **vii** $\dfrac{(A - B)}{C}$

You should now:

- understand the continuous nature of measure
- understand that measurements given are only approximate to the degree of accuracy used in recording them
- know what is meant by the upper and lower bounds
- know how to calculate the maximum and minimum values of expressions given the measurements and their accuracy.

Summary exercise 40

1   Copy and complete the table below.

Measurement	Accuracy	Lower bound	Upper bound
57 cm	nearest integer		
420 mm	nearest 10 mm		
5000 h	nearest 100 h		
8.46 m	nearest cm		
5.8 l	1 decimal place		
5.197 g	4 significant figures		

2   The base and height of a parallelogram are measured as 16 cm and 12 cm, each correct to the nearest integer. Find:
   a the maximum area
   b the minimum area.

3   The sides of a right-angled triangle are measured as 3 cm, 4 cm and 5 cm, each correct to the nearest integer. Find the range within which **a** the perimeter and **b** the area could lie.

4   The area of a rectangle is measured as 50 cm^2 correct to the nearest 10 cm^2. Its length is measured as 8.6 cm to the nearest millimetre. Find the range within which the breadth could lie.

5   The sides of a cube are measured as 5.4 cm, each correct to 1 decimal place. Find:
   a the maximum volume
   b the minimum surface area.

6   A car travels 84 miles correct to 2 significant figures at an average speed of 56 mph correct to 2 significant figures. Find the range within which the time taken to travel this distance could lie.

   Give your answers in **a** hours and **b** hours and minutes.

7   The density and volume of a solid were measured as 4.56 g/cm^3 and 14.8 cm^3, each correct to 3 significant figures. Find the range within which the mass of the solid could lie.

8   The length and diagonal of a rectangle are measured as 6.8 cm and 9.4 cm, each correct to 1 decimal place. Find the range within which the breadth could lie.

9   P and Q were measured as 7.8 and 4.9, each correct to 1 decimal place.
   a Find the maximum value of:
      i PQ ii P^2 iii $P - Q$
   b Find the minimum value of:
      i $P + Q$ ii $\sqrt{Q}$ iii $\dfrac{P}{Q}$

10 The values X, Y and Z were measured as 4500, 3000 and 2800, each correct to the nearest 100.

   a Find the maximum value of:

     i $X + Y$ **ii** ZY **iii** Z^2 **iv** $X - Y$

     v $\dfrac{Y}{Z}$ **vi** $\dfrac{(X - Y)}{Z}$ **vii** $\dfrac{(X - Z)}{Y}$

   b Find the minimum value of:

     i XZ **ii** $Y + Z$ **iii** $\sqrt{Y}$

     iv $Y - Z$ **v** $\dfrac{Z}{X}$

Examination questions

These questions are from examination papers where you may use a calculator.

Use 'Topic Tracker' at www.ccea.org.uk to find more exam questions.

1 A set of models have square bases. Widths are measured to the nearest millimetre. One model has a base of width 12.0 cm. What is the upper limit of the area of the base?

2 a, b and c are three values, each correct to 3 significant figures.
$a = 23.1$
$b = 25.6$
$c = 18.7$
Calculate the minimum value of d where $d = a + b + 3c$.

3 The two shorter sides of a right-angled triangle are 80 cm and 120 cm, both to 2 significant figures. What is the smallest possible size of the smallest angle in the triangle?

4 Find the least and greatest total length of nine pencils, each measuring 7 cm to the nearest cm.

CHAPTER 41

Transformations

This chapter is about:

- transforming shapes by reflection, rotation, translation, enlargement
- combining transformations
- understanding what is meant by the inverse of a transformation.

You should already know:

- how to plot and read points given in co-ordinate form
- how to use $y = mx + c$ as the equation of a straight line
- what is meant by clockwise and anti-clockwise turns
- how to find the reciprocal of a number.

Transformation

A transformation is when a shape is moved from one position to another. This can be described in one of four ways:

- reflection
- rotation
- translation
- enlargement.

The position a shape is moved to is called its **image**. We say that the shape has been mapped to this image.

Reflection

To find the image after a reflection in a line you:

- count the **perpendicular** distance from each corner to the line
- count the **same** distance on the other side.

When a shape is reflected it stays the **same** size and shape. Its position is changed (either back to front, upside down or diagonally).

Drawing the image of a shape under reflection

Examples 1 and 2 show how to draw a shape under reflection. The drawings show the original shape and its reflection.

EXAMPLE 1

Draw the image of quadrilateral Q after a reflection in $x = 2$.

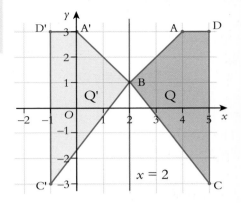

SOLUTION

A is 2 squares to the right of $x = 2$. So we count 2 squares to the left.

B is on the line $x = 2$. So it stays in the same place.

C is 3 squares to the right of $x = 2$. So we count 3 squares to the left.

D is 3 squares to the right of $x = 2$. So we count 3 squares to the left.

EXAMPLE 2

Draw the image of triangle T after a reflection in $y = x$.

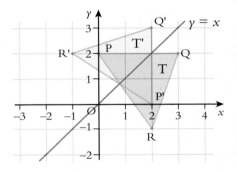

SOLUTION

P is 1 diagonal to the left of $y = x$. So we count 1 diagonal to the right.

Q is $\frac{1}{2}$ a diagonal to the right of $y = x$.
So we count $\frac{1}{2}$ diagonals to the left.

R is $1\frac{1}{2}$ diagonals to the right of $y = x$.
So we count $1\frac{1}{2}$ diagonals to the left.

Exercise 41.1

1   Plot and join A(2, 1), B(3, 4), C(4, 1). Draw the image of ABC after reflection in the x-axis.

2   Plot and join D(−3, 2), E(−1, 3), F(2, −1). Draw the image of DEF after reflection in the y-axis.

3   Plot and join G(−4, −2), H(−5, −1), I(−2, 1). Draw the image of GHI after reflection in the line $x = 1$.

4   Plot and join J(2, −1), K(3, −4), L(4, −2). Draw the image of JKL after reflection in the line $y = 2$.

5   Plot and join M(2, 3), N(3, 6), P(5, 2). Draw the image of MNP after reflection in the line $x = -2$.

6   Plot and join Q(−2, 2), R(−1, 4), S(0, 1). Draw the image of QRS after reflection in the line $y = -3$.

7   Plot and join T(2, 5), U(3, 7), V(4, 2). Draw the image of TUV after reflection in the line $y = x$.

8   Plot and join X(−1, −3), Y(−3, −2), Z(−4, −5). Draw the image of XYZ after reflection in the line $y = -x$.

Drawing the original shape

EXAMPLE 3

T' is the image of T under a reflection in the line $y = -2$. Draw T on the grid.

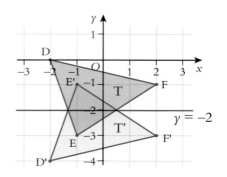

SOLUTION

The **inverse** of a reflection is just the **same** reflection. So we just reflect T' in $y = -2$.

D' is 2 squares below $y = -2$. So we count 2 squares above.

E' is 1 square above $y = -2$. So we count 1 square below.

F' is 1 square below $y = -2$. So we count 1 square above.

Exercise 41.2

1 Plot and join A'(3, 5), B'(4, 1), C'(1, −1). A'B'C' is the image of ABC under reflection in the x-axis. Draw ABC on your diagram.

2 Plot and join A'(1, −2), B'(2, −4), C'(3, 0). A'B'C' is the image of ABC under reflection in the line $x = -1$. Draw ABC on your diagram.

3 Plot and join A'(−4, 5), B'(−3, 2), C'(−1, 4). A'B'C' is the image of ABC under reflection in the line $y = x$. Draw ABC on your diagram.

4 Plot and join A'(−3, −5), B'(−2, −3), C'(0, −4). A'B'C' is the image of ABC under reflection in the y-axis. Draw ABC on your diagram.

5 Plot and join A'(2, 7), B'(3, 5), C'(5, 6). A'B'C' is the image of ABC under reflection in the line $y = 3$. Draw ABC on your diagram.

6 Plot and join A'(3, −5), B'(4, −2), C'(6, −3). A'B'C' is the image of ABC under reflection in the line $y = -x$. Draw ABC on your diagram.

Describing a reflection fully

To describe a reflection fully, you must give both of these:

• the name of the transformation (reflection)

• the equation of the line in which the reflection takes place.

EXAMPLE 4

Describe the transformation fully that maps T to T'.

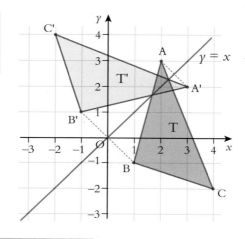

SOLUTION

Rules

• Join A to A'.

• Join B to B'.

• Draw the line joining the midpoints of AA' and BB' (which is $y = x$).

Answer. Reflection in the line $y = x$.

Exercise 41.3

Describe **fully** the transformation that maps T to T' in each diagram.

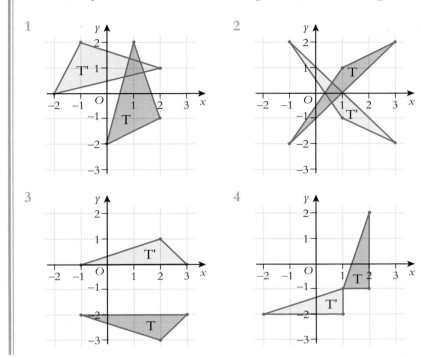

Rotation

To find the image after a rotation about a point you turn the shape in the correct direction (clockwise or anti-clockwise) using tracing paper about the centre of rotation.

When a shape is rotated it stays the **same** size and shape.
Its orientation changes.

Drawing the image of a shape under rotation

EXAMPLE 5

Draw the image of triangle T after a 180° rotation about C(1, −2).

SOLUTION

Mark the centre C on the grid.

Trace T and turn the tracing paper through $\frac{1}{2}$ a turn about C.

It does not matter whether you turn clockwise or anti-clockwise when you have a 180° rotation.

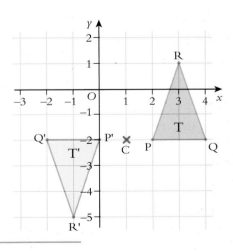

EXAMPLE 6

Draw the image of triangle T after a 90° clockwise rotation about O.

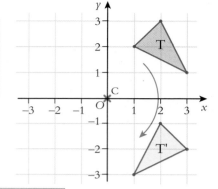

SOLUTION

Mark the centre O on the grid.

Trace T and turn the tracing paper through $\frac{1}{4}$ of a turn clockwise about C.

Exercise 41.4

1   Plot and join A(2, 1), B(3, 4), C(4, 1). Draw the image of ABC after a rotation of 180° about O.

2   Plot and join D(−3, 2), E(−1, 3), F(2, −1). Draw the image of DEF after a 90° clockwise rotation about O.

3   Plot and join G(−4, −2), H(−5, −1), I(−2, 1). Draw the image of GHI after a 90° anti-clockwise rotation about (1, 3).

4   Plot and join J(2, −1), K(3, −4), L(4, −2). Draw the image of JKL after a rotation of 180° about (1, 2).

5   Plot and join M(2, 3), N(3, 6), P(5, 2). Draw the image of MNP after a 90° anti-clockwise rotation about O.

6   Plot and join Q(−2, 2), R(−1, 4), S(0, 1). Draw the image of QRS after a 90° clockwise rotation about (3, 2).

7   Plot and join T(2, 5), U(3, 7), V(4, 2). Draw the image of TUV after a 90° anti-clockwise rotation about (1, 0).

8   Plot and join X(−1, −3), Y(−3, −2), Z(−4, −5). Draw the image of XYZ after a 90° clockwise rotation about O.

Drawing the original shape

EXAMPLE 7

T' is the image of T after a 90° clockwise rotation about (2, 1). Draw T on the grid.

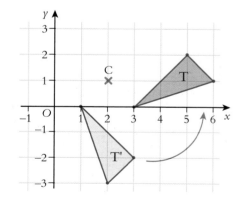

SOLUTION

Mark the centre C on the grid.

Trace T' and turn the tracing paper through $\frac{1}{4}$ of a turn **anti-clockwise** about C.

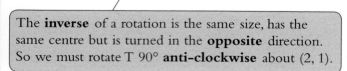

The **inverse** of a rotation is the same size, has the same centre but is turned in the **opposite** direction. So we must rotate T 90° **anti-clockwise** about (2, 1).

Exercise 41.5

1 Plot and join A'(3, 5), B'(4, 1), C'(1, −1). A'B'C' is the image of ABC after a 90° clockwise rotation about (2, 0). Draw ABC on your diagram.

2 Plot and join A'(1, −2), B'(2, −4), C'(3, 0). A'B'C' is the image of ABC after a 90° anti-clockwise rotation about (1, 1). Draw ABC on your diagram.

3 Plot and join A'(−4, 5), B'(−3, 2), C'(−1, 4). A'B'C' is the image of ABC after a 90° clockwise rotation about (−2, 1). Draw ABC on your diagram.

4 Plot and join A'(−3, −5), B'(−2, −3), C'(0, −4). A'B'C' is the image of ABC after a 90° anti-clockwise rotation about (−1, −2). Draw ABC on your diagram.

5 Plot and join A'(2, 7), B'(3, 5), C'(5, 6). A'B'C' is the image of ABC after a 90° anti-clockwise rotation about O. Draw ABC on your diagram.

6 Plot and join A'(3, −5), B'(4, −2), C'(6, −3.) A'B'C' is the image of ABC after a 90° clockwise rotation about O. Draw ABC on your diagram.

Describing a rotation fully

To describe a rotation fully, you must give

- the name of the transformation (rotation)
- the size and direction of the rotation
- the centre.

EXAMPLE 8

Describe the transformation fully that maps T to T'.

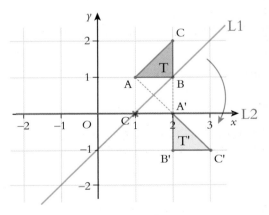

SOLUTION

Rules

- Join A to A'.
- Join B to B'.
- Draw the perpendicular bisectors of AA' and BB' (labelled L1 and L2 on the diagram).
- The perpendicular bisectors cross at the centre.

Answer: 90° clockwise rotation about (1, 0).

Exercise 41.6

Describe **fully** the transformation that maps T to T' in each diagram.

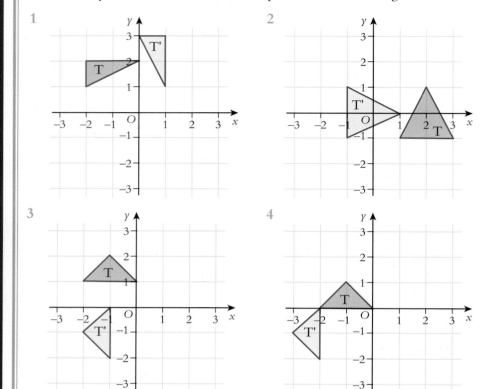

Translation

To find the image after a translation you move each point horizontally and vertically as given by the translation vector $\begin{pmatrix} a \\ b \end{pmatrix}$.

a (the x component of the translation) tells you how far to move across.

- If a is positive you move each point to the right.
- If a is negative you move each point to the left.

b (the y component of the translation) tells you how far to move vertically.

- If b is positive you move each point up.
- If b is negative you move each point down.

When a shape is translated it stays the **same** size and shape.
Its keeps the same orientation.

Drawing the image of a shape under translation

The next example shows how to draw the image of a shape under translation. The drawing shows the shape before and after the translation.

EXAMPLE 9

Draw the image of quadrilateral Q after the translation $\begin{pmatrix} 3 \\ -2 \end{pmatrix}$.

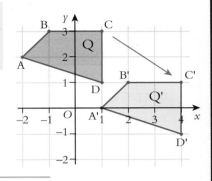

SOLUTION

The translation vector means 'move 3 squares to the right and 2 squares down'. Thus,

A is mapped to A'(1, 0).   B is mapped to B'(2, 1).
C is mapped to C'(4, 1).   D is mapped to D'(4, −1).

Exercise 41.7

1   Plot and join A(2, 1), B(3, 4), C(4, 1).
    Draw the image of ABC after the translation $\begin{pmatrix} 2 \\ -1 \end{pmatrix}$.

2   Plot and join D(−3, 2), E(−1, 3), F(2, −1).
    Draw the image of DEF after the translation $\begin{pmatrix} -2 \\ 5 \end{pmatrix}$.

3   Plot and join G(−4, −2), H(−5, −1), I(−2, 1).
    Draw the image of GHI after the translation $\begin{pmatrix} 3 \\ -2 \end{pmatrix}$.

4   Plot and join J(2, −1), K(3, −4), L(4, −2).
    Draw the image of JKL after the translation $\begin{pmatrix} -1 \\ -3 \end{pmatrix}$.

5   Plot and join M(2, 3), N(3, 6), P(5, 2).
    Draw the image of MNP after the translation $\begin{pmatrix} -2 \\ 0 \end{pmatrix}$.

6   Plot and join Q(−2, 2), R(−1, 4), S(0, 1).
    Draw the image of QRS after the translation $\begin{pmatrix} 1 \\ -4 \end{pmatrix}$.

7   Plot and join T(2, 5), U(3, 7), V(4, 2).
    Draw the image of TUV after the translation $\begin{pmatrix} 0 \\ 3 \end{pmatrix}$.

8   Plot and join X(−1, −3), Y(−3, −2), Z(−4, −5).
    Draw the image of XYZ after the translation $\begin{pmatrix} -2 \\ -5 \end{pmatrix}$.

Drawing the original shape

EXAMPLE 10

T' is the image of T under the translation $\begin{pmatrix} -1 \\ 3 \end{pmatrix}$.
Draw T on the grid.

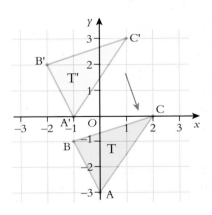

SOLUTION

The **inverse** of a translation is when you move the points in the **opposite** direction. Thus we need to move each point 1 square to the **right** and 3 squares **down**.

A' is mapped to A(0, −3).
B' is mapped to B(−1, −1).
C' is mapped to C(2, 0).

Exercise 41.8

1 Plot and join A'(3, 5), B'(4, 1), C'(1, −1). A'B'C' is the image
   of ABC after the translation $\begin{pmatrix} 2 \\ -1 \end{pmatrix}$. Draw ABC on your diagram.

2 Plot and join A'(1, −2), B'(2, −4), C'(3, 0). A'B'C' is the image
   of ABC after the translation $\begin{pmatrix} 4 \\ 3 \end{pmatrix}$. Draw ABC on your diagram.

3 Plot and join A'(−4, 5), B'(−3, 2), C'(−1, 4). A'B'C' is the image
   of ABC after the translation $\begin{pmatrix} -2 \\ -5 \end{pmatrix}$. Draw ABC on your diagram.

4 Plot and join A'(−3, −5), B'(−2, −3), C'(0, −4). A'B'C' is the
   image of ABC after the translation $\begin{pmatrix} -1 \\ 2 \end{pmatrix}$. Draw ABC on your diagram.

5 Plot and join A'(2, 7), B'(3, 5), C'(5, 6). A'B'C' is the image of
   ABC after the translation $\begin{pmatrix} 4 \\ -3 \end{pmatrix}$. Draw ABC on your diagram.

6 Plot and join A'(3, −5), B'(4, −2), C'(6, −3). A'B'C' is the image
   of ABC after the translation $\begin{pmatrix} -2 \\ 4 \end{pmatrix}$. Draw ABC on your diagram.

Describing a translation fully

To describe a translation fully, you must give

- the name of the transformation (translation)
- **both** components of the translation vector.

EXAMPLE 11

Describe the transformation fully that maps T to T'.

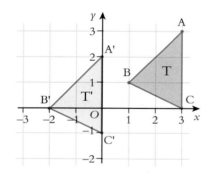

SOLUTION

Rules

- Count horizontally from A to A'.
- Count vertically from A to A'.
- Write your answer in proper component form.

Answer: Translation $\begin{pmatrix} -3 \\ -1 \end{pmatrix}$.

Exercise 41.9

Describe **fully** the transformation that maps T to T' in each diagram.

1

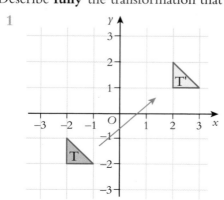

2

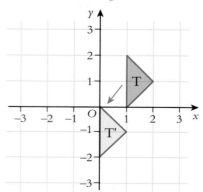

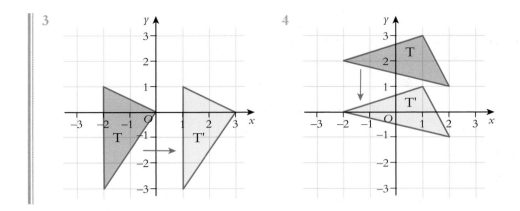

Enlargement

To find the image after an enlargement you

- count horizontally **from the centre** to each corner in turn and multiply your answer by the scale factor
- count the new horizontal distance **from the centre**
- count vertically **from the centre** to each corner in turn and multiply your answer by the scale factor
- count the new vertical distance **from the centre**.

When a shape is enlarged the angles all remain unchanged but all the lengths are multiplied by the scale factor.

Drawing the image of a shape under enlargement

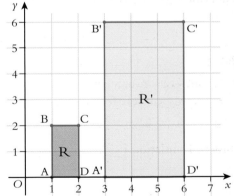

EXAMPLE 12

Draw the image of rectangle R after an enlargement, centre O, scale factor 3.

SOLUTION

O to A(1, 0) is 1 square to the right.

Since the scale factor is 3 then O to A' will be 3 squares to the right, i.e. A'(3, 0).

Similarly O to B(1, 2) is 1 square to the right and 2 squares up.

Thus O to B' will be 3 squares to the right and 6 squares up, i.e. B'(3, 6).

EXAMPLE 13

Draw the image of triangle PQR after an enlargement, centre C(2, 1), scale factor $\frac{1}{2}$.

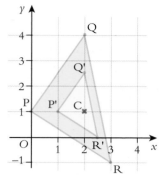

SOLUTION

C to P(0, 1) is 2 squares to the left.

Since the scale factor is $\frac{1}{2}$ then C to P' will be 1 square to the left **from C**, i.e. P'(1, 1).

Similarly C to Q(2, 4) is 3 squares up.

Thus C to Q' will be $1\frac{1}{2}$ squares up, i.e. Q'(2, $2\frac{1}{2}$).

C to R(3, −1) is 1 square to the right and 2 squares down.

Thus C to R' will be $\frac{1}{2}$ square to the right and 1 square down, i.e. R'($2\frac{1}{2}$, 0).

Negative scale factor

When there is a negative scale factor you must

- join the centre to each point in turn
- extend these lines in the **opposite** direction
- always measure from the centre.

EXAMPLE 14

Draw the image of triangle PQR after an enlargement, centre C(1, −2), scale factor −2.

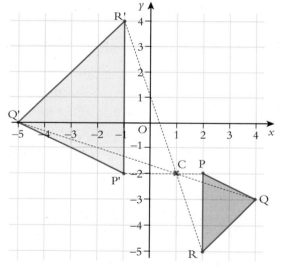

SOLUTION

C to P(2, −2) is 1 square to the right.

Since the scale factor is −2 then C to P' will be 2 squares to the **left from C**, i.e. P'(−1, −2).

Similarly C to Q(4, −3) is 3 to the right and 1 down.

Thus C to Q' will be 6 to the left and 2 up, i.e. Q'(0, −5).

C to R(2, −5) is 1 square to the right and 3 squares down.

Thus C to R' will be 2 squares to the left and 6 squares up, i.e. R'(−1, 4).

Exercise 41.10

1 Plot and join A(2, 1), B(3, 4), C(4, 1). Draw the image of ABC after an enlargement, centre O, scale factor 2.

2 Plot and join D(−3, 2), E(−1, 3), F(2, −1). Draw the image of DEF after an enlargement, centre (1, 1), scale factor $1\frac{1}{2}$.

3 Plot and join G(−4, −2), H(−5, −1), I(−2, 1.) Draw the image of GHI after an enlargement, centre O, scale factor −2.

4 Plot and join J(2, −1), K(3, −4), L(4, −2). Draw the image of JKL after an enlargement, centre (1, 0), scale factor 3.

5 Plot and join M(2, 3), N(3, 6), P(5, 2) Draw the image of MNP after an enlargement, centre O, scale factor $\frac{1}{2}$

6 Plot and join Q(−2, 2), R(−1, 4), S(0, 1). Draw the image of QRS after an enlargement, centre (−1, 1), scale factor $2\frac{1}{2}$.

7 Plot and join T(2, 5), U(3, 7), V(4, 2). Draw the image of TUV after an enlargement, centre O, scale factor $-\frac{1}{2}$.

8 Plot and join X(−1, −3), Y(−3, −2), Z(−4, −5). Draw the image of XYZ after an enlargement, centre O, scale factor $1\frac{1}{2}$.

Drawing the original shape

EXAMPLE 15

T' is the image of T after an enlargement, centre (0, 2), scale factor 2. Draw T on the grid.

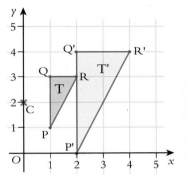

SOLUTION

The **inverse** of an enlargement has the same centre but the scale factor is the **reciprocal** of the given scale factor. So we must enlarge T' by a scale factor of $\frac{1}{2}$ about (0, 2).

C to P'(2, 0) is 2 squares to the right and 2 squares down

Since the scale factor is $\frac{1}{2}$ then C to P will be 1 square to the right and 1 square down **from C**, i.e. P(1, 1).

Similarly C to Q'(2, 4) is 2 squares to the right and 2 squares up.

Thus C to Q will be 1 square to the right and 1 square up, i.e. Q(1, 3).

C to R'(4, 4) is 4 squares to the right and 2 squares up.

Thus C to R will be 2 squares to the right and 1 square up, i.e. R(2, 3).

Exercise 41.11

1 Plot and join A'(3, 5), B'(4, 1), C'(1, −1). A'B'C' is the image of ABC after an enlargement, centre O, scale factor 2. Draw ABC.

2 Plot and join A'(1, −2), B'(2, −4), C'(3, 0). A'B'C' is the image of ABC after an enlargement, centre (1, −1), scale factor $\frac{1}{2}$. Draw ABC.

3 Plot and join A'(−4, 5), B'(−3, 2), C'(−1, 4). A'B'C' is the image of ABC after an enlargement, centre O, scale factor −2. Draw ABC.

4 Plot and join A'(−3, −5), B'(−2, −3), C'(0, −4). A'B'C' is the image of ABC after an enlargement, centre (0, 1), scale factor $\frac{1}{3}$. Draw ABC.

5 Plot and join A'(2, 7), B'(3, 5), C'(5, 6). A'B'C' is the image of ABC after an enlargement, centre O, scale factor 2. Draw ABC.

6 Plot and join A'(3, −5), B'(4, −2), C'(6, −3). A'B'C' is the image of ABC after an enlargement, centre (2, 1), scale factor 2. Draw ABC.

Describing an enlargement fully

To describe an enlargement fully you must give

- the name of the transformation (enlargement)
- the centre of the enlargement
- the scale factor of the enlargement.

EXAMPLE 16

Describe the transformation fully that maps PQR to P'Q'R'.

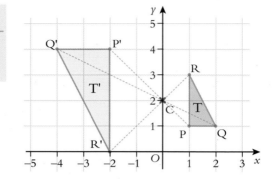

SOLUTION

Rules

- Join P to P', Q to Q' and R to R'.
- The centre of the enlargement is where these lines cross, i.e. (0, 2).
- The scale factor is found by $\dfrac{P'Q'}{PQ}$ or $\dfrac{P'R'}{PR} = \dfrac{-2}{1} = -2$.

Answer: Enlargement, centre (0, 2), scale factor −2. ◄─── This is a negative scale factor.

Exercise 41.12

Describe **fully** the transformation that maps T to T' in each diagram.

1

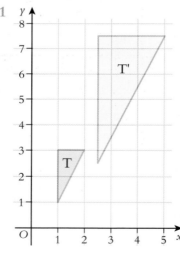

2

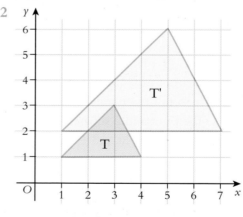

3

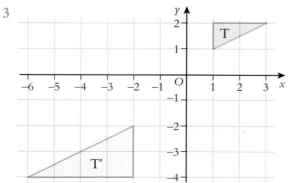

4

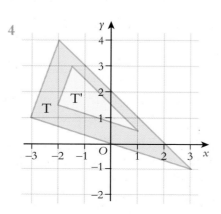

5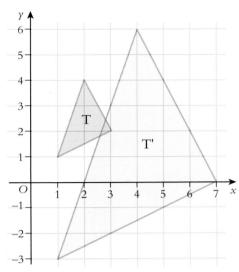

6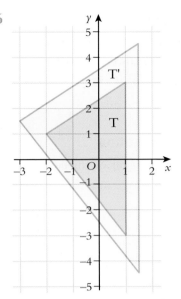

Combination of transformations

EXAMPLE 17

Draw the image of the triangle T after a
reflection in $y = x$ followed by a 90°
anti-clockwise rotation about (0, 1).

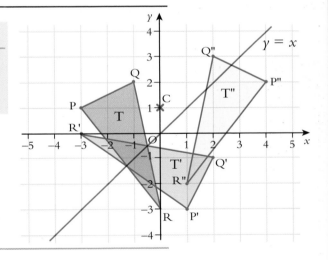

SOLUTION

We do the reflection first to get T' and then
rotate T' to get T".

Exercise 41.13

1 Plot and join A(2, 1), B(3, 4), C(4, 1). Draw the image of ABC
  after a reflection in the x-axis followed by the translation $\begin{pmatrix} -3 \\ 1 \end{pmatrix}$.

2 Plot and join D(−3, 2), E(−1, 3), F(2, −1). Draw the image of
  DEF after a 90° anti-clockwise rotation about (1, 0) followed by a
  reflection in $y = x$.

3 Plot and join G(−4, −2), H(−5, −1), I(−2, 1). Draw the image
  of GHI after a translation $\begin{pmatrix} -1 \\ 2 \end{pmatrix}$ followed by an enlargement, centre
  O, scale factor 2.

4 Plot and join J(2, −1), K(3, −4), L(4, −2). Draw the image of JKL
  after a 90° clockwise rotation about (2, 0) followed by a reflection
  in the y-axis.

5 Plot and join M(2, 3), N(3, 6), P(5, 2). Draw the image of MNP
   after a reflection in $y = -x$ followed by a 180° rotation about (3, 1).

6 Plot and join Q(−2, 2), R(−1, 4), S(0, 1). Draw the image of QRS
   after an enlargement, centre O, scale factor −2, followed
   by a translation $\begin{pmatrix} -2 \\ -1 \end{pmatrix}$.

Recognising transformations

- An enlargement gives a bigger or smaller image.
- A translation leaves the image in a similar position.
- A reflection leaves the image upside down, back to front or
  bent diagonally.
- A rotation leaves the image turned round.

Describing transformations fully

- Pick out the type of transformation first.
- Describe it fully using the techniques learnt earlier.

EXAMPLE 18

Describe the following
transformations:

T to A   T to B

T to C   T to D.

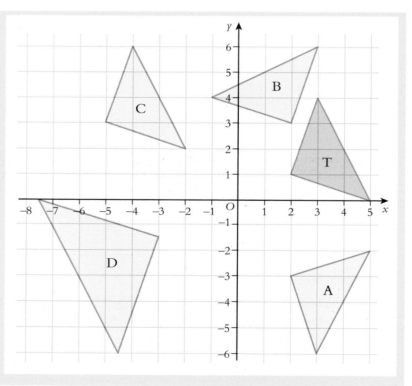

SOLUTION

T to A: turned upside down − reflection in $y = -1$.

T to B: turned round − anti-clockwise rotation of 90° about (1, 2).

T to C: in a similar orientation − translation $\begin{pmatrix} -7 \\ 2 \end{pmatrix}$.

T to D: bigger − enlargement, centre O, scale factor $-1\frac{1}{2}$.

Exercise 41.14

Describe the **single** transformation that maps T to T' in each of the following diagrams.

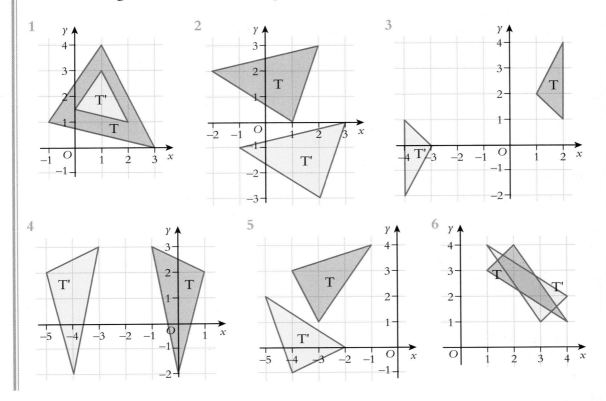

Summary exercise 41

1 Plot and join G(−2, 5), H(0, 6), I(5, −1). Draw the image of GHI after reflection in the line $x = 1$.

2 Plot and join A'(−3, −5), B'(0, −2), C'(2, −3). A'B'C' is the image of ABC under reflection in the line $y = -x$. Draw ABC on your diagram.

3 Plot and join A(−2, 1), B(1, −3), C(4, 2). Draw the image of ABC after a rotation of 180° about (1, −1).

4 Plot and join A'(−1, −2), B'(−2, −4), C'(−3, 1). A'B'C' is the image of ABC after a 90° anti-clockwise rotation about (1, 2).

5 Plot and join D(5, −2), E(3, 1), F(2, −4). Draw the image of DEF after the translation $\begin{pmatrix} 2 \\ -3 \end{pmatrix}$.

6 Plot and join A(1, 3), B(4, 1), C(5, 4). Draw the image of ABC after an enlargement, centre (3, 2), scale factor 2.

7 Plot and join A'(−3, 2), B'(−1, 5), C'(1, 0). A'B'C' is the image of ABC after an enlargement, centre O, scale factor 2. Draw ABC.

8 Plot and join M(1, −1), N(3, 0), P(4, −2). Draw the image of MNP after a reflection in $y = x$ followed by a 90° clockwise rotation about (1, 2).

9 Plot and join Q(−2, −2), R(−1, −4), S(0, 2). Draw the image of QRS after an enlargement, centre O, scale factor $\frac{1}{2}$, followed by a translation $\begin{pmatrix} 2 \\ -1 \end{pmatrix}$.

10 Describe the **single** transformation which maps

    a T to A   **b** T to B   **c** T to C   **d** T to D.

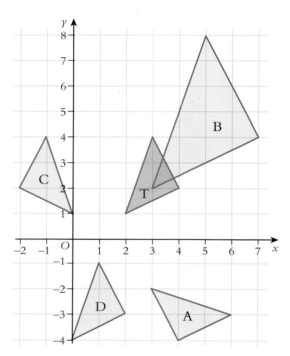

Use 'Topic Tracker' at www.ccea.org.uk to find more exam questions.

Question **1** is from an examination paper where you may not use a calculator.

1 **a** Copy the diagram. On your grid, draw a reflection of the shape S in the line $y = 5$.

   b On your grid, draw an enlargement of the shape S, scale factor 2, centre $(0, 0)$.

   c Describe fully the transformation that maps the shape S onto the shape T.

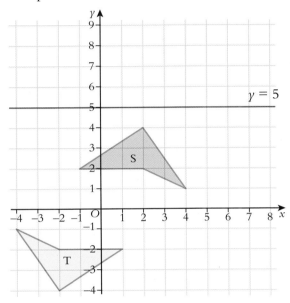

Question **2** is from an examination paper where you may use a calculator.

2 Copy the diagram. On your grid, draw a rotation of the given shape by 90° clockwise about the origin.

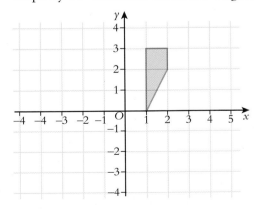

CHAPTER 42

Questionnaires

This chapter is about:

- carrying out the data handling cycle
- designing and using recording sheets
- designing and using a questionnaire
- testing hypotheses.

You should already know:

- how to use tally marks
- the rules of inequalities.

The data handling cycle

Whenever you have to carry out an investigation or survey, you should follow the data handling cycle as detailed below:

1 Specifying and planning.
2 Collecting the appropriate data.
3 Processing and representing appropriately the data collected.
4 Interpreting and analysing the results found.
5 Reflecting on your investigation.
6 Repeating the cycle for a new hypothesis.

Example of a data handling cycle

1 Specifying and planning

Specifying
This is where we state as clearly as possible what we are going to do, for example:

- a hypothesis we wish to test
- a survey we wish to carry out
- a question we wish to answer.

We could test the hypothesis: 'Girls are better than boys.' But this is not a good hypothesis as it is not specified in a measurable or investigative way.

Alternatively, we could test the hypothesis: 'Girls do better in exams than boys.'

Planning

We now need to plan how we are going to investigate this hypothesis.

We could say we will collect as much data as possible. However, this is not a good plan as it is too vague. We need to be more precise in what we intend to do.

Alternatively we could say that we will

- collect data
- process the data appropriately
- represent the data effectively
- analyse the data
- make a conclusion on what we have found so far.

This is now very clear and allows us to plan the next step.

2 Collecting the appropriate data

We need to make clear what data is to be collected, how it is to be collected and why it is to be collected.

For example, we could

- collect all the GCSE exam results in our school over the last 5 years
- do this by accessing the results from the school database
- use the database to search these results by gender to compare how well boys and girls have done.

3 Processing and representing the data collected appropriately

Processing

This is where we do something with the data, for example we might want to work out

- the mean of the boys' and girls' exam grades
- the median of the boys' and girls' exam grades
- the range of the boys' and girls' exam grades.

Representing

This is where we represent the data collected and/or processed by

- putting the data in appropriate tabular form
- using appropriate pictorial forms, for example bar charts, pie charts, scatter graphs, etc.

4 Interpreting and analysing the results found

Interpreting

This is where we look at our tables and graphs and, from them, present conclusions to try to answer our original hypothesis.

Analysing

This is where we look a bit more deeply at our conclusions. We might want to consider how accurate or valid our work has been. We might want to think about how much credibility we can give to our conclusions.

5 Reflecting on your investigation

This is where we would review

- what we did
- what limitations there are to our work
- how we could improve our work
- how we could narrow the focus to get a more specific result.

6 Repeating

We could now test a new hypothesis, for example: 'Year 12 girls do better in exams than Year 12 boys' or 'Girls do better in English than boys'.

EXAMPLE 1

Suppose you wanted to answer the question: 'What is the favourite subject in school?'

   a   Write down three different sets of data you would collect.

   b   Write down how you would collect the data sets.

   c   Write down one possible limitation in your plan.

   d   Suggest what further question you might wish to answer after carrying out this investigation.

SOLUTION

   a   Suitable sets of data are:
   - Number of students in Year 11 choosing each subject for GCSE
   - Favourite subject in the whole of Year 8
   - Asking students in Year 10 at random what is their favourite subject.

   b   Possible ways of collecting the data are:
   - Number of students in Year 11 choosing each subject for GCSE: ask the teachers
   - Favourite subject in Year 8: design and use a questionnaire
   - Asking students in Year 10 at random what is their favourite subject: conduct a random poll of the Year 10 students

   c   Students do not choose all their subjects, for example they have to do Maths.

   d   You could ask the question: 'What is the favourite subject chosen by Year 11 girls to study at GCSE level in school?'

Exercise 42.1

1 Cadence was going to investigate the following hypotheses. Suggest, for each one, a better alternative which would be more measurable.
   a Most people travel by bus in Belfast.
   b The food in our school canteen is healthy.
   c Some newspapers are easier to read.
   d Dance music is the best.
   e Gaelic football is the most popular.

2 Suppose you wanted to answer the question:
   'What is the favourite lunch in school?'
   a Write down three different sets of data you could collect.
   b Write down how you would collect the data sets.
   c Write down one possible limitation in your plan.
   d Suggest what further question you might wish to answer after carrying out this investigation.

3 Suppose you wanted to answer the question:
   'Which is the cheapest supermarket in Lisburn?'
   a Write down three different sets of data you would collect.
   b Write down how you would collect the data sets.
   c Write down one possible limitation in your plan.
   d Suggest what further question you might wish to answer after carrying out this investigation.

4 Suppose you wanted to test the hypothesis:
   'The most common pet is a dog'.
   a Write down three different sets of data you would collect.
   b Write down how you would collect the data sets.
   c Write down one possible limitation in your plan.
   d Suggest what further question you might wish to answer after carrying out this investigation.

5 Suppose you wanted to test the hypothesis:
   'There are more shoppers in Newry on a Saturday than on other days of the week'.
   a Write down three different sets of data you would collect.
   b Write down how you would collect the data sets.
   c Write down one possible limitation in your plan.
   d Suggest what further question you might wish to answer after carrying out this investigation.

6 Suppose you wanted to carry out a survey to find the most popular car colour.
   a Write down three different sets of data you would collect.
   b Write down how you would collect the data sets.
   c Write down one possible limitation in your plan.
   d Suggest what further question you might wish to answer after carrying out this investigation.

Recording sheets

A questionnaire is a means of asking different questions in order to collect sufficient and appropriate data to get a clearer picture of whatever issue we want to explore.

A recording sheet is used to record the answers from a questionnaire. It is best to ask questions the answers to which can be categorised and recorded in a table using tally marks as appropriate, as in the example below.

1 Are you under 16?

Yes	No
~~HHH~~ //	~~HHH~~ ////

2 Do you agree that Maths is difficult?

Strongly disagree	Disagree	Neither agree nor disagree	Agree	Strongly agree
~~HHH~~	~~HHH~~ /	///	~~HHH~~ //	~~HHH~~ ~~HHH~~

When designing a recording sheet you must

- first decide on the different categories you want to investigate
- then construct a suitable table.

EXAMPLE 2

Design a recording sheet to investigate the cars passing a school.

SOLUTION

We must first decide on the different categories we want to investigate and then construct a suitable table. We could focus on

- the colour of the cars
- the make of the cars
- the number of people in the cars
- the number of doors in the cars.

For the colour of cars, we could then use a table such as:

Red	Blue	White	Green	Silver	Black	Other

Exercise 42.2

Design recording sheets for the following investigations.

1 The types of houses that the students live in.

2 How the students come to school.

3 How the students spend their weekends.

4 The activities in a youth club.

5 The career hopes of final-year students.

6 The part-time jobs of students in the school.

7 The different types of work undertaken by students in a school day.

8 The favourite types of music of students.

9 The tasks undertaken by teachers each week.

10 The courses offered in a leisure centre.

Designing a questionnaire

When you design a questionnaire you must make sure that you follow certain rules.

- The questionnaire consists of at least three or four questions.
- The questions are as short as possible.
- The questions are clear and precise.
- The questions are equally balanced.
- The questions are closed.
- The questions are not biased.
- Any groups used are clearly and uniquely defined.
- There are no gaps in the groups.

Balanced questions

Suppose we want to explore the use of mobile phones. We could ask the question:

Do you use your mobile phone frequently?

Strongly disagree ☐   Neither agree nor disagree ☐   Agree ☐   Strongly agree ☐

This is an unbalanced question because there are two answers to choose from if you agree, but only one if you disagree. We would need to insert an extra response:

Disagree ☐

Closed questions

Suppose we want to explore the issue of the favourite sport of a group of students. We could ask the question:

Which of these sports is your favourite?

Football ☐   Rugby ☐   Cricket ☐

Tennis ☐   Netball ☐   Hockey ☐

This is not a closed question because the student whose favourite sport is boxing could not give a response. We would need to insert an extra response:

Other sport ☐

Biased questions

Suppose we want to explore the issue of how students spend their pocket money. We could ask the question:

Which of these do you spend your pocket money on?

Make-up ☐   Handbags ☐   Perfume ☐   Other ☐

This is a biased question towards girls as there is no option for boys except 'Other'. We would need to insert three responses targeted at boys to make the question unbiased and balanced:

Football magazines ☐   Aftershave ☐   Car accessories ☐

Wrongly defined groups

You must make sure that the groups you use are defined so that each response can only go in one of the groups, and there is a group for each response.

For example, consider the following question and possible responses:

Which age group do you belong to?

A 1–10   **B** 11–20   **C** 21–30   **D** 31–40   **E** 41–50

This is wrongly defined as it does not include babies under 1 or people over 50. We would need to insert two further responses at either end:

Under 1   Over 50

Consider the following question:

How many homeworks did you get last week?

A 0–2   **B** 3–6   **C** 6–8   **D** Over 8

This is wrongly defined as it is unclear which group to use if you had six homeworks. We would need to change group B or C, e.g.

B 3–5   **C** 6–8   or   **B** 3–6   **C** 7–8

Consider the following question:

How tall are you in metres?

A Under 1.3   **B** 1.3–1.4   **C** 1.5–1.6   **D** 1.7–1.8   **E** Over 1.8

This is wrongly defined as there is nowhere to record a height of 1.64 m. You could clearly define the variable (height) and the groups as follows:

What is your height, h, in metres?

A Under 1.3   **B** $1.3 \leqslant h < 1.5$ **C** $1.5 \leqslant h < 1.7$

D $1.7 \leqslant h < 1.8$ **E** Equal to or more than 1.8

Gaps in groups

Consider the following question:

How many questions did you get wrong?

A none   **B** 1–4   **C** 7–9   **D** more than 9

This is wrongly defined as there is a gap between 4 and 7. We would need to add another group as follows:

A none   **B** 1–4   **C** 5–6   **D** 7–9   **E** more than 9

Exercise 42.3

These are questions from different questionnaires. For each:

    a   say what is wrong with the question

    b   suggest alternative responses to improve the question.

1   How would you describe solving equations?

   Very difficult ☐   Difficult ☐   Some difficult, some easy ☐   Easy ☐

2   How many pets do you have?

   0 ☐   Less than 3 ☐   3–5 ☐   More than 5 ☐

3   What is your favourite subject?

   Maths ☐   PE ☐   Drama ☐   RE ☐

   Art ☐   French ☐   English ☐   Science ☐

4   How many GCSEs are you taking?

   Less than 3 ☐   4–5 ☐   6–8 ☐   More than 8 ☐

5   How much pocket money do you get each week?

   £1 or more but less than £10 ☐   £15 or more but less than £18 ☐

   £10 or more but less than £15 ☐   £18 or more but less than £20 ☐

6   How long, l, are the objects in a box in centimetres?

   $0 < l \leqslant 5$ $5 < l \leqslant 15$ $15 < l \leqslant 20$ $l \geqslant 20$

7   Do you agree that all homework should be done at home?

   Totally ☐   Mostly ☐   It depends ☐   Sometimes ☐   Rarely ☐

8   What is the mass, m, in grams of a set of objects?

   $0 \leqslant m < 10$ $10 \leqslant m < 20$ $20 \leqslant m < 30$ $30 \leqslant m < 40$ $m > 40$

9   How many brothers or sisters do you have?

   1 ☐   2 ☐   3 ☐   More than 3 ☐

10   What is the age, A, in years of the people in a club?

   $A \leqslant 20$ $20 \leqslant A < 40$ $40 \leqslant A < 50$ $50 \leqslant A < 70$ $A \geqslant 70$

Unsuitable questions

Consider the question:

Don't you think there is too much sport on television?

This is unsuitable because it is too leading and suggestive a question.
A better alternative question would be more open and include different categories of response, for example:

Do you think there is too much sport on television?

Yes ☐   No ☐   Unsure ☐

Exercise 42.4

Say why each of the following questions is unsuitable and give an alternative question each time.

1 Don't you think that students are not as hard working now as 10 years ago?

2 Is pizza your favourite food?

3 How much television do you watch at the weekend?

4 What do you think of Maths tests?

5 Which Spanish resort would you want to go to on holiday?

6 Which university do you want to go to when you finish school?

7 Which sport is your favourite hobby?

8 Which war film is your favourite film?

9 What do you think of hospitals?

10 Don't you think that school is for helping you pass exams?

Hypotheses

A hypothesis is a statement which may or may not be true.
We can test a hypothesis by constructing a questionnaire.

EXAMPLE 3

Design a questionnaire to test the hypothesis: 'Men are better drivers than women'.

SOLUTION

We need to consider specific areas relating to the hypothesis and then write appropriate questions based on these.

TOPICS TO BE CONSIDERED

Gender	Male or Female
Driving test success	Passed first or second or third time, etc.
Driving experience	0 or 1 or 2 accidents, etc./number of years' driving
Penalty points	3 or 6 or 9, etc.
Convictions	Yes or No

Once we have thought out the relevant areas we can construct the questions, remembering the rules from before.

Hypothesis: 'Men are better drivers than women'

QUESTIONNAIRE

1 Are you   Male ☐   Female ☐?

2 When did you pass your driving test?
The first time ☐   The second time ☐   The third time ☐
After more than three attempts ☐   Not yet ☐

3   How many accidents have you been responsible for?

None ☐   1 ☐   2 or 3 ☐   4 or more ☐

4   How many years, y, have you been driving?

$y \leqslant 1$ ☐ $1 < y \leqslant 3$ ☐ $3 < y \leqslant 10$ ☐ $10 < y \leqslant 20$ ☐ $y > 20$ ☐

5   How many penalty points have you received?

0 ☐   1–3 ☐   4–9 ☐   10 or more ☐

6   Have you had any convictions?   Yes ☐   No ☐

Exercise 42.5

Design questionnaires to test the following hypotheses.
You must include at least four questions each time.

1   Students don't revise enough.

2   Girls do better in exams than boys.

3   Most students dislike Maths.

4   Teenagers use mobile phones much more than any other age group.

5   Women can estimate time better than men.

6   The most popular pet is a dog.

7   Most students do not walk to school.

8   School meals are boring.

9   The letter 'e' is the most frequently occurring letter in written work.

10   GCSE Maths is harder now than it was 10 years ago.

You should now:

- understand and know how to use the handling data cycle
- be able to design a recording sheet
- be able to design a questionnaire
- know the rules for designing questions in a questionnaire
- be able to say why questions are unsuitable
- be able to suggest alternative questions
- be able to design a questionnaire to test a hypothesis.

Summary exercise 42

Design recording sheets for the following investigations.

1   The different types of work experience that Year 12 students went on.

2   The different extra-curricular activities students are involved in at school.

For questions **3** to **6**:

    a Say what is wrong with each of the following questions from different questionnaires.

    b Suggest alternative responses to improve these questions.

3 What is your favourite type of magazine?

Car racing ☐   Fishing ☐   Motor bikes ☐   Other ☐

4 What is the volume, V litres, of a set of liquids?

$0 < V \leqslant 3$ ☐ $3 < V \leqslant 9$ ☐ $8 < V \leqslant 20$ ☐ $20 < V \leqslant 22$ ☐ $V > 22$ ☐

5 How much of your pocket money, P, in £ would you save on average per week?

$0 < P \leqslant 1$ ☐ $1 < P \leqslant 2$ ☐ $2 < P \leqslant 3$ ☐ $P > 3$ ☐

6 How long do you watch television at night?

    Less than 2 hours ☐   2 or 3 hours ☐   More than 3 hours ☐

7 Say why the following question is unsuitable and give an alternative question.

What is your favourite type of dance music?

8 Design a questionnaire to test the hypothesis: 'Students who are good at Maths are good at Science'.

9 Faye was going to investigate the following hypothesis:

'Fewer young people go to church'.

Suggest a better alternative which would be more measurable.

10 Suppose you wanted to carry out a survey to find the most popular boy's name.

    a Write down three different sets of data you would collect.

    b Write down how you would collect the data sets.

    c Write down one possible limitation in your plan.

    d Suggest what further question you might wish to answer after carrying out this investigation.

Examination question

This question is from an examination paper where you may use a calculator.

1 A questionnaire on the benefits of fitness is to be given out at a fitness centre.

    a In each case give a reason why the following questions are not good.

        i Are you fit?

        ii Are you fat?

    b For this questionnaire design a question with a response section.

Use 'Topic Tracker' at www.ccea.org.uk to find more exam questions.

CHAPTER 43

Statistical diagrams

This chapter is about:

- drawing and using frequency tables
- drawing and using frequency polygons
- drawing and using stem and leaf diagrams
- drawing and using scatter graphs
- drawing and using flow diagrams.

You should already know:

- how to use tally marks
- how to find the range, median and mode
- how to work out fractions and percentages
- how to round to a number of significant figures
- how to plot points given in co-ordinate form.

Displaying statistical information

In Chapter 42 we looked at ways of collecting data. Data is numerical information about something. It can be **discrete** or **continuous**.

- Discrete data is data that can only take certain values, e.g. the number of children in a family.
- Continuous data is data that can take any value, e.g. any measurement such as length, age, etc.

The frequency of an event means how many times the event has happened. For data, **frequency** means how many times a particular value appears in the data set. When finding the frequency, it is best to use tally marks, counting in 5s. The data needs to be ordered (normally from smallest to largest) and grouped (where the spread of the data is too big).

It is much easier to understand statistical data when it is presented in pictorial form via tables, charts and graphs than when it is presented simply as numbers. The data should be organised in groups where appropriate and categorised as necessary. The method is slightly different, depending on whether the data is discrete or continuous.

Frequency diagrams for discrete data

Listed below are the marks out of 10 scored by 30 pupils in a mental maths test.

7	6	9	8	5	7	6	5	9	10
4	7	5	1	6	8	3	9	9	7
8	7	9	10	8	5	6	4	7	6

This data is discrete.
We can organise the data in a frequency distribution table by:

- ordering the marks from 1 to 10
- tallying each mark
- converting the tallies into frequencies.

The frequency distribution table shows how this is done for the data on page 481.

Mark	Tally	Frequency
1	/	1
2		0
3	/	1
4	//	2
5	////	4
6	////	5
7	//// /	6
8	////	4
9	////	5
10	//	2

We can then display the data graphically in a frequency diagram or bar chart.

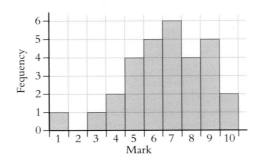

Frequency diagrams for continuous data

The lengths of 104 objects measured in cm, correct to the nearest mm, are shown below.

0.6	16.0	12.5	24.8	11.9	30.7	19.8	22.8	17.3	25.2	20.1	22.3	34.7	17.5	29.3
31.7	26.7	21.8	20.0	15.0	16.4	8.3	12.3	26.4	10.7	19.3	5.0	18.6	33.9	32.6
15.7	32.9	30.0	20.7	19.9	27.0	7.1	20.0	32.9	9.2	29.8	2.5	25.0	10.0	26.3
22.6	29.9	34.1	15.2	21.7	16.9	31.1	27.8	3.8	18.7	13.8	28.1	7.7	25.7	15.6
11.5	28.5	6.4	33.8	18.9	27.3	8.6	24.6	17.8	34.1	20.9	10.8	16.7	21.4	15.8
4.1	25.8	13.9	34.9	32.9	9.7	30.4	28.7	26.1	14.2	33.7	3.9	17.9	23.6	11.2
7.0	10.2	19.5	6.3	11.8	14.4	25.9	28.8	18.4	22.0	1.7	20.3	28.9	21.1	

This data is continuous. We can organise the data in a frequency distribution table by:

- selecting appropriate groups
- defining the groups explicitly
- ordering the groups
- tallying each length in the appropriate group
- converting the tallies into frequencies.

We can then display the data graphically in a frequency diagram.

Appropriate groups

The lengths range from 0.6 cm to 34.9 cm.
The groups should be the same size.
We could therefore group the lengths in intervals of 5 cm from 0 to 35 cm.

Defining the groups explicitly

We need to:

- define the variable, e.g. length, l
- define each group so that:
  - i **all** pieces of data can be placed in a group
  - ii there is **only** one place in which any particular piece of data can be placed, e.g. $0 < l \leqslant 5$, etc.

The grouped frequency distribution table for the length data for the 104 objects is shown below, with the frequency diagram on the right.

Length, l (cm)	Tally	Frequency
$0 < l \leqslant 5$	~~////~~ //	7
$5 < l \leqslant 10$	~~////~~ ////	9
$10 < l \leqslant 15$	~~////~~ ~~////~~ ~~////~~	15
$15 < l \leqslant 20$	~~////~~ ~~////~~~~////~~ ~~////~~ //	22
$20 < l \leqslant 25$	~~////~~~~////~~~~////~~ /	16
$25 < l \leqslant 30$	~~////~~ ~~////~~ ~~////~~ ~~////~~	20
$30 < l \leqslant 35$	~~////~~~~////~~ ~~////~~	15

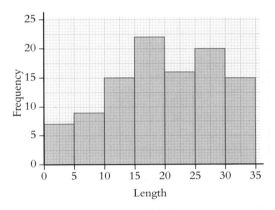

When we draw a frequency diagram to represent continuous data we **must** use a continuous scale.

Exercise 43.1

For the data in each of questions 1 and 2:
    a   set up a frequency distribution table
    b   draw a frequency diagram.

1 Number of brothers or sisters.

0	3	1	2	1	2	3	1	1	4
2	1	0	3	0	1	2	5	4	1
2	0	3	1	2	0	1	3	1	4
3	4	0	1	2	5	0	1	2	4
0	3	1	0	2	0	1	2	3	5
2	0	1	4	0	2	3	0	1	2

2 Number of goals scored in football matches last Saturday.

2	1	3	2	1	4	4	3	2	3	2	1	5	4	2	3	3	2	7	3
4	2	4	3	2	1	3	0	3	2	1	8	3	2	7	3	2	3	4	5
3	4	1	2	4	3	1	2	6	1	3	8	2	1	0	4	3	4	2	4
1	3	2	3	4	1	3	4	2	3	1	2	3	7	4	2	3	0	1	3
2	3	1	2	3	0	2	1	3	2	3	2	1	3	2	6	4	1	5	2

For the data in each of questions 3 and 4:

    a   set up a grouped frequency distribution table

    b   draw a frequency diagram.

3   Breadths of objects (cm). Use the groups 1–5, 6–10, etc.

14	2	16	7	11	20	18	13	18	10
21	16	18	12	9	4	22	15	17	22
17	22	14	17	22	13	6	19	8	11
27	24	28	30	21	28	25	29	24	25
12	10	13	3	6	15	8	16	12	23

4   Mass of objects, M (kg). Use the groups $5 < M \leqslant 7, 7 < M \leqslant 9$, etc.

6	12	8	14	9	12	11	15	14	11	13	15
15	10	13	17	9	10	8	7	12	15	19	13
13	9	7	10	12	6	9	12	9	7	8	16
10	8	15	6	12	9	8	10	7	8	10	12
11	15	7	11	13	15	18	13	9	14	13	11

For the data in each of questions 5 and 6:

    a   set up a grouped frequency distribution table, choosing appropriate equal class intervals

    b   draw a frequency diagram.

5   Heights of different solids, h (cm).

3	6	9	12	2	23	16	9	14	22	13	18	19	3	23
25	1	3	16	18	24	18	14	10	6	3	23	17	13	19
5	13	21	18	25	23	7	10	15	16	21	19	22	3	6
17	18	23	12	8	2	15	11	23	18	16	18	12	5	11

6   Capacity of different boxes, V (cm^3).

32	45	12	36	42	18	27	38	41	50	12	16	23	42	31	37
13	27	43	35	12	18	50	41	39	31	27	16	23	41	38	28
21	18	35	48	12	47	33	20	40	16	19	31	46	39	28	41

Interpreting frequency diagrams

Now we will look at how you can extract the data from a frequency diagram.

The frequency diagram opposite shows the points scored when different people played a computer game.

Use the frequency diagram to:

    a   construct a frequency distribution table

    b   find the range of the points

    c   find the mode of the points

    d   express the number of times that the points scored were less than or equal to 70 as a fraction of the total number of times the points were recorded

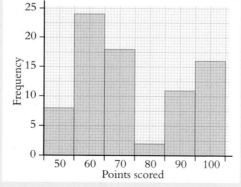

    e   write the number of times that the points scored were greater than or equal to 90 as a percentage of the total number of times the points were recorded.

SOLUTION

a

Points scored	Frequency
50	8
60	24
70	18
80	2
90	11
100	16

> Take these values from the diagram.

b The **range** is given by:
biggest number − smallest number = $100 - 50 = 50$

c The **mode** is the number that occurs the most often, so the mode is 60 as it occurs 24 times.

d There are $8 + 24 + 18 = 50$ times when the points scored were less than or equal to 70.
The total number of times the points were recorded is
$8 + 24 + 18 + 2 + 11 + 16 = 79$.
Answer: $\dfrac{50}{79}$

e The number of times the points scored were greater than or equal to 90 is $11 + 16 = 27$
So we have $\dfrac{27}{79} \times 100 = 34.17\%$, which rounds to 34.2%.

EXAMPLE 2

The frequency diagram shows the heights of different objects in cm.

a Construct a grouped frequency distribution table.

b Give the limits of the modal class.

c Find the percentage of heights greater than 14 cm.

d Give the ratio of the numbers of heights less than or equal to 14 cm compared with the number more than 21 cm.

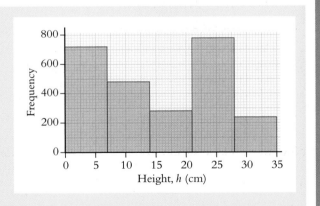

SOLUTION

a

Height, h (cm)	Frequency
$0 < h \leqslant 7$	720
$7 < h \leqslant 14$	480
$14 < h \leqslant 21$	280
$21 < h \leqslant 28$	780
$28 < h \leqslant 35$	240

b The highest frequency is 780, so this is the modal class. Therefore the limits of the modal class are 21 and 28.

> The modal class is the group or class that contains the mode. See Chapter 44.

c The number greater than 14 cm is: 280 + 780 + 240 = 1300.
The total number is: 720 + 480 + 280 + 780 + 240 = 2500.
So the percentage is worked out as follows:
$$\frac{1300}{2500} \times 100 = 52\%$$

d The number of heights less than or equal to 14 cm is 720 + 480 = 1200.

The number of heights greater than 21 cm is 780 + 240 = 1020.

Ratio = 1200 : 1020
= 120 : 102   (cancelling by 10)
= 20 : 17   (cancelling by 6)

Exercise 43.2

1 The frequency diagram shows the times worked by different employees in a company on Friday.
  a Copy and complete the frequency distribution table below.

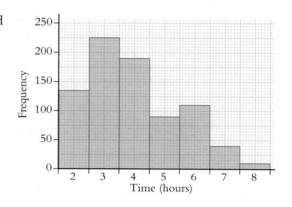

Time (hours)	Frequency
2	
3	
8	

  b Work out the range of the distribution.
  c Work out the mode of the distribution.
  d Work out the number of employees who worked more than 4 hours as a percentage of the total number of employees.
  e Work out the ratio of the number of employees who worked 2 hours to those who worked 6 hours, giving your answer in its simplest form.

2 The frequency diagram shows the points scored by different players in a computer game.
  a Construct a frequency distribution table.
  b Work out the range of the distribution.
  c Work out the mode of the distribution.
  d Work out the number of players who scored less than or equal to 45 points as a fraction of the total number of players, giving your answer in its simplest form.
  e $33\frac{1}{3}\%$ of the players who scored 90 points played the game again. How many played the game again?

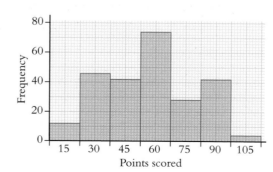

3 The frequency diagram shows the volumes of different containers in litres.
   a Construct a grouped frequency distribution table.
   b State the limits of the modal class.
   c What fraction of all the containers has a greater volume than 18 litres? Give your answer in its simplest form.
   d What percentage of all the containers has volumes less than or equal to 12 litres? Give your answer to 3 significant figures.
   e Work out the ratio of the number of containers with volume less than or equal to 6 litres to those with volume less than or equal to 18 litres. Give your answer in its simplest form.

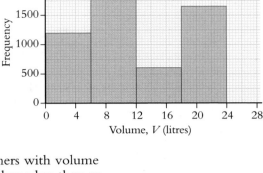

4 The frequency diagram shows the areas of different shapes in cm².
   a Construct a grouped frequency distribution table.
   b State the limits of the modal class.
   c Find the total number of areas less than or equal to 20 cm².
   d Find the fraction of areas in the range $15 < A \leqslant 20$.
   e Areas less than or equal to 5 cm² and more than 25 cm² are discarded. What fraction is kept?

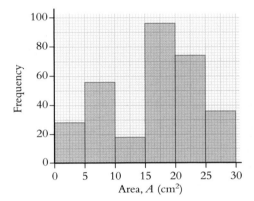

Frequency polygons

Frequency polygons are used to compare two sets of data. A frequency polygon is really a line graph drawn by joining the midpoints of each successive group by a line segment. The frequency polygon will then show the shape of the grouped frequency distribution.

Drawing a frequency polygon

The order for drawing a frequency polygon is shown below.
- Find the midpoint of each group.
- Plot the frequency of each group at its midpoint.
- Join successive points with straight lines.
- Where possible you should start from, and end at, 0 on the horizontal axis.

EXAMPLE 3

The table below shows the marks for boys and girls in a test.

Score, S	$10 < S \leqslant 20$	$20 < S \leqslant 30$	$30 < S \leqslant 40$	$40 < S \leqslant 50$	$50 < S \leqslant 60$
boys	46	52	68	48	12
girls		74	62	58	32

   a Draw a frequency polygon to show this data.
   b Write down one conclusion based on a comparison of the data.

SOLUTION

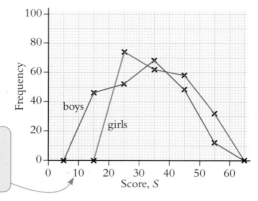

a   We must first find the midpoint of each group,
i.e. 15, 25, 35, 45, 55.
We can then plot the frequency for each group
at the midpoints, e.g. for boys, value 46 is
plotted at 15, 52 at 25, and so on. For girls,
value 74 is plotted at 25, 62 at 35, and so on.

> Note that we must plot 0 at 5 and 65 on the
> horizontal axis for the boys, but we must plot 0 at 15
> and 65 on the horizontal axis for the girls.

b   Possible conclusions:
The scores for the boys are more spread out than the scores for
the girls. The girls in general have the higher marks.

Interpreting frequency polygons

We now look at how to interpret a frequency polygon.

EXAMPLE 4

The frequency polygon here
shows the masses in kg of
25 males and females.

a   Set up the corresponding
frequency distribution table.

b   Write down one conclusion
based on a comparison of
the data.

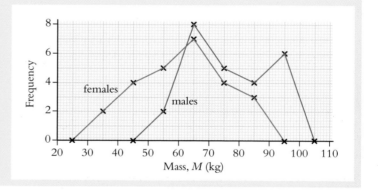

SOLUTION

a   Males: The first non-zero frequency is plotted at 55 and so the
first group for the males must be $50 < M \leqslant 60$.

Females: The first non-zero frequency is plotted at 35 and so the
first group for the females must be $30 < M \leqslant 40$.

Thus we can set up the frequency table below.

Mass, M (kg)	$30 < M \leqslant 40$	$40 < M \leqslant 50$	$50 < M \leqslant 60$	$60 < M \leqslant 70$	$70 < M \leqslant 80$	$80 < M \leqslant 90$	$90 < M \leqslant 100$
males			2	8	5	4	6
females	2	4	5	7	4	3	

b   The males are generally heavier than the females.

Exercise 43.3

In each of questions 1 to 4:
a draw a frequency polygon to show the data
b write down one conclusion based on a comparison of the data.

1 The table shows the Maths and Science marks for 60 students.

Mark, m	35 < m ≤ 40	40 < m ≤ 45	45 < m ≤ 50	50 < m ≤ 55	55 < m ≤ 60	60 < m ≤ 65
Maths		4	9	7	4	6
Science	7	8	7	8		

2 The table shows the number of goals scored by the 20 teams
in a football league in 2009 and 2010.

Goals, G	46 < G ≤ 50	50 < G ≤ 54	54 < G ≤ 58	58 < G ≤ 62	62 < G ≤ 66	66 < G ≤ 70
2009	3	5	7	2	1	2
2010		6	5	4	2	3

3 The table shows the temperatures in Belfast and in Athens in June.

Temperature, T (°C)	18 < T ≤ 20	20 < T ≤ 22	22 < T ≤ 24	24 < T ≤ 26	26 < T ≤ 28	28 < T ≤ 30
Belfast	6	13	9	2		
Athens			9	7	8	6

4 The table shows the lengths of words in the first 100 words in a
child's book and a teenager's book.

Length, l (letters)	0 < l ≤ 2	2 < l ≤ 4	4 < l ≤ 6	6 < l ≤ 8	8 < l ≤ 10	10 < l ≤ 12
child's book	17	39	34	4	5	1
teenager's book	4	30	34	19	7	6

In questions 5 and 6 look at the frequency polygons. For each:
a set up the corresponding frequency distribution tables
b write down one conclusion based on a comparison of the data.

5

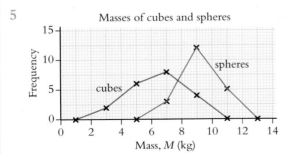

6

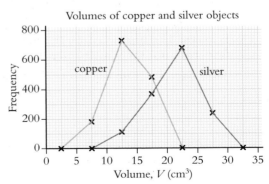

Stem and leaf diagrams

A stem and leaf diagram is another way to represent data graphically. All
the data can be seen and the range, mode and median are easy to find as
the numbers are all in order.

In a stem and leaf diagram each number is split into two parts, the stem and the leaf, separated by a vertical line. The stem is on the left of the vertical line and the leaf is on the right of the vertical line.

The stem and the leaves **must** be ordered (either from smallest to largest or vice versa).

A key **must** be given.

Drawing stem and leaf diagrams

To draw a stem and leaf diagram there are some rules to follow.

- Rewrite the data in order.
- Choose the stem.
- Add a key.

This process is illustrated in the following example.

EXAMPLE 5

The lengths of a set of objects in cm are given below.

9.7 6.6 8.2 6.3 7.7 9.5 6.2 7.4 8.2 7.0 9.6 6.5 9.9 8.1 7.7 9.2

Show this data in a stem and leaf diagram.

SOLUTION

The ordered data are:

6.2 6.3 6.5 6.6 7.0 7.4 7.7 7.7 8.1 8.2 8.2 9.2 9.5 9.6 9.7 9.9

The stem will be 6, 7, 8, 9.

```
6 | 2  3  5  6
7 | 0  4  7  7
8 | 1  2  2
9 | 2  5  6  7  9
```

Key: 6 | 2 = 6.2 cm

 HINT
Don't forget to add the key. Include the unit.

Back-to-back stem and leaf diagrams

Back-to-back stem and leaf diagrams can be used to compare two sets of data. Both sets of data must be ordered, and there must be two keys.

EXAMPLE 6

The ages of men and women in a club are given below.

Men: 54 46 76 32 68 53 31 45 65 47 42 50 71 62

Women: 75 57 64 76 58 43 73 32 56 41 62 44 55

   a Draw a back-to-back stem and leaf diagram to show the data for the ages of the men and women.

   b Write one comment comparing the data.

SOLUTION

a First, put the data in order.
Men: 31 32 42 45 46 47 50 53 54 62 65 68 71 76
Women: 32 41 43 44 55 56 57 58 62 64 73 75 76

The stem will be 3, 4, 5, 6, 7, giving this diagram:

women			men
	2	3	1 2
4 3 1		4	2 5 6 7
8 7 6 5		5	0 3 4
	4 2	6	2 5 8
6 5 3		7	1 6

Key: 2 | 3 = 32 years (women)
3 | 1 = 31 years (men)

b There are more men under 50 than women.

Exercise 43.4

For questions 1 to 4, draw stem and leaf diagrams to show the data given.

1 Temperatures in °F.
46   55   35   54   45   32   51   54   31   46   42   32   47
33   44   50

2 Lengths in cm.
5.9   2.6   3.8   4.6   3.7   2.5   5.4   2.6   5.9   4.7   5.4   3.4   2.3
4.5   2.1   5.9   3.6   3.0   4.2   5.1

3 Distances in km.
4.5   5.9   3.6   5.4   2.5   4.6   3.4   2.6   2.3   4.3   3.5   5.8
4.2   3.8   5.1   2.5   5.6   4.1   2.2   3.7   3.9   2.7   3.4   5.1

4 Volumes in litres.
68   66   48   37   63   43   56   31   69   42   54   46   65
67   39   59   45   31   62   57   48   32   46   37   51   65

For questions 5 to 8, draw back-to-back stem and leaf diagrams to show the data given and make one comparison each time.

5 Marks in a test.
Boys: 79   78   51   65   73   41   55   46   61   68   75   72
        64   45   51   66   53   42   50   77

Girls: 67   79   60   41   64   52   76   44   63   78   72   51
        43   56   61   51   42   67   55   76

6 Heights and lengths of objects in cm.
Lengths: 71   65   47   58   76   52   45   68   57   61   79
           56   77   43   63   74   41   54   46   71

Heights: 73   65   55   41   67   53   42   54   44   79   79
           64   42   56   78   62   51   66   77   67

7   Amount spent on shopping in £.
    Men: 88   84   61   55   75   68   85   56   76   73   52
              81   72   51   64   53   61   65

    Women: 75   88   86   62   89   74   52   85   65   86   51
             72   87   50   82   63   54   71

8   Masses of round and flat objects in kg.
    Round: 3.6   5.9   5.7   2.5   5.2   4.5   2.3   5.8   3.4   5.1   4.3
             3.2   3.5   2.1   5.8   3.1   5.1   2.6   4.1   4.7

    Flat: 4.5   3.1   4.3   2.1   3.4   4.4   2.3   3.9   2.8   5.3   4.2
             3.6   2.7   4.3   2.4   4.1   3.1   2.5   3.2   5.1

Interpreting stem and leaf diagrams

Now we will look at how to interpret a stem and leaf diagram.

EXAMPLE 7

Find a the range, b the mode and c the median of the following widths.

```
4 | 1   3   3   4
5 | 2   3   5   6
6 | 1   1   1   4   7
```

Key: 4 | 1 = 41 cm

SOLUTION

a   Range = biggest number − smallest number
    Range = 67 − 41 = 26 cm.

b   Mode is the number that occurs most often.
    Mode = 61 cm.

c   The median is the number in the middle.
    There are 13 numbers.
    $\frac{13}{2}$ = 6.5 and so the 7th number is the median, i.e. 55 cm.

EXAMPLE 8

Find i the range, ii the mode and iii the median of
   a   the boys' marks and
   b   the girls' marks.
   c   Hence, make one comparison between the boys and the girls.

```
      girls              boys
          2   1 | 6 | 1   4   6
      6   5   3 | 7 | 0   5   5   8
      8   8   4 | 8 | 2   3   7   9
  9   7   5   3 | 9 | 8
```

Key: 1 | 6 = 61 (girls)
         6 | 1 = 61 (boys)

SOLUTION

a Boys

   i   Range = 98 − 61 = 37

   ii Mode = 75

   iii There are 12 numbers.

      $\frac{12}{2}$ = 6 and so the median is the number halfway between the 6th and the 7th numbers

      6th number = 75

      7th number = 78

      So the median is 76.5

b Girls

   i   Range = 99 − 61 = 38

   ii Mode = 88

   iii There are 12 numbers.

      $\frac{12}{2}$ = 6 and so the median is the number halfway between the 6th and the 7th numbers

      6th number = 84

      7th number = 88

      So the median is 86

c The median mark for the girls is much higher than the median mark for the boys, which means that the girls in general have done better.

Exercise 43.5

For each of the following stem and leaf diagrams find
a the range, b the mode and c the median.

1

1	0	0	1		
2	1	1	2	3	3
3	2	4	5	5	5	6
4	1	2	7	8	

Key: 1 | 0 = 10 mm

2

4	2	5	6				
5	1	3	3	7	8		
6	1	0	1	2	3	6	9
7	2	6					

Key: 4 | 2 = 42 marks

3

7	2	3	5	5	6	7	8	
8	4	5	6	6	7	7	9	
9	2	2	3	3	3	3	4	5

Key: 7 | 2 = 72 litres

4

1	1	2	3	5	5	6	7	
2	2	3	4	4	4	7	9	9
3	3	3	5	6	7	8		
4	1	2	4	4	5	6	6	7

Key: 1 | 1 = 11 kg

For each of the following back-to-back stem and leaf diagrams find
a the range, b the mode and c the median for both distributions.
Use these values to make a comparison between the distributions.

5

				girls			boys				

```
            4   3   2   0 | 5 | 1   4   5   6   6
        5   5   3   1   1 | 6 | 2   3   5   5   6   7
    8   8   6   2   2   2 | 7 | 3   4   4   4   4   6   7
        3   2   1   1   0 | 8 | 5   8   8   8   9
            5   4   4   1 | 9 | 2   3   5   5   6   7
```

Key: 0 | 5 = 50 (girls)   5 | 1 = 51 (boys)

6

width   length

```
        5   4   1   1   1 | 3 | 2   5   6   7   7
    6   5   3   3   2   2 | 4 | 4   5   5   6   8
    8   8   6   2   2   2 | 7 | 3   4   4   4   4   6   7
    7   5   4   4   3   1 | 5 | 1   1   1   3   5   6
    7   6   5   5   3   2 | 6 | 2   4   5   6   6   7   8
```

Key: 1 | 3 = 3.1 cm (width)   3 | 2 = 3.2 cm (length)

7

volume   mass

```
        6   5   2   2   2   1 | 4 | 0   0   2   7   8   9
    7   4   3   2   2   0   0 | 5 | 1   3   3   4   5   5
    6   6   5   4   2   2   1 | 6 | 2   4   4   4   5   6   7
    9   7   7   5   4   4   3 | 7 | 0   0   1   2   2   3   4   5
```

Key: 1 | 4 = 41 cm³   4 | 0 = 4.0 g

8

male   female

```
        4   3   3   2   1 | 4 | 1   2   2   3   5
    8   7   1   0   0   0 | 5 | 3   4   5   5   6   7
    7   6   6   5   3   2 | 6 | 1   2   2   2   4   5   6
    7   6   5   4   4   1 | 7 | 0   1   3   3   5
```

Key: 1 | 4 = £41 spent on clothes by males   4 | 1 = £41 spent on clothes by females

Scatter graphs

A scatter graph is used to see if there is a relationship between two sets of data.

We scale one set of data on the horizontal axis and the other set on the vertical axis. We then plot each pair of data in the same way as we would plot co-ordinates.

Correlation

The relationship between the two sets of data is called the correlation. There are three types of correlation:

1 **positive correlation** – this is when as one data set increases (or decreases) the other data set increases (or decreases)

2 **negative correlation** – this is when as one data set increases (or decreases) the other data set decreases (or increases)

3 **zero correlation** – this is when there is no relationship between the points.

Line of best fit

A line of best fit should be drawn roughly through the middle of the points with roughly the same number of points below and above it.

It might be useful to draw an envelope round the points before drawing the line of best fit.

The line of best fit should only be drawn when there is positive or negative correlation.

The gradient of the line of best fit shows the type of correlation, i.e.

• a positive gradient shows there is positive correlation

• a negative gradient shows there is negative correlation.

We can use the line of best fit to predict the value of one data set if we know the value of the other data set.

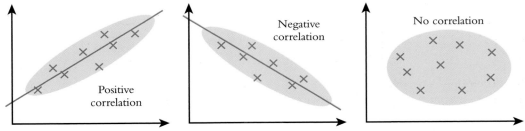

Exercise 43.6

For each of the graphs below, describe the correlation.

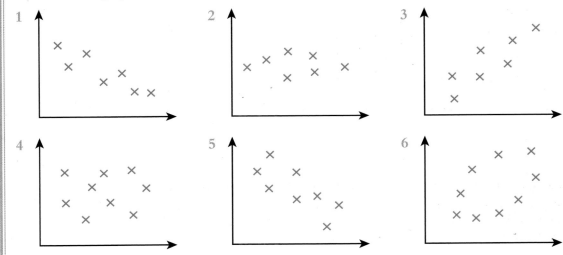

EXAMPLE 9

The marks of seven students in a History test and a Geography test are given below.

History mark	34	52	64	22	48	38	61
Geography mark	47	61	79	31	64	48	77

a   Draw a scatter graph to illustrate this data.

b   Describe the correlation.

c   Describe the relationship between the marks.

d   Draw a line of best fit.

e   Use the line of best fit to estimate

   i   the Geography mark for a student who scored 42 in History

   ii   the History mark for a student who scored 72 in Geography.

SOLUTION

a   We scale the History marks on the horizontal axis and the Geography marks on the vertical axis. We then plot each pair of data in exactly the same way as we would plot co-ordinates.

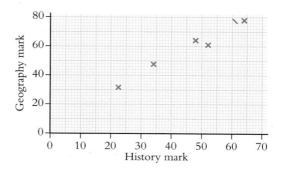

b   We can then draw an envelope round the points to help us see the correlation more clearly.
Since the envelope is sloping upwards, the correlation is positive.

c   As the History marks increase the Geography marks increase.

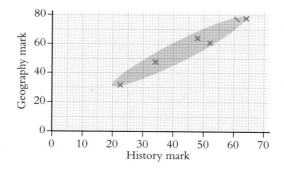

d   To draw the line of best fit, we use the envelope and draw a straight line roughly parallel to the sides of the envelope splitting the points in half.

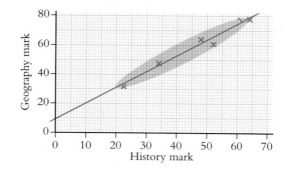

e i Go to 42 on the horizontal History axis.
        Draw vertically up to the line of best fit
        and across to the Geography axis.
        Read off the Geography mark.
        Answer: 55
   ii Go to 72 on the vertical Geography axis.
        Draw horizontally across to the line of
        best fit and down to the History axis.
        Read off the History mark.
        Answer: 57.5

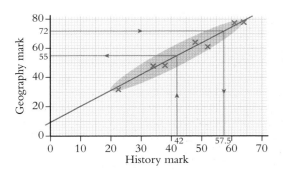

Exercise 43.7

1 The times, in minutes, and the distances travelled in miles for eight
   journeys are shown below.

Time (minutes)	36	50	72	48	64	28	53	62
Distance (miles)	26	37	57	34	55	12	42	47

   a Draw a scatter graph to illustrate this data.
   b Describe the correlation.
   c Describe the relationship.
   d Draw a line of best fit.
   e Use the line of best fit to estimate
      i   the distance travelled in 68 minutes
      ii the time to travel 33 miles.

2 The costs in £ and the number of books ordered by eight different
   departments in a school are shown below.

Cost (£)	840	1150	960	1060	1240	1030	1110	920
Number	42	53	50	54	61	53	60	44

   a Draw a scatter graph to illustrate this data.
   b Describe the correlation.
   c Describe the relationship.
   d Draw a line of best fit.
   e Use the line of best fit to estimate
      i   the number of books that could be bought with £1080
      ii the cost of 47 books.

3 The volumes and densities of eight different objects are shown below.

Volume (cm^3)	5	2	14	26	8	32	18	12
Density (g/cm^3)	1.2	5.4	1.1	0.4	1.3	0.3	0.5	0.8

   a Draw a scatter graph to illustrate this data.
   b Describe the correlation.
   c Describe the relationship.
   d Draw a line of best fit.
   e Use the line of best fit to estimate
      i   the density of a solid with volume $22\,cm^3$
      ii the volume of a solid with density $3.7\,g/cm^3$.

4 The marks in both a Numeracy and a Literacy test sat by eight students are shown below.

Numeracy mark	38	54	76	44	82	67	51	27
Literacy mark	54	42	31	49	28	38	40	61

a Draw a scatter graph to illustrate this data.
b Describe the correlation.
c Describe the relationship.
d Draw a line of best fit.
e Use the line of best fit to estimate
  i the Literacy mark for a student who got 48 in Numeracy
  ii the Numeracy mark for a student who got 48 in Literacy.

5 The table shows the average number in each group in a youth club and the amount collected for charity.

Number in group	16	34	26	42	18	53
Charity collection (£)	23	51	38	60	26	74

a Draw a scatter graph to illustrate this data.
b Describe the correlation.
c Describe the relationship.
d Draw a line of best fit.
e Use the line of best fit to estimate
  i the charity collection of a group of 20
  ii the number in a group that would collect £66.

6 The table shows the values and ages of eight cars for sale.

Value (£)	4300	1600	3900	1300	8800	2300	5700	1800
Age (years)	4	10	5	11	1	6	2	9

a Draw a scatter graph to illustrate this data.
b Describe the correlation.
c Describe the relationship.
d Draw a line of best fit.
e Use the line of best fit to estimate
  i the age of a car valued at £4800
  ii the value of an 8-year-old car.

Flow diagrams

A flow diagram is a diagram where instructions are given in an ordered sequence. You begin at the top and follow the direction of the arrows, reading each box in turn. You must do whatever the instruction in the box says or answer questions to determine which box you go on to next.

There are a number of different types of boxes used in flow diagrams, which have special shapes.

Start and stop boxes

These are found at the start and end of the flow diagram.

$\left(\text{START}\right)$ $\left(\text{STOP}\right)$

Input boxes

- Input boxes are parallelograms.
- They tell you what variables to start with.

$\overline{/\ \text{INPUT } A\ /}$

Instruction boxes

- Instruction boxes are rectangles.
- They tell you what to do.

$\boxed{C = A + 10}$

Decision or question boxes

- Decision or question boxes are rhombuses.
- They ask a question to which the answer is 'Yes' or 'No'.
- You follow the path corresponding to the answer to the question.
- When you return to a previous box a **loop** is said to be formed.

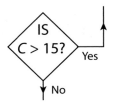

EXAMPLE 10

Look at this flow diagram.

Starting with $A = 35$ and $B = 16$ follow the instructions of the flow diagram. What is the result?

SOLUTION

The first instruction box says $Q = A^2 - B$.

We substitute $A = 35$ and $B = 16$ to get $Q = 35^2 - 16 = 1209$.

We now follow the arrow to the question box.

$1209 < 1600$ and so the answer to the question is 'No'.

We then follow the arrow to the instruction box which says:

$A = A + 2$

We substitute A on the right-hand side to get a new value for A.

$A = 35 + 2 = 37$

Similarly for B:

$B = B - 1 = 16 - 1 = 15$

We now return to the instruction box $Q = A^2 - B$.

Using the new values of A and B, i.e. $A = 37$ and $B = 15$, we get $Q = 37^2 - 15 = 1354$.

But $1354 < 1600$, so we have to go through the loop again.

$A = 37 + 2 = 39$
$B = 15 - 1 = 14$

giving $Q = 39^2 - 14 = 1507$

But $1507 < 1600$, so we have to go through the loop again.

$A = 39 + 2 = 41$
$B = 14 - 1 = 13$

giving $Q = 41^2 - 13 = 1668$

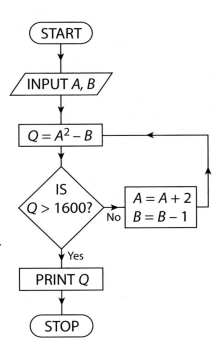

This time when we go to the question box we have 1668 > 1600 and so the answer is 'Yes'.

We then go to the final instruction box which says to print Q and then stop. Thus our answer is 1668.

Exercise 43.8

Look at the flow diagrams below and follow the instructions until you get the answer.

1 Start with $B = 40$ and $C = 18$.

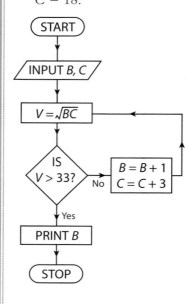

2 Start with $L = 50$ and $M = 2$.

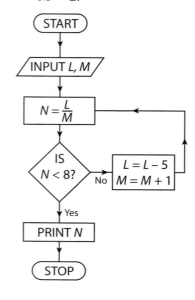

3 Start with $A = 1$ and $M = 11$.

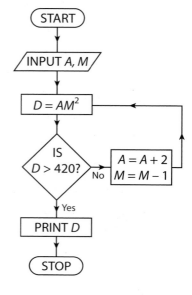

4 Start with $N = 8$ and $x = 1$.

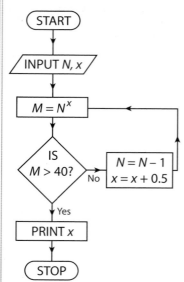

5 Start with $x = 8$ and $y = 12$.

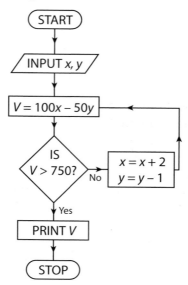

6 Start with $a = 5.8$ and $b = 4.6$.

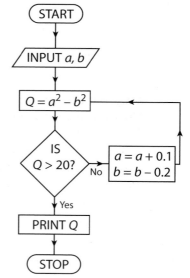

Summary exercise 43

1 A dice is thrown 60 times and the results are shown below.

```
3   2   4   1   5   4   2   3   1   6   5   4   2   5   6   6   4   5   3   4   1
6   5   2   3   4   6   1   2   3   4   3   1   2   6   5   4   2   3   6   1   4
2   3   5   6   4   5   4   2   1   3   6   2   5   4   2   6   1   3
```

   a Set up a frequency distribution table.
   b Draw a frequency diagram.

2 The frequency diagram shows the points scored by different people on a computer game.

   a Copy and complete the frequency distribution table below.

Points scored	Frequency
50	
100	
350	

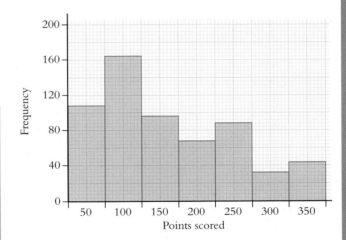

   b Work out the range of the distribution.
   c Work out the mode of the distribution.
   d Work out the total number of players.
   e Work out the total number of points scored.
   f Work out the ratio of the number of players who scored 100 points to those who scored 200 points, giving your answer in its simplest form.

3   This frequency diagram shows the heights of different objects in cm.

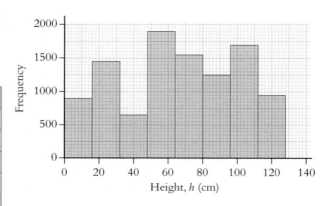

a   Copy and complete the grouped frequency distribution table below.

Height, h (cm)	Frequency
$0 < h \leqslant 16$	
$16 < h \leqslant 32$	
$112 < h \leqslant 128$	

b   State the limits of the modal class.
c   How many heights are there in the range $48 < h \leqslant 80$?
d   Work out the number of objects shorter than or equal to 32 cm as a fraction of the total number of objects, giving your answer in its simplest form.
e   Work out the number of objects taller than 96 cm as a percentage of the total number of objects, giving your answer correct to 3 significant figures.

4   Draw a stem and leaf diagram to show the following lengths (all in cm).
5.7   5.6   3.5   4.8   3.4   4.2   3.7   5.2   4.9   3.7   4.1   4.8

5   The lists below show the marks for boys and girls in a test.
Boys: 38   56   24   46   31   23   42   54   37   58   45
      38   57
Girls: 49   54   47   25   50   32   21   41   47   34   23
      48   25   36   56

a   Draw a back-to-back stem and leaf diagram to show the data.
b   Write one conclusion about the data.

6   The back-to-back stem and leaf diagram below shows the masses in grams of different objects in two boxes A and B.

```
      box A              box B
    6  5  2 │ 1 │ 2  3  4  4  5
 6  5  5  4 │ 2 │ 3  6  6  6  7
    8  7  1 │ 3 │ 4  8
 8  5  4  2 │ 4 │ 1  5
```

Key: $2 \mid 1 = 1.2\,\text{g}$ (box A) $1 \mid 2 = 1.2\,\text{g}$ (box B)

a   Find i the range, ii the mode, and iii the median of the masses in box A.
b   Find i the range, ii the mode, and iii the median of the masses in box B.
c   Write one comparison about the data.

7 The number of bottles of water sold by a supermarket each week and the average weekly temperature in °C are shown below.

Number of bottles	3400	5700	2800	6200	4500	5300	8100
Temperature (°C)	19	26	17	27	23	25	33

a Draw a scatter graph to illustrate this data.
b Describe the correlation.
c Describe the relationship.
d Draw a line of best fit.
e Use the line of best fit to estimate:
   i the temperature when 6200 bottles are sold
   ii the number of bottles of water sold when the temperature is 21 °C.

8 Look at the flow diagram opposite and follow the instructions until you get the answer, starting with $a = 6$ and $b = 30$.

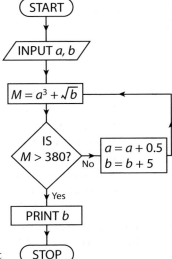

9 The table shows the amount of time spent on mobile phones last night in minutes by girls and boys in a youth club.

Time t (min)	$20 < t \leqslant 40$	$40 < t \leqslant 60$	$60 < t \leqslant 80$	$80 < t \leqslant 100$	$100 < t \leqslant 120$	$120 < t \leqslant 140$	$140 < t \leqslant 160$	$160 < t \leqslant 180$
girls			6	9	8	5	8	7
boys	6	4	9	11	7	6		

a Draw a frequency polygon to show the data.
b Write down one conclusion based on a comparison of the data.

10 The frequency polygon shows the English and History marks for 300 students.
a Set up the corresponding frequency distribution table.
b Write down one conclusion based on a comparison of the data.

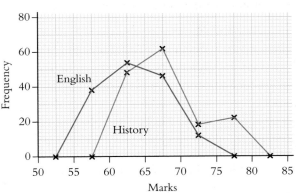

Examination questions

Use 'Topic Tracker' at www.ccea.org.uk to find more exam questions.

Questions **1** and **2** are from examination papers where you may not use a calculator.

1 A firm recorded the sales resulting from advertising campaigns, together with the advertising costs.

Sales (thousands £)	Advertising costs (£)
8	100
24	180
25	300
38	450
36	540
53	680
52	820

a On graph paper, draw a scatter graph for the data.

b Draw a line of best fit on the scatter graph.

c For the next campaign, the firm is aiming for sales of £45 000. Use the graph to estimate the advertising costs to achieve this.

d Write down one word to describe the correlation.

2 At an MOT centre, the waiting times, t minutes, for tests were recorded.

Time, t (min)	$0 \leqslant t < 4$	$4 \leqslant t < 8$	$8 \leqslant t < 12$	$12 \leqslant t < 16$	$16 \leqslant t < 20$	$20 \leqslant t < 24$
Frequency	28	12	16	3	4	1

Draw a frequency polygon to illustrate this data.

Question **3** is from an examination paper where you may use a calculator.

3 Ages of members of cycling club

```
1 | 5  6  6  7  7  8
2 | 0  2  3  3  4  5  6  6  7  9
3 | 1  3  4  5  6  6  7
```

Key: 1 | 5 means 15 years old

Two new members joined the club.
One was 19 years old and one was 40.
Copy and complete the stem and leaf diagram to include the new members.

CHAPTER 44

Statistical averages and spread

This chapter is about:

- calculating the mean, median, mode and range of frequency distributions
- calculating the mean, median, mode and range of grouped frequency distributions
- comparing sets of data.

You should already know:

- how to find the mean, median and mode of discrete data
- how to find midpoints
- how to solve equations.

Averages and spread

There are three types of statistical average:

- **mode** – the value that occurs most often
- **median** – the middle value (or halfway between the two middle values when there is an even number of values) of an ordered list
- **mean** – $\dfrac{\text{total of all the values}}{\text{number of values}}$

The **spread** of a distribution is measured by the range where:

range = highest value − lowest value

Frequency distributions

Here are some rules to follow when finding the different averages for frequency distributions.

Mode

- To find the mode of a frequency distribution, choose the value with the highest frequency.

Median

- Add up the frequencies to get the total (= Σf).
- Divide the total by 2 (= $\dfrac{\Sigma f}{2}$).
- Construct a **cumulative frequency** column (by adding on each **successive** frequency).

> Σ means 'sum of', so we add all the values.

- Find the value in the table corresponding to $\frac{\Sigma f}{2}$.
  - If there is an even number of values, then the median is halfway between this value and the next value in the table.
  - If there is an odd number of values, then the median is the next value in the table.

Mean

- Multiply each value (x) by its frequency (f) to get fx.
- Add up the fx values to get Σfx.
- Mean = $\frac{\Sigma fx}{\Sigma f}$.

EXAMPLE 1

For the following frequency distribution, find:

    a   the range   b   the mode   c   the median   d   the mean.

Value (x)	4	6	8	10	12	14	16	18
Frequency (f)	3	8	11	8	4	6	8	2

SOLUTION

    a   Range = $18 - 4 = 14$.

    b   The highest frequency is 11 and so the mode is 8.

    c   We must first find $\Sigma f = 3 + 8 + 11 + 8 + 4 + 6 + 8 + 2 = 50$

        $\frac{50}{2} = 25$ ←————————————————— Divide Σf by 2.

So the median is the number halfway between the 25th and the 26th values. We can now set up a cumulative frequency table.

x	f	Cumulative frequency
4	3	3
6	8	11 (3 + 8)
8	11	22 (11 + 11)
10	8	30 (22 + 8)
12	4	34 (30 + 4)
14	6	40 (34 + 6)
16	8	48 (40 + 8)
18	2	50 (48 + 2)

The 25th number = 10 and the 26th number = 10 and so the median = 10.

d   We need to set up an *fx* column by multiplying *f* by *x*.

x	f	fx
4	3	12 (4 × 3)
6	8	48 (6 × 8)
8	11	88
10	8	80
12	4	48
14	6	84
16	8	128
18	2	36
	$\Sigma f = 50$	$\Sigma fx = 524$

$$\text{Mean} = \frac{524}{50} = \frac{52.4}{5} = 10.48 \text{ (dividing by 10 and then by 5)}$$

EXAMPLE 2

For the following frequency distribution, find:

a   the range   b   the mode
c   the median   d   the mean.

Value (x)	1.5	1.6	1.7	1.8	1.9
Frequency (f)	13	7	9	8	3

SOLUTION

a   Range = 1.9 − 1.5 = 0.4

b   The highest frequency is 13 and so the mode is 1.5

c   We must first find $\Sigma f = 13 + 7 + 9 + 8 + 3 = 40$

$$\frac{40}{2} = 20$$

So the median is the number halfway between the 20th and the 21st values. We can now set up a cumulative frequency table.

The 20th number = 1.6 and the 21st number = 1.7 and so the median is halfway between 1.6 and 1.7 = 1.65.

x	f	Cumulative frequency
1.5	13	13
1.6	7	20
1.7	9	29
1.8	8	37
1.9	3	40

d   We need to set up an *fx* column by multiplying *f* by *x*.

x	f	fx
1.5	13	19.5
1.6	7	11.2
1.7	9	15.3
1.8	8	14.4
1.9	3	5.7
	$\Sigma f = 40$	$\Sigma fx = 66.1$

$$\text{Mean} = \frac{66.1}{40} = \frac{6.61}{4} = 1.6525$$

Do not round your answers when they work out exactly (if we rounded the mean we would get 1.65, which is the answer for the median).

Exercise 44.1

For the following frequency distributions where x is the value and f the frequency, find:

    a the range   b the mode   c the median   d the mean.

1

x	7	8	9	10	11	12
f	2	5	6	8	1	3

2

x	10	15	20	25	30	35
f	9	2	5	1	2	1

3

x	0	4	8	12	16	20
f	5	8	14	4	17	2

4

x	1	1.5	2	2.5	3	3.5
f	3	7	5	1	2	2

5

x	0	3	6	9	12	15
f	9	7	3	8	11	2

6

x	1	1.2	1.4	1.6	1.8	2
f	3	5	4	2	3	3

7

x	0	6	12	18	24	30
f	18	14	13	18	14	23

8

x	20	30	40	50	60	70
f	2	5	1	3	1	4

9

x	0	7	14	21	28	35	42
f	3	6	4	2	1	1	3

10

x	6	6.2	6.4	6.6	6.8	7	7.2
f	9	10	8	4	9	4	6

Grouped frequency distributions

Mode and median

We cannot find the exact mode or median of a grouped frequency distribution, but we can give the limits of the group or class in which the mode or median lies. These classes are called the **modal class** and the **median class**.

Mean

We cannot find the exact mean of a grouped frequency distribution, but we can calculate an estimate for the mean by choosing the midpoint of each group or class to represent the group, i.e. taking the midpoint to be the x value.

EXAMPLE 3

    a The table below shows the lengths of 80 objects in cm. Find:

        i   the limits of the modal class

        ii the limits of the median class.

    b Calculate an estimate of the mean.

Length, l (cm)	$0 < l \leqslant 4$	$4 < l \leqslant 8$	$8 < l \leqslant 12$	$12 < l \leqslant 16$	$16 < l \leqslant 20$
Frequency	13	32	17	10	8

SOLUTION

    a i   The highest frequency is 32 and so the modal class is $4 < l \leqslant 8$.

       ii We are told that $\Sigma f = 80$.

$$\frac{80}{2} = 40$$

So the median is the number halfway between the 40th and the 41st values. We can now set up a cumulative frequency table.

Both the 40th and the 41st values are in the group $4 < l \leqslant 8$, so the median class is $4 < l \leqslant 8$.

Length, l (cm)	f	Cumulative frequency
$0 < l \leqslant 4$	13	13
$4 < l \leqslant 8$	32	45
$8 < l \leqslant 12$	17	62
$12 < l \leqslant 16$	10	72
$16 < l \leqslant 20$	8	80

b We need to work out the midpoints of each group, for example:

For the group $0 < l \leqslant 4$:

$0 + 4 = 4$ and $\dfrac{4}{2} = 2$ and so we take $x = 2$ in the first group.

For the group $4 < l \leqslant 8$

$4 + 8 = 12$ and $\dfrac{12}{2} = 6$ and so we take $x = 6$ in the second group.

We need to set up a fx column by multiplying f by x.

x	f	fx
2	13	26
6	32	192
10	17	170
14	10	140
18	8	144
	$\Sigma f = 80$	$\Sigma fx = 672$

$$\text{Mean} = \frac{672}{80} = 8.4$$

EXAMPLE 4

a The table below shows the ages of 50 people. Find:
  i the limits of the modal class
  ii the limits of the median class.
b Calculate an estimate of the mean.

Age (years)	1–16	17–32	33–48	49–64
Frequency	12	17	20	1

SOLUTION

a i The highest frequency is 20 and so the modal class is 33–48.

  ii We are told that $\Sigma f = 50$

  $$\frac{50}{2} = 25$$

  So the median is the number halfway between the 25th and the 26th values. We can now set up a cumulative frequency table.

  Both the 25th and the 26th values are in the group 17–32, so the median class is 17–32.

Age	f	Cumulative frequency
1–16	12	12
17–32	17	29
33–48	20	49
49–64	1	50

b   We need to work out the midpoints of each group, for example:

For the group 1–16:

$1 + 16 = 17$ and $\dfrac{17}{2} = 8.5$ and so we take $x = 8.5$ in the first group

For the group 17–32:

$17 + 32 = 49$ and $\dfrac{49}{2} = 24.5$ and so we take $x = 24.5$ in the second group.

We need to set up an fx column by multiplying f by x.

x	f	fx
8.5	12	102
24.5	17	416.5
40.5	20	810
56.5	1	56.5
	$\Sigma f = 50$	$\Sigma fx = 1385$

$$\text{Mean} = \frac{1385}{50} = 27.7$$

Exercise 44.2

For each of the following grouped distributions:

a   find the limits of

  i   the modal class   ii   the median class.

b   calculate an estimate of the mean.

1
Length, l (mm)	$0 < l \le 4$	$4 < l \le 8$	$8 < l \le 12$	$12 < l \le 16$	$16 < l \le 20$
Frequency	8	7	4	3	18

2
Height, h (cm)	$0 < h \le 8$	$8 < h \le 16$	$16 < h \le 24$	$24 < h \le 32$	$32 < h \le 40$
Frequency	9	7	6	8	10

3
Price, P (£)	$10 < P \le 15$	$15 < P \le 20$	$20 < P \le 25$	$25 < P \le 30$	$30 < P \le 35$	$35 < P \le 40$
Frequency	33	22	18	17	9	1

4
Mass, M (mg)	$11 < M \le 12$	$12 < M \le 13$	$13 < M \le 14$	$14 < M \le 15$
Frequency	2	7	6	5

5
Area, A (cm^2)	$0 < A \le 25$	$25 < A \le 50$	$50 < A \le 75$	$75 < A \le 100$
Frequency	18	11	12	9

6
Dollars, D ($)	$0 < D \le 6$	$6 < D \le 12$	$12 < D \le 18$	$18 < D \le 24$	$24 < D \le 30$
Frequency	14	3	7	11	5

7
Volume, V (cm^3)	$10 < V \le 24$	$24 < V \le 38$	$38 < V \le 52$	$52 < V \le 66$
Frequency	3	4	8	5

8
Age (years)	1–10	11–20	21–30	31–40	41–50
Frequency	13	17	21	24	5

9	Width (mm)	1–5	6–10	11–15	16–20	21–25
	Frequency	2	6	4	7	1

10	Absences	1–3	4–6	7–9	10–12	13–15	16–18
	Frequency	13	10	12	10	3	2

Finding a missing frequency in a frequency distribution

If you know the mean of a frequency distribution or a grouped frequency distribution, you can find the value of a single missing frequency.

EXAMPLE 5

The mean of the following frequency distribution is 4.525. Find n.

x	2	3	4	5	6	7
f	6	n	5	9	4	8

SOLUTION

$$\Sigma f = 6 + n + 5 + 9 + 4 + 8 = n + 32$$
$$\Sigma fx = 12 + 3n + 20 + 45 + 24 + 56 = 3n + 157$$
$$\text{Total} = 4.525(n + 32) = 4.525n + 144.8$$

So
$$4.525n + 144.8 = 3n + 157$$
$$4.525n - 3n = 157 - 144.8$$
$$1.525n = 12.2$$
$$n = \frac{12.2}{1.525} = 8$$

> **Rules**
> - Find Σf and Σfx.
> - Multiply the mean by Σf to get the total.
> - Put $\Sigma fx =$ the total and solve the equation.

EXAMPLE 6

The mean of the following grouped frequency distribution is 6.56. Find n.

Group	1–3	4–6	7–9	10–12	13–15
f	6	8	5	n	2

SOLUTION

We must first work out the midpoints of each group. Then we can produce a frequency table.

x	2	5	8	11	14
f	6	8	5	n	2

Then, as before, we have:
$$\Sigma f = 6 + 8 + 5 + n + 2 = n + 21$$
$$\Sigma fx = 12 + 40 + 40 + 11n + 28 = 11n + 120$$
$$\text{Total} = 6.56(n + 21) = 6.56n + 137.76$$

So
$$11n + 120 = 6.56n + 137.76$$
$$11n - 6.56n = 137.76 - 120$$
$$4.44n = 17.76$$
$$n = \frac{17.76}{4.44} = 4$$

Exercise 44.3

1 The mean of the following frequency distribution is 1.68. Find n.

x	0	1	2	3	4
f	4	8	7	n	2

2 The mean of the following frequency distribution is 9. Find n.

x	5	7	9	11	13
f	2	6	5	n	3

3 The mean of the following frequency distribution is 4.48. Find n.

x	4	4.2	4.4	4.6	4.8
f	2	7	3	n	8

4 The mean of the following grouped frequency distribution is 5.3. Find n.

Group	1–2	3–4	5–6	7–8	9–10
f	3	n	1	4	4

5 The mean of the following grouped frequency distribution is 12.3125. Find n.

Group	$0 < x \leqslant 5$	$5 < x \leqslant 10$	$10 < x \leqslant 15$	$15 < x \leqslant 20$	$20 < x \leqslant 25$
f	13	n	17	14	15

6 The mean of the following grouped frequency distribution is 8.225. Find n.

Group	1–3	4–6	7–9	10–12	13–15
f	8	6	n	9	8

7 The mean of the following grouped frequency distribution is 10.8. Find n.

Group	$0 < x \leqslant 4$	$4 < x \leqslant 8$	$8 < x \leqslant 12$	$12 < x \leqslant 16$	$16 < x \leqslant 20$
f	n	5	3	7	3

8 The mean of the following grouped frequency distribution is 15.38. Find n.

Group	1–6	7–12	13–18	19–24	25–30
f	11	27	24	29	n

Problems involving means

We can also have problems where we know the means of all the different subsets within a question. From this information we can then work out the mean of the whole population.

EXAMPLE 7

The table below shows the mean amount spent by men, women and teenagers on a weekend break.

People	Mean amount spent (£)
8 men	184.64
9 women	157.58
3 teenagers	79.48

Calculate the mean amount spent by all the people.

SOLUTION

Total number of people $= 8 + 9 + 3 = 20$

Total amount spent $= 184.64 \times 8 + 157.58 \times 9 + 79.48 \times 3$

$\qquad\qquad\qquad\quad = £3133.78.$

Mean amount spent $= \dfrac{£3133.78}{20} = £156.689$, which approximates to £156.69.

Rules

- Find the total number of people.
- Find the total amount spent.
- Divide the total amount spent by the total number of people.

EXAMPLE 8

The table below shows the mean age of men and women in a club.

People	Mean age (years)
24 men	38
16 women	n

The mean age of all the people is 36.4 years. Find n.

SOLUTION

$$\text{Total of all the ages} = 40 \times 36.4 = 1456$$
$$\text{Total of all the ages of the men} = 24 \times 38 = 912$$
$$\text{Total of all the ages of the women} = 1456 - 912 = 544$$
$$\text{Mean age of the women} = \frac{544}{16} = 34 \text{ years.}$$

Rules

- Find the total of all the ages by multiplying.
- Find the total of all the ages of the men by multiplying.
- Subtract the two totals to get the total of all the ages of the women.
- Divide this total by the number of women.

Exercise 44.4

1 The mean height of 10 objects is 6.8 m. The mean height of a different 15 objects is 8.4 m. Find the mean height of all the objects.

2 The mean pocket money of 16 girls is £7.50. The mean pocket money of 9 boys is £6. Find the mean pocket money of all the children.

3 The mean volume of 27 objects is 6.4 litres. The mean volume of another 23 objects is 3.8 litres. Find the mean volume of all the objects.

4 The mean age of 9 men in a club is 47 years. The mean age of 6 women in this club is 42 years. The mean age of 10 children in this club is 13 years. Find the mean age of everyone in this club.

5 The mean mass of 36 containers is 8.4 kg. The mean mass of a different 14 containers is 7.6 kg. Find the mean mass of all the containers.

6 There are 16 men and 9 women in a small company. The mean savings of the men is £36. The mean savings of everyone is £33.12. Find the mean savings of the women.

7 There are 28 red and 22 green objects in a box. The mean length of the red objects is 6.8 cm. The mean length of all the objects is 6.976 cm. Find the mean length of the green objects.

8 There are 25 students in a class of which 7 are girls. In a test the mean mark of the class is 59.68 and the mean mark of the girls is 64. Find the mean mark of the boys.

Comparing sets of data

We can compare sets of data by calculating the range, mode, median and mean.

EXAMPLE 9

The heights of blue and yellow objects are given in the table.

Make three conclusions about these objects and make an overall comparison.

Height (cm)	8	9	10	11
Number of blue objects	6	8	13	13
Number of yellow objects	17	22	11	

SOLUTION

Range

Blue: range = 11 − 8 = 3 cm
Yellow: range = 10 − 8 = 2 cm

Conclusion: The blue objects have the larger range.

> **Rules**
> - Find the range and the statistical averages.
> - Compare these.

Mean

Blue

x	f	fx
8	6	48
9	8	72
10	13	130
11	13	143
	$\Sigma f = 40$	$\Sigma fx = 393$

Yellow

x	f	fx
8	17	136
9	22	198
10	11	110
	$\Sigma f = 50$	$\Sigma fx = 444$

Mean $= \dfrac{393}{40} = 9.825$ cm

Mean $= \dfrac{444}{50} = 8.88$ cm

Conclusion: The blue objects have the higher mean.

Median

Blue

x	f	Cumulative frequency
8	6	6
9	8	14
10	13	27
11	13	40

Yellow

x	f	Cumulative frequency
8	17	17
9	22	39
10	11	50

$\dfrac{40}{2} = 20$

Median is halfway between the 20th and the 21st height = 10 cm.

$\dfrac{50}{2} = 25$

Median is halfway between the 25th and the 26th height = 9 cm.

Conclusion: The blue objects have the higher median.

Mode

The blue objects do not have a mode and so we cannot compare the modes.

Overall comparison

The heights of the blue objects are more spread out with a higher mean and median. The heights of the yellow objects are closer together with a lower mean and median.

Exercise 44.5

For each of these distributions, make three conclusions and an overall comparison.

1 Class marks

Mark	30	31	32	33	34
Boys	4	5	3	4	4
Girls	1	8	6		

2 Visits to a leisure centre in June

Number	5	6	7	8	9
Men	4	7	9		
Women		3	5	5	7

3 Absences last fortnight

Absences	0	1	2	3	4	5
Boys	14	2	3	4	1	1
Girls	17	4	3	1		

4 Ages in a youth club

Age	15	16	17	18	19
Boys	5	6	9	4	1
Girls	7	10	8		

5 Number of cars for sale in a garage

Age of car (years)	1	2	3	4	5	6
British	14	18	15	12	24	17
Foreign	19	27	18	21	15	

6 Number of late arrivals yesterday

Number	0	1	2	3	4
Bus	5	6	8	9	2
Train	5	5	14	6	

Choosing the appropriate statistical average

Sometimes it is better to choose a particular statistical average rather than either of the other two. You should use the following as a rough guide to help you choose the most appropriate average.

- When all the values have to be taken into account choose the **mean**.
- When there are one or two very small or very large values that distort the mean choose the **median**.
- When you want half the values to be above or below the average choose the **median**.
- When you want the most popular value choose the **mode**.
- When all the values are not numerical choose the **mode**.

EXAMPLE 10

A class voted on where to go for a day out and the results are shown below.

Museum	Cinema	Shopping	Sports centre	Seaside
3	5	13	4	2

Which would be the most appropriate statistical average to use?
Give a reason for your choice.

SOLUTION

The mode, because not all the values are numerical and so you could not work out the mean.

EXAMPLE 11

The marks of a class test are given below.

| 21 | 23 | 23 | 23 | 26 | 27 | 28 | 29 | 30 | 30 | 31 | 34 | 35 | 38 | 97 |

Which would be the most appropriate statistical average to use?
Give a reason for your choice.

SOLUTION

The mean would not be appropriate because the mark of 97 would distort the mean. The mode (= 23) would not be appropriate because this is the second lowest mark. Therefore the median (= 29) is the most appropriate.

EXAMPLE 12

The table below shows the rate of pay per hour for different employees in a company.

Rate (£)	5.35	5.80	6.45	7.25
Number	3	7	9	2

Which would be the most appropriate statistical average to use?
Give a reason for your choice.

SOLUTION

The mean, because all the values have to be taken into account.

Exercise 44.6

For each of the following, which would be the most appropriate statistical average to use? Give a reason for your choice.

1 Choosing the average shoe size in a class.

2 Finding the average amount of crisps in a packet.

3 Choosing a figure to represent the average cost of a holiday, costs in £ below.

   250   255   255   285   295   305   310   315   320   795

4 A class mini-company take a vote on what price to charge for their product and the results are given below.

Price (£)	2	2.50	3	3.50
Number	7	11	8	4

5   Time waiting for the school bus in minutes.

    7   8   9   9   10   11   12   13   14   14   15

6   Results of a class vote for favourite type of music, shown below.

Rock	Rap	House	Garage	Indie
3	5	2	6	12

7   Number of detentions in a class.

Detentions	0	1	2	3
Number	10	7	2	5

8   Goals scored by teams in a league.

Goals	0	1	2	3
Number	5	7	6	2

9   A class voted on what to have for lunch on a field trip.

Lunch	Sandwich	Chips	Pizza	Burger	Packed lunch
Number	3	5	12	6	2

10   Percentage of fat in 10 different yoghurts.

    0%   15%   18%   18%   19%   20%   23%   24%   24%   24%

You should now:

- be able to define and distinguish between mode, median and mean
- understand what is meant by the range
- be able to calculate the range, mode, median and mean of a frequency distribution
- be able to find the limits of the median and modal class of a grouped frequency distribution
- be able to calculate the mean of a grouped frequency distribution
- be able to use means in problems
- be able to compare distributions
- be able to choose the most appropriate statistical average.

Summary exercise 44

1   For the following frequency distribution find: **a** the range, **b** the mode, **c** the median and **d** the mean.

x	1.5	2.5	3.5	4.5	5.5
f	2	4	5	7	2

2   For the following grouped frequency distribution:
   a find **i** the limits of the modal class and **ii** the limits of the
       median class
   b calculate an estimate of the mean.

Group	$0 < x \leqslant 5$	$5 < x \leqslant 10$	$10 < x \leqslant 15$	$15 < x \leqslant 20$	$20 < x \leqslant 25$
Frequency	23	24	17	22	14

3 The mean of the following frequency distribution is 4.95. Find n.

x	0	2	4	6	8	10
f	7	9	4	n	8	7

4 The mean of the following grouped frequency distribution is 15.8. Find n.

Group	1–5	6–10	11–15	16–20	21–25	26–30
Frequency	3	8	n	14	8	4

5 The mean weekly wage for 36 men in a factory is £246.50 and the mean weekly wage for 24 women is £217.50. Calculate the mean weekly wage for everybody.

6 20 people went on holiday at a mean cost of £439.90. Nine went on a seaside holiday at a mean cost of £347. Four went on a cruise at a mean cost of £675. The rest went skiing. Calculate the mean cost for skiing.

7 The table below shows the daily rainfall in mm in April in Belfast and Bonn.

Rainfall (mm)	0	1	2	3	4	5
Belfast	8	7	9	6		
Bonn	4	6	8	5	2	5

Make three conclusions about the rainfall and make an overall comparison.

8 A class voted for its favourite subject and the results are shown below.

Subject	Maths	PE	Science	Art	Music
Votes	3	6	8	7	12

a Which would be the most appropriate statistical average to use?
b Give a reason for your choice.

9 A teacher wants to set a test from which she will choose the top half of the class to do Additional Maths.
a Which would be the most appropriate statistical average to use?
b Give a reason for your choice.

10 The table below shows the time spent by the students in a class getting to their classroom after lunch.

Time (minutes)	1	1.5	2	2.5
Number of students	8	9	3	4

a Which would be the most appropriate statistical average to use?
b Give a reason for your choice.

Examination questions

Use 'Topic Tracker' at www.ccea.org.uk to find more exam questions.

These questions are from examination papers where you may use a calculator.

1 A teacher recorded the weekly wages of 60 students with part-time jobs. The information is recorded in the table.

Weekly wage, £W	Number of students
Under £8	2
£8 ≤ £W < £16	13
£16 ≤ £W < £24	17
£24 ≤ £W < £32	25
£32 ≤ £W < £40	3

Using the midpoint of each interval, calculate an estimate for the mean weekly wage.

2 The hourly rates, £H, for workers in a company are shown in the table.

Hourly rate, £H	Frequency	Mid-value (£)
5 < H ≤ 7	30	6
7 < H ≤ 9	25	
9 < H ≤ 11	14	
11 < H ≤ 13	9	
13 < H ≤ 15	5	

a Which is the modal class interval?

b Calculate the mean hourly rate.

CHAPTER 45

Cumulative frequency curves and box plots

This chapter is about:

- constructing and analysing cumulative frequency curves
- using cumulative frequency curves to estimate the median and the inter-quartile range
- drawing and using a box plot.

You should already know:

- the meaning of median and range
- how to find percentages.

Cumulative frequency curves

A cumulative frequency curve is drawn by plotting the cumulative frequency (on the vertical axis) against the limits or boundaries of the groups (on the horizontal axis), as appropriate.

Limits and boundaries

Consider the groups 1–5, 6–10, 11–15, …

The values 1 and 5 are the limits of the first group; the values 6 and 10 are the limits of the second group, and so on. Limits like these would be appropriate where the data is discrete.

However, when the data is continuous we need to use boundaries that allow for the continuous values of the data. So,

- 0.5 and 5.5 become the boundaries of the first group
- 5.5 and 10.5 become the boundaries of the second group
- 10.5 and 15.5 become the boundaries of the third group.

Cumulative frequency curves are used to show the spread of a set of data. We can easily use these curves to identify the median, the quartiles and the inter–quartile range.

Quartiles

The quartiles divide the distribution into four equal parts.

- **Lower quartile** or **Q1** – this determines the lowest quarter of the distribution.
- **Median** or **Q2** – this divides the distribution into two equal halves.
- **Upper quartile** or **Q3** – this determines the highest quarter of the distribution.

Spread

The spread of a distribution can be measured by either the **range** or the **inter-quartile range**.

Range

range = highest value − lowest value

This is sometimes not a very good measure as it can include very extreme and unrepresentative values.

Inter-quartile range

inter-quartile range = Q3 − Q1

This is a better measure of the spread of a distribution as it focuses on the middle 50%, thereby avoiding very extreme values.

Using cumulative frequency curves to find quartiles and the inter-quartile range

All cumulative frequency curves have a similar shape and they can all be used in the same way to find the quartiles and the inter-quartile range.

Finding the quartiles

- Find Q2 first by dividing N by 2 where N is the final cumulative total.
- Go to $\frac{N}{2}$ on the vertical axis, draw across to the curve and read off the answer on the horizontal axis.
- Find Q1 next by dividing $\frac{N}{2}$ by 2 to get $\frac{N}{4}$ (or divide N by 4).
- Go to $\frac{N}{4}$ on the vertical axis, draw across to the curve and read off the answer on the horizontal axis.
- Find Q3 by multiplying $\frac{N}{4}$ by 3 to get $\frac{3N}{4}$ (or multiply N by $\frac{3}{4}$).
- Go to $\frac{3N}{4}$ on the vertical axis, draw across to the curve and read off the answer on the horizontal axis.

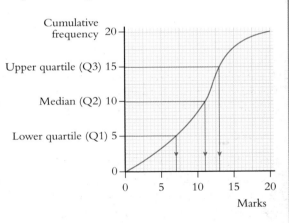

Finding the inter-quartile range

To find the inter-quartile range, subtract Q1 from Q3.

EXAMPLE 1

The table shows the lengths of 240 objects in cm.

Length, l (cm)	$0 < l \leqslant 6$	$6 < l \leqslant 12$	$12 < l \leqslant 18$	$18 < l \leqslant 24$	$24 < l \leqslant 30$	$30 < l \leqslant 36$
Frequency	14	38	64	68	44	12

a Set up a cumulative frequency table.
b Draw the cumulative frequency curve.
c Use your cumulative frequency curve to estimate
   i   the median   ii   the inter-quartile range.
d What percentage of the objects are over 28 cm long?

SOLUTION

a

(handwritten: cumulative freq table.)

Length, l (cm)	0	6	12	18	24	30	36
Frequency	0	14	52 (14 + 38)	116 (52 + 64)	184 (116 + 68)	228 (184 + 44)	240 (228 + 12)

b, c

i $N = 240$

$$Q2: \frac{240}{2} = 120$$

Go to 120 on the vertical axis and read across and down to get Q2 = 18.5

ii $Q1: \frac{240}{2} = 60$

Go to 60 on the vertical axis and read across and down to get Q1 = 13

Q3: $60 \times 3 = 180$

Go to 180 on the vertical axis and read across and down to get Q3 = 23.5

Inter-quartile range = 23.5 − 13 = 10.5

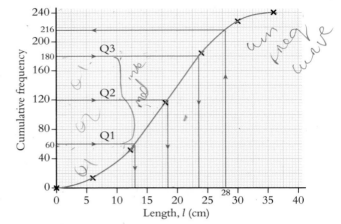

(handwritten: cum freq curve)

d Go to 28 on the horizontal axis and read up and across to get 216.
This means that 216 objects are **less than** 28 cm long.
Thus 240 − 216 = 24 objects are over 28 cm long.

EXAMPLE 2

The table shows the time in minutes taken by 80 runners to complete a race.

Time, T (minutes)	150–154	155–159	160–164	165–169	170–174	175–179	180–184
Frequency	3	8	10	35	12	7	5

a Set up a cumulative frequency table.
b Draw the cumulative frequency curve.
c Use your cumulative frequency curve to estimate
   i   the median   ii   the inter-quartile range.
d Find the times within which the fastest 10% finished.

SOLUTION

a We have to use the boundaries of each group.

Time < T (minutes)	149.5	154.5	159.5	164.5	169.5	174.5	179.5	184.5
Frequency	0	3	11	21	56	68	75	80

b, c

i $N = 80$

$$Q2: \frac{80}{2} = 40$$

Go to 40 on the vertical axis of the cumulative frequency curve
on page 523 and read across and down to get Q2 = 167

ii Q1: $\dfrac{40}{2} = 20$

Go to 20 on the vertical axis and read across and down to get Q1 = 164

Q3: 20 × 3 = 60

Go to 60 on the vertical axis and read across and down to get Q3 = 171

Inter-quartile range = 171 − 164 = 7

d 10% of 80 = $\dfrac{10}{100} × 80 = 8$

Go to 8 on the vertical axis and read across and down to get 158 minutes.

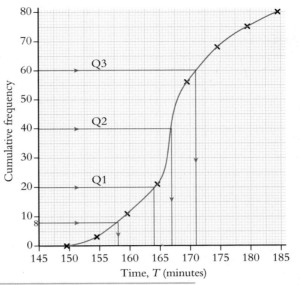

Exercise 45.1

1 The table shows the heights of 180 objects in cm.

Height, h (cm)	$0 < h \leqslant 4$	$4 < h \leqslant 8$	$8 < h \leqslant 12$	$12 < h \leqslant 16$	$16 < h \leqslant 20$	$20 < h \leqslant 24$	$24 < h \leqslant 28$
Frequency	4	16	28	90	24	12	6

a Copy and complete the cumulative frequency table.

Height $\leqslant h$ (cm)	0	4	8	12	16	20	24	28
Cumulative frequency	0	4						180

b Draw the cumulative frequency curve.
c Use your cumulative frequency curve to estimate
  i the median   **ii** the inter-quartile range.
d Estimate the number of heights less than 21 cm.

2 The table shows the marks of 60 students.

Mark	1–10	11–20	21–30	31–40	41–50	51–60
Frequency	2	5	21	25	4	3

a Copy and complete the cumulative frequency table.

Mark ($\leqslant$)	0	10	20	30	40	50	60
Cumulative frequency	0	2					60

b Draw the cumulative frequency curve.
c Use your cumulative frequency curve to estimate
  i the median   **ii** the inter-quartile range.
d Estimate the pass mark if 70% pass.

3 The table shows the ages of 240 people.

Age (years)	Over 10 and up to and including 16	Over 16 and up to and including 22	Over 22 and up to and including 28	Over 28 and up to and including 34	Over 34 and up to and including 40	Over 40 and up to and including 46	Over 46 and up to and including 52
Frequency	8	24	38	88	42	28	12

a Copy and complete the cumulative frequency table.

Age ($\leqslant$) (years)	10	16	22	28	34	40	46	52
Cumulative frequency	0	8						240

b Draw the cumulative frequency curve.
c Use your cumulative frequency curve to estimate
   i the median   ii the inter-quartile range.
d Estimate the percentage of people older than 36.

4 The table shows the masses of 120 objects in kg.

Mass, M (kg)	$10 < M \leqslant 12$	$12 < M \leqslant 14$	$14 < M \leqslant 16$	$16 < M \leqslant 18$	$18 < M \leqslant 20$	$20 < M \leqslant 22$	$22 < M \leqslant 24$	$24 < M \leqslant 26$
Frequency	2	7	12	38	37	15	5	4

a Copy and complete the cumulative frequency table.

Mass $\leqslant M$ (kg)	10	12	14	16	18	20	22	24	26
Cumulative frequency	0	2							120

b Draw the cumulative frequency curve.
c Use your cumulative frequency curve to estimate
   i the median   ii the inter-quartile range.
d Estimate the number of masses between 11 and 17 kg.

5 The table shows the points scored by 56 players of a computer game.

Points	1–50	51–100	101–150	151–200	201–250	251–300	301–350	351–400
Frequency	2	5	8	14	12	8	4	3

a Copy and complete the cumulative frequency table.

Points ($\leqslant$)	0	50	100	150	200	250	300	350	400
Cumulative frequency	0	2							56

b Draw the cumulative frequency curve.
c Use your cumulative frequency curve to estimate
   i the median   ii the inter-quartile range.
d Estimate the number of players who scored more than 280 points.

6 The table shows the widths of 220 objects in cm.

Width, w (cm)	$0 < w \leqslant 8$	$8 < w \leqslant 16$	$16 < w \leqslant 24$	$24 < w \leqslant 32$	$32 < w \leqslant 40$	$40 < w \leqslant 48$	$48 < w \leqslant 56$	$56 < w \leqslant 64$	$64 < w \leqslant 72$
Frequency	8	12	23	38	64	34	25	10	6

a Copy and complete the cumulative frequency table.

Width, $\leqslant w$ (cm)	0	8	16	24	32	40	48	56	64	72
Frequency	0	8								220

b Draw the cumulative frequency curve.
c Use your cumulative frequency curve to estimate
   i the median   ii the inter-quartile range.
d Estimate the number of widths between 43 and 58 cm.

7 The table shows the miles driven by a salesman each day.

Miles	1–15	16–30	31–45	46–60	61–75	76–90	91–105	106–120
Frequency	4	8	18	48	52	22	6	2

a Copy and complete the cumulative frequency table below

Miles ($\leqslant$)	0.5								120.5
Cumulative frequency	0								160

b Draw the cumulative frequency curve.
c Use your cumulative frequency curve to estimate
   i the median   ii the inter-quartile range.
d Estimate the percentage number of days the salesman travelled
   at least 92 miles.

8 The table shows the areas of 196 objects in cm^2.

Area, A cm^2	$40 < A \leqslant 44$	$44 < A \leqslant 48$	$48 < A \leqslant 52$	$52 < A \leqslant 56$	$56 < A \leqslant 60$	$60 < A \leqslant 64$	$64 < A \leqslant 68$	$68 < A \leqslant 72$
Frequency	3	9	18	64	67	22	8	5

a Copy and complete the cumulative frequency table.

Area $\leqslant A$ (cm^2)	40								72
Cumulative frequency	0								196

b Draw the cumulative frequency curve.
c Use your cumulative frequency curve to estimate
   i the median   ii the inter-quartile range.
d Estimate the number of areas greater than 65 cm^2.

9 The table shows the lengths of 124 objects in cm.

Length, l (cm)	$0 < l \leqslant 20$	$20 < l \leqslant 40$	$40 < l \leqslant 60$	$60 < l \leqslant 80$	$80 < l \leqslant 100$	$100 < l \leqslant 120$	$120 < l \leqslant 140$	$140 < l \leqslant 160$	$160 < l \leqslant 180$
Frequency	2	5	10	22	40	25	9	7	4

a Copy and complete the cumulative frequency table

Length $\leqslant l$ (cm)	0								180
Cumulative frequency	0								124

b Draw the cumulative frequency curve.
c Use your cumulative frequency curve to estimate
   i the median   ii the inter-quartile range.
d Estimate the number of lengths between 54 and 148 cm.

10 The table shows the money spent by 280 customers at a supermarket in £.

Cost, C (£)	Over 80 up to 90	Over 90 up to 100	Over 100 up to 110	Over 110 up to 120	Over 120 up to 130	Over 130 up to 140	Over 140 up to 150	Over 150 up to 160
Frequency	14	32	38	52	58	40	28	18

  a Copy and complete the cumulative frequency table.

Cost ≤ C (£)	80								160
Cumulative frequency	0								280

  b Draw the cumulative frequency curve.
  c Use your cumulative frequency curve to estimate
    i the median   **ii** the inter-quartile range.
  d Estimate the number of customers who spent more than £116.

Interpreting cumulative frequency curves

We now look at how you can extract information from a cumulative frequency curve

EXAMPLE 3

The cumulative frequency curve shows the lengths, *l* cm, of 1680 objects.

Use the curve to

  a construct a frequency distribution table
  b estimate the median and the inter-quartile range.

SOLUTION

  a We have to subtract the previous cumulative frequency from the next cumulative frequency each time to find the frequency for each group.

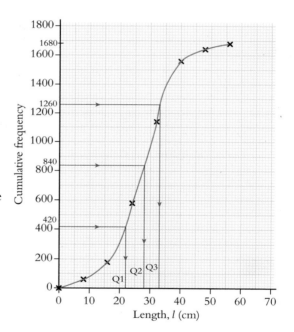

Length, *l* (cm)	Frequency
$0 < l \leqslant 8$	60
$8 < l \leqslant 16$	120 (180 − 60)
$16 < l \leqslant 24$	400 (580 − 180)
$24 < l \leqslant 32$	560 (1140 − 580)
$32 < l \leqslant 40$	420 (1560 − 1140)
$40 < l \leqslant 48$	80 (1640 − 1560)
$48 < l \leqslant 56$	40 (1680 − 1640)

  b Median:
  $$\frac{1680}{2} = 840$$

  Go to 840 on the vertical axis , read across and down to get Q2 = 28

Inter-quartile range:

Q1: $\dfrac{840}{2}$ = 420

Go to 420 on the vertical axis and read across and down to get
Q1 = 22

Q3: 420 × 3 = 1260

Go to 1260 on the vertical axis and read across and down to get
Q3 = 33

Inter-quartile range = 33 − 21 = 12

Exercise 45.2

In the following questions
    a   complete the frequency distribution table
    b   estimate the median and the inter-quartile range.

1 Volume in litres of 120 objects.

Volume, V (litres)	Frequency
$0 < V \leqslant 16$	

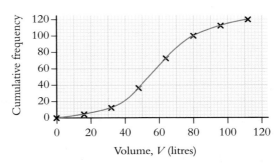

2 Heights in centimetres of 640 objects.

Height, h (cm)	Frequency
$130 < h \leqslant 135$	

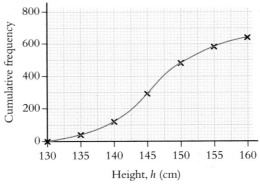

3 Number of downloads for 160 teenagers.

Number	Frequency
1–20	

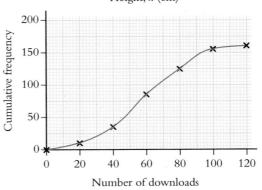

4 Costs in £ of 60 televisions.

Costs (£)	Frequency
Over 200 and up to and including 240	

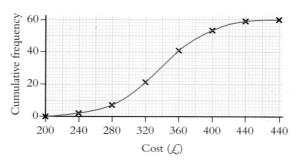

5 Ages of 1200 children.

Age (years)	Frequency
5–6	

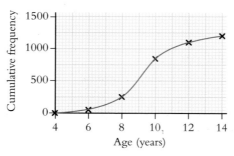

6 Masses of 210 objects in kg.

Mass, M (g)	Frequency
$10 < M \leqslant 14$	

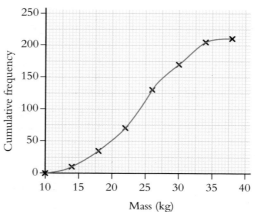

Box plots

A box plot is a statistical graph in which the following are plotted:
- the minimum value
- the lower quartile (Q1)
- the median (Q2)
- the upper quartile (Q3)
- the maximum value.

The box shows the inter-quartile range.

Horizontal lines are drawn from the sides of the box to the minimum and maximum values and these are sometimes called the whiskers. The box plot can also be called a box and whisker diagram.

Box plots can be used effectively to compare two or more data sets.

Drawing box plots

EXAMPLE 4

Draw a box plot to show the following data on the masses in kg of a set of objects.

Minimum	4
Lower quartile	22
Median	28
Upper quartile	40
Maximum	56

SOLUTION

We need to:

- scale the horizontal axis
- draw small vertical lines at the minimum and maximum values
- draw longer vertical lines at the lower quartile, median and the upper quartile
- complete the box around the inter-quartile range
- join the minimum and maximum values to the box by horizontal lines.

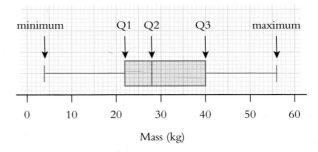

Mass (kg)

Exercise 45.3

Draw box plots to show the following data.

1 Cost in £ of computer games.

Minimum	38
Lower quartile	43
Median	49
Upper quartile	52
Maximum	54

2 Area in cm² of different shapes.

Minimum	26
Lower quartile	38
Median	42
Upper quartile	47
Maximum	60

3 Width in mm of pieces of wood.

Minimum	42
Lower quartile	47
Median	51
Upper quartile	53
Maximum	58

4 Age in years of people in a club.

Minimum	23
Lower quartile	36
Median	42
Upper quartile	45
Maximum	48

5 Volume in litres of a set of containers.

Minimum	130
Lower quartile	142
Median	156
Upper quartile	163
Maximum	168

6 Masses in kg of a group of people.

Minimum	64
Lower quartile	72
Median	79
Upper quartile	84
Maximum	86

Interpreting box plots

We now look at how you can extract information from box plots.

EXAMPLE 5

The table shows different values for Geography and History marks in a year group.

a Show the data on a box plot.

b Give three conclusions about the data with reasons.

	Geography	History
Minimum	4.5	3
Lower quartile	12	11
Median	18	19
Upper quartile	26	27
Maximum	28	31

SOLUTION

a

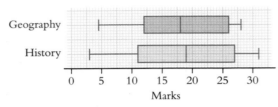

b Three possible conclusions are:

- The History marks are more spread out (a bigger range).
- The middle 50% of the History marks are more spread out (a bigger box).
- Students have done better in History (higher maximum value, higher upper quartile, higher median).

Exercise 45.4

Look at the box plots in each of the questions below.
Give two conclusions about the data with reasons.

1 Marks from Years 8 and 12.

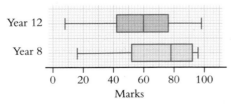

2 Hours spent revising for a test by boys and girls.

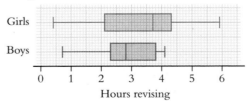

3 DVDs owned by teenagers and adults.

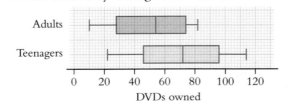

4 Mistakes made in driving tests by men and women.

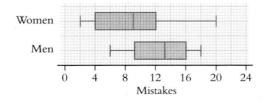

5 Wages in £ for men and women in a company.

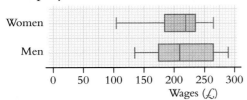

6 Science and Maths marks.

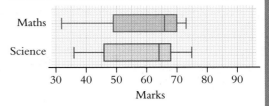

Drawing cumulative frequency curves and box plots

We can draw cumulative frequency curves to find the median and the quartiles to help us draw box plots

EXAMPLE 6

The table shows the amount of money in £ spent on clothes by 280 people.

a Set up a cumulative frequency table.
b Draw the cumulative frequency curve.
c Use your cumulative frequency curve to estimate
   i   the median
   ii   the lower quartile
   iii the upper quartile.
d Hence draw a box plot to show the data.

Amount, A (£)	Frequency
$0 < A \leq 20$	15
$20 < A \leq 40$	30
$40 < A \leq 60$	50
$60 < A \leq 80$	95
$80 < A \leq 100$	50
$100 < A \leq 120$	25
$120 < A \leq 140$	15

SOLUTION

a

Amount ≤ A (£)	Cumulative frequency
0	0
20	15
40	45
60	95
80	190
100	240
120	265
140	280

b

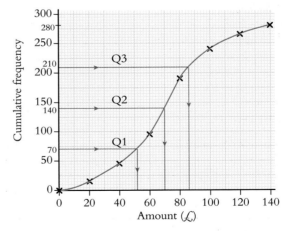

c i   Median: $\dfrac{280}{2} = 140$ so Q2 = 70

   ii Lower quartile: $\dfrac{140}{2} = 70$ so Q1 = 52

   iii Upper quartile: $70 \times 3 = 210$ so Q3 = 86

d Minimum value = 0
   Maximum value = 140

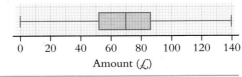

Exercise 45.5

Carry out the following for each of the questions.
a   Set up a cumulative frequency table.
b   Draw the cumulative frequency curve.
c   Use your cumulative frequency curve to estimate
   i   the median
   ii   the lower quartile
   iii   the upper quartile.
d   Hence draw a box plot to show the data.

1 Marks in a test.

Mark	Frequency
1–10	5
11–20	9
21–30	26
31–40	35
41–50	22
51–60	7
61–70	4

2 Lengths of objects.

Length, l (cm)	Frequency
$0 < l \leqslant 6$	14
$6 < l \leqslant 12$	36
$12 < l \leqslant 18$	72
$18 < l \leqslant 24$	58
$24 < l \leqslant 30$	42
$30 < l \leqslant 36$	18

3 Ages of football players.

Age (years)	Frequency
Over 15 and up to and including 18	6
Over 18 and up to and including 21	14
Over 21 and up to and including 24	32
Over 24 and up to and including 27	54
Over 27 and up to and including 30	38
Over 30 and up to and including 33	12
Over 33 and up to and including 36	8

4 Masses of objects in grams.

Mass, M (g)	Frequency
$0 < M \leqslant 8$	12
$8 < M \leqslant 16$	28
$16 < M \leqslant 24$	42
$24 < M \leqslant 32$	37
$32 < M \leqslant 40$	25
$40 < M \leqslant 48$	16

5 Costs of car services in £ rounded to the nearest £.

Cost, C (£)	Frequency
61–80	5
81–100	12
101–120	25
121–140	27
141–160	11
161–180	8

6 Lifetimes of batteries in hours.

Lifetime, L (hours)	Frequency
$9 < L \leqslant 10$	3
$10 < L \leqslant 11$	9
$11 < L \leqslant 12$	24
$12 < L \leqslant 13$	38
$13 < L \leqslant 14$	48
$14 < L \leqslant 15$	21
$15 < L \leqslant 16$	8
$16 < L \leqslant 17$	5

Summary exercise 45

1   The table shows the marks of 148 students in a mock GCSE exam.

Mark	1–16	17–32	33–48	49–64	65–80	81–96
Frequency	4	13	49	58	15	9

  a Copy and complete the cumulative frequency table.

Mark (<)	0.5						96.5
Cumulative frequency	0						148

  b Draw the cumulative frequency curve.
  c Use your cumulative frequency curve to estimate
    i   the median   **ii** the inter-quartile range.
  d Estimate the pass mark if 40% fail.
  e The top 15 students get grade A.
    What is the lowest possible mark to get a grade A?

2   The table shows the heights of 840 objects in cm.

Height, h (cm)	Frequency
$115 < h \leqslant 120$	30
$120 < h \leqslant 125$	70
$125 < h \leqslant 130$	125
$130 < h \leqslant 135$	195
$135 < h \leqslant 140$	205
$140 < h \leqslant 145$	110
$145 < h \leqslant 150$	85
$150 < h \leqslant 155$	20

  a Copy and complete the cumulative frequency table.

Height $\leqslant h$ (cm)	115						155
Cumulative frequency	0						840

  b Draw the cumulative frequency curve.
  c Use your cumulative frequency curve to estimate
    i   the median   **ii** the inter-quartile range.
  d Estimate the percentage of heights greater than 144 cm.

3 The cumulative frequency curve shows the lengths,
   l cm, of 128 objects.
   a Complete the frequency distribution table.

Length, l (cm)	Frequency
$0 < l \leq 40$	

   b Estimate the median and the inter-quartile range.
   c Estimate the number of lengths between 65 cm
      and 215 cm.
   d The smallest $\frac{1}{8}$ of the lengths are thrown away.
      What is the least length kept?

4 The table shows different values for the
   number of text messages sent by boys and girls in
   a youth group.
   a Show the data on a box plot.
   b Give two conclusions about the data
      with reasons.

	Boys	Girls
Minimum	32	17
Lower quartile	41	45
Median	49	57
Upper quartile	53	63
Maximum	69	67

5 The box plot shows the times, in minutes, taken by students to
   travel to school and to return home from school.

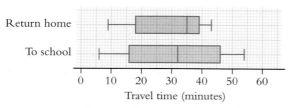

   Give two conclusions about the data with reasons.

6 The table shows the costs of DVDs in a shop.

   a Set up a cumulative frequency table.
   b Draw the cumulative frequency curve.
   c Use your cumulative frequency curve
      to estimate
      i the median
      ii the lower quartile
      iii the upper quartile.
   d Hence draw a box plot to show the data.

Costs in £	Frequency
Over 5 and up to and including 8	12
Over 8 and up to and including 11	21
Over 11 and up to and including 14	35
Over 14 and up to and including 17	53
Over 17 and up to and including 20	32
Over 20 and up to and including 23	12
Over 23 and up to and including 26	7

Examination questions

Use 'Topic Tracker' at www.ccea.org.uk to find more exam questions.

Question **1** is from an examination paper where you may not use a calculator.

1 The cumulative frequency graph gives information about the percentage marks obtained by 300 candidates in an examination. Use the graph to estimate:

   a the median percentage mark

   b the interquartile range

   c the percentage mark separating the top 20 candidates from the others.

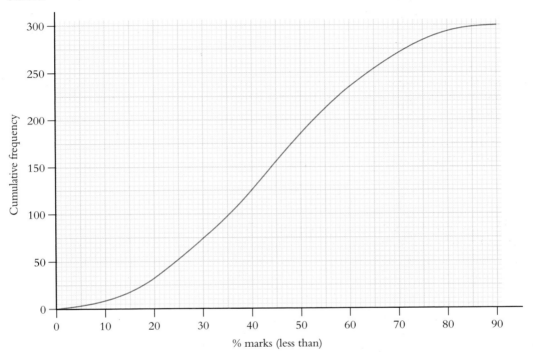

Questions **2** and **3** are from examination papers where you may use a calculator.

2 Peter is a gardener. He recorded how much he earned each week for 40 weeks. The lowest amount Peter earned was £185 and the highest amount was £315. The median amount was £235 and the quartiles £217 and £256. Draw a box plot to illustrate Peter's earnings.

3 The hourly rates for workers in a company for 2004 were recorded. The lowest rate was £6, the highest £15, the median £8, the quartiles £6.80 and £10. Here is a box plot for this data.

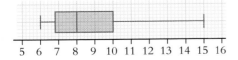

The modal hourly rate was £12. Explain why this is not an appropriate average to use.

CHAPTER 46

Histograms and sampling

> **This chapter is about:**
> - drawing and using histograms
> - understanding and using sampling schemes.
>
> **You should already know:**
> - how to find class boundaries
> - how to use class limits.

Histograms

A histogram is a pictorial way of presenting data contained in a grouped frequency distribution. The data is represented by columns or bars. The **area** of each bar represents the frequency.

The data must be scaled on a **continuous** scale on the horizontal axis. The **frequency density** is plotted on the vertical axis.

The frequency density is calculated as follows:

$$\text{frequency density} = \frac{\text{frequency}}{\text{class width}}$$

The **class width** is calculated in one of two ways, depending on the way the data is presented in the question.

When data is presented as 1–5, 6–15, …
then the class width would be $5.5 - 0.5 = 5$ and $15.5 - 5.5 = 10$, and so on. For this sort of data:

> class width = upper boundary – lower boundary

When data is presented as $0 < h \leqslant 6, 6 < h \leqslant 16, \dots$
then the class width would be $6 - 0 = 6$ and $16 - 6 = 10$, and so on. For this sort of data:

> class width = upper limit – lower limit

Drawing histograms

- Work out the class widths for each group.
- Calculate the frequency density for each group.
- Plot a continuous scale on the horizontal axis.
- Plot the frequency density on the vertical axis.
- Draw the bars using the class widths and the frequency density.

The data can be grouped in equal class intervals but also in unequal class intervals.

Equal class intervals

The following example shows how to draw a histogram when the class intervals are equal.

EXAMPLE 1

Draw a histogram to show the following test marks for a class.

Test marks	Frequency
1–5	3
6–10	7
11–15	5
16–20	8
21–25	2

SOLUTION

We need to work out the boundaries for each group first. We take the numbers halfway between each limit. This gives us $0.5 - 5.5$, $5.5 - 10.5$, $10.5 - 15.5$, $15.5 - 20.5$ and $20.5 - 25.5$.

We can then work out the class widths by subtracting the boundaries:

$5.5 - 0.5 = 5$
$10.5 - 5.5 = 5$ and so on.

> These will all be 5 as all the intervals are equal.

We can then work out the frequency density for each group as shown in the table.

> We divide the frequency by the class width to get the frequency density.

Mark	Class boundaries	Class width	Frequency	Frequency density
1–5	0.5 – 5.5	5	3	$\frac{3}{5} = 0.6$
6–10	5.5 – 10.5	5	7	$\frac{7}{5} = 1.4$
11–15	10.5 – 15.5	5	5	$\frac{5}{5} = 1$
16–20	15.5 – 20.5	5	8	$\frac{8}{5} = 1.6$
21–25	20.5 – 25.5	5	2	$\frac{2}{5} = 0.4$

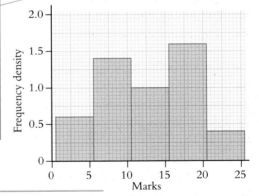

We can now plot the class boundaries (on the horizontal axis) against the frequency density (on the vertical axis).

Unequal class intervals

The examples below show how to draw a histogram when the class intervals are unequal.

EXAMPLE 2

1   The marks in an RE exam are shown in the table.
Show this data on a histogram.

RE marks	Frequency
1 – 10	470
11 – 15	320
16 – 40	800
41 – 60	1160
61 – 65	240

SOLUTION

We need to work out the boundaries for each group first. We take the numbers halfway between each limit. This gives us $0.5 - 10.5$, $10.5 - 15.5$, $15.5 - 40.5$, $40.5 - 60.5$, $60.5 - 65.5$.

We can then work out the class widths by subtracting the boundaries:

$$10.5 - 0.5 = 10$$
$$15.5 - 10.5 = 5$$
$$40.5 - 15.5 = 25$$
$$60.5 - 40.5 = 20$$
$$65.5 - 60.5 = 5$$

We can then work out the frequency density for each group as shown in the table.

Mark	Class boundaries	Class width	Frequency	Frequency density
$1-10$	$0.5 - 10.5$	10	470	$\frac{470}{10} = 47$
$11-15$	$10.5 - 15.5$	5	320	$\frac{320}{5} = 64$
$16-40$	$15.5 - 40.5$	25	800	$\frac{800}{25} = 32$
$41-60$	$40.5 - 60.5$	20	1160	$\frac{1160}{20} = 58$
$61-65$	$60.5 - 65.5$	5	240	$\frac{240}{5} = 48$

We can now plot the class boundaries (on the horizontal axis) against the frequency density (on the vertical axis).

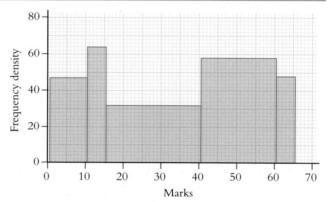

EXAMPLE 3

The lengths of different objects in cm are shown in the table.

Show this data on a histogram.

Length, l (cm)	Frequency
$0 < l \leqslant 4$	14
$4 < l \leqslant 6$	15
$6 < l \leqslant 16$	64
$16 < l \leqslant 21$	19
$21 < l \leqslant 25$	38
$25 < l \leqslant 35$	23

SOLUTION

We can find the class widths by subtracting the limits of each group as follows:

$$4 - 0 = 4$$
$$6 - 4 = 2$$
$$16 - 6 = 10$$
$$21 - 16 = 5$$
$$25 - 21 = 4$$
$$35 - 25 = 10$$

We can then work out the frequency density for each group as shown in the table.

Length, l (cm)	Class width	Frequency	Frequency density
$0 < l \leqslant 4$	4	14	$\frac{14}{4} = 3.5$
$4 < l \leqslant 6$	2	15	$\frac{15}{2} = 7.5$
$6 < l \leqslant 16$	10	64	$\frac{64}{10} = 6.4$
$16 < l \leqslant 21$	5	19	$\frac{19}{5} = 3.8$
$21 < l \leqslant 25$	4	38	$\frac{38}{4} = 9.5$
$25 < l \leqslant 35$	10	23	$\frac{23}{10} = 2.3$

We can now plot the class boundaries (on the horizontal axis) against the frequency density (on the vertical axis).

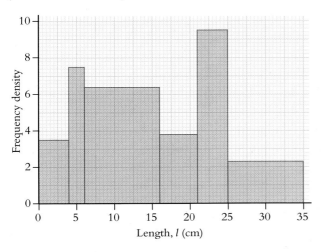

Exercise 46.1

Draw histograms to show the following data.

1 Masses of apples in a bag.

Mass m (g)	Frequency
61 – 70	8
71 – 80	12
81 – 90	10
91 – 100	7
101 – 110	2

2 Costs of radios.

Cost, C (£)	Frequency
1 – 6	21
7 – 11	28
12 – 15	10
16 – 25	48
26 – 30	8
31 – 35	16

3 Heights.

Height, h (cm)	Frequency
$0 < h \leqslant 3$	162
$3 < h \leqslant 8$	120
$8 < h \leqslant 18$	420
$18 < h \leqslant 33$	510
$33 < h \leqslant 35$	84

4 Perimeters.

Perimeter, P (cm)	Frequency
$30 < P \leqslant 34$	72
$34 < P \leqslant 44$	130
$44 < P \leqslant 46$	56
$46 < P \leqslant 51$	110
$51 < P \leqslant 61$	90

5 Scores out of 30.

Number	Frequency
1 – 4	6
5 – 9	14
10 – 19	6
19 – 20	5
21 – 25	9
26 – 30	4

6 Times to finish a race.

Time, t (minutes)	Frequency
$30 < t \leqslant 32$	8
$32 < t \leqslant 35$	6
$35 < t \leqslant 40$	30
$40 < t \leqslant 50$	120
$50 < t \leqslant 60$	580
$60 < t \leqslant 65$	260

Interpreting histograms

We now look at how you can extract information from a histogram.

EXAMPLE 4

The histogram shows the ages of people in a church.

Copy and complete the frequency table for this data.

Age (years)	Frequency
31−40	

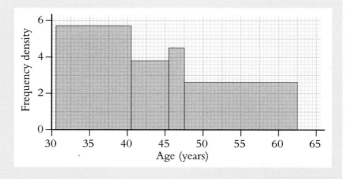

SOLUTION

From the histogram, the boundaries for the groups are:

30.5 − 40.5 and so the limits are 31−40
40.5 − 45.5 and so the limits are 41−45
45.5 − 47.5 and so the limits are 46−47
47.5 − 62.5 and so the limits are 48−62

The class widths for each group are:

40.5 − 30.5 = 10
45.5 − 40.5 = 5
47.5 − 45.5 = 2
62.5 − 47.5 = 15

The frequency density for each group is:

5.7   3.8   4.5   2.6

Thus the frequencies are:

10 × 5.7 = 57
5 × 3.8 = 19
2 × 4.5 = 9
15 × 2.6 = 39

We can now complete the table.

Age (years)	Frequency
31−40	57
41−45	19
46−47	9
48−62	39

> **Rules**
> - Find the limits for each group.
> - Complete the 'Age' column.
> - Find the class widths for each group.
> - Find the frequency density for each group.
> - Multiply the class widths by the frequency density to get the frequencies.
> - Complete the 'Frequency' column.

EXAMPLE 5

The histogram shows the volumes of containers in litres.

Copy and complete the frequency table for this data.

Volume, V (litres)	Frequency
$0 < V \leqslant 8$	

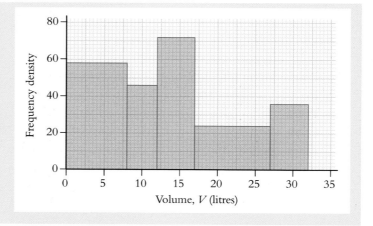

SOLUTION

The limits for each group are:	The class widths for each group are:	The frequency density for each group is:
0 and 8	$8 - 0 = 8$	58
8 and 12	$12 - 8 = 4$	46
12 and 17	$17 - 12 = 5$	72
17 and 27	$27 - 17 = 10$	24
27 and 32	$32 - 27 = 5$	36

Thus the frequencies are:

$8 \times 58 = 464$
$4 \times 46 = 184$
$5 \times 72 = 360$
$10 \times 24 = 240$
$5 \times 36 = 180$

We can now complete the table.

Volume, V (litres)	Frequency
$0 < V \leqslant 8$	464
$8 < V \leqslant 12$	184
$12 < V \leqslant 17$	360
$17 < V \leqslant 27$	240
$27 < V \leqslant 32$	180

Exercise 46.2

1 The histogram shows the costs of computer games in £. Copy and complete the frequency table for this data.

Cost, C (£)	Frequency
1–6	

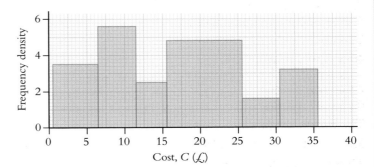

2 The histogram shows the heights of different objects. Copy and complete the frequency table for this data.

Height, h (cm)	Frequency
$0 < h \leqslant 3$	

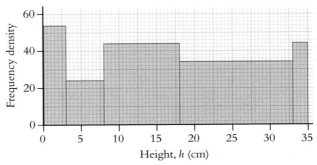

3 The histogram shows the prices of air fares of a budget plane company. Copy and complete the frequency table for this data.

Price, P (£)	Frequency
1–4	

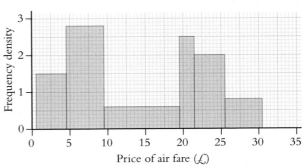

4   The histogram shows the times of
    different journeys.
    Copy and complete the frequency
    table for this data.

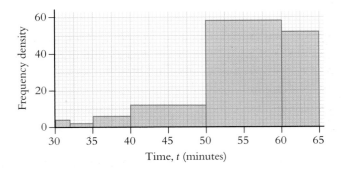

Time, t (minutes)	Frequency
$30 < t \leqslant 32$	

Sampling

The **population** is the complete set of data. When information is required
from this complete set it is often impossible or impractical to ask everyone.
A **sample** of the population would then be taken. The sample should be

- large enough to make the results meaningful
- representative of the complete data set
- unbiased. ◄—————————

> An unbiased sample is one in which
> **every** piece of data has an equal
> chance of being chosen.

Different types of sampling

Random sampling

A **random** sample is a sample in which all pieces of data are equally likely
to be chosen. They would be chosen completely at random. For example
we could give each piece of data a different number and then choose
numbers at random.

Positive point: All the data set has an equal chance of being chosen.

Negative point: There is no guarantee that the data set in the sample
would be representative of the population.

Systematic random sampling

This is when the data set in the sample is chosen at random according to
some rule, for example every fifth item is chosen.

Positive point: All the data set has an equal chance of being chosen.

Negative point: There is no guarantee that the data set in the sample
would be representative of the population.

Stratified random sampling

This method ensures that the data set will be representative of the
population by dividing the population into separate groups or strata and
choosing data sets from these groups in the **same** proportion as in the
population. This is statistically the best method of sampling.

Positive points: All the data set has an equal chance of being chosen.
The data set in the sample is representative of the
population.

Hypothesis

An **hypothesis** is a statement which may or may not be true. The aim of the investigation is to gather data to find out whether the hypothesis is correct. The sampling method that you should use depends on what information is being gathered.

Exercise 46.3

In questions 1 to 6 say whether:

a the sample is a random sample or a systematic sample

b it is a representative sample and if not give a reason why.

1   *Hypothesis:* 'Trains are unreliable.'
    Sampling method: Giving a questionnaire to 10% of the passengers on 10% of the trains one morning.

2   *Hypothesis:* 'Girls do better in exams than boys.'
    Sampling method: Get exam results for 50 boys and 50 girls.

3   *Hypothesis:* 'Fewer people are putting salt on their chips.'
    Sampling method: Note whether every tenth person adds salt or not.

4   *Hypothesis:* 'The most popular colour of car is black.'
    Sampling method: Note every fourth car's colour.

5   *Hypothesis:* 'Football is the most popular sport.'
    Sampling method: Ask 100 people their favourite sport.

6   *Hypothesis:* 'More women do grocery shopping than men.'
    Sampling method: Record the sex of shoppers in a supermarket from noon to 1 pm on Saturday.

In questions 7 to 10, say why the sampling method is biased.

7   *Hypothesis:* 'There should be more time given to PE in school.'
    Sampling method: Ask the members of the rugby and netball teams.

8   *Hypothesis:* 'Church is boring.'
    Sampling method: Ask half the members of Sunday school.

9   *Hypothesis:* 'Young people spend too much time on the computer.'
    Sampling method: Ask one in every four parents at a parents' night.

10   *Hypothesis:* 'Students like Maths.'
    Sampling method: Ask the students in the Additional Maths classes.

Stratified random sampling

We have already noted that the best method of sampling is stratified random sampling. We now look at this method in more detail.

EXAMPLE 9

The number of people taking driving lessons with the different driving instructors at a driving school is shown in the table.
A stratified sample of 80 students is to be taken.
How many should be selected from each driving instructor?

Instructor A	Instructor B	Instructor C	Instructor D
120	192	96	72

Total = 120 + 192 + 96 + 72 = 480

Instructor A $\dfrac{120}{480} \times 80 = 20$

Instructor B $\dfrac{192}{480} \times 80 = 32$

Instructor C $\dfrac{96}{480} \times 80 = 16$

Rules
- Find the total number in the population.
- Find the fraction of the total for each stratum.
- Multiply each fraction by the number in the sample.

Instructor D $\qquad \dfrac{72}{480} \times 80 = 12$

So for a stratified random sample, there should be 20 students from instructor A, 32 students from instructor B, 16 students from instructor C and 12 students from instructor D.

EXAMPLE 10

The number of people who did their shopping at four different supermarkets on Friday is shown in the table. A stratified sample of 40 shoppers is to be taken. How many more shoppers will be in the sample from supermarket 3 than from supermarket 2?

Supermarket 1	Supermarket 2	Supermarket 3	Supermarket 4
1116	248	744	372

SOLUTION

Total = 1116 + 248 + 744 + 372 = 2480

Supermarket 3: $\qquad \dfrac{744}{2480} \times 40 = 12$

Supermarket 2: $\qquad \dfrac{248}{2480} \times 40 = 4$

$$12 - 4 = 8 \text{ shoppers}$$

In the sample there are eight more shoppers from supermarket 3 than from supermarket 2.

Exercise 46.4

1 The number of discs in a box is shown in the table. A stratified sample of 50 is to be taken. How many should be selected from each colour?

Red	Yellow	Blue	Green
216	648	972	864

2 The number of cars sold in the first quarter of 2010 is shown in the table. A stratified sample of 48 is to be taken. How many should be selected from each make of car?

Ford	Renault	Volkswagen	Skoda
462	770	924	308

3 The number of people taking ICT classes last year is shown in the table. A stratified sample of 54 is to be taken. How many males should be selected?

Boys	Girls	Men	Women
471	314	785	1256

4   The number of people going to four different destinations on holiday is shown
    in the table. A stratified sample of 60 is to be taken. How many should be
    selected from each destination?

Spain	Italy	France	Portugal
768	864	1056	192

5   The number of people choosing different main courses in a hotel is shown in
    the table. A stratified sample of 48 is to be taken. How many should be selected
    from each course?

Chicken	Turkey	Beef	Vegetarian
380	608	532	304

6   The number of students choosing their favourite sports is shown in the table.
    A stratified sample of 56 is to be taken. How many should be selected from each?

Football	Rugby	Netball	Hockey
464	580	232	348

7   The number of people staying at a range of hotels is shown in the table. A
    stratified sample of 42 is to be taken. How many should be selected from those
    who chose full or half board?

Full board	Half board	Bed and breakfast	Room only
172	430	516	688

8   The number of people going to different sports is shown in the table. A stratified
    sample of 63 is to be taken. How many should be selected from each sport?

Tennis	Motor racing	Ice hockey	Hurling
345	460	920	690

9   The number of people travelling to work is shown in the table. A stratified
    sample of 44 is to be taken. How many should be selected from each method of
    transport?

Train	Car	Walk	Bus
204	340	408	544

10 The number of people buying different flavours of crisps is shown in the table.
    A stratified sample of 36 is to be taken. How many more will be in the sample
    of those who bought Cheese and onion than those who bought Smoky bacon?

Smoky bacon	Cheese and onion	Salt and vinegar
324	432	540

Examples where we do not know the total number in the population set

Sometimes we will not know the total number in the population set.
However, if we know the total number of one of the subsets and the
breakdown of the stratified sample we can work out the number for all of
the other subsets and the population itself.

EXAMPLE 11

A stratified sample was taken of the men, women and children on a holiday.
There were 9 men, 18 women and 12 children in the sample.
There were 876 women on the holiday.
How many a men and b children were on the holiday?

SOLUTION

Total in the sample = 9 + 18 + 12 = 39

Women: $\dfrac{18}{39}$

So total population = $876 \times \dfrac{39}{18} = 1898$

   a Men: $\dfrac{9}{39} \times 1898 = 438$

   b Children: $\dfrac{12}{39} \times 1898 = 584$

Rules
- Find the total number in the sample.
- Find the fraction of women in the sample.
- Use this fraction to find the population.
- Find the fraction of men and children in the sample.
- Multiply these fractions by the population.

Exercise 46.5

1 A stratified sample was taken of the red, blue, green and orange counters in a box. There were 3 red, 6 blue, 12 green and 15 orange counters in the sample.
There were 485 orange counters in the box.
How many a red, b blue, c green counters were in the box?

2 A stratified sample was taken of the men, women, boys and girls on a cruise. There were 6 men, 9 women, 18 boys and 21 girls in the sample.
There were 291 women on the cruise.
How many a men, b boys, c girls were on the cruise?

3 A stratified sample was taken of the three newspapers read on holiday. 20 people in the sample read *The Times*, 25 read *The Mirror* and 30 read *The Mail*.
Altogether 654 read *The Mail*.
How many read a *The Times*, b *The Mirror*?

4 A stratified sample was taken of the cars driven by tourists on holiday.
Twelve people in the sample drove a Mini, 16 drove a Fiesta, 20 drove an Audi and 24 drove a Clio. Altogether 726 drove a Clio.
How many drove a a Mini, b a Fiesta, c an Audi?

5 A stratified sample was taken of the activities chosen in a leisure centre. Four people in the sample chose the gym, 10 chose swimming and 12 chose badminton.
Altogether 365 chose swimming.
How many chose a the gym, b badminton?

6 A stratified sample was taken of the numbers in a school studying Irish, Spanish and French. Four people in the sample study Irish, 16 study Spanish and 20 study French. Altogether 476 study Spanish.
How many study a Irish, b French?

7 A stratified sample was taken of the ways people travel to work. Six people in the sample walk, 9 come by train, 15 come by bus and 18 drive. Altogether 405 come by bus.
How many **a** walk, **b** come by train, **c** drive?

8 A stratified sample was taken of the ways people spend their weekends. Eight people in the sample visit friends, 14 go to the cinema and 16 stay at home. Altogether 861 go to the cinema.
How many **a** visit friends, **b** stay at home.

9 A stratified sample was taken of the men, women, boys and girls at a concert. There were 6 men, 15 women, 21 boys and 24 girls in the sample. There were 335 women at the concert.
How many **a** men, **b** boys, **c** girls were at the concert?

10 A stratified sample was taken of the places where people would like to go on holiday. In the sample 4 wanted to go to Australia, 16 wanted to go to America, 20 wanted to go to Egypt and 24 wanted to go to Mexico. Altogether 522 wanted to go to Mexico.
How many wanted to go to **a** Australia, **b** America, **c** Egypt?

Examples where we only know the number of one subset in the sample

Sometimes we will only know the number in one of the subsets in the stratified sample. However, if we know the total number of each of the subsets in the population then we can work out the number in all of the other subsets in the stratified sample.

EXAMPLE 12

There were 128 black, 192 white, 320 brown and 64 pink coloured tokens in a box. A stratified sample was taken in which six were white. How many of each of the other colours were in this sample?

SOLUTION

White: $\dfrac{192}{6} = 32$

Black: $\dfrac{128}{32} = 4$

Brown: $\dfrac{320}{32} = 10$

Pink: $\dfrac{64}{32} = 2$

Rules
- Divide the number of whites in the population by the number of whites in the sample.
- Divide this answer into the number of each colour in the population.

Exercise 46.6

1 There were 74 men, 148 women, and 296 children on holiday. A stratified sample was taken in which six were women.
How many **a** men, **b** children were in this sample?

2 252 vehicles passing a school were lorries, 168 were motor bikes and 420 were cars. A stratified sample was taken in which 15 were lorries.
How many **a** motor bikes, **b** cars were in this sample?

3   There were 128 cubes, 384 cones, and 448 cylinders in a warehouse.
    A stratified sample was taken in which 24 were cones.
    How many **a** cubes, **b** cylinders were in this sample?

4   There were 376 students in Years 8 and 9, 282 students in Years 10
    and 11 and 470 students in Years 12 and 13.
    A stratified sample was taken in which 35 were in Years 12 and 13.
    How many were in **a** Years 8 and 9, **b** Years 10 and 11 in this sample?

5   There were 237 marbles, 158 dice, 316 counters and 395 beads in a
    Maths store. A stratified sample was taken in which eight were dice.
    How many **a** marbles, **b** counters, **c** beads were in this sample?

6   There were 1924 carp, 962 perch, 2405 pike and 2886 trout in a
    lake. A stratified sample was taken in which 18 were trout.
    How many of each of the other fish were in this sample?

7   There were 225 Linfield, 600 Cliftonville, 300 Ballymena and 525
    Glenavon supporters at a football tournament.
    A stratified sample was taken in which 20 were Ballymena supporters.
    How many of each of the other supporters were in this sample?

8   There were 142 men, 426 women, and 355 children on holiday.
    A stratified sample was taken in which 24 were women.
    How many **a** men, **b** children were in this sample?

You should now:

- **be able to draw histograms**
- **be able to interpret histograms**
- **understand population and sample**
- **understand bias**
- **know the different sampling methods**
- **be able to use stratified random sampling.**

Summary exercise 46

1   The masses of different objects
    in kg are shown in the table.
    Show this data on a histogram.

Mass, M (kg)	Frequency
$0 < M \leqslant 10$	540
$10 < M \leqslant 15$	365
$15 < M \leqslant 40$	950
$40 < M \leqslant 60$	1280
$60 < M \leqslant 70$	430

2   The ages of people at a football
    match are shown in the table.
    Show this data on a histogram.

Age (years)	Frequency
4 – 13	37
14 – 20	28
21 – 25	31
26 – 40	72
41 – 60	156
61 – 65	23

3 The histogram shows the costs of
   portable televisions in £.
   Copy and complete the frequency
   table for this data.

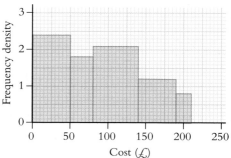

Cost (£)	Frequency
over 0 and up to and including 50	

4 Give an example of a random sample to test the hypothesis:
   'Older students are better at estimating time'.

5 Consider the hypothesis and sampling method below.
   Hypothesis: 'More Year 12 students eat packed lunch
               than Year 8.'
   Sampling method: Ask every fifth Year 8 and every fifth Year 12
               student.

   a Is the sample random or systematic?

   b Is it a representative sample? If not, give a reason why.

6 Say why the sampling method below is biased.
   Hypothesis: 'Students revise hard for exams.'
   Sampling method: Ask every other Year 12 student after a
               GCSE exam.

7 The heights, h metres, of different students are shown in the table.
   A stratified sample of 34 is to be taken.
   How many should be selected from each group?

$h < 1.45$	$1.45 \leqslant h < 1.70$	$h \geqslant 1.70$
292	438	511

8 The number of people who travelled by train, boat and plane is shown
   in the table. A stratified sample of 38 is to be taken. How many more
   people in the sample will have travelled by plane than by train?

Train	Boat	Plane
580	696	928

9 A stratified sample was taken of the people who drink juice, tea, water
   and coffee at work. In the sample two drank juice, five drank tea, four
   drank water and six drank coffee. 316 people altogether drank water.
   How many altogether drank **a** juice, **b** tea, **c** coffee?

10 There were 201 chicken sandwiches, 335 tuna sandwiches, 268
    beef sandwiches and 134 salad sandwiches made for a reception. A
    stratified sample was taken in which there were 14 salad sandwiches.
    How many of each of the other sandwiches were in this sample?

Examination questions

Use 'Topic Tracker' at www.ccea.org.uk to find more exam questions.

Question **1** is from an examination paper where you may not use a calculator.

1   A number of students responded to a survey about the amount of money they earned per week from their Saturday jobs.

   The result of the survey is illustrated by the histogram.

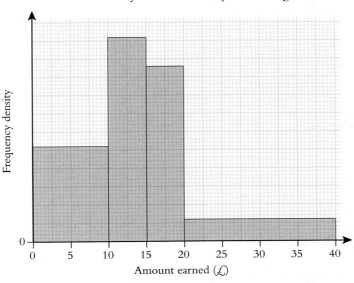

   a Twenty-six students earned less than £10. Calculate the total number of students who responded to the survey.

   b A stratified sample of 16 of the students who earned more than £10 was taken. How many of the students in the sample earned between £15 and £20?

Questions **2** and **3** are from examination papers where you may use a calculator.

2   A change in the road tax system for private cars was proposed. A sample of motorists stopping at a service centre on a motorway was questioned to get their opinion on the change. Give two reasons why the sample would be biased.

3   **a** Describe one way of choosing a **random** sample.

   b An investigation is to be carried out into the television viewing habits of students at an 11–18 co-educational school. There are 700 girls and 300 boys attending the school. A sample of 100 students is to be chosen.
      The sample should be representative of the school population, State **two** factors which should be taken into consideration when choosing the sample.

CHAPTER 47

Probability

This chapter is about:

- using relative frequency as an estimate of probability
- finding the probability of an event not happening
- using the addition law of probability
- calculating the probability of a combined event happening
- drawing and using probability trees.

You should already know:

- how to find the probability of a single event happening
- how to calculate the expected frequency of an event happening
- how to round to a given number of significant figures
- the rules of decimals and fractions
- how to determine which numbers are prime
- how to find multiples and factors of numbers
- how to find squares and cubes of numbers.

Probability

The probability of an event happening is given by the rule:

$$\text{probability of an event} = \frac{\text{the number of desirable outcomes}}{\text{the number of possible outcomes}}$$

But this rule is only true when the outcomes are unbiased, i.e. when all the outcomes are equally likely.

When all the events are possible then the events are said to be **exhaustive**.

Consider a football team playing a match. The possible outcomes are Win, Lose or Draw. However these are not all equally likely, depending on different factors such as the current form of the team or the quality of the opposition.

In this and similar cases we can use **relative frequency** as an estimate for probability.

Relative frequency

The relative frequency of an event happening is given by the rule:

$$\begin{array}{r} \text{relative frequency} \\ \text{of an event} \end{array} = \frac{\begin{array}{c}\text{the number of times the event happens in}\\ \text{an experiment or survey}\end{array}}{\begin{array}{c}\text{the total number of times the experiment}\\ \text{or survey took place}\end{array}}$$

EXAMPLE 1

A dice was thrown 1000 times and the results are shown in the table.

Number	1	2	3	4	5	6
Frequency	127	213	208	173	121	158

a   Is this a biased dice?

b   Find the relative frequency for each number.

c   Hence find how many 2s you would expect if the dice were thrown 2400 times.

SOLUTION

a   The outcomes of an unbiased dice should all have approximately the same frequency ($\frac{1000}{6} = 166$ approximately).

The frequencies are quite different from this, so this dice is biased.

b $RF(1) = \frac{127}{1000}$

$RF(2) = \frac{213}{1000}$

$RF(3) = \frac{208}{1000} = \frac{26}{125}$ ← Here we can cancel by dividing top and bottom by 8.

$RF(4) = \frac{173}{1000}$

$RF(5) = \frac{121}{1000}$

$RF(6) = \frac{158}{1000} = \frac{79}{500}$

c   Expected frequency = probability $\times$ number of times

Using RF(2) as an estimate for the probability of getting 2 we have:

Expected frequency = $\frac{213}{1000} \times 2400 = 511.2$

Answer: 511 times.

EXAMPLE 2

A record was kept of a football team's results and the relative frequency of a win was calculated after every 20 games. The results are shown in the table.

Number of games	Number of wins	RF(win)
20	9	$\frac{9}{20} = 0.45$
40	14	$\frac{14}{40} = 0.35$
60	17	$\frac{17}{60} = 0.2833...$ or $0.28\dot{3}$
80	23	$\frac{23}{80} = 0.2875$
100	25	$\frac{25}{100} = 0.25$
120	25	$\frac{25}{120} = 0.20833...$ or $0.208\dot{3}$
140	26	$\frac{26}{140} = 0.186$
160	33	$\frac{33}{160} = 0.20625$
180	37	$\frac{37}{180} = 0.2055...$ or $0.20\dot{5}$
200	41	$\frac{41}{200} = 0.205$

SOLUTION

a   The relative frequency that gives the best estimate is 0.205, as this
    is based on the **largest** number of games (200 games).

b $0.205 \times 200 = 41$
    So the team might expect to win 41 of the next 200 games.

c   We do not know who the team will be playing in the next 200
    games or if the team is going to change personnel over these
    games (or any of the other unknowns).

Exercise 47.1

1   A drawing pin is dropped 150 times and the
    results are shown in the table.
    Find:
    a   the relative frequency of the pin landing point up
    b   the relative frequency of the pin landing point down
    c   how many times you would expect the pin to land
        point up if it was dropped 320 times.

Outcome	Frequency
Landing 'point up'	54
Landing 'point down'	96

2   A spinner has the letters P, Q, R, S and T on it. It is spun
    100 times and the results are shown in the table.
    The spinner landed on S and T an equal number of times.
    Find:
    a   the relative frequency of each letter
    b   how many times you would expect the letter Q to turn up
        after 260 spins.

Outcome	Frequency
P	24
Q	17
R	19
S	
T	

3   There are 60 counters in a bag. They are either blue or green.
    A counter is withdrawn at random, its colour noted
    and then replaced.
    The table shows the results after every 40 withdrawals.
    a   Calculate the relative frequency of getting a blue
        counter after 40, 80, 120, 160 and 200 withdrawals.
    b   Which of these relative frequencies gives the best
        estimate for the probability and why?
    c   Use this relative frequency to estimate the number of blues
        and greens in the bag.

Number of withdrawals	Number of blues
40	27
80	51
120	76
160	101
200	129

4   A man records the colour of a set of traffic lights he has to pass
    every morning on his way to work.
    a   Calculate the relative frequency to 3 significant figures of each
        colour.
    b   Hence estimate how many more red lights than green lights he
        would expect in 250 journeys to work.

Colour	Number
Red	75
Amber	24
Green	32

5 Thomas records how many questions he gets
wrong in every 10 Maths questions he does.

Question numbers	1–10	11–20	21–30	31–40	41–50	51–60	61–70
Number wrong	4	4	3	4	3	2	2

a Copy and complete the relative frequency table.

Number of questions	Total number wrong	Relative frequency to 3 significant figures if necessary
10	4	0.4
20	8	
30		
40		
50		
60		
70		

b Which of these relative frequencies gives the best estimate for
the probability and why?

c Use this relative frequency to estimate the number of questions
he will have got wrong after 150 questions.

6 Arlene spins a spinner which has the numbers 1, 3, 5, 7 and 9 on it
and records the results for every 60 spins.

Number of spins	Number of 1s	Number of 3s	Number of 5s	Number of 7s	Number of 9s
1–60	6	11	7	18	18
61–120	8	12	5	19	16
121–180	9	8	9	21	13
181–240	11	7	6	17	19
241–300	10	13	7	22	8
301–360	9	11	10	20	10

a Calculate the relative frequency to 3 significant figures of
getting 1, 3, 5, 7 and then 9 after 360 spins.

b Arlene then spins the spinner 160 times.
How many times will she expect to get i 1, ii 9?

Probability of certain success

The probability of an outcome that is certain to happen is 1, so the sum of
all the possible outcomes will be 1.

Thus if you know the probability of all the possible outcomes except one
of them, to find the missing probability you should:

- add up all the other probabilities
- subtract this total from 1.

EXAMPLE 3

The probabilities of rolling each number on a biased dice are given in the table. Find the probability of rolling 4.

Number	1	2	3	4	5	6
Probability	0.12	0.2	0.15		0.22	0.16

SOLUTION

$$0.12 + 0.2 + 0.15 + 0.22 + 0.16 = 0.85$$
$$P(4) = 1 - 0.85 = 0.15$$

EXAMPLE 4

The probabilities of getting each letter on a spinner are given in the table. Find the probability of getting the letter C.

Letter	A	B	C	D
Probability	$\frac{1}{4}$	$\frac{2}{5}$		$\frac{3}{10}$

SOLUTION

Remember that we need a lowest common denominator to add fractions.

$$\frac{1}{4} + \frac{2}{5} + \frac{3}{10} = \frac{5}{20} + \frac{8}{20} + \frac{6}{20} = \frac{19}{20}$$
$$P(C) = 1 - \frac{19}{20} = \frac{20}{20} - \frac{19}{20} = \frac{1}{20}$$

Probability of an event not happening

The probability of an outcome that is certain to happen is 1. Therefore the probability of an event happening added to the probability of an event not happening must equal 1.

$$P(\text{event A}) + P(\text{not event A}) = 1$$

Thus $\qquad P(\text{not event A}) = 1 - P(\text{event A})$

So, to find the probability of an event **not** happening, subtract the probability of it happening from 1.

EXAMPLE 5

The probability it rains tomorrow is $\frac{16}{25}$.
Find the probability it won't rain tomorrow.

SOLUTION

$$P(\text{no rain tomorrow}) = 1 - \frac{16}{25} = \frac{25}{25} - \frac{16}{25} = \frac{9}{25}$$

1   Sam makes a train journey once each week. The probability that he
    makes the journey on a particular day of the week is given in the
    table.
    Find the probability he takes the train on a Friday.

Day	Sunday	Monday	Tuesday	Wednesday	Thursday	Friday	Saturday
Probability	0.03	0.23	0.11	0.13	0.12		0.07

2   The probabilities of getting each number on a spinner are given in
    the table. Find the probability of getting a 500.

Number	10	20	30	50	100	500
Probability	$\frac{5}{12}$	$\frac{1}{4}$	$\frac{1}{8}$	$\frac{1}{12}$	$\frac{1}{12}$	

3   A family has chips for tea once a week. The probabilities of chips
    for tea on a particular day of the week are given in the table.
    Find the probability of getting chips for tea on Wednesday.

Day	Sunday	Monday	Tuesday	Wednesday	Thursday	Friday	Saturday
Probability	$\frac{1}{40}$	$\frac{3}{20}$	$\frac{1}{10}$		$\frac{1}{20}$	$\frac{3}{10}$	$\frac{1}{4}$

4   The probability of passing a test is 0.73. Find the probability of
    failing the test.

5   The probability a baby is a girl is $\frac{19}{40}$. Find the probability the baby
    is a boy.

6   The probability there is a Maths homework tonight is 0.84.
    Find the probability there is no Maths homework tonight.

7   The probability that a hockey match is cancelled is $\frac{2}{25}$.
    Find the probability it is not cancelled.

8   The probability there is sport on television tonight is $\frac{17}{20}$.
    Find the probability there is no sport on television tonight.

9   The probability that a girl will come first in a Maths test is 0.64.
    Find the probability that a boy will come first in the Maths test.

Mutually exclusive events

Mutually exclusive events are events that **cannot** happen at the same time.

- When throwing a dice, getting a number less than 3 or a number
  greater than 5 are mutually exclusive events.
- When throwing a dice getting an even number or a prime number are
  not mutually exclusive events since 2 is even **and** prime.

Addition law of probability

When events A and B are mutually exclusive then the probability that event A **or** event B happens is found by adding the probability that event A happens to the probability that event B happens, i.e.

$$P(A \text{ or } B) = P(A) + P(B)$$

> This law only works when the events are mutually exclusive.

Mutually exclusive events

When throwing a dice find the probability of getting a number less than 3 or a number greater than 5.

Desirable outcomes = 1, 2, 6

Possible outcomes = 1, 2, 3, 4, 5, 6

Thus P(a number less than 3 or a number greater than 5) = $\frac{3}{6}$

But P(a number less than 3) = $\frac{2}{6}$

And P(a number greater than 5) = $\frac{1}{6}$

And $\frac{3}{6} = \frac{2}{6} + \frac{1}{6}$

Events that are not mutually exclusive

When throwing a dice find the probability of getting an even number or a prime number.

P(even) = $\frac{3}{6}$ (evens: 2, 4, 6)

P(prime) = $\frac{3}{6}$ (primes: 2, 3, 5)

P(even or prime) = $\frac{3}{6} + \frac{3}{6} = \frac{6}{6} = 1$ which means it is certain.

But 1 is neither even nor prime.

Thus we cannot use the law this time as the events are not mutually exclusive.

In such a question we would need to list the desirable outcomes:

Desirable outcomes: 2, 4, 6, 3, 5

Possible outcomes: 1, 2, 3, 4, 5, 6

P(even or prime) = $\frac{5}{6}$

EXAMPLE 6

A bag contains 6 red, 8 green and 12 white beads. One bead is drawn out at random. Find the probability it is red or white.

SOLUTION

These events are mutually exclusive.

Total number = 6 + 8 + 12 = 26

P(red or white) = $\frac{6}{26} + \frac{12}{26} = \frac{18}{26} = \frac{9}{13}$

EXAMPLE 7

The probabilities of each number on a biased dice are given in the table.

Number	1	2	3	4	5	6
Probability	0.14	0.23	0.11			

a   Find the probability of getting a 1 or a 3.

b   Find the probability of not getting a 2.

c   The probability of getting a prime number is 0.53.
     Find the probability of getting a 5.

d   It is equally likely to get a 4 or a 6.
     Find the probability of getting a 4.

SOLUTION

a   1 and 3 are mutually exclusive.
     So P(1 or 3) = 0.14 + 0.11 = 0.25

b   P(not 2) = 1 − P(2) = 1 − 0.23 = 0.77

c   The prime numbers are 2, 3 and 5
     P(2 or 3) = 0.23 + 0.11 = 0.34
     P(5) = 0.53 − 0.34 = 0.19

d   P(1 or 2 or 3 or 5) = 0.14 + 0.53 = 0.67   ← Here we add P(1) to P(2 or 3 or 5) from part c.
     So P(4 or 6) = 1 − 0.67 = 0.33
     But it is equally likely to get a 4 or a 6.
     So P(4) = $\frac{0.33}{2}$ = 0.165

Exercise 47.3

1   A box contains 16 cards, each of which has a shape drawn on it. Of
    these, five are rectangles, eight are triangles and three are kites. What
    is the probability of picking a card with
    a   a rectangle or a triangle   b   a rectangle or a kite?

2   The probability that Laura is first in Maths is 0.17 and the
    probability that Colin is first in Maths is 0.28. What is the
    probability that Laura or Colin is first in Maths?

3   The probabilities of rolling each number on a biased dice are given
    in the table.

Number	1	2	3	4	5	6
Probability	$\frac{1}{8}$	$\frac{1}{5}$	$\frac{3}{20}$	$\frac{1}{10}$	$\frac{13}{40}$	

Find the probability of rolling:
a   6   b   1 or 2   c   3 or 5   d   4 or 6   e   2 or 5.

4   The probabilities of getting each number on a spinner are given in the table.

Number	1	2	5	20	50
Probability	0.14		0.32		

a   Find the probability of getting a 1 or a 5.
b   Find the probability of not getting a 5.
c   The probability of getting a factor of 10 is 0.62.
    Find the probability of getting a 2.
d   It is equally likely to get a 20 or a 50.
    Find the probability of getting a 20.

5   The probabilities of getting each number on a spinner are given in the table.

Number	1	2	3	4	5
Probability	$\frac{2}{9}$	$\frac{1}{3}$			

a   Find the probability of getting a number less than 3.
b   Find the probability of not getting 1.
c   The probability of getting a square number is $\frac{7}{18}$.
    Find the probability of getting a 4.
d   It is equally likely to get a 3 or a 5.
    Find the probability of getting a 3.

6   The probabilities of rolling each number on a biased dice are given in the table.

Number	1	2	3	4	5	6
Probability		0.19		0.23		

a   Find the probability of rolling a 2 or a 4.
b   Find the probability of not rolling a 4.
c   The probability of rolling a factor of 8 is 0.53.
    Find the probability of rolling a 1.
d   The probability of rolling a factor of 20 is 0.6.
    Find the probability of rolling a 5.
e   It is three times as likely to roll a 6 as it is to roll a 3.
    Find the probability of rolling i a 3, ii a 6.

7   The table shows the probability of picking different colours from a box.

Colour	red	green	white	blue	pink
Probability		$\frac{2}{5}$		$\frac{1}{6}$	

a   Find the probability of picking a green or blue.
b   Find the probability of not picking a green.
c   The probability of picking a green or a pink is $\frac{11}{20}$.
    Find the probability of picking a pink.
d   It is twice as likely to pick a red as it is to pick a white.
    Find the probability of picking i a white, ii a red.

8   The probability that Paedar chooses one of five drinks for breakfast
    is shown in the table.

Drink	tea	milk	coffee	orange juice	hot chocolate
Probability	0.14		0.23		

a   Find the probability he chooses tea or coffee.
b   Find the probability he doesn't choose tea.

The probability he chooses milk, orange juice or hot chocolate is in
the ratio 2:3:5. Find the probability he chooses:
c   milk
d   tea or orange juice
e   milk or hot chocolate.

9   Joseph chooses a number from 1 to 16 inclusive.
    a   Find the probability he chooses:
        i   a number less than 10 or greater than 12
        ii an even number or a cube number.
    b   Find the probability he does not choose a square number.

10 The probability that a class do different activities in games is shown
    in the table.

Activity	Swimming	Badminton	Running	Volleyball
Probability	0.27			

It is twice as likely that they will run as swim.
a   Find the probability they run.

It is twice as likely that they will swim as play badminton.
b   Find the probability they play badminton.
c   Find the probability they play volleyball.
d   Find the probability they run or play volleyball.
e   Find the probability they do not play badminton.

Independent events

When two events are independent the outcome of the first event has no
effect on the outcome of the second event.

Multiplication law of probability

If A and B are independent events, then:

$$P(A \text{ and } B) = P(A) \times P(B)$$

Suppose a dice is thrown and a coin is tossed.
Then the possible outcomes are:

1, H   2, H   3, H   4, H   5, H   6, H
1, T   2, T   3, T   4, T   5, T   6, T

So $P(1 \text{ and a head}) = \frac{1}{12}$

But $P(1) = \frac{1}{6}$ and $P(\text{head}) = \frac{1}{2}$

and $\frac{1}{6} \times \frac{1}{2} = \frac{1}{12}$

> There is only one of the
> 12 outcomes that gives
> both a 1 and a head.

> Note that the probability of the outcome
> being both 1 and a head is less than the
> probability of the outcome being 1 or the
> probability of the outcome being a head.
>
> $P(1 \text{ and a head}) = \frac{1}{12} < \frac{1}{6} = P(1)$
>
> $P(1 \text{ and a head}) = \frac{1}{12} < \frac{1}{2} = P(\text{head})$

Combined events

Sometimes the first event affects the probability of the second event, for example if you take a card from a pack and do not replace it before you draw a second card.

The examples below show how to deal with problems like this.

EXAMPLE 8

There are eight black, two white and six cream beads in a box. One is selected at random and then replaced. Another bead is then selected. Find the probability that:

    a   the first bead is black and the second bead is cream

    b   one bead is white and the other is cream

    c   both beads are black

    d   at least one bead is cream.

SOLUTION

Total number of beads = 8 + 2 + 6 = 16

Because the bead is replaced, there will be 16 to choose from each time.

    a $P(b \text{ and } c) = P(b) \times P(c) = \dfrac{8}{16} \times \dfrac{6}{16} = \dfrac{3}{16}$

    b   If one is white and the other is cream then we have **two** possible outcomes: The first can be white or cream, i.e.

        $P(w \text{ and } c) = \dfrac{2}{16} \times \dfrac{6}{16} = \dfrac{3}{64}$

        or

        $P(c \text{ and } w) = \dfrac{6}{16} \times \dfrac{2}{16} = \dfrac{3}{64}$

        We must then use the addition law to get the final answer.

        $\dfrac{3}{64} + \dfrac{3}{64} = \dfrac{3}{32}$

        The probability that one bead is white and one is cream is $\dfrac{3}{32}$.

    c $P(b \text{ and } b) = \dfrac{8}{16} \times \dfrac{8}{16} = \dfrac{1}{4}$

    d   'At least' one is cream means either:

        • the first is cream and the second is not cream

        • the first is not cream and the second is cream

        • the first is cream and the second is cream.

        That is:

        $P(c \text{ and not } c) + P(\text{not } c \text{ and } c) + P(c \text{ and } c)$

        $P(c \text{ and not } c) = \dfrac{6}{16} \times \dfrac{10}{16} = \dfrac{15}{64}$

        $P(\text{not } c \text{ and } c) = \dfrac{10}{16} \times \dfrac{6}{16} = \dfrac{15}{64}$

        $P(c \text{ and } c) = \dfrac{6}{16} \times \dfrac{6}{16} = \dfrac{9}{64}$

        We must then use the addition law to get the final answer.

        $\dfrac{15}{64} + \dfrac{15}{64} + \dfrac{9}{64} = \dfrac{39}{64}$

        The probability that at least one bead is cream is $\dfrac{39}{64}$.

Alternative method

An alternative method for answering part d is to find the probability of no creams and then subtract this from 1.

$$P(\text{not c and not c}) = \frac{10}{16} \times \frac{10}{16} = \frac{25}{64}$$

$$\text{So } P(\text{at least one cream}) = 1 - \frac{25}{64} = \frac{64}{64} - \frac{25}{64} = \frac{39}{64}$$

EXAMPLE 9

There are six 5p coins, ten 2p coins and four 1p coins in a bag.
Two are selected at random. Find the probability that:

    a   the first is a 5p and the second is a 2p

    b   neither are 5p

    c   the total value is 3p

    d   at most one is 1p.

SOLUTION

Total number of coins = 6 + 10 + 4 = 20

    a $P(5 \text{ and } 2) = P(5) \times P(2) = \frac{6}{20} \times \frac{10}{19} = \frac{3}{19}$

    b $P(\text{not } 5) \times P(\text{not } 5) = \frac{14}{20} \times \frac{13}{19} = \frac{91}{190}$

> Because two coins are selected this implies that after the first coin is selected it is **not** replaced. Thus, the first selection has 20 possible outcomes but the second selection has only 19 possible outcomes.

> Because there is no replacement only 13 coins will now not be 5p.

    c   To get a total value of 3p we need either 2p and 1p, or 1p and 2p.

$$P(2 \text{ and } 1) = P(2) \times P(1) = \frac{10}{20} \times \frac{4}{19} = \frac{2}{19}$$

$$P(1 \text{ and } 2) = P(1) \times P(2) = \frac{4}{20} \times \frac{10}{19} = \frac{2}{19}$$

We must then use the addition law to get the final answer.

$$P(\text{total value is 3p}) = \frac{2}{19} + \frac{2}{19} = \frac{4}{19}$$

    d   'At most' one is 1p means either:

      •   the first is 1p and the second is not 1p

      •   the first is not 1p and the second is 1p

      •   the first is not 1p and the second is not 1p.

$$P(1 \text{ and not } 1) = P(1) \times P(\text{not } 1) = \frac{4}{20} \times \frac{16}{19} = \frac{16}{95}$$

$$P(\text{not } 1 \text{ and } 1) = P(\text{not } 1) \times P(1) = \frac{16}{20} \times \frac{4}{19} = \frac{16}{95}$$

$$P(\text{not } 1 \text{ and not } 1) = P(\text{not } 1) \times P(\text{not } 1) = \frac{16}{20} \times \frac{15}{19} = \frac{12}{19}$$

We must then use the addition law to get the final answer.

$$\frac{16}{95} + \frac{16}{95} + \frac{12}{19} = \frac{92}{95}$$

Alternative method

An alternative method for part d is to find the probability of both coins being 1p and then subtract this from 1.

$$P(1p \text{ and } 1p) = \frac{4}{20} \times \frac{3}{19} = \frac{3}{95}$$

$$\text{So } P(\text{at most one 1p}) = 1 - \frac{3}{95} = \frac{92}{95}$$

Exercise 47.4

1 There are 15 pens and 10 pencils in a box. One object is selected at random and then replaced. Another is then selected. Find the probability that:
   a   the first object selected is a pen and the second is a pencil
   b   one is a pen and the other is a pencil
   c   both are pencils
   d   at least one is a pen.

2 There are 10 toffee and 5 caramel sweets in a box. Alan eats two sweets at random. Find the probability that:
   a   the first is toffee and the second is caramel
   b   one is toffee and the other is caramel
   c   both are toffee
   d   neither are toffee
   e   at most one is a caramel.

3 There are nine 50p stamps and eighteen 40p stamps in a drawer. Two stamps are chosen. Find the probability that the total value is:
   a   £1   b   80p   c   90p.

4 A dice is thrown twice. Find the probability that:
   a   the first throw is a 4 and the second is a 3
   b   one throw is an even number and the other is a 5
   c   both throws are odd
   d   at least one throw is bigger than 2.

5 A spinner can either land on a shaded section or a blank section. The probability it lands on a shaded section is 0.4.
   a   Find the probability it lands on a blank section.

   The spinner is spun twice. Find the probability it lands on:
   b   a shaded section and then a blank section
   c   a shaded section on one spin and then a blank section on the other spin
   d   a blank section on both spins.

6 There are 12 green, 8 white and 4 red discs in a box. One is selected at random and then replaced. Another disc is then selected. Find the probability that:
   a   the first disc is green and the second disc is red
   b   the first disc is white and the second disc is green
   c   one disc is white and the other is red
   d   both discs are red
   e   neither disc is white
   f   at least one disc is red.

7　There are 15 hazel nuts, 10 Brazil nuts, 5 walnuts and 20 peanuts in a bag. Two are eaten at random. Find the probability that:

　　a　the first was a hazel nut and the second was a peanut
　　b　the first was a Brazil nut and the second was a walnut
　　c　one was a hazel nut and the other was a walnut
　　d　both were Brazil nuts
　　e　neither were peanuts
　　f　at least one was a hazel nut.

8　A game contains 30 place cards, 45 person cards, 20 activity cards and 5 object cards. One is selected and then replaced. Another is then selected. Find the probability that:

　　a　a place card is selected first followed by an object card
　　b　a person card is selected first followed by an activity card
　　c　one of the cards is a place card and the other card is an activity card
　　d　neither of the cards is a person card
　　e　both the cards are activity cards
　　f　at most one of the cards is an object card.

9　John collects football programs. He has 16 Crusaders programs, 12 Distillery programs, 24 Coleraine programs and 8 Newry programs. He chooses two programs at random to bring in to work. Find the probability that:

　　a　one is a Crusaders program and the other is a Coleraine program
　　b　both are Distillery programs
　　c　neither are Newry programs
　　d　at least one is a Coleraine program.

Tree diagrams

We can also solve the probability of combined events by drawing a tree diagram.

A tree diagram is where we show the different outcomes in a sketch where the lines are called the branches of the tree diagram.

EXAMPLE 10

There are eight red and four yellow balls in a box. One ball is withdrawn and not replaced. Another ball is withdrawn.

　　a　Draw a tree diagram to show all the possible outcomes.
　　b　Use the tree diagram to find the probability of getting one red and one yellow ball.
　　c　Use the tree diagram to find the probability of getting two yellow balls.

SOLUTION

　　a

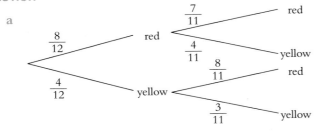

b   Do not cancel down the probabilities on each branch as it is easier
    to work out the next probability from the uncancelled fraction.

$\frac{7}{11} + \frac{4}{11} = 1$ and $\frac{8}{11} + \frac{3}{11} = 1$ ◄───

Note that the sum of
the probabilities on
each branch is always 1.

$$P(r \text{ and } y) = \frac{8}{12} \times \frac{4}{11} = \frac{8}{33}$$

or

$$P(y \text{ and } r) = \frac{4}{12} \times \frac{8}{11} = \frac{8}{33}$$

So $\frac{8}{33} + \frac{8}{33} = \frac{16}{33}$

c $P(y \text{ and } y) = \frac{4}{12} \times \frac{3}{11} = \frac{1}{11}$

EXAMPLE 11

There are red, green and white discs in a bag. The probability of choosing
a red disc from the bag is 0.5 and the probability of choosing a green disc
from the bag is 0.2.

   a   What is the probability of choosing a white disc from the bag?

Two discs are chosen one after the other, the first being replaced.

   b   Draw a tree diagram to show all the possible outcomes.
   c   Use the tree diagram to find the probability of choosing a red
        and a white.
   d   Use the tree diagram to find the probability of choosing no
        green discs.
   e   Use the tree diagram to find the probability of choosing at least
        one white.

SOLUTION

a   0.5 + 0.2 = 0.7

    1 − 0.7 = 0.3

    So P(white) = 0.3

b

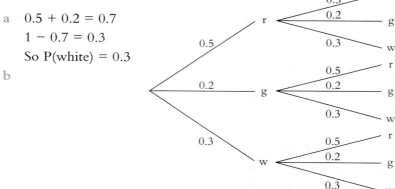

c $P(r \text{ and } w) = 0.5 \times 0.3 = 0.15$

    or

    $P(w \text{ and } r) = 0.3 \times 0.5 = 0.15$

    So 0.15 + 0.15 = 0.3

d $P(g) = 0.2$ and so $P(\text{not } g) = 0.8$

    $P(\text{not } g) \times P(\text{not } g) = 0.8 \times 0.8 = 0.64$

e $P(\text{not } w \text{ and not } w) = 0.7 \times 0.7 = 0.49$

    So 1 − 0.49 = 0.51

Exercise 47.5

1 There are six pens and three pencils in a box. One object is withdrawn and not replaced. Another object is withdrawn.
   a Draw a tree diagram to show all the possible outcomes.

   Use the tree diagram to find the probability of getting:
   b two pens   c one pen   d no pens.

2 There are 10 CDs and 5 DVDs in a box. One is withdrawn and not replaced. Another is withdrawn.
   a Draw a tree diagram to show all the possible outcomes.

   Use the tree diagram to find the probability of getting:
   b two CDs   c one CD   d no CDs.

3 There are 20 white draughts pieces and 24 black draughts pieces in a box. One piece is withdrawn and replaced. Another piece is withdrawn.
   a Draw a tree diagram to show all the possible outcomes.

   Use the tree diagram to find the probability of getting:
   b two blacks   c two whites   d a black and a white.

4 There are 8 red, 10 white and 7 yellow beads in a box.
   Two are selected one after the other without replacement.
   a Draw a tree diagram to show all the possible outcomes.

   Use the tree diagram to find the probability of selecting:
   b a red and a yellow   c two whites
   d no reds   e at least one yellow.

5 The probability each set of traffic lights is red is 0.55 and the probability each set of traffic lights is amber is 0.2.
   a Find the probability each set of traffic lights is green.
   b Draw a tree diagram to show all the possible outcomes for two sets of traffic lights.

   Use the tree diagram to find the probability of:
   c both sets being red   d neither set being green
   e one set being amber   f at least one set being red.

6 The probability a netball team wins each match is $\frac{5}{12}$ and the probability the team draws each match is $\frac{1}{3}$.
   a Find the probability the team loses each match.
   b Draw a tree diagram to show all the possible outcomes for two matches.

   Use the tree diagram to find the probability the team:
   c loses both matches
   d wins one match
   e draws at least one match.

7   There are 80 people in a club. Of these, 50 are adults and 10 are girls.
    One person is to be chosen at random from the 80 in the club.
    Find the probability of choosing:
    a   an adult   b   a girl   c   a boy.

    Two people are to be chosen at random from the 80 in the club.
    d   Draw a tree diagram to show all the possible outcomes.
    Use the tree diagram to find the probability of choosing:
    e   two adults   d   two children   e   at most one boy.

8   There are 20 yoghurts for sale. Of these, 4 are raspberry, 6 are
    strawberry and the rest are banana. Two are sold.
    a   Draw a tree diagram to show all the possible outcomes.

    Use the tree diagram to find the probability that the two sold were:
    b   a strawberry and a banana
    c   both raspberry
    d   not strawberry.

Dependent events

Two events are dependent when the outcome of the first event has an
effect on the outcome of the second event.

EXAMPLE 12

The probability it is wet tomorrow is 0.76.
If it is wet the probability I go swimming is 0.8.
Otherwise the probability I go swimming is 0.15.
    a   Draw a tree diagram to show all the possible outcomes.
    b   Hence find the probability that I go swimming.

SOLUTION

a   P(wet) = 0.76 and so P(not wet) = 1 − 0.76 = 0.24
    P(swim) = 0.8 and so P(don't swim) = 1 − 0.8 = 0.2
    P(swim) = 0.15 and so P(don't swim) = 1 − 0.15 = 0.85

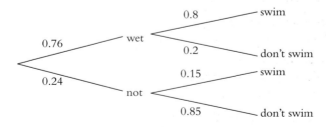

b   There are two possible outcomes, i.e.
    P(wet and I swim) = 0.76 × 0.8 = 0.608 or
    P(not wet and I swim) = 0.24 × 0.15 = 0.036
    So P(I swim) = 0.608 + 0.036 = 0.644

EXAMPLE 13

Alice plays a game in which she rolls a dice. If she gets a number less than 3 she wins. Otherwise she rolls again.

   a   Draw a tree diagram to show all the possible outcomes after three rolls.

Hence find the probability that:

   b   Alice wins before the third roll

   c   Alice has not won after three rolls.

SOLUTION

   a $P(\text{win}) = \frac{2}{6}$ and so $P(\text{not win}) = \frac{4}{6}$

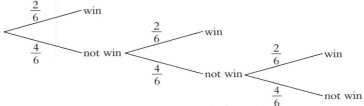

   b   There are two possible outcomes, i.e.

   $P(\text{Alice wins on the first roll}) = \frac{2}{6}$

   or

   $P(\text{Alice wins on the second roll}) = \frac{4}{6} \times \frac{2}{6} = \frac{2}{9}$

   Thus $P(\text{Alice wins before the third roll}) = \frac{2}{6} + \frac{2}{9} = \frac{5}{9}$

   c $P(\text{Alice has not won after 3 rolls}) = \frac{4}{6} \times \frac{4}{6} \times \frac{4}{6} = \frac{8}{27}$

Exercise 47.6

1   The probability George revises is 0.35.
   If he revises the probability he passes his test is 0.84.
   Otherwise the probability he passes his test is 0.05.
   a   Draw a tree diagram to show all the possible outcomes.
   b   Hence, find the probability that he passes his test.

2   The probability Sinead buys a take-away for lunch is $\frac{3}{10}$.
   If she buys a take-away the probability she has a drink of juice is $\frac{4}{5}$.
   Otherwise the probability she has a drink of juice is $\frac{2}{3}$.
   a   Draw a tree diagram to show all the possible outcomes.
   b   Hence, find the probability that she has a drink of juice.

3   A spinner is equally likely to point to any number between 1 and 20 inclusive. Ann plays a game spinning this spinner. If the spinner points to a factor of 20, Ann wins and the game stops. Otherwise she continues to spin the spinner.
   a   Draw a tree diagram to show all the possible outcomes after three spins.
   Hence, find the probability that:
   b   Ann wins on the second spin
   c   she is still playing after three spins.

4   The probability a train is on time is 0.48.
    If it is on time the probability I miss it is 0.4.
    Otherwise the probability I miss it is 0.35.
    a   Draw a tree diagram to show all the possible outcomes.
    b   Hence, find the probability that I miss the train.

5   72% of senior citizens choose to be vaccinated against the flu.
    The probability of catching the flu if you are vaccinated is 0.12.
    Otherwise the probability of catching the flu is 0.72.
    a   Draw a tree diagram to show all the possible outcomes.
    b   Hence, find the probability that a senior citizen catches the flu.

6   A rugby team plays 56% of its matches at home.
    The probability it wins when it plays at home is 0.72.
    Otherwise the probability it wins is 0.18.
    a   Draw a tree diagram to show all the possible outcomes.
    b   Hence, find the probability that it wins a match.

7   The probability Colin goes to the seaside is 0.48.
    If he goes to the seaside the probability that he buys an ice-cream
    is 0.88.
    Otherwise the probability that he buys an ice-cream is 0.28.
    a   Draw a tree diagram to show all the possible outcomes.
    b   Hence, find the probability that Colin buys an ice-cream.

8   The probability that Colette wins the first tennis match is $\frac{3}{8}$.
    If she wins the tennis match, the probability that she wins the
    second tennis match is $\frac{2}{5}$.
    Otherwise the probability that she wins the second tennis match is $\frac{1}{6}$.
    a   Draw a tree diagram to show all the possible outcomes.
    b   Hence, find the probability that she loses the second tennis match.

You should now:

- understand and be able to use relative frequency as an estimate of probability
- know and be able to use the fact that the sum of all the probabilities is 1
- know that the probability of something happening is 1 minus the probability of it not happening
- know what is meant by mutually exclusive events
- know what is meant by independent events
- know what is meant by dependent events
- know and be able to use the addition law of probability
- know and be able to use the multiplication law of probability
- be able to find the probability of combined events
- be able to use tree diagrams for independent events
- be able to use tree diagrams for dependent events.

Summary exercise 47

1 Four students Frank, Gillian, Harry and Aishling work together in a group to test whether a dice is biased. They each roll it and record the number of sixes in a table, as shown here.

Student	Number of rolls	Number of sixes
Frank	67	24
Gillian	95	32
Harry	55	17
Aishling	107	46

   a Calculate the relative frequency to 3 significant figures of getting a six using the results from each student.

   b Calculate the relative frequency to 3 significant figures of getting a six using the results from all students.

   c Which of these relative frequencies gives the best estimate for the probability and why?

   d Use this relative frequency to estimate the number of sixes after 950 rolls.

2 The probability of getting each number on a biased spinner labelled 1 to 5 is shown in the table. Find the probability of getting 5.

Number	1	2	3	4	5
Probability	$\frac{2}{9}$	$\frac{1}{3}$	$\frac{1}{9}$	$\frac{5}{18}$	

3 There are five houses in a school which has 1200 students. The table shows the number of students in some of these houses.

House	Apple	Beech	Oak	Pine	Sycamore
Number	260	185			

   The ratio of students in Apple:Oak is 4:3.
   There is an equal number of students in Pine and Sycamore.
   Find the probability a student chosen at random:

   a is in Oak

   b is in Apple or Sycamore

   c is not in Pine.

4 The table shows the probability of each of five meals being chosen at a take-away.

Meal	Burger	Pizza	Sausage	Nuggets	Fish
Probability	0.24	0.17		0.15	

   Find the probability that:

   a a Burger or a Pizza meal is chosen

   b a Nuggets meal is not chosen.

   It is equally likely that a sausage meal or a fish meal is chosen.

   c If there are 450 customers, how many would you expect to choose a sausage meal?

5 A girl has six bottles of shampoo, four bottles of conditioner and five bottles of shower gel. She lifts two at random.
   Find the probability that:

   a both are shampoo

   b one is conditioner

   c neither is shower gel.

6 There are 24 dotted, 10 striped and 16 plain cards in a box. One is selected at random and then replaced. Another card is then selected. Find the probability that:

   a the first card is dotted and the second card is striped

   b the first card is plain and the second card is dotted

   c one card is plain and the other is striped

   d both cards are dotted

   e neither card is striped

   f at least one card is plain.

7 Patrick collects stamps. He has 15 Australian stamps, 36 Russian stamps, 42 Chinese stamps and 7 Indian stamps. He chooses two stamps at random to swap. Find the probability that:

   a one is a Russian stamp and the other is an Indian stamp

   b both are Australian stamps

   c neither are Indian stamps

   d at least one is a Russian stamp.

8 There are 24 red, 19 white and 7 yellow beads in a box. Two are selected one after the other without replacement.

   a Draw a tree diagram to show all the possible outcomes.

   Use the tree diagram to find the probability of selecting:

   b a red and a yellow   **c** two yellows

   d no reds   **e** at least one yellow.

9 The probability a student goes to the chess club is $\frac{3}{20}$.

   If she goes to the chess club the probability she enters the chess competition is $\frac{5}{6}$. Otherwise the probability she enters the chess competition is $\frac{2}{9}$.

   a Draw a tree diagram to show all the possible outcomes.

   b Use the tree diagram to find the probability she enters the chess competition.

10 The probability a boy gets up when his alarm goes off is 0.36. If he gets up when his alarm goes off the probability he has breakfast is 0.74. Otherwise the probability he has breakfast is 0.22.

   a Draw a tree diagram to show all the possible outcomes.

   b Use the tree diagram to find the probability he has breakfast.

Examination questions

Questions **1** and **2** are from examination papers where you may not use a calculator.

Use 'Topic Tracker' at www.ccea.org.uk to find more exam questions.

1 A spinner has sections marked A, B, C, D, E. The probabilities of landing on some of these letters are given in the table:

Letter	A	B	C	D	E
Probability	0.2	0.3	0.15	0.25	

What is the probability of the spinner landing on

a the letter E

b a letter of the word ABBA

c a letter not in the word ABBA?

2 On Monday to Thursday, the probability that Keith travels home from school by bus is 0.7. On Friday the probability is 0.4.

a Complete the tree diagram for Keith's method of travel on a school day chosen at random.

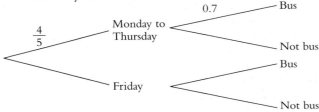

b Calculate the probability that, on a school day chosen at random, Keith travels home from school by bus.

c Calculate the probability that a school day chosen at random is a Wednesday on which Keith does not travel home from school by bus.

Question **3** is from an examination paper where you may use a calculator.

3 A bag contains 3 red dice, 5 blue dice and 8 black dice.

a I pick a dice and replace it in the bag. I do this 80 times. Estimate how many times I would expect to get a red dice.

b One dice is picked at random, without replacement. A second dice is then picked at random.

   i What is the probability that I have picked two black dice?

   ii What is the probability that I have picked two dice which are different in colour?

Index

3D/3D objects
  Pythagoras' theorem and
    356–8
  surface areas 369–71
  trigonometry and 356–8
  volumes 369–71
  see also shapes

A
addition 18–19
  algebraic fractions
    213–14
  decimals 27
  dimensions 416
  fractions 40–1
  inequalities 311
  mixed numbers 41–2
  negative numbers 33–4
  probability 558
  in standard form 97–8
algebra 116–21
  conventions 116–17
  index notation 117–18
algebraic expressions 116
  factorising 167–76
  simplification 125–6, 175
  substitution into 119–20
algebraic fractions 211–17
  addition 213–14
  division 215–16
  multiplication 214–15
  in quadratic equations
    224–5
  simplification 211–12
  subtraction 213–14
alternate segment theorem
  332–3
angles
  bisectors 425
  in circles 326–35
    alternate segment
      theorem 332–3
    subtended by arcs
      412–13
  in cyclic quadrilaterals
    330
  in polygons 337–42
  in sectors 412–13
  in similar shapes 361,
    365
  in triangles
    cosine rule 378–9
    sine rule 376

trigonometry and
  352–3
  see also right angles
appreciation 85–6
appropriate degree of
  accuracy 60
approximation 50–2
arcs 326
  angles subtended by
    412–13
  length 411–13
areas
  circles 390–1
  compound shapes 384–5
  dimensions 415
  parallelograms 392
  sectors 412
  segments 414
  semicircles 391
  trapeziums 393
  triangles 379–80
  see also surface areas
arrival times 436–7
asymptotes 256
averages 505
  choosing appropriate
    515–16
  see also mean; median;
    mode
average speed 438
  from travel graphs 271–3
  see also speed

B
balanced questions 475
bases (index notation) 123
bearings 354, 422–3
biased questions 476
bisectors
  of angles 425
  perpendicular 424
BODMAS 9, 56–8
  calculators and 59–62
  substitution 119
bounds 445–8
  expressions 448
  measurements 445,
    446–7
box plots 528–31
box and whisker diagrams
  528–31
brackets 132–8

changing subject of
  formulae with 184
  in equations 143–5
  expanding 132–4, 167
  factorisation and 167–76
  multiplying together
    135–8

C
calculators
  BODMAS rule 59–62
  multistep calculations
    60–1
  reciprocals 93–4
  single-step calculations
    59–60
  square roots 60
  standard form 101
cancelling down
  algebraic fractions
    211–12
  fractions 38–9, 43
  ratios 64–5
chords 326
  tangents to 332–3
circles
  alternate segment
    theorem 332–3
  angle properties 328–9
  arcs 326, 411–13
  area 390–1
  chords 326, 332–3
  circumference 326,
    386–7
  diameter 326
  as loci 426
  quadrants 389
  radius 326, 331–2
  sectors 327, 412–13
  segments 327, 332–3,
    414
  tangents to 326, 331–2
circumference 326, 386–7
class width 536
  see also grouped data
closed questions 476
combined events 562–3
  tree diagrams 565–6
common denominator 5, 39
common difference 159,
  234
common factors 5, 12–13,
  14, 167–8

common multiples 13–14
compound interest 84–5
compound measures
  433–42
compound shapes/solids
  384–5, 410
cones 402–5
  frustums of 406–7
constant of proportionality
  194, 198
constants 232
constant speed 433
  see also speed
constructions
  bearings 422–3
  bisectors
    angles 425
    perpendicular 424
  loci 426–7
  perpendiculars 425
  triangles 421–2
continuous data 481
  frequency diagrams for
    482–3
conversion graphs 270
correlation 495
cosine 349
  cosine rule 377–9
  graphs of 261, 263
cosine rule 377–9
costs graphs 270–1
counter-examples 5, 8
cross-multiplication 145–7
cube roots 5, 6, 7
cubes (numbers) 5, 6, 7
cubic equations 204
  solving graphically
    301–2
cubic functions 255
  graphs of 255–6, 263,
    301–2
cuboids 357, 394
cumulative frequency 505
cumulative frequency curves
  520–7, 531
currency exchange 86, 87, 88
cyclic quadrilaterals 330
cylinders 397–8

D
data
  comparing 513–14, 528
  continuous 481, 482–3